C0-AWL-833

THE MODERN LIBRARY

OF THE WORLD'S BEST BOOKS

SELECTED WRITINGS OF WASHINGTON IRVING

Selected Writings of
WASHINGTON IRVING

EDITED, WITH AN INTRODUCTION

BY SAXE COMMINS

THE MODERN LIBRARY
NEW YORK

Distributed in Canada
by Random House of Canada Limited, Toronto

THE MODERN LIBRARY
is published by RANDOM HOUSE, INC.
BENNETT CERF • DONALD S. KLOPFER

Manufactured in the United States of America by H. Wolff

Contents

Introduction

AMERICANS are just beginning to refresh their national memory. We are finding pride, and no little solace for an uncertain present and an unpredictable future, in the rediscovery of our past. The tendency to run away from that past into a geographical and cultural expatriatism has finally given way to a revival of interest in a nation and a history that have been a century and a half in coming of age.

In that time we have groped our way among the European cultures, borrowing their philosophy, accepting their science, proclaiming their literature, memorizing their music and imitating their art, only to come back a little less provincial after each journey from home and always a little more acutely hopeful of regaining some portion of our own heritage.

In a sense that general pattern can be traced back to the first professional writer of the American Republic, who was born in 1783, the year when the Treaty of Paris brought the American Revolution to an end, and lived to become the first man of letters from the United States to win international fame. In the life and travels and works of Washington Irving, it is possible to read the cycle of a nation born, finding its lifelong attachments in childhood, moving restlessly in youth, seeking permanence of place and expression in middle age, and returning to its origins at the end, trying to summon remembrance of things past.

The main events in Washington Irving's life lend force to speculation on this ever-recurring design. The New York in which he was born still carried the relics of the Indian native and the manners of the Dutch occupation, and it is especially remarkable that his first, and perhaps his greatest, achievement was in a satirical memoir of the city of his birth, recalling a time just past with the humor of a Laurence Sterne and the impaling irony of a Dean Swift. Diedrich Knickerbocker's *A History of New York* was an auspicious beginning. It enabled the young author to take flight to Europe and become exposed to its influence, as so many subsequent writers, from Longfellow to Hemingway, were to do. There under the guidance of Sir Walter

Scott, W. M. Thackeray, Thomas Moore and others, Irving expanded his outlook and became far more than the recorder of his quaint homeland. He wrote of England and English ways, but still the recollection of his Hudson River Valley days impelled him to recount such stories as "Rip Van Winkle" and "The Legend of Sleepy Hollow" from foreign soil.

Failure in the law and business, disappointment of the heart and insecurity about the future brought the writer to Europe for the second time. He remained an expatriate for seventeen years. It is significant, for the purposes of this speculation, that he wrote, then and later when he became Minister to Spain, the biographical works whose subjects had their birth and existence far from home, and the history, *The Conquest of Granada,* of a land and a people far removed from his Manhattan companions of the Salmagundi days. Even his *Alhambra,* with its evocation of Moorish splendor, is in the romantic mood and resurrects a lost world with the loving care of the antiquarian and the precision of the archeologist.

It is perhaps evidence of the shyness of a young author and later the continued self-consciousness of a man writing in alien lands that Washington Irving did not issue a single book under his own name until he had passed his fiftieth year. His first letters to newspapers, when he was a boy, were signed "Jonathan Oldstyle." As one of the three contributors to the magazine *Salmagundi* he appeared in the guise of "Anthony Evergreen, Gent." *A History of New York* was under the authorship of "Diedrich Knickerbocker," a name far more closely identified with New York than that English Duke's for which the city was renamed. *The Conquest of Granada* bore the imposing pseudonym of "Fray Antonio Agapida," and *The Sketch Book, Tales of a Traveller* and *Bracebridge Hall* were credited to "Geoffrey Crayon, Gent."

With the return of the native, after so long an absence, interest was revived in familiar scenes, and themes closer to the heart of his own land made demands on Irving's pen. *Astoria, The Adventures of Captain Boneville* and *A Tour on the Prairies* were exciting and in the best sense patriotic accounts of the opening of our West. The wanderer had come home and had rediscovered America.

Most meaningful, perhaps, is that the crowning work of Irving's life was the five-volume biography of George Washington. The cycle was complete. Irving, the pleasure-loving, genial, imperturbable traveler and gentle hedonist, the man without much interest in his time or the world's convulsions, unless these inconvenienced him, the professional man of letters, the respected but inconspicuous diplomat, the always fluent and imaginative story-teller—Irving, first in a long succession of American authors, established the inevitable pattern: early growth and achievement in the land of his birth; the attraction of and flight to an older culture; and, finally, homecoming and the exploration of the world that was at first too familiar and taken for granted and then became an inexhaustible treasury of remembrance.

So much for hypothesis, even if it depends upon evidence chosen to support a thesis. The actual facts of Washington Irving's life are perhaps even simpler. When he became the eleventh child of William Irving, merchant, and his wife, the former Sarah Sanders, New York was hardly a metropolis.

Its population of 23,000 inhabitants was concentrated near the Battery and became thinned out at the northern fringe in the vicinity of what is now City Hall Park and the approaches to the Brooklyn Bridge. The Revolutionary War had left its mark, especially where a great fire had burned down half the city. The cluster of high-gabled Dutch houses, surmounted by gay weathercocks, gave only mild promise of developing into a city which would become the center of the world's commerce. Certainly this predominantly Dutch community could not vie with Philadelphia, the heart of the intellectual and artistic life in America.

The home at 131 William Street into which Washington Irving was born had no Dutch equanimity or Quaker tolerance; it was so severely and angrily religious that nearly every one of the children who managed to survive ultimately revolted against the father's stern Scotch Covenanter doctrines. Washington himself seemed to learn quite early in youth that the wages of pleasure could very frequently be a more abundant life.

After a casual schooling which lasted until he was sixteen, he entered a law office, where his reading went beyond the law. At this period he spent a summer in Westchester County and explored the Sleepy Hollow region. In 1800 he made his first voyage up the Hudson River to visit his sisters in Albany. On such excursions he steeped himself in the legends of the river and the Dutch and Indian lore of all the settlements along its 150-mile course. In 1802, all of nineteen years old and a law clerk in the office of Josiah Hoffman, our author, disguised as Jonathan Oldstyle, contributed a series of letters to the *Morning Chronicle* protesting with admirable chivalry against jesting at maiden ladies, and other such local follies.

Because of ill health, Irving was persuaded by his brothers to take passage for Europe in 1804. He arrived in France while Napoleon was at the height of his glory. The young visitor was too active cultivating the society of well-situated families to worry much about the meaning to France and Europe of the Corsican's dream of power. In Italy music and painting held the interest of the traveler for a little while; in London the chief attraction was the theatre; and elsewhere it was a fete or the opera or the companionship of charming and light-hearted friends.

To come back to New York and the practice of law after such a grand tour was a dismal prospect. There had to be distraction, and soon it was found among those convivial lads who called themselves the "Nine Worthies" and carried on their milder revelries in New York and their more secret roisterings in an old country house on the Passaic River. In this group were Washington's eldest brother, William, and James Paulding. These three Manhattan bravos collaborated to issue a semi-monthly magazine which they dubbed *Salmagundi*, and whose avowed intention was to "amuse, edify and castigate the town." It ran through twenty numbers and created a genuine stir. Irving's contributions represented a considerable improvement in content and style over the adolescent seriousness of purpose in the writings of Jonathan Oldstyle. In fact, the pieces in *Salmagundi* foreshadowed the writer of fluency and felicity, of graciousness and gentleness, the whole world was soon to recognize.

Meanwhile the young lawyer tried in vain to make some headway in his profession. A foray into politics on the side of the Federalists and an attempt to win a civil appointment at

Albany failed. He actually attended, as counsel, the trial of Aaron Burr in Richmond, but his role was inconspicuous.

With *Salmagundi* no longer in existence, Washington and his brother Peter conceived the idea of a satirical and burlesque account of their native city. Peter was summoned to Europe, and Washington, perhaps because of his profound distaste for the law or perhaps even for want of something better to do, undertook to complete the task alone.

Thus the first great work of imaginative literature in the American Republic came into being. It appeared in 1809, when its author, hiding behind the pseudonym of Diedrich Knickerbocker, was twenty-six years old. *A History of New York* is far more than its title suggests. As satire, as a richly embellished re-creation of Gargantuan figures and of fabulous history, it is improvisation on a grand scale that ranges from out-and-out burlesque to epic grandeur of scene and action. This gay and whimsical account of the rise of the Dutch from the days of Wouter Van Twiller, the Doubter, to the grandiose reign and pathetic end of Peter Stuyvesant, the Headstrong, deservedly belongs among the most admired books of all American literature.

Even before the completion of *A History of New York*, a tragic episode, which many biographers insist influenced all the rest of Irving's life and career, marked the end of his youth. Matilda Hoffman, the daughter of the lawyer in whose offices Washington was employed, awakened a deeply ardent emotion in the heart of the aspiring writer. Marriage was impossible until an assured means of livelihood could be found. Tragically, Matilda Hoffman died in her eighteenth year, and Irving was crushed. All his life he cherished a painfully nostalgic memory of his childhood sweetheart, and never married. Especially touching and in the best romantic mood of the period is the story that after his death there was found hidden in a strong-box a miniature, a lock of hair and a yellowing piece of paper on which Irving had inscribed "Matilda Hoffman." Biographers with less respect for the romantic tradition have revealed how in the Dresden period Irving loved, wooed and lost a lady, Miss Emily Foster, whose heart was stronger.

The acclaim of the *History* was more than heartening; it helped determine the choice of Irving's career. Sir Walter Scott was one of the first to sing its praises. "I have never," he declared, "read anything so closely resembling the style of Dean Swift as the annals of Diedrich Knickerbocker. I have been employed these few evenings in reading them aloud, and our sides have been absolutely sore with laughing. I think, too, there are passages which indicate that the author possesses power of a different kind, and has some touches which remind me of Sterne."

Still Irving had misgivings as to the earning power of his pen. Success meant more leisure and more gaiety, which required funds. A loose partnership with his brothers in the hardware business involved him in no serious duties, and he could enjoy the amenities of social life in New York, Baltimore and Washington. In the capital he was entertained by President Madison, and life for the author of a single successful book was a round of cotillions and carousals.

The War of 1812 gave Irving some concern and brought a halt to his pursuit of pleasure. He began to work as editor of the *Analectic Magazine*, but the effort involved was distasteful to him. A period of sloth followed, and writing was forgotten for idleness in the country, theatregoing in the city and general indifference to the factors in the world which brought his country to war. Finally he awakened from his apathy and volunteered his services. The war was over in February of 1815, and he was too late. Three months afterwards he sailed for England on what he thought would be a brief visit. It lasted seventeen years.

The pleasures of life in England were marred by troubles in the hardware business. Matters went from bad to worse, and when bankruptcy finally caught up with the partners, Washington had to think seriously of other ways to earn his living. Ideas for books, since the success of his *History* ten years earlier, had been stirring in his mind, and, in 1819, when Irving was thirty-six years old, the first number of *The Sketch Book* was published in America. It created a sensation. England took the author of "Rip Van Winkle" to its heart, and Irving was in no hurry to go home now. With Sir Walter Scott and Lord Byron, he became one of the three idols of the English-reading public. Praise flowed from the highest sources and money in a golden stream from the publishers. Life was pleasant again.

With his brother Peter as companion, the successful author

crossed the Channel to France. By steamboat they traveled to Rouen, and were impressed with the possibilities of steam navigation, then in its infancy. Nearly all of Washington Irving's literary earnings were soon lost in the business of promoting a steamboat company.

In the year that he remained in Paris, Irving's closest friends were Thomas Moore and John Howard Payne, author of "Home, Sweet Home." Payne, down on his luck, was afflicted with a form of genius mania and it expressed itself in grandiose schemes for the drama. Irving, with his love for the theatre, needed little persuasion to become his collaborator.

Bracebridge Hall, Irving's third book, was sold to Murray, the publisher, for £1,000, and, with fresh funds, the traveling author returned to the continent, this time in search of relief from the recurring malady of eczema. After leisurely visits to most of the German cities, he arrived in Dresden, where the romance with Emily Foster, about which future biographers were to become so concerned, blossomed for six or seven months and then wilted.

Back in Paris, the spurned lover assuaged his grief in violent activity in playwriting with Payne. Although not listed in any of his works, there is good evidence that he collaborated in the creation of such plays as *Charles II, Richelieu, Abu Hassan* and *The Wild Huntsman,* all of which remained unknown to the world until disinterred by a painstaking bibliophile more than one hundred years after they were written.

In 1824 Irving collected a sufficient number of pieces to make *The Tales of a Traveller* and sold the book to Murray for the then unprecedented sum of 1,500 guineas. In spite of one of the unsung brief masterpieces in this sheaf of sketches—"The Poor-Devil Author"—it added very little to Irving's literary reputation. In fact, the reception of this book was decidedly unfavorable, and so affected him that he forsook writing of this kind for many years.

After losing more of his literary earnings in another ill-advised investment—this time it was Bolivian mines—Irving applied to Alexander Everett, American Minister to Madrid, for a post with the Legation. In complying, the diplomat suggested that the author undertake a translation of Don Martin Fernandez de Navarette's *Voyages of Columbus.* By this fortunate circumstance, the richest phases of Irving's life and work awaited him.

Arrived in Madrid in February of 1826, the recently appointed attaché to the Court of Ferdinand VII found no great difficulty in adjusting himself to his new career, since its demands were chiefly social. Paying formal calls and attending functions at the various embassies and homes of the diplomatic colony, observing and enjoying the ceremonials of court and finding excitement at the bull fights seemed to be his official assignment.

Unofficially, this was the most active and productive period of Irving's life. Originally it was his intention to translate some historical documents pertaining to Christopher Columbus which had just been unearthed and edited by Navarette. The more he examined these papers, containing so many hitherto-unknown facts on the discovery of America, the more was the translator inclined to become the author. Forthwith he decided to write a biography of Columbus which would include the mass of data available in the libraries of Madrid and the private collections of Spanish colonial history, as well as whatever he could glean from Navarette.

After two years of the most arduous labor performed by Irving in the forty-four years of his life, the biography of Columbus was ready for publication. In these twenty-four months, as a respite from his researches on the explorer and as a pure labor of love, he wrote what he himself considered the best book to come from his pen up to then, *The Conquest of Granada,* and almost all of the book which his admirers still hold in greatest affection, *The Alhambra,* although this account of the moldering Moorish citadel was not published until 1832. In addition to these Herculean accomplishments by a man who loved ease and leisure, he collected material for the history of the Conquest of Mexico which many years later he turned over, with a generosity almost unexampled among literary men, to William H. Prescott.

Prescott's Introduction to *The Conquest of Mexico* makes acknowledgment to the debt owed Irving in this manner:

"In the Preface to the *History of Ferdinand and Isabella,* I lamented, that, while occupied with that subject, two of its most attractive parts had engaged the attention of the most popular of American authors, Washington Irving. By a singular chance, something like the reverse of this has taken place in the composition of the present history, and I have found myself unconsciously taking up ground which he was preparing to occupy. It was not till I had become master of my rich collection of materials, that I was acquainted with this circumstance; and, had he persevered in his design, I should unhesitatingly have abandoned my own, if not from courtesy, at least from policy; for, though armed with the weapons of Achilles, this could give me no hope of success in a competition with Achilles himself. But no sooner was that distinguished writer informed of the preparations I had made, than, with the gentlemanly spirit which will surprise no one who has the pleasure of his acquaintance, he instantly announced to me his intention of leaving the subject open to me."

As an indication of Irving's popularity as a writer and as a sidelight on the earning powers of a best-selling author of more than one hundred years ago, the sums paid for his books are suggestive. It must be remembered that they were bought outright and there were no royalties. For the English rights to the *Life and Voyages of Columbus,* he received £3,150; for *The Conquest of Granada* 2,000 guineas.

Of far greater importance, however, was the critical and public acclaim with which these two books were greeted. Samuel Taylor Coleridge was among the first to voice his praise; the Royal Society of Literature in London awarded Irving its gold medal and Oxford University the degree of D.C.L. William Makepeace Thackeray hailed Irving as "The first ambassador whom the New World of Letters sent to the Old."

Advancement in the form of an appointment as Secretary of the Legation to the Court of St. James's came from the State Department, and Irving moved to London and a general renewal of his social activities there, but more particularly the revival of his old friendship with Sir Walter Scott, now declining in years and in power as a writer.

In May of 1832, after an absence of seventeen years, Washington Irving returned to America as a conquering hero. New York had grown to a flourishing city of 200,000 inhabitants, and it seemed that every one of them was eager to do him honor. Lavish entertainments and banquets were prepared for the "Dutch Herodotus, Diedrich Knickerbocker." Invitations from all over the country came in a deluge, but Irving quickly realized how far he had traveled from his origins, and he wanted above everything else to avoid attention so that he could attempt to re-discover his native land.

In the autumn of that year he found escape from the clamor of his insistent admirers by leaving for an exploration of the West, starting from Fort Gibson on the Arkansas River. The trip took him into the Pawnee country, and out of it he brought that adventurous account of the plains, *A Tour on the Prairie* and, subsequently, *The Adventures of Captain Boneville*, precursors of those pioneering tales now generically called "Westerns."

With the considerable sums of money earned by his writings, Irving now could afford a place of his own, and he found it near the Sleepy Hollow haunts of his boyhood at Tarrytown on the east bank of the Hudson. The farm which he purchased boasted but one small, stone, Dutch cottage, but Irving immediately set to work to make additions until it grew into a rambling, picturesque residence which he decided to call "Sunnyside."

Here for ten years, until his appointment as Minister to Spain, Irving lived as a country squire who clung to his old, honored and highly profitable profession. As a contributor to *Knickerbocker Magazine* he earned $2,000 a year. His championship of international copyrights to protect American literature has earned infinitely more in gratitude from every generation of American writers since and is quite as notable as anything else he did during this decade of his life. Out of it came, besides the two aforementioned books on the West, *Recollections of Abbotsford* and *Newstead Abbey, The Legends of the Conquest of Spain* and *Astoria*, that strange book conceived as what today might be called a public-relations release for a magnate, John Jacob Astor, and a paid advertisement for his fur company, which turned out to be one of the most enthralling stories of the opening of the northwestern continent in the annals of our literature. The race between the two expeditions—one by sea and the other overland—for the goal at the mouth of the Columbia River is melodrama of breathtaking action. Incidentally, it was Washington Irving who prevailed upon John Jacob Astor to found the Astor Library, the nucleus for the incomparable New York Public Library.

In this period there were also written many scattered pieces which were later collected in a volume under the title *Wolfert's Roost and Other Papers.* At this time, too, considerable work was done on the *Life of Goldsmith* and *Mahomet and His Successors,* although neither of these last-named books saw publication until five years later, when Irving had already begun his research for the monumental *Life of Washington.*

In 1842, at the age of fifty-nine, Washington Irving was offered the **post of Minister** to Madrid, partly as a gesture to him personally and partly as recognition of the political value of his international reputation as a man of letters and especially one who had written so much on Spain. Daniel Webster made the nomination and it was approved by Henry Clay.

For four and a half years Irving remained at his post in Madrid. Although adequately equipped for his rather ornamental duties, he was never conspicuous for the originality or forcefulness of his statesmanship. The truth is that he cared too little for diplomacy to devote himself to it. The habits of a lifetime and his obsession to get on with the writing of his biography of Washington probably made him look upon this appointment as a golden opportunity to finish his *magnum opus* under the conditions of leisure and repose rather than as a means of staking out a new career for his old age.

When, in 1846, he came back to Sunnyside, it was all too apparent that he wanted nothing more than to complete his work in tranquillity at home. That work was: to conclude, in 1849, the *Life of Goldsmith* and *Mahomet and His Successors* in 1850, and finally to give his last efforts to the five-volume biography of George Washington, issued from 1855 to 1859.

The date of 1859 is significant. It marked the completion of a task begun soon after the end of the Revolutionary War, just as the new century dawned, and brought to a conclusion with an analysis and a tribute to the first President of the United States. To this formidable undertaking the last years of Irving's life were consecrated. Now the final word of many manuscripts, comprising twenty imposing volumes, had been written, and it was time to die, without ostentation or offense to anyone, quietly, harmlessly and resignedly. The first American expatriate writer had come home and had found his own country good.

The selections in this volume were made with the purpose of achieving the widest possible representation and variety within the limitations imposed by a book of 670 pages. A primary condition for inclusion was that each item be given in its entirety; nothing was to be abridged or garbled. This offered no serious difficulty with the short stories and essays and sketches, but it automatically excluded the biographies: *The Life of Washington,* which runs to 2,900 pages; *The Life and Voyages of Columbus,* 1,100; *Oliver Goldsmith* and *Mahomet and His Successors* another 1,000. The Western accounts, *Astoria, The Adventures of Captain Boneville, A Tour on the Prairies,* are of a comparable length. *The Conquest of Granada* would require an entire volume.

Because *A History of New York* is regarded by almost unanimous consent among students and critics of Irving's works as his most humorous and imaginative, yet basically authentic, contribution to historical writing, it is included here without the deletion of a word. In this unabridged form, it still has the spontaneity and capricious gaiety it held for readers one hundred and thirty-five years ago, and by making it available, intact, it is not too presumptuous to believe that we are helping to preserve one of the most valuable assets of our national literature.

The eight selections from *The Sketch Book* include, of course, "Rip Van Winkle" and "The Legend of Sleepy Hollow," together with pieces representative of the English influence on Irving after his first residence in Britain. From *Bracebridge Hall* are taken the classic little tale, "The Stout Gentleman," as British as Dickens, and "The Haunted House," as American of the period as the legends of Captain Kidd along the banks of the Hudson.

Because that gem of literary travesty, "The Poor-Devil Author," with its introductory pieces "Literary Life," "A Literary Dinner" and "The Club of Queer Fellows," has been overlooked for so long, it is revived in these pages with the hope that it will receive the recognition it has been denied for more than a century.

The mood and the legends of Moorish Spain are conveyed in the selections from *The Alhambra.* These eight pieces must serve to represent that great body of Irving's Spanish writings which are perforce inadmissible to a book of this size because they cannot be excerptized or condensed without doing violence to them. In these selections from *The Alhambra* the descriptive opulence of the Moorish palace-fortress, its strange traditions and fanciful legends convey how completely Irving had immersed himself in Spanish lore and history.

"Wolfert's Roost" was chosen to represent the Hudson River Valley mood of the later Irving period, when he had returned from Europe and had become re-identified with the quaint Dutch ways along the banks of the river. Finally, a word about "A Time of Unexampled Prosperity" and "The Great Mississippi Bubble." Irving's own experience with bad investments qualified him, with great authority and no little bitterness, to expose the meteoric career of that Scotch financial adventurer and rogue, John Law. Those who remember with sorrow the collapse of our own boom in 1929 will read this tale of the ascent into the astronomical realms of finance, and the sudden descent to earth, with sadder and wiser understanding.

The representative character of this volume, it is hoped, will whet interest in all the writings of our first man of letters and encourage the revival urged by his living literary descendants in the United States. Such books as *The World of Washington Irving* by Van Wyck Brooks are taking up the cause as a debt we owe to our progenitors. The editors of the Modern Library feel that this volume can become a genuine contribution in the reawakening of interest in the pioneers of our national literature.

Saxe Commins

I. From *The Sketch Book*

Rip Van Winkle

A POSTHUMOUS WRITING OF

DIEDRICH KNICKERBOCKER

By Woden, God of Saxons,
From whence comes Wensday, that is Wodensday,
Truth is a thing that ever I will keep
Unto thylke day in which I creep into
My sepulchre —

CARTWRIGHT

[The following Tale was found among the papers of the late Diedrich Knickerbocker, an old gentleman of New York, who was very curious in the Dutch history of the province, and the manners of the descendants from its primitive settlers. His historical researches, however, did not lie so much among books as among men; for the former are lamentably scanty on his favorite topics; whereas he found the old burghers, and still more their wives, rich in that legendary lore, so invaluable to true history. Whenever, therefore, he happened upon a genuine Dutch family, snugly shut up in its low-roofed farmhouse, under a spreading sycamore, he looked upon it as a little clasped volume of black-letter, and studied it with the zeal of a book-worm.

The result of all these researches was a history of the province during the reign of the Dutch governors, which he published some years since. There have been various opinions as to the literary character of his work, and, to tell the truth, it is not a whit better than it should be. Its chief merit is its scrupulous accuracy, which indeed was a little questioned on its first appearance, but has since been completely established; and it is now admitted into all historical collections, as a book of unquestionable authority.

The old gentleman died shortly after the publication of his work, and now that he is dead and gone, it cannot do much harm to his memory to say that his time might have been much better employed in weightier labors. He, however, was apt to ride his hobby his own way; and though it did now and then kick up the dust a little in the eyes of his neighbors, and grieve the spirit of some friends, for whom he felt the truest deference and affection; yet his errors and follies are remembered "more in sorrow than in anger," and it begins to be suspected, that he never intended to injure or offend. But however his memory may be appreciated by critics, it is still held dear by many folks, whose good opinion is well worth having; particularly by certain biscuit-bakers, who have gone so far as to imprint his likeness on their new-year cakes; and have thus given him a chance for immortality, almost equal to the being stamped on a Waterloo Medal, or a Queen Anne's Farthing.]

WHOEVER has made a voyage up the Hudson must remember the Kaatskill mountains. They are a dismembered branch of the great Appalachian family, and are seen away to the west of the river, swelling up to a noble height, and lording it over the surrounding country. Every change of season, every change of weather, indeed, every hour of the day, produces some change in the magical hues and shapes of these mountains, and they are regarded by all the good wives, far and near, as perfect barometers. When the weather is fair and settled, they are clothed in blue and purple, and print their bold outlines on the clear evening sky; but, sometimes, when the rest of the landscape is cloudless, they will gather a hood of gray vapors about their summits, which, in the last rays of the setting sun, will glow and light up like a crown of glory.

At the foot of these fairy mountains, the voyager may have descried the light smoke curling up from a village, whose shingle-roofs gleam among the trees, just where the blue tints of the upland melt away into the fresh green of the nearer landscape. It is a little village of great antiquity, having been founded by some of the Dutch colonists, in the early times of the province, just about the beginning of the government of the good Peter Stuyvesant (may he rest in peace!), and there were some of the houses of the original settlers standing within a few years, built of small yellow bricks brought from Holland, having latticed windows and gable fronts, surmounted with weather-cocks.

In that same village, and in one of these very houses (which, to tell the precise truth, was sadly time-worn and weather-beaten), there lived many years since, while the country was yet a province of Great Britain, a simple good-natured fellow of the name of Rip Van Winkle. He was a descendant of the Van

Winkles who figured so gallantly in the chivalrous days of Peter Stuyvesant, and accompanied him to the siege of Fort Christina. He inherited, however, but little of the martial character of his ancestors. I have observed that he was a simple good-natured man; he was, moreover, a kind neighbor, and an obedient henpecked husband. Indeed, to the latter circumstance might be owing that meekness of spirit which gained him such universal popularity; for those men are most apt to be obsequious and conciliating abroad, who are under the discipline of shrews at home. Their tempers, doubtless, are rendered pliant and malleable in the fiery furnace of domestic tribulation; and a curtain lecture is worth all the sermons in the world for teaching the virtues of patience and long-suffering. A termagant wife may, therefore, in some respects, be considered a tolerable blessing; and if so, Rip Van Winkle was thrice blessed.

Certain it is that he was a great favorite among all the good wives of the village, who, as usual, with the amiable sex, took his part in all family squabbles; and never failed, whenever they talked those matters over in their evening gossipings, to lay all the blame on Dame Van Winkle. The children of the village, too, would shout with joy whenever he approached. He assisted at their sports, made their playthings, taught them to fly kites and shoot marbles, and told them long stories of ghosts, witches, and Indians. Whenever he went dodging about the village, he was surrounded by a troop of them, hanging on his skirts, clambering on his back, and playing a thousand tricks on him with impunity; and not a dog would bark at him throughout the neighborhood.

The great error in Rip's composition was an insuperable aversion to all kinds of profitable labor. It could not be from the want of assiduity or perseverance; for he would sit on a wet rock, with a rod as long and heavy as a Tartar's lance, and fish all day without a murmur, even though he should not be encouraged by a single nibble. He would carry a fowling-piece on his shoulder for hours together, trudging through woods and swamps, and up hill and down dale, to shoot a few squirrels or wild pigeons. He would never refuse to assist a neighbor even in the roughest toil, and was a foremost man at all country frolics for husking Indian corn, or building stone-fences; the women of the village, too, used to employ him to run their errands, and to do such little odd jobs as their less obliging husbands would not do for them. In a word Rip was ready to attend to anybody's business but his own; but as to doing family duty, and keeping his farm in order, he found it impossible.

In fact, he declared it was of no use to work on his farm; it was the most pestilent little piece of ground in the whole country; every thing about it went wrong, and would go wrong, in spite of him. His fences were continually falling to pieces; his cow would either go astray, or get among the cabbages; weeds were sure to grow quicker in his fields than anywhere else; the rain always made a point of setting in just as he had some outdoor work to do; so that though his patrimonial estate had dwindled away under his management, acre by acre, until there was little more left than a mere patch of Indian corn and potatoes, yet it was the worst conditioned farm in the neighborhood.

His children, too, were as ragged and wild as if they belonged to nobody. His son Rip, an urchin begotten in his own likeness, promised to inherit the habits, with the old clothes of his father. He was generally seen trooping like a colt at his mother's heels, equipped in a pair of his father's cast-off galligaskins, which he had much ado to hold up with one hand, as a fine lady does her train in bad weather.

Rip Van Winkle, however, was one of those happy mortals, of foolish, well-oiled dispositions, who take the world easy, eat white bread or brown, whichever can be got with least thought or trouble, and would rather starve on a penny than work for a pound. If left to himself, he would have whistled life away in perfect contentment; but his wife kept continually dinning in his ears about his idleness, his carelessness, and the ruin he was bringing on his family. Morning, noon, and night, her tongue was incessantly going, and everything he said or did was sure to produce a torrent of household eloquence. Rip had but one way of replying to all lectures of the kind, and that, by frequent use, had grown into a habit. He shrugged his shoulders, shook his head, cast up his eyes, but said nothing. This, however, always provoked a fresh volley from his wife; so that he was fain to draw off his forces, and take to the outside of the house—the only side which, in truth, belongs to a hen-pecked husband.

Rip's sole domestic adherent was his dog Wolf, who was as much hen-pecked as his master; for Dame Van Winkle regarded them as companions in idleness, and even looked upon Wolf with an evil eye, as the cause of his master's going so often astray. True it is, in all points of spirit befitting an honorable dog, he was as courageous an animal as ever scoured the woods—but what courage can withstand the ever-during and all-besetting terrors of a woman's tongue? The moment Wolf entered the house his crest fell, his tail drooped to the ground, or curled between his legs, he sneaked about with a gallows air, casting many a sidelong glance at Dame Van Winkle, and at the least flourish of a broomstick or ladle, he would fly to the door with yelping precipitation.

Times grew worse and worse with Rip Van Winkle as years of matrimony rolled on; a tart temper never mellows with age, and a sharp tongue is the only edged tool that grows keener with constant use. For a long while he used to console himself, when driven from home, by frequenting a kind of perpetual club of the sages, philosophers, and other idle personages of the village; which held its sessions on a bench before a small inn, designated by a rubicund portrait of His Majesty George the Third. Here they used to sit in the shade through a long lazy summer's day, talking listlessly over village gossip, or telling endless sleepy stories about nothing. But it would have been worth any statesman's money to have heard the profound discussions that sometimes took place, when by chance an old newspaper fell into their hands from some passing traveller. How solemnly they would listen to the contents, as drawled out by Derrick Van Bummel, the schoolmaster, a dapper learned little man, who was not to be daunted by the most gigantic word in the dictionary; and how sagely they would deliberate upon public events some months after they had taken place.

The opinions of this junto were completely controlled by Nicholas Vedder, a patriarch of the village, and landlord of the inn, at the door of which he took his seat from morning till night, just moving sufficiently to avoid the sun and keep in the shade of a large tree; so that the neighbors could tell the hour by his movements as accurately as by a sun-dial. It is true he was rarely heard to speak, but smoked his pipe incessantly. His adherents, however (for every great man has his adherents), perfectly understood him, and knew how to gather his opinions. When any thing that was read or related displeased him, he was observed to smoke his pipe vehemently, and to send forth short, frequent and angry puffs; but when pleased, he would inhale the smoke slowly and tranquilly, and emit it in light and placid clouds; and sometimes, taking the pipe from his mouth, and letting the fragrant vapor curl about his nose, would gravely nod his head in token of perfect approbation.

From even this stronghold the unlucky Rip was at length routed by his termagant wife, who would suddenly break in upon the tranquillity of the assemblage and call the members all to naught; nor was that august personage, Nicholas Vedder himself, sacred from the daring tongue of this terrible virago, who charged him outright with encouraging her husband in habits of idleness.

Poor Rip was at last reduced almost to despair; and his only alternative, to escape from the labor of the farm and clamor of his wife, was to take gun in hand and stroll away into the woods. Here he would sometimes seat himself at the foot of a tree, and share the contents of his wallet with Wolf, with whom he sympathized as a fellow-sufferer in persecution. "Poor Wolf," he would say, "thy mistress leads thee a dog's life of it; but never mind, my lad, whilst I live thou shalt never want a friend to stand by thee!" Wolf would wag his tail, look wistfully in his master's face, and if dogs can feel pity I verily believe he reciprocated the sentiment with all his heart.

In a long ramble of the kind on a fine autumnal day, Rip had unconsciously scrambled to one of the highest parts of the Kaatskill mountains. He was after his favorite sport of squirrel shooting, and the still solitudes had echoed and re-echoed with the reports of his gun. Panting and fatigued, he threw himself, late in the afternoon, on a green knoll, covered with mountain herbage, that crowned the brow of a precipice. From an opening between the trees he could overlook all the lower country for many a mile of rich woodland. He saw at a distance the lordly Hudson, far, far below him, moving on its silent but majestic course, with the reflection of a purple cloud, or the sail of a lagging bark, here and there sleeping on its glassy bosom, and at last losing itself in the blue highlands.

On the other side he looked down into a deep mountain glen, wild, lonely, and shagged, the bottom filled with fragments from the impending cliffs, and scarcely lighted by the reflected rays of the setting sun. For some time Rip lay musing on this scene; evening was gradually advancing; the mountains began to throw their long blue shadows over the valleys; he saw that it would be dark long before he could reach the village, and he heaved a heavy sigh when he thought of encountering the terrors of Dame Van Winkle.

As he was about to descend, he heard a voice from a distance, hallooing, "Rip Van Winkle! Rip Van Winkle!" He looked round, but could see nothing but a crow winging its solitary flight across the mountain. He thought his fancy must have deceived him, and turned again to descend, when he heard the same cry ring through the still evening air; "Rip Van Winkle! Rip Van Winkle!"—at the same time Wolf bristled up his back, and giving a low growl, skulked to his master's side, looking fearfully down into the glen. Rip now felt a vague apprehension stealing over him; he looked anxiously in the same direction, and perceived a strange figure slowly toiling up the rocks, and bending under the weight of something he carried on his back. He was surprised to see any human being in this lonely and unfrequented place, but supposing it to be some one of the neighborhood in need of his assistance, he hastened down to yield it.

On nearer approach he was still more surprised at the singularity of the stranger's appearance. He was a short square-built old fellow, with thick bushy hair, and a grizzled beard. His dress was of the antique Dutch fashion—a cloth jerkin strapped round the waist—several pair of breeches, the outer one of ample volume, decorated with rows of buttons down the sides, and bunches at the knees. He bore on his shoulder a stout keg, that seemed full of liquor, and made signs for Rip to approach and assist him with the load. Though rather shy and distrustful of this new acquaintance, Rip complied with his usual alacrity; and mutually relieving one another, they clambered up a narrow gully, apparently the dry bed of a mountain torrent. As they ascended, Rip every now and then heard long rolling peals, like distant thunder, that seemed to issue out of a deep ravine, or rather cleft, between lofty rocks, toward which their rugged path conducted. He paused for an instant, but supposing it to be the muttering of one of those transient thunder-showers which often take place in mountain heights, he proceeded. Passing through the ravine, they came to a hollow, like a small amphitheatre, surrounded by perpendicular precipices, over the brinks of which impending trees shot their branches, so that you only caught glimpses of the azure sky and the bright evening cloud. During the whole time Rip and his companion had labored on in silence; for though the former marvelled greatly what could be the object of carrying a keg of liquor up this wild mountain, yet there was something strange and incomprehensible about the unknown, that inspired awe and checked familiarity.

On entering the amphitheatre, new objects of wonder presented themselves. On a level spot in the centre was a company of odd-looking personages playing at nine-pins. They were dressed in a quaint outlandish fashion; some wore short doublets, others jerkins, with long knives in their belts, and most of them had enormous breeches, of similar style with that of the guide's. Their visages, too, were peculiar: one had a large beard, broad face, and small piggish eyes: the face of another seemed to consist entirely of nose, and was surmounted by a white sugar-loaf hat set off with a little red cock's tail. They all had beards, of various shapes and colors. There was one who seemed to be the commander. He was a stout old gentleman, with a weather-beaten countenance; he wore a laced doublet, broad belt and hanger, high-crowned hat and feather, red stockings, and high-heeled shoes, with roses in them. The whole group reminded Rip of the figures in an old Flemish painting, in the parlor of Dominie Van Shaick, the village parson, and which had been brought over from Holland at the time of the settlement.

What seemed particularly odd to Rip was, that though these folks were evidently amusing themselves, yet they maintained the gravest faces, the most mysterious silence, and were, withal, the most melancholy party of pleasure he had ever witnessed. Nothing interrupted the stillness of the scene but the noise of the balls, which, whenever they were rolled, echoed along the mountains like rumbling peals of thunder.

As Rip and his companion approached them, they suddenly desisted from their play, and stared at him with such fixed statue-like gaze, and such strange, uncouth, lack-lustre countenances, that his heart turned within him, and his knees smote together. His companion now emptied the contents of the keg into large flagons, and made signs to him to wait upon the company. He obeyed with fear and trembling; they quaffed the liquor in profound silence, and then returned to their game.

By degrees Rip's awe and apprehension subsided. He even ventured, when no eye was fixed upon him, to taste the beverage, which he found had much of the flavor of excellent Hollands. He was naturally a thirsty soul, and was soon tempted to repeat the draught. One taste provoked another; and he reiterated his visits to the flagon so often that at length his senses were overpowered, his eyes swam in his head, his head gradually declined, and he fell into a deep sleep.

On waking, he found himself on the green knoll whence he had first seen the old man of the glen. He rubbed his eyes—it was a bright sunny morning. The birds were hopping and twittering among the bushes, and the eagle was wheeling aloft, and breasting the pure mountain breeze. "Surely," thought Rip, "I have not slept here all night." He recalled the occurrences before he fell asleep. The strange man with a keg of liquor—the mountain ravine—the wild retreat among the rocks—the woebegone party at nine-pins—the flagon—"Oh! that flagon! that wicked flagon!" thought Rip—"what excuse shall I make to Dame Van Winkle!"

He looked round for his gun, but in place of the clean well-oiled fowling-piece, he found an old firelock lying by him, the barrel incrusted with rust, the lock falling off, and the stock worm-eaten. He now suspected that the grave roysters of the mountain had put a trick upon him, and, having dosed him with liquor, had robbed him of his gun. Wolf, too, had disappeared, but he might have strayed away after a squirrel or partridge. He whistled after him and shouted his name, but all in vain; the echoes repeated his whistle and shout, but no dog was to be seen.

He determined to revisit the scene of the last evening's gambol, and if he met with any of the party, to demand his dog and gun. As he rose to walk, he found himself stiff in the joints, and wanting in his usual activity. "These mountain beds do not agree with me," thought Rip, "and if this frolic should lay me up with a fit of the rheumatism, I shall have a blessed time with Dame Van Winkle." With some difficulty he got down into the glen: he found the gully up which he and his companion had ascended the preceding evening; but to his astonishment a mountain stream was now foaming down it, leaping from rock to rock, and filling the glen with babbling murmurs. He, however, made shift to scramble up its sides, working his toilsome way through thickets of birch, sassafras, and witch-hazel, and sometimes tripped up or entangled by the wild grapevines that twisted their coils or tendrils from tree to tree, and spread a kind of network in his path.

At length he reached to where the ravine had opened through the cliffs to the amphitheatre; but no traces of such opening remained. The rocks presented a high impenetrable wall over which the torrent came tumbling in a sheet of feathery foam, and fell into a broad deep basin, black from the shadows of the surrounding forest. Here, then, poor Rip was brought to a stand. He again called and whistled after his dog; he was only answered by the cawing of a flock of idle crows, sporting high in air about a dry tree that overhung a sunny precipice; and who, secure in their elevation, seemed to look down and scoff at the poor man's perplexities. What was to be done? the morning was passing away, and Rip felt famished for want of his breakfast. He grieved to give up his dog and gun; he dreaded to meet his wife; but it would not do to starve among the mountains. He shook his head, shouldered the rusty firelock, and, with a heart full of trouble and anxiety, turned his steps homeward.

As he approached the village he met a number of people, but none whom he knew, which somewhat surprised him, for he had thought himself acquainted with every one in the country round. Their dress, too, was of a different fashion from that to which he was accustomed. They all stared at him with equal marks of surprise, and whenever they cast their eyes upon him, invariably stroked their chins. The constant recurrence of this gesture induced Rip, involuntarily, to do the same, when, to his astonishment, he found his beard had grown a foot long!

He had now entered the skirts of the village. A troop of strange children ran at his heels, hooting after him, and pointing at his gray beard. The dogs, too, not one of which he recognized for an old acquaintance, barked at him as he passed. The very village was altered; it was larger and more populous. There were rows of houses which he had never seen before, and those which had been his familiar haunts had disappeared. Strange names were over the doors—strange faces at the windows—every thing was strange. His mind now misgave him; he began to doubt whether both he and the world around him were not bewitched. Surely this was his native village, which he had left but the day before. There stood the Kaatskill mountains—there ran the silver Hudson at a distance—there was every hill and dale precisely as it had always been—Rip was sorely perplexed—"That flagon last night," thought he, "has addled my poor head sadly!"

It was with some difficulty that he found the way to his own house, which he approached with silent awe, expecting every moment to hear the shrill voice of Dame Van Winkle. He found the house gone to decay—the roof fallen in, the windows shattered, and the doors off the hinges. A half-starved dog that looked like Wolf was skulking about it. Rip called him by name, but the cur snarled, showed his teeth, and passed on. This was an unkind cut indeed—"My very dog," sighed poor Rip, "has forgotten me!"

He entered the house, which, to tell the truth, Dame Van Winkle had always kept in neat order. It was empty, forlorn, and apparently abandoned. This desolateness overcame all his connubial fears—he called loudly for his wife and children—the lonely chambers rang for a moment with his voice, and then all again was silence.

He now hurried forth, and hastened to his old resort, the village inn—but it too was gone. A large rickety wooden building stood in its place, with great gaping windows, some of them broken and mended with old hats and petticoats, and over the door was painted, "the Union Hotel, by Jonathan Doolittle." Instead of the great tree that used to shelter the quiet little Dutch inn of yore, there now was reared a tall naked pole, with something on the top that looked like a red night-cap, and from it was fluttering a flag, on which was a singular assemblage of stars and stripes—all this was strange and incomprehensible. He recognized on the sign, however, the ruby face of King George, under which he had smoked so many a peaceful pipe; but even this was singularly metamorphosed. The red coat was changed for one of blue and buff, a sword was held in the hand instead of a sceptre, the head was decorated with a cocked hat, and underneath was painted in large characters, GENERAL WASHINGTON.

There was, as usual, a crowd of folk about the door, but none that Rip recollected. The very character of the people seemed changed. There was a busy, bustling, disputatious tone about it, instead of the accustomed phlegm and drowsy tranquillity. He looked in vain for the sage Nicholas Vedder, with his broad face, double chin, and fair long pipe, uttering clouds of tobacco-smoke instead of idle speeches; or Van Bummel, the schoolmaster, doling forth the contents of an ancient newspaper. In place of these, a lean, bilious-looking fellow, with his pockets full of handbills, was haranguing vehemently about rights of citizens—elections—members of congress—liberty—Bunker's Hill—heroes of seventy-six—and other words, which were a perfect Babylonish jargon to the bewildered Van Winkle.

The appearance of Rip, with his long grizzled beard, his rusty fowling-piece, his uncouth dress, and an army of women and children at his heels, soon attracted the attention of the tavern politicians. They crowded round him, eyeing him from head to foot with great curiosity. The orator bustled up to him, and, drawing him partly aside, inquired "on which side he voted?" Rip stared in vacant stupidity. Another short but busy little fellow pulled him by the arm, and, rising on tiptoe, inquired in his ear, "Whether he was Federal or Democrat?" Rip was equally at a loss to comprehend the question; when a knowing, self-important old gentleman, in a sharp cocked hat, made his way through the crowd, putting them to the right and left with his elbows as he passed, and planting himself before Van Winkle, with one arm akimbo, the other resting on his cane, his keen eyes and sharp hat penetrating, as it were, into his very soul, demanded in an austere tone, "what brought him to the election with a gun on his shoulder, and a mob at his heels, and whether he meant to breed a riot in the village?"—"Alas! gentlemen," cried Rip, somewhat dismayed, "I am a poor quiet man, a native of the place, and a loyal subject of the king, God bless him!"

Here a general shout burst from the by-standers—"A tory! a tory! a spy! a refugee! hustle him! away with him!" It was with great difficulty that the self-important man in the cocked hat restored order; and, having assumed a tenfold austeriy of brow, demanded again of the unknown culprit, what he came there for, and whom he was seeking? The poor man humbly assured him that he meant no harm, but merely came there in search of some of his neighbors, who used to keep about the tavern.

"Well—who are they?—name them."

Rip bethought himself a moment, and inquired, "Where's Nicholas Vedder?"

There was a silence for a little while, when an old man replied, in a thin piping voice, "Nicholas Vedder! why, he is dead and gone these eighteen years! There was a wooden tombstone in the church-yard that used to tell all about him, but that's rotten and gone too."

"Where's Brom Dutcher?"

"Oh, he went off to the army in the beginning of the war; some say he was killed at the storming of Stony Point—others say he was drowned in a squall at the foot of Antony's Nose. I don't know—he never came back again."

"Where's Van Bummel, the schoolmaster?"

"He went off to the wars too, was a great militia general, and is now in congress."

Rip's heart died away at hearing of these sad changes in his home and friends, and finding himself thus alone in the world. Every answer puzzled him too, by treating of such enormous lapses of time, and of matters which he could not understand: war—congress—Stony Point—he had no courage to ask after any more friends, but cried out in despair, "Does nobody here know Rip Van Winkle?"

"Oh, Rip Van Winkle!" exclaimed two or three, "Oh, to be sure! that's Rip Van Winkle yonder, leaning against the tree."

Rip looked, and beheld a precise counterpart of himself, as he went up the mountain: apparently as lazy, and certainly as ragged. The poor fellow was now completely confounded. He doubted his own identity, and whether he was himself or another man. In the midst of his bewilderment, the man in the cocked hat demanded who he was, and what was his name?

"God knows," exclaimed he, at his wit's end; "I'm not myself—I'm somebody else—that's me yonder—no—that's somebody else got into my shoes—I was myself last night, but I fell asleep on the mountain, and they've changed my gun, and every thing's changed, and I'm changed, and I can't tell what's my name, or who I am!"

The by-standers began now to look at each other, nod, wink significantly, and tap their fingers against their foreheads. There was a whisper, also, about securing the gun, and keeping the old fellow from doing mischief, at the very suggestion of which the self-important man in the cocked hat retired with some precipitation. At this critical moment a fresh comely woman pressed through the throng to get a peep at the gray-bearded man. She had a chubby child in her arms, which, frightened at his looks, began to cry. "Hush, Rip," cried she, "hush, you little fool; the old man won't hurt you." The name of the child, the air of the mother, the tone of her voice, all awakened a train of recollections in his mind. "What is your name, my good woman?" asked he.

"Judith Gardenier."

"And your father's name?"

"Ah, poor man, Rip Van Winkle was his name, but it's twenty years since he went away from home with his gun, and never has been heard of since—his dog came home without him; but whether he shot himself, or was carried away by the Indians, nobody can tell. I was then but a little girl."

Rip had but one question more to ask; but he put it with a faltering voice:

"Where's your mother?"

"Oh, she too had died but a short time since; she broke a blood-vessel in a fit of passion at a New-England peddler."

There was a drop of comfort, at least, in this intelligence. The honest man could contain himself no longer. He caught his daughter and her child in his arms. "I am your father!" cried he—"Young Rip Van Winkle once—old Rip Van Winkle now! Does nobody know poor Rip Van Winkle?"

All stood amazed, until an old woman, tottering out from among the crowd, put her hand to her brow, and peering under it in his face for a moment, exclaimed, "Sure enough! it is Rip Van Winkle—it is himself! Welcome home again, old neighbor —Why, where have you been these twenty long years?"

Rip's story was soon told, for the whole twenty years had been to him but as one night. The neighbors stared when they heard it; some were seen to wink at each other, and put their tongues in their cheeks: and the self-important man in the cocked hat, who, when the alarm was over, had returned to the field, screwed down the corners of his mouth, and shook his head—upon which there was a general shaking of the head throughout the assemblage.

It was determined, however, to take the opinion of old Peter Vanderdonk, who was seen slowly advancing up the road. He was a descendant of the historian of that name, who wrote one of the earliest accounts of the province. Peter was the most ancient inhabitant of the village, and well versed in all the wonderful events and traditions of the neighborhood. He recollected Rip at once, and corroborated his story in the most satisfactory manner. He assured the company that it was a fact, handed down from his ancestor the historian, that the Kaatskill mountains had always been haunted by strange beings. That it was affirmed that the great Hendrick Hudson, the first discoverer of the river and country, kept a kind of vigil there every twenty years, with his crew of the Half-moon; being permitted in this way to revisit the scenes of his enterprise, and keep a guardian eye upon the river, and the great city called by his name. That his father had once seen them in their old Dutch dresses playing at nine-pins in a hollow of the mountain; and that he himself had heard, one summer afternoon, the sound of their balls, like distant peals of thunder.

To make a long story short, the company broke up, and returned to the more important concerns of the election. Rip's daughter took him home to live with her; she had a snug, well-furnished house, and a stout cheery farmer for a husband, whom Rip recollected for one of the urchins that used to climb upon his back. As to Rip's son and heir, who was the ditto of himself, seen leaning against the tree, he was employed to work on the farm; but evinced an hereditary disposition to attend to any thing else but his business.

Rip now resumed his old walks and habits; he soon found many of his former cronies, though all rather the worse for the wear and tear of time; and preferred making friends among the rising generation, with whom he soon grew into great favor.

Having nothing to do at home, and being arrived at that happy age when a man can be idle with impunity, he took his place once more on the bench at the inn door, and was reverenced as one of the patriarchs of the village, and a chronicle of the old times "before the war." It was some time before he could get into the regular track of gossip, or could be made to comprehend the strange events that had taken place during his torpor. How that there had been a revolutionary war—that the country had thrown off the yoke of old England—and that, instead of being a subject of his Majesty George the Third, he was now a free citizen of the United States. Rip, in fact, was no politician; the changes of states and empires made but little impression on him; but there was one species of despotism under which he had long groaned, and that was—petticoat government. Happily that was at an end; he had got his neck out of the yoke of matrimony, and could go in and out whenever he pleased, without dreading the tyranny of Dame Van Winkle. Whenever her name was mentioned, however, he shook his head, shrugged his shoulders, and cast up his eyes; which might pass either for an expression of resignation to his fate, or joy at his deliverance.

He used to tell his story to every stranger that arrived at Mr. Doolittle's hotel. He was observed, at first, to vary on some points every time he told it, which was, doubtless, owing to his having so recently awaked. It at last settled down precisely to the tale I have related, and not a man, woman, or child in the neighborhood, but knew it by heart. Some always pretended to doubt the reality of it, and insisted that Rip had been out of his head, and that this was one point on which he always remained flighty. The old Dutch inhabitants, however, almost universally gave it full credit. Even to this day they never hear a thunderstorm of a summer afternoon about the Kaatskill, but they say Hendrick Hudson and his crew are at their game of nine-pins; and it is a common wish of all hen-pecked husbands in the neighborhood, when life hangs heavy on their hands, that they might have a quieting draught out of Rip Van Winkle's flagon.

NOTE

The foregoing Tale, one would suspect, had been suggested to Mr. Knickerbocker by a little German superstition about the Emperor Frederick *der Rothbart*, and the Kypphaüser mountain: the subjoined note, however, which he had appended to the tale, shows that it is an absolute fact, narrated with his usual fidelity:

"The story of Rip Van Winkle may seem incredible to many, but nevertheless I give it my full belief, for I know the vicinity of our old Dutch settlements to have been very subject to marvellous events and appearances. Indeed, I have heard many stranger stories than this, in the villages along the Hudson; all of which were too well authenticated to admit of a doubt. I have even talked with Rip Van Winkle myself, who, when last I saw him, was a very venerable old man, and so perfectly rational and consistent on every other point, that I think no conscientious person could refuse to take this into the bargain; nay, I have seen a certificate on the subject taken before a country justice and signed with a cross, in the justice's own handwriting. The story, therefore, is beyond the possibility of doubt.

D. K."

POSTSCRIPT

The following are travelling notes from a memorandum-book of Mr. Knickerbocker:

The Kaatsberg, or Catskill mountains, have always been a region full of fable. The Indians considered them the abode of spirits, who influenced the weather, spreading sunshine or clouds over the landscape, and sending good or bad hunting seasons. They were ruled by an old squaw spirit, said to be their mother. She dwelt on the highest peak of the Catskills, and had charge of the doors of day and night to open and shut them at the proper hour. She hung up the new moons in the skies, and cut up the old ones into stars. In times of drought, if properly propitiated, she would spin light summer clouds out of cobwebs and morning dew, and send them off from the crest of the mountain, flake after flake, like flakes of carded cotton, to float in the air; until, dissolved by the heat of the sun, they would fall in gentle showers, causing the grass to spring, the fruits to ripen, and the corn to grow an inch an hour. If displeased, however, she would brew up clouds black as ink, sitting in the midst of them like a bottle-bellied spider in the midst of its web; and when these clouds broke, woe betide the valleys!

In old times, say the Indian traditions, there was a kind of Manitou or Spirit, who kept about the wildest recesses of the Catskill Mountains, and took a mischievous pleasure in wreaking all kinds of evils and vexations upon the red men. Sometimes he would assume the form of a bear, a panther, or a deer, lead the bewildered hunter a weary chase through tangled forests and among ragged rocks; and then spring off with a loud ho! ho! leaving him aghast on the brink of a beetling precipice or raging torrent.

The favorite abode of this Manitou is still shown. It is a great rock or cliff on the loneliest part of the mountains, and, from the flowering vines which clamber about it, and the wild flowers which abound in its neighborhood, is known by the name of the Garden Rock. Near the foot of it is a small lake, the haunt of the solitary bittern, with water-snakes basking in the sun on the leaves of the pond-lilies which lie on the surface. This place was held in great awe by the Indians, insomuch that the boldest hunter would not pursue his game within its precincts. Once upon a time, however, a hunter who had lost his way, penetrated to the garden rock, where he beheld a number of gourds placed in the crotches of trees. One of these he seized and made off with it, but in the hurry of his retreat he let it fall among the rocks, when a great stream gushed forth, which washed him away and swept him down precipices, where he was dashed to pieces, and the stream made its way to the Hudson, and continues to flow to the present day; being the identical stream known by the name of the Kaaters-kill.

The Legend of Sleepy Hollow

FOUND AMONG THE PAPERS OF THE
LATE DIEDRICH KNICKERBOCKER

A pleasing land of drowsy head it was,
Of dreams that wave before the half-shut eye;
And of gay castles in the clouds that pass,
Forever flushing round a summer sky.

CASTLE OF INDOLENCE

IN the bosom of one of those spacious coves which indent the eastern shore of the Hudson, at that broad expansion of the river denominated by the ancient Dutch navigators the Tappan Zee, and where they always prudently shortened sail, and implored the protection of St. Nicholas when they crossed, there lies a small market-town or rural port, which by some is called Greensburgh, but which is more generally and properly known by the name of Tarry Town. This name was given, we are told, in former days, by the good housewives of the adjacent country, from the inveterate propensity of their husbands to linger about the village tavern on market days. Be that as it may, I do not vouch for the fact, but merely advert to it, for the sake of being precise and authentic. Not far from this village, perhaps about two miles, there is a little valley, or rather lap of land, among high hills, which is one of the quietest places in the whole world. A small brook glides through it, with just murmur enough to lull one to repose; and the occasional whistle of a quail, or tapping of a woodpecker, is almost the only sound that ever breaks in upon the uniform tranquillity.

I recollect that, when a stripling, my first exploit in squirrel-shooting was in a grove of tall walnut-trees that shades one side of the valley. I had wandered into it at noon time, when all nature is peculiarly quiet, and was startled by the roar of my own gun, as it broke the Sabbath stillness around, and was prolonged and reverberated by the angry echoes. If ever I should wish for a retreat, whither I might steal from the world and its distractions, and dream quietly away the remnant of a troubled life, I know of none more promising than this little valley.

From the listless repose of the place, and the peculiar character of its inhabitants, who are descendants from the original Dutch settlers, this sequestered glen has long been known by the name of SLEEPY HOLLOW, and its rustic lads are called the Sleepy Hollow Boys throughout all the neighboring country. A drowsy, dreamy influence seems to hang over the land, and to pervade the very atmosphere. Some say that the place was bewitched by a high German doctor, during the early days of the settlement; others, that an old Indian chief, the prophet or wizard of his tribe, held his pow-wows there before the country was discovered by Master Hendrick Hudson. Certain it is, the place still continues under the sway of some witching power, that holds a spell over the minds of the good people, causing them to walk in a continual reverie. They are given to all kinds of marvellous beliefs; are subject to trances and visions; and frequently see strange sights, and hear music and voices in the air. The whole neighborhood abounds with local tales, haunted spots, and twilight superstitions; stars shoot and meteors glare oftener across the valley than in any other part of the country, and the nightmare, with her whole nine fold, seems to make it the favorite scene of her gambols.

The dominant spirit, however, that haunts this enchanted region, and seems to be commander-in-chief of all the powers of the air, is the apparition of a figure on horseback without a head. It is said by some to be the ghost of a Hessian trooper, whose head had been carried away by a cannon-ball, in some nameless battle during the revolutionary war; and who is ever and anon seen by the country folk, hurrying along in the gloom of night, as if on the wings of the wind. His haunts are not confined to the valley, but extend at times to the adjacent roads, and especially to the vicinity of a church at no great distance. Indeed, certain of the most authentic historians of those parts, who have been careful in collecting and collating the floating facts concerning this spectre, allege that the body of the trooper, having been buried in the church-yard, the ghost rides forth to the scene of battle in nightly quest of his head; and that the rushing speed with which he sometimes passes along the Hollow, like a midnight blast, is owing to his being belated, and in a hurry to get back to the church-yard before daybreak.

Such is the general purport of this legendary superstition, which has furnished materials for many a wild story in that region of shadows; and the spectre is known, at all the country firesides, by the name of the Headless Horseman of Sleepy Hollow.

It is remarkable that the visionary propensity I have mentioned is not confined to the native inhabitants of the valley, but is unconsciously imbibed by every one who resides there for a time. However wide awake they may have been before they entered that sleepy region, they are sure, in a little time, to inhale the witching influence of the air, and begin to grow imaginative —to dream dreams, and see apparitions.

I mention this peaceful spot with all possible laud; for it is in such little retired Dutch valleys, found here and there embosomed in the great State of New-York, that population, manners, and customs, remain fixed; while the great torrent of migration and improvement, which is making such incessant changes in other parts of this restless country, sweeps by them unobserved. They are like those little nooks of still water which border a rapid stream; where we may see the straw and bubble riding quietly at anchor, or slowly revolving in their mimic harbor, undisturbed by the rush of the passing current. Though many years have elapsed since I trod the drowsy shades of Sleepy Hollow, yet I question whether I should not still find the same trees and the same families vegetating in its sheltered bosom.

In this by-place of nature, there abode, in a remote period of American history, that is to say, some thirty years since, a worthy wight of the name of Ichabod Crane; who sojourned, or, as he expressed it, "tarried," in Sleepy Hollow, for the purpose of instructing the children of the vicinity. He was a native of Connecticut; a State which supplies the Union with pioneers for the mind as well as for the forest, and sends forth yearly its legions of frontier woodsmen and country schoolmasters. The cognomen of Crane was not inapplicable to his person. He was tall, but exceedingly lank, with narrow shoulders, long arms and legs, hands that dangled a mile out of his sleeves, feet that might have served for shovels, and his whole frame most loosely hung together. His head was small, and flat at top, with huge ears, large green glassy eyes, and a long snipe nose, so that it looked like a weather-cock, perched upon his spindle neck, to tell which way the wind blew. To see him striding along the profile of a hill on a windy day, with his clothes bagging and fluttering about him, one might have mistaken him for the genius of famine descending upon the earth, or some scarecrow eloped from a cornfield.

His school-house was a low building of one large room, rudely constructed of logs; the windows partly glazed, and partly patched with leaves of old copy-books. It was most ingeniously secured at vacant hours, by a withe twisted in the handle of the door, and stakes set against the window shutters; so that, though a thief might get in with perfect ease, he would find some embarrassment in getting out; an idea most probably borrowed by the architect, Yost Van Houten, from the mystery of an eel-pot. The school-house stood in a rather lonely but pleasant situation, just at the foot of a woody hill, with a brook running close by, and a formidable birch tree growing at one end of it. From hence the low murmur of his pupils' voices, conning over their lessons, might be heard in a drowsy summer's day, like the hum of a beehive; interrupted now and then by the authoritative voice of the master, in the tone of menace or command; or, peradventure, by the appalling sound of the birch, as he urged some tardy loiterer along the flowery path of knowledge. Truth to say, he was a conscientious man, and ever bore in mind the golden maxim, "Spare the rod and spoil the child." Ichabod Crane's scholars certainly were not spoiled.

I would not have it imagined, however, that he was one of those cruel potentates of the school, who joy in the smart of their subjects; on the contrary, he administered justice with discrimination rather than severity; taking the burthen off the backs of the weak, and laying it on those of the strong. Your mere puny stripling, that winced at the least flourish of the rod, was passed by with indulgence; but the claims of justice were satisfied by inflicting a double portion on some little, tough, wrong-headed, broad-skirted Dutch urchin, who sulked and swelled and grew dogged and sullen beneath the birch. All this he called "doing his duty by their parents;" and he never inflicted a chastisement without following it by the assurance, so consolatory to the smarting urchin, that "he would remember it, and thank him for it the longest day he had to live."

When school hours were over, he was even the companion and playmate of the larger boys; and on holiday afternoons would convoy some of the smaller ones home, who happened to have pretty sisters, or good housewives for mothers, noted for the comforts of the cupboard. Indeed it behooved him to keep on good terms with his pupils. The revenue arising from his school was small, and would have been scarcely sufficient to furnish him with daily bread, for he was a huge feeder, and though lank, had the dilating powers of an anaconda; but to help out his maintenance, he was, according to country custom in those parts, boarded and lodged at the houses of the farmers, whose children he instructed. With these he lived successively a week at a time; thus going the rounds of the neighborhood, with all his worldly effects tied up in a cotton handkerchief.

That all this might not be too onerous on the purses of his rustic patrons, who are apt to consider the costs of schooling a grievous burden, and schoolmasters as mere drones, he had various ways of rendering himself both useful and agreeable. He assisted the farmers occasionally in the lighter labors of their farms; helped to make hay; mended the fences; took the horses to water; drove the cows from pasture; and cut wood for the winter fire. He laid aside, too, all the dominant dignity and absolute sway with which he lorded it in his little empire, the school, and became wonderfully gentle and ingratiating. He found favor in the eyes of the mothers, by petting the children, particularly the youngest; and like the lion bold, which whilom so magnanimously the lamb did hold, he would sit with a child on one knee, and rock a cradle with his foot for whole hours together.

In addition to his other vocations, he was the singing-master of the neighborhood, and picked up many bright shillings by instructing the young folks in psalmody. It was a matter of no little vanity to him, on Sundays, to take his station in front of the church gallery, with a band of chosen singers; where, in his own mind, he completely carried away the palm from the parson. Certain it is, his voice resounded far above all the rest of the congregation; and there are peculiar quavers still to be heard in that church, and which may even be heard half a mile off, quite to the opposite side of the mill-pond, on a still Sunday morning, which are said to be legitimately descended from the nose of Ichabod Crane. Thus, by divers little make-shifts in that ingenious way which is commonly denominated "by hook and by crook," the worthy pedagogue got on tolerably enough, and was thought, by all who understood nothing of the labor of headwork, to have a wonderfully easy life of it.

The schoolmaster is generally a man of some importance in the female circle of a rural neighborhood; being considered a kind of idle gentlemanlike personage, of vastly superior taste and accomplishments to the rough country swains, and, indeed, inferior in learning only to the parson. His appearance, therefore, is apt to occasion some little stir at the tea-table of a farmhouse, and the addition of a supernumerary dish of cakes or sweetmeats, or, peradventure, the parade of a silver tea-pot. Our man of letters, therefore, was peculiarly happy in the smiles of all the country damsels. How he would figure among them in the churchyard, between services on Sundays! gathering grapes for them from the wild vines that overrun the surrounding trees; reciting for their amusement all the epitaphs on the tombstones; or sauntering, with a whole bevy of them, along the banks of the adjacent mill-pond; while the more bashful country bumpkins hung sheepishly back, envying his superior elegance and address.

From his half itinerant life, also, he was a kind of travelling gazette, carrying the whole budget of local gossip from house to house; so that his appearance was always greeted with satisfaction. He was, moreover, esteemed by the women as a man of great erudition, for he had read several books quite through, and was a perfect master of Cotton Mather's history of New England Witchcraft, in which, by the way, he most firmly and potently believed.

He was, in fact, an odd mixture of small shrewdness and simple credulity. His appetite for the marvellous, and his powers of digesting it, were equally extraordinary; and both had been increased by his residence in this spellbound region. No tale was too gross or monstrous for his capacious swallow. It was often his delight, after his school was dismissed in the afternoon, to stretch himself on the rich bed of clover, bordering the little brook that whimpered by his school-house, and there con over old Mather's direful tales, until the gathering dusk of the evening made the printed page a mere mist before his eyes. Then, as he wended his way, by swamp and stream and awful woodland, to the farm-house where he happened to be quartered, every sound of nature, at that witching hour, fluttered his excited imagination: the moan of the whip-poor-will * from the hill-side; the boding cry of the tree-toad, that harbinger of storm; the dreary hooting of the screech-owl, or the sudden rustling in the thicket of birds frightened from their roost. The fire-flies, too, which sparkled most vividly in the darkest places, now and then startled him, as one of uncommon brightness would stream across his path; and if, by chance, a huge blockhead of a beetle came winging his blundering flight against him, the poor varlet was ready to give up the ghost, with the idea that he was struck with a witch's token. His only resource on such occasions, either to drown thought, or drive away evil spirits, was to sing psalm tunes; and the good people of Sleepy Hollow, as they sat by their doors of an evening, were often filled with awe, at hearing his nasal melody, "in linked sweetness long drawn out," floating from the distant hill, or along the dusky road.

Another of his sources of fearful pleasure was, to pass long winter evenings with the old Dutch wives, as they sat spinning by the fire, with a row of apples roasting and spluttering along the hearth, and listen to their marvellous tales of ghosts and goblins, and haunted fields, and haunted brooks, and haunted bridges, and haunted houses, and particularly of the headless horseman, or galloping Hessian of the Hollow, as they sometimes called him. He would delight them equally by his anecdotes of witchcraft, and of the direful omens and portentous sights and sounds in the air, which prevailed in the earlier times of Connecticut; and would frighten them wofully with speculations upon comets and shooting stars; and with the alarming fact that the world did absolutely turn round, and that they were half the time topsy-turvy!

But if there was a pleasure in all this, while snugly cuddling in the chimney corner of a chamber that was all of a ruddy glow

* The whip-poor-will is a bird which is only heard at night. It receives its name from its note, which is thought to resemble those words.

from the crackling wood fire, and where, of course, no spectre dared to show his face, it was dearly purchased by the terrors of his subsequent walk homewards. What fearful shapes and shadows beset his path amidst the dim and ghastly glare of a snowy night!—With what wistful look did he eye every trembling ray of light streaming across the waste fields from some distant window!—How often was he appalled by some shrub covered with snow, which, like a sheeted spectre, beset his very path!—How often did he shrink with curdling awe at the sound of his own steps on the frosty crust beneath his feet; and dread to look over his shoulder, lest he should behold some uncouth being tramping close behind him!—and how often was he thrown into complete dismay by some rushing blast, howling among the trees, in the idea that it was the Galloping Hessian on one of his nightly scourings!

All these, however, were mere terrors of the night, phantoms of the mind that walk in darkness; and though he had seen many spectres in his time, and been more than once beset by Satan in divers shapes, in his lonely perambulations, yet daylight put an end to all these evils; and he would have passed a pleasant life of it, in despite of the devil and all his works, if his path had not been crossed by a being that causes more perplexity to mortal man than ghosts, goblins, and the whole race of witches put together, and that was—a woman.

Among the musical disciples who assembled, one evening in each week, to receive his instructions in psalmody, was Katrina Van Tassel, the daughter and only child of a substantial Dutch farmer. She was a blooming lass of fresh eighteen; plump as a partridge; ripe and melting and rosy cheeked as one of her father's peaches, and universally famed, not merely for her beauty, but her vast expectations. She was withal a little of a coquette, as might be perceived even in her dress, which was a mixture of ancient and modern fashions, as most suited to set off her charms. She wore the ornaments of pure yellow gold, which her great-great-grandmother had brought over from Saardam; the tempting stomacher of the olden time; and withal a provokingly short petticoat, to display the prettiest foot and ankle in the country round.

Ichabod Crane had a soft and foolish heart towards the sex;

and it is not to be wondered at, that so tempting a morsel soon found favor in his eyes; more especially after he had visited her in her paternal mansion. Old Baltus Van Tassel was a perfect picture of a thriving, contented, liberal-hearted farmer. He seldom, it is true, sent either his eyes or his thoughts beyond the boundaries of his own farm; but within those every thing was snug, happy, and well-conditioned. He was satisfied with his wealth, but not proud of it; and piqued himself upon the hearty abundance, rather than the style in which he lived. His stronghold was situated on the banks of the Hudson, in one of those green, sheltered, fertile nooks, in which the Dutch farmers are so fond of nestling. A great elm-tree spread its broad branches over it; at the foot of which bubbled up a spring of the softest and sweetest water, in a little well, formed of a barrel; and then stole sparkling away through the grass, to a neighboring brook, that bubbled along among alders and dwarf willows. Hard by the farmhouse was a vast barn, that might have served for a church; every window and crevice of which seemed bursting forth with the treasures of the farm; the flail was busily resounding within it from morning to night; swallows and martins skimmed twittering about the eaves; and rows of pigeons, some with one eye turned up, as if watching the weather, some with their heads under their wings, or buried in their bosoms, and others swelling, and cooing, and bowing about their dames, were enjoying the sunshine on the roof. Sleek unwieldy porkers were grunting in the repose and abundance of their pens; whence sallied forth, now and then, troops of sucking pigs, as if to snuff the air. A stately squadron of snowy geese were riding in an adjoining pond, convoying whole fleets of ducks; regiments of turkeys were gobbling through the farmyard, and guinea fowls fretting about it, like ill-tempered housewives, with their peevish discontented cry. Before the barn door strutted the gallant cock, that pattern of a husband, a warrior, and a fine gentleman, clapping his burnished wings, and crowing in the pride and gladness of his heart—sometimes tearing up the earth with his feet, and then generously calling his ever-hungry family of wives and children to enjoy the rich morsel which he had discovered.

The pedagogue's mouth watered, as he looked upon this sumptuous promise of luxurious winter fare. In his devouring mind's eye, he pictured to himself every roasting-pig running about with a pudding in his belly, and an apple in his mouth; the pigeons were snugly put to bed in a comfortable pie, and tucked in with a coverlet of crust; the geese were swimming in their own gravy; and the ducks pairing cosily in dishes, like snug married couples, with a decent competency of onion sauce. In the porkers he saw carved out the future sleek side of bacon, and juicy relishing ham; not a turkey but he beheld daintily trussed up, with its gizzard under its wing, and, peradventure, a necklace of savory sausages; and even bright chanticleer himself lay sprawling on his back, in a side-dish, with uplifted claws, as if craving that quarter which his chivalrous spirit disdained to ask while living.

As the enraptured Ichabod fancied all this, and as he rolled his great green eyes over the fat meadow-lands, the rich fields of wheat, of rye, of buckwheat, and Indian corn, and the orchards burthened with ruddy fruit, which surrounded the warm tenement of Van Tassel, his heart yearned after the damsel who was to inherit these domains, and his imagination expanded with the idea, how they might be readily turned into cash, and the money invested in immense tracts of wild land, and shingle palaces in the wilderness. Nay, his busy fancy already realized his hopes, and presented to him the blooming Katrina, with a whole family of children, mounted on the top of a wagon loaded with household trumpery, with pots and kettles dangling beneath; and he beheld himself bestriding a pacing mare, with a colt at her heels, setting out for Kentucky, Tennessee, or the Lord knows where.

When he entered the house the conquest of his heart was complete. It was one of those spacious farmhouses, with high-ridged, but lowly-sloping roofs, built in the style handed down from the first Dutch settlers; the low projecting eaves forming a piazza along the front, capable of being closed up in bad weather. Under this were hung flails, harness, various utensils of husbandry, and nets for fishing in the neighboring river. Benches were built along the sides for summer use; and a great spinning-wheel at one end, and a churn at the other, showed the various uses to which this important porch might be devoted. From this piazza the wondering Ichabod entered the hall, which formed the centre of the mansion and the place of usual residence. Here, rows of resplendent pewter, ranged on a long dresser, dazzled his eyes. In one corner stood a huge bag of wool ready to be spun; in another a quantity of linsey-woolsey just from the loom; ears of Indian corn, and strings of dried apples and peaches, hung in gay festoons along the walls, mingled with the gaud of red peppers; and a door left ajar gave him a peep into the best parlor, where the claw-footed chairs, and dark mahogany tables, shone like mirrors; and irons, with their accompanying shovel and tongs, glistened from their covert of asparagus tops; mock-oranges and conch-shells decorated the mantelpiece; strings of various colored birds' eggs were suspended above it: a great ostrich egg was hung from the centre of the room, and a corner cupboard, knowingly left open, displayed immense treasures of old silver and well-mended china.

From the moment Ichabod laid his eyes upon these regions of delight, the peace of his mind was at an end, and his only study was how to gain the affections of the peerless daughter of Van Tassel. In this enterprise, however, he had more real difficulties than generally fell to the lot of a knight-errant of yore, who seldom had any thing but giants, enchanters, fiery dragons, and such like easily-conquered adversaries, to contend with; and had to make his way merely through gates of iron and brass, and walls of adamant, to the castle keep, where the lady of his heart was confined; all which he achieved as easily as a man would carve his way to the centre of a Christmas pie; and then the lady gave him her hand as a matter of course. Ichabod, on the contrary, had to win his way to the heart of a country coquette, beset with a labyrinth of whims and caprices, which were for ever presenting new difficulties and impediments; and he had to encounter a host of fearful adversaries of real flesh and blood, the numerous rustic admirers, who beset every portal to her heart; keeping a watchful and angry eye upon each other, but ready to fly out in the common cause against any new competitor.

Among these the most formidable was a burly, roaring, roystering blade, of the name of Abraham, or, according to the Dutch abbreviation, Brom Van Brunt, the hero of the country round, which rang with his feats of strength and hardihood. He was broad-shouldered and double-jointed, with short curly black hair, and a bluff, but not unpleasant countenance, having a mingled air of fun and arrogance. From his Herculean frame and great powers of limb, he had received the nickname of Brom Bones, by which he was universally known. He was famed for great knowledge and skill in horsemanship, being as dexterous on horseback as a Tartar. He was foremost at all races and cock-fights; and, with the ascendency which bodily strength acquires in rustic life, was the umpire in all disputes, setting his hat on one side, and giving his decisions with an air and tone admitting of no gainsay or appeal. He was always ready for either a fight or a frolic; but had more mischief than ill-will in his composition; and, with all his overbearing roughness, there was a strong dash of waggish good humor at bottom. He had three or four boon companions, who regarded him as their model, and at the head of whom he scoured the country, attending every scene of feud or merriment for miles round. In cold weather he was distinguished by a fur cap, surmounted with a flaunting fox's tail; and when the folks at a country gathering descried this well-known crest at a distance, whisking about among a squad of hard riders, they always stood by for a squall. Sometimes his crew would be heard dashing along past the farmhouses at midnight, with whoop and halloo, like a troop of Don Cossacks; and the old dames, startled out of their sleep, would listen for a moment till the hurry-scurry had clattered by, and then exclaim, "Ay, there goes Brom Bones and his gang!" The neighbors looked upon him with a mixture of awe, admiration, and good will; and when any madcap prank, or rustic brawl, occurred in the vicinity, always shook their heads, and warranted Brom Bones was at the bottom of it.

This rantipole hero had for some time singled out the blooming Katrina for the object of his uncouth gallantries, and though his amorous toyings were something like the gentle caresses and endearments of a bear, yet it was whispered that she did not altogether discourage his hopes. Certain it is, his advances were signals for rival candidates to retire, who felt no inclination to cross a lion in his amours; insomuch, that when his horse was seen tied to Van Tassel's paling, on a Sunday night, a sure sign that his master was courting, or as it is termed, "sparking," within, all other suitors passed by in despair, and carried the war into other quarters.

Such was the formidable rival with whom Ichabod Crane had to contend, and, considering all things, a stouter man than he would have shrunk from the competition, and a wiser man would have despaired. He had, however, a happy mixture of pliability and perseverance in his nature; he was in form and spirit like a supple-jack—yielding, but tough; though he bent, he never broke; and though he bowed beneath the slightest pressure, yet, the moment it was away—jerk! he was as erect, and carried his head as high as ever.

To have taken the field openly against his rival would have been madness; for he was not a man to be thwarted in his amours, any more than that stormy lover, Achilles. Ichabod, therefore, made his advances in a quiet and gently-insinuating manner. Under cover of his character of singing-master, he made frequent visits at the farmhouse; not that he had any thing to apprehend from the meddlesome interference of parents, which is so often a stumbling-block in the path of lovers. Balt Van Tassel was an easy indulgent soul; he loved his daughter better even than his pipe, and, like a reasonable man and an excellent father, let her have her way in every thing. His notable little wife, too, had enough to do to attend to her housekeeping and manage her poultry; for, as she sagely observed, ducks and geese are foolish things, and must be looked after, but girls can take care of themselves. Thus while the busy dame bustled about the house, or plied her spinning-wheel at one end of the piazza, honest Balt would sit smoking his evening pipe at the other, watching the achievements of a little wooden warrior, who, armed with a sword in each hand, was most valiantly fighting the wind on the pinnacle of the barn. In the mean time, Ichabod would carry on his suit with the daughter by the side of the spring under the great elm, or sauntering along in the twilight, that hour so favorable to the lover's eloquence.

I profess not to know how women's hearts are wooed and won. To me they have always been matters of riddle and admiration. Some seem to have but one vulnerable point, or door of access; while others have a thousand avenues, and may be captured in a thousand different ways. It is a great triumph of skill to gain the former, but a still greater proof of generalship to maintain possession of the latter, for the man must battle for his fortress at every door and window. He who wins a thousand common hearts is therefore entitled to some renown; but he who keeps undisputed sway over the heart of a coquette, is indeed a hero. Certain it is, this was not the case with the redoubtable Brom Bones; and from the moment Ichabod Crane made his advances, the interests of the former evidently declined; his horse was no longer seen tied at the palings on Sunday nights, and a deadly feud gradually arose between him and the preceptor of Sleepy Hollow.

Brom, who had a degree of rough chivalry in his nature, would fain have carried matters to open warfare, and have settled their pretensions to the lady, according to the mode of those most concise and simple reasoners, the knights-errant of yore—by single combat; but Ichabod was too conscious of the superior might of his adversary to enter the lists against him: he had overheard a boast of Bones, that he would "double the schoolmaster up, and lay him on a shelf of his own schoolhouse;" and he was too wary to give him an opportunity. There was something extremely provoking in this obstinately pacific system; it left Brom no alternative but to draw upon the funds of rustic waggery in his disposition, and to play off boorish practical jokes upon his rival. Ichabod became the object of whimsical persecution to Bones, and his gang of rough riders. They harried his hitherto peaceful domains; smoked out his singing school, by stopping up the chimney; broke into the school-house at night, in spite of its formidable fastenings of withe and window stakes, and turned every thing topsy-turvy: so that the poor schoolmaster began to think all the witches in the country held their meetings there. But what was still more annoying, Brom took all opportunities of turning him into ridicule in presence of his mistress, and had a scoundrel dog whom he taught to whine in the most ludicrous manner, and introduced as a rival of Ichabod's to instruct her in psalmody.

In this way matters went on for some time, without producing any material effect on the relative situation of the contending powers. On a fine autumnal afternoon, Ichabod, in pensive mood, sat enthroned on the lofty stool whence he usually watched all the concerns of his little literary realm. In his hand he swayed a ferule, that sceptre of despotic power; the birch of justice reposed on three nails, behind the throne, a constant terror to evil doers; while on the desk before him might be seen sundry contraband articles and prohibited weapons, detected upon the persons of idle urchins; such as half-munched apples, popguns, whirligigs, fly-cages, and whole legions of rampant little paper game-cocks. Apparently there had been some appalling act of justice recently inflicted, for his scholars were all busily intent upon their books, or slyly whispering behind them with one eye kept upon the master; and a kind of buzzing stillness reigned throughout the school-room. It was suddenly interrupted by the appearance of a Negro, in tow-cloth jacket and trousers, a round-crowned fragment of a hat, like the cap of Mercury, and mounted on the back of a ragged, wild, half-broken colt, which he managed with a rope by way of halter. He came clattering up to the school door with an invitation to Ichabod to attend a merry-making or "quilting frolic," to be held that evening at Mynheer Van Tassel's; and having delivered his message with that air of importance, and effort at fine language, which a Negro is apt to display on petty embassies of the kind, he dashed over the brook, and was seen scampering away up the hollow, full of the importance and hurry of his mission.

All was now bustle and hubbub in the late quiet school-room. The scholars were hurried through their lessons, without stopping at trifles; those who were nimble skipped over half with impunity, and those who were tardy, had a smart application now and then in the rear, to quicken their speed, or help them over a tall word. Books were flung aside without being put away on the shelves, inkstands were overturned, benches thrown down, and the whole school was turned loose an hour before the usual time, bursting forth like a legion of young imps, yelping and racketing about the green, in joy at their early emancipation.

The gallant Ichabod now spent at least an extra half hour at his toilet, brushing and furbishing up his best, and indeed only, suit of rusty black, and arranging his looks by a bit of broken looking-glass, that hung up in the school-house. That he might make his appearance before his mistress in the true style of a cavalier, he borrowed a horse from the farmer with whom he was domiciliated, a choleric old Dutchman, of the name of Hans Van Ripper, and, thus gallantly mounted, issued forth, like a knight-errant in quest of adventures. But it is meet I should, in the true spirit of romantic story, give some account of the looks and equipments of my hero and his steed. The animal he bestrode was a broken-down plough-horse, that had outlived almost every thing but his viciousness. He was gaunt and shagged, with a ewe neck and a head like a hammer; his rusty mane and tail were tangled and knotted with burrs; one eye had lost its pupil, and was glaring and spectral; but the other had the gleam of a genuine devil in it. Still he must have had fire and mettle in his day, if we may judge from the name he bore of Gunpowder. He had, in fact, been a favorite steed of his master's, the choleric Van Ripper, who was a furious rider, and had infused, very probably, some of his own spirit into the animal; for, old and broken-down as he looked, there was more of the lurking devil in him than in any young filly in the country.

Ichabod was a suitable figure for such a steed. He rode with short stirrups, which brought his knees nearly up to the pommel of the saddle; his sharp elbows stuck out like grasshoppers'; he carried his whip perpendicularly in his hand, like a sceptre, and, as his horse jogged on, the motion of his arms was not unlike the flapping of a pair of wings. A small wool hat rested on the top of his nose, for so his scanty strip of forehead might be called; and the skirts of his black coat fluttered out almost to the horse's tail. Such was the appearance of Ichabod and his steed, as they shambled out of the gate of Hans Van Ripper, and it was altogether such an apparition as is seldom to be met with in broad daylight.

It was, as I have said, a fine autumnal day, the sky was clear and serene, and nature wore that rich and golden livery which we always associate with the idea of abundance. The forests had put on their sober brown and yellow, while some trees of the tenderer kind had been nipped by the frosts into brilliant dyes of orange, purple, and scarlet. Streaming files of wild ducks began to make their appearance high in the air; the bark of the squirrel might be heard from the groves of beech and hickory nuts, and the pensive whistle of the quail at intervals from the neighboring stubble-field.

The small birds were taking their farewell banquets. In the fulness of their revelry, they fluttered, chirping and frolicking, from bush to bush, and tree to tree, capricious from the very profusion and variety around them. There was the honest cock-robin, the favorite game of stripling sportsmen, with its loud querulous note; and the twittering blackbirds flying in sable clouds; and the golden-winged woodpecker, with his crimson crest, his broad black gorget, and splendid plumage; and the cedar bird, with its red-tipt wings and yellow-tipt tail, and its little monteiro cap of feathers; and the blue-jay, that noisy coxcomb, in his gay light-blue coat and white under-clothes; screaming and chattering, nodding and bobbing and bowing, and pretending to be on good terms with every songster of the grove.

As Ichabod jogged slowly on his way, his eye, ever open to every symptom of culinary abundance, ranged with delight over the treasures of jolly autumn. On all sides he beheld vast store of apples; some hanging in oppressive opulence on the trees; some gathered into baskets and barrels for the market; others heaped up in rich piles for the cider-press. Farther on he beheld great fields of Indian corn, with its golden ears peeping from their leafy coverts, and holding out the promise of cakes and hasty pudding; and the yellow pumpkins lying beneath them, turning up their fair round bellies to the sun, and giving ample prospects of the most luxurious of pies; and anon he passed the fragrant buckwheat fields, breathing the odor of the bee-hive, and as he beheld them, soft anticipations stole over his mind of dainty slapjacks, well buttered, and garnished with honey or treacle, by the delicate little dimpled hand of Katrina Van Tassel.

Thus feeding his mind with many sweet thoughts and "sugared suppositions," he journeyed along the sides of a range of hills which look out upon some of the goodliest scenes of the mighty Hudson. The sun gradually wheeled his broad disk down into the west. The wide bosom of the Tappan Zee lay motionless and glassy, excepting that here and there a gentle undulation waved and prolonged the blue shadow of the distant mountain. A few amber clouds floated in the sky, without a breath of air to move them. The horizon was of a fine golden tint, changing gradually into a pure apple green, and from that into the deep blue of the mid-heaven. A slanting ray lingered on the woody crests of the precipices that overhung some parts of the river, giving greater depth to the dark-gray and purple of their rocky sides. A sloop was loitering in the distance, dropping slowly down with the tide, her sail hanging uselessly against the mast; and as the reflection of the sky gleamed along the still water, it seemed as if the vessel was suspended in the air.

It was toward evening that Ichabod arrived at the castle of the Heer Van Tassel, which he found thronged with the pride and flower of the adjacent country. Old farmers, a spare leathern-faced race, in homespun coats and breeches, blue stockings, huge shoes, and magnificent pewter buckles. Their brisk withered little dames, in close crimped caps, long-waisted short-gowns, homespun petticoats, with scissors and pincushions, and gay calico pockets hanging on the outside. Buxom lasses, almost as antiquated as their mothers, excepting where a straw hat, a fine ribbon, or perhaps a white frock, gave symptoms of city innovation. The sons, in short square-skirted coats with rows of stupendous brass buttons, and their hair generally queued in the fashion of the times, especially if they could procure an eel-skin for the purpose, it being esteemed, throughout the country, as a potent nourisher and strengthener of the hair.

Brom Bones, however, was the hero of the scene, having come to the gathering on his favorite steed Daredevil, a creature, like himself, full of mettle and mischief, and which no one but himself could manage. He was, in fact, noted for preferring vicious animals, given to all kinds of tricks, which kept the rider in constant risk of his neck, for he held a tractable well-broken horse as unworthy of a lad of spirit.

Fain would I pause to dwell upon the world of charms that burst upon the enraptured gaze of my hero, as he entered the state parlor of Van Tassel's mansion. Not those of the bevy of buxom lasses, with their luxurious display of red and white; but the ample charms of a genuine Dutch country tea-table, in the sumptuous time of autumn. Such heaped-up platters of cakes of various and almost indescribable kinds, known only to experienced Dutch housewives! There was the doughty dough-nut, the tenderer oly koek, and the crisp and crumbling cruller; sweet cakes and short cakes, ginger cakes and honey cakes, and the whole family of cakes. And then there were apple pies and peach pies and pumpkin pies; besides slices of ham and smoked beef; and moreover delectable dishes of preserved plums, and peaches, and pears, and quinces; not to mention broiled shad and roasted chickens; together with bowls of milk and cream, all mingled higgledy-piggledy, pretty much as I have enumerated them, with the motherly tea-pot sending up its clouds of vapor from the midst—Heaven bless the mark! I want breath and time to discuss this banquet as it deserves, and am too eager to get on with my story. Happily, Ichabod Crane was not in so great a hurry as his historian, but did ample justice to every dainty.

He was a kind and thankful creature, whose heart dilated in proportion as his skin was filled with good cheer; and whose spirits rose with eating as some men's do with drink. He could not help, too, rolling his large eyes round him as he ate, and chuckling with the possibility that he might one day be lord of all this scene of almost unimaginable luxury and splendor. Then, he thought, how soon he'd turn his back upon the old schoolhouse; snap his fingers in the face of Hans Van Ripper, and every other niggardly patron, and kick any itinerant pedagogue out of doors that should dare to call him comrade!

Old Baltus Van Tassel moved about among his guests with a face dilated with content and good humor, round and jolly as the harvest moon. His hospitable attentions were brief, but expressive, being confined to a shake of the hand, a slap on the shoulder, a loud laugh, and a pressing invitation to "fall to, and help themselves."

And now the sound of the music from the common room, or hall, summoned to the dance. The musician was an old gray-headed Negro, who had been the itinerant orchestra of the neighborhood for more than half a century. His instrument was as old and battered as himself. The greater part of the time he scraped on two or three strings, accompanying every movement of the bow with a motion of the head; bowing almost to the ground, and stamping with his foot whenever a fresh couple were to start.

Ichabod prided himself upon his dancing as much as upon his vocal powers. Not a limb, not a fibre about him was idle; and to have seen his loosely hung frame in full motion, and clattering about the room, you would have thought Saint Vitus himself, that blessed patron of the dance, was figuring before you in person. He was the admiration of all the Negroes; who, having gathered, of all ages and sizes, from the farm and the neighborhood, stood forming a pyramid of shining black faces at every door and window, gazing with delight at the scene, rolling their white eye-balls, and showing grinning rows of ivory from ear to ear. How could the flogger of urchins be otherwise than animated and joyous? the lady of his heart was his partner in the dance, and smiling graciously in reply to all his amorous oglings; while Brom Bones, sorely smitten with love and jealousy, sat brooding by himself in one corner.

When the dance was at an end, Ichabod was attracted to a knot of the sager folks, who, with old Van Tassel, sat smoking at one end of the piazza, gossiping over former times, and drawing out long stories about the war.

This neighborhood, at the time of which I am speaking, was one of those highly-favored places which abound with chronicle and great men. The British and American line had run near it during the war; it had, therefore, been the scene of marauding, and infested with refugees, cow-boys, and all kinds of border chivalry. Just sufficient time had elapsed to enable each story-teller to dress up his tale with a little becoming fiction, and, in the indistinctness of his recollection, to make himself the hero of every exploit.

There was the story of Doffue Martling, a large blue-bearded Dutchman, who had nearly taken a British frigate with an old iron nine-pounder from a mud breastwork, only that his gun burst at the sixth discharge. And there was an old gentleman who shall be nameless, being too rich a mynheer to be lightly mentioned, who, in the battle of White-plains, being an excellent master of defence, parried a musket ball with a small sword, insomuch that he absolutely felt it whiz round the blade, and glance off at the hilt: in proof of which, he was ready at any time to show the sword, with the hilt a little bent. There were several more that had been equally great in the field, not one of whom but was persuaded that he had a considerable hand in bringing the war to a happy termination.

But all these were nothing to the tales of ghosts and apparitions that succeeded. The neighborhood is rich in legendary treasures of the kind. Local tales and superstitions thrive best in these sheltered long-settled retreats; but are trampled under foot by the shifting throng that forms the population of most of our country places. Besides, there is no encouragement for ghosts in most of our villages, for they have scarcely had time to finish their first nap, and turn themselves in their graves, before their surviving friends have travelled away from the neighborhood; so that when they turn out at night to walk their rounds, they have no acquaintance left to call upon. This is perhaps the reason why we so seldom hear of ghosts except in our long-established Dutch communities.

The immediate cause, however, of the prevalence of supernatural stories in these parts, was doubtless owing to the vicinity of Sleepy Hollow. There was a contagion in the very air that blew from that haunted region; it breathed forth an atmosphere of dreams and fancies infecting all the land. Several of the Sleepy Hollow people were present at Van Tassel's, and, as usual, were doling out their wild and wonderful legends. Many dismal tales were told about funeral trains, and mourning cries and wailings heard and seen about the great tree where the unfortunate Major André was taken, and which stood in the neighborhood. Some mention was made also of the woman in white, that haunted the dark glen at Raven Rock, and was often heard to shriek on winter nights before a storm, having perished there in the snow. The chief part of the stories, however, turned upon the favorite spectre of Sleepy Hollow, the headless horseman, who had been heard several times of late, patrolling the country; and, it was said, tethered his horse nightly among the graves in the church-yard.

The sequestered situation of this church seems always to have made it a favorite haunt of troubled spirits. It stands on a knoll, surrounded by locust-trees and lofty elms, from among which its decent whitewashed walls shine modestly forth, like Christian purity beaming through the shades of retirement. A gentle slope descends from it to a silver sheet of water, bordered by high trees, between which, peeps may be caught at the blue hills of the Hudson. To look upon its grass-grown yard, where the sunbeams seem to sleep so quietly, one would think that there at least the dead might rest in peace. On one side of the church extends a wide woody dell, along which raves a large brook among broken rocks and trunks of fallen trees. Over a deep black part of the stream, not far from the church, was formerly thrown a wooden bridge; the road that led to it, and the bridge itself, were thickly shaded by overhanging trees, which cast a gloom about it, even in the daytime; but occasioned a fearful darkness at night. This was one of the favorite haunts of the headless horseman; and the place where he was most frequently encountered. The tale was told of old Brouwer, a most heretical disbeliever in ghosts, how he met the horseman returning from his foray into Sleepy Hollow, and was obliged to get up behind him; how they galloped over bush and brake, over hill and swamp, until they reached the bridge; when the horseman suddenly turned into a skeleton, threw old Brouwer into the brook, and sprang away over the tree-tops with a clap of thunder.

This story was immediately matched by a thrice marvellous adventure of Brom Bones, who made light of the galloping Hessian as an arrant jockey. He affirmed that, on returning one night from the neighboring village of Sing Sing, he had been overtaken by this midnight trooper; that he had offered to race with him for a bowl of punch, and should have won it too, for Daredevil beat the goblin horse all hollow, but, just as they came to the church bridge, the Hessian bolted, and vanished in a flash of fire.

All these tales, told in that drowsy undertone with which men talk in the dark, the countenances of the listeners only now and then receiving a casual gleam from the glare of a pipe, sank deep in the mind of Ichabod. He repaid them in kind with large extracts from his invaluable author, Cotton Mather, and added many marvellous events that had taken place in his native State of Connecticut, and fearful sights which he had seen in his nightly walks about Sleepy Hollow.

The revel now gradually broke up. The old farmers gathered together their families in their wagons, and were heard for some time rattling along the hollow roads, and over the distant hills. Some of the damsels mounted on pillions behind their favorite swains, and their light-hearted laughter, mingling with the clatter of hoofs, echoed along the silent woodlands, sounding fainter and fainter until they gradually died away—and the late scene of noise and frolic was all silent and deserted. Ichabod only lingered behind, according to the custom of country lovers, to have a tête-à-tête with the heiress, fully convinced that he was now on the high road to success. What passed at this interview I will not pretend to say, for in fact I do not know. Something, however, I fear me, must have gone wrong, for he certainly sallied forth, after no very great interval, with an air quite desolate and shop-fallen.--Oh these women! these women! Could that girl have been playing off any of her coquettish tricks?—Was her encouragement of the poor pedagogue all a mere sham to secure her conquest of his rival?—Heaven only knows, not I!—Let it suffice to say, Ichabod stole forth with the air of one who had been sacking a hen-roost, rather than a fair lady's heart. Without looking to the right or left to notice the scene of rural wealth, on which he had so often gloated, he went straight to the stable, and with several hearty cuffs and kicks, roused his steed most uncourteously from the comfortable quarters in which he was soundly sleeping, dreaming of mountains of corn and oats, and whole valleys of timothy and clover.

It was the very witching time of night that Ichabod, heavy-hearted and crest-fallen, pursued his travel homewards, along the sides of the lofty hills which rise above Tarry Town, and which he had traversed so cheerily in the afternoon. The hour was as dismal as himself. Far below him, the Tappan Zee spread its dusky and indistinct waste of waters, with here and there the tall mast of a sloop, riding quietly at anchor under the land. In the dead hush of midnight, he could even hear the barking of the watch dog from the opposite shore of the Hudson; but it was so vague and faint as only to give an idea of his distance from this faithful companion of man. Now and then, too, the long-drawn crowing of a cock, accidentally awakened, would sound far, far off, from some farmhouse away among the hills—but it was like a dreaming sound in his ear. No signs of life occurred near him, but occasionally the melancholy chirp of a cricket, or perhaps the guttural twang of a bull-frog, from a neighboring marsh, as if sleeping uncomfortably, and turning suddenly in his bed.

All the stories of ghosts and goblins that he had heard in the afternoon, now came crowding upon his recollection. The night grew darker and darker; the stars seemed to sink deeper in the sky, and driving clouds occasionally hid them from his sight. He had never felt so lonely and dismal. He was, moreover, approaching the very place where many of the scenes of the ghost stories had been laid. In the centre of the road stood an enormous tulip-tree, which towered like a giant above all the other trees of the neighborhood, and formed a kind of landmark. Its limbs were gnarled, and fantastic, large enough to form trunks for ordinary trees, twisting down almost to the earth, and rising again into the air. It was connected with the tragical story of the unfortunate André, who had been taken prisoner hard by; and was universally known by the name of Major André's tree. The common people regarded it with a mixture of respect and superstition, partly out of sympathy for the fate of its ill-starred namesake, and partly from the tales of strange sights and doleful lamentations told concerning it.

As Ichabod approached this fearful tree, he began to whistle: he thought his whistle was answered—it was but a blast sweeping sharply through the dry branches. As he approached a little nearer, he thought he saw something white, hanging in the midst of the tree—he paused and ceased whistling; but on looking more narrowly, perceived that it was a place where the tree had been scathed by lightning, and the white wood laid bare. Suddenly he heard a groan—his teeth chattered and his knees smote against the saddle: it was but the rubbing of one huge bough upon another, as they were swayed about by the breeze. He passed the tree in safety, but new perils lay before him.

About two hundred yards from the tree a small brook crossed the road, and ran into a marshy and thickly-wooded glen, known by the name of Wiley's swamp. A few rough logs, laid side by side, served for a bridge over this stream. On that side of the road where the brook entered the wood, a group of oaks and chestnuts, matted thick with wild grapevines, threw a cavernous gloom over it. To pass this bridge was the severest trial. It was at this identical spot that the unfortunate André was captured, and under the covert of those chestnuts and vines were the sturdy yeomen concealed who surprised him. This has ever since been considered a haunted stream, and fearful are the feelings of the schoolboy who has to pass it alone after dark.

As he approached the stream his heart began to thump; he

summoned up, however, all his resolution, gave his horse half a score of kicks in the ribs, and attempted to dash briskly across the bridge; but instead of starting forward, the perverse old animal made a lateral movement, and ran broadside against the fence. Ichabod, whose fears increased with the delay, jerked the reins on the other side, and kicked lustily with the contrary foot: it was all in vain; his steed started, it is true, but it was only to plunge to the opposite side of the road into a thicket of brambles and alder bushes. The schoolmaster now bestowed both whip and heel upon the starveling ribs of old Gunpowder, who dashed forward, snuffling and snorting, but came to a stand just by the bridge, with a suddenness that had nearly sent his rider sprawling over his head. Just at this moment a plashy tramp by the side of the bridge caught the sensitive ear of Ichabod. In the dark shadow of the grove, on the margin of the brook, he beheld something huge, misshapen, black and towering. It stirred not, but seemed gathered up in the gloom, like some gigantic monster ready to spring upon the traveller.

The hair of the affrighted pedagogue rose upon his head with terror. What was to be done? To turn and fly was now too late; and besides, what chance was there of escaping ghost or goblin, if such it was, which could ride upon the wings of the wind? Summoning up, therefore, a show of courage, he demanded in stammering accents—"Who are you?" He received no reply. He repeated his demand in a still more agitated voice. Still there was no answer. Once more he cudgelled the sides of the inflexible Gunpowder, and, shutting his eyes, broke forth with involuntary fervor into a psalm tune. Just then the shadowy object of alarm put itself in motion, and, with a scramble and a bound, stood at once in the middle of the road. Though the night was dark and dismal, yet the form of the unknown might now in some degree be ascertained. He appeared to be a horseman of large dimensions, and mounted on a black horse of powerful frame. He made no offer of molestation or sociability, but kept aloof on one side of the road, jogging along on the blind side of old Gunpowder, who had now got over his fright and waywardness.

Ichabod, who had no relish for this strange midnight companion, and bethought himself of the adventure of Brom Bones with the Galloping Hessian, now quickened his steed, in hopes of leaving him behind. The stranger, however, quickened his horse to an equal pace. Ichabod pulled up, and fell into a walk, thinking to lag behind—the other did the same. His heart began to sink within him; he endeavored to resume his psalm tune, but his parched tongue clove to the roof of his mouth, and he could not utter a stave. There was something in the moody and dogged silence of this pertinacious companion that was mysterious and appalling. It was soon fearfully accounted for. On mounting a rising ground, which brought the figure of his fellow-traveller in relief against the sky, gigantic in height, and muffled in a cloak, Ichabod was horror-struck, on perceiving that he was headless!—but his horror was still more increased, on observing that the head, which should have rested on his shoulders, was carried before him on the pommel of the saddle: his terror rose to desperation; he rained a shower of kicks and blows upon Gunpowder, hoping, by a sudden movement, to give his companion the slip—but the spectre started full jump with him. Away then they dashed, through thick and thin; stones flying, and sparks flashing at every bound. Ichabod's flimsy garments fluttered in the air, as he stretched his long lank body away over his horse's head, in the eagerness of his flight.

They had now reached the road which turns off to Sleepy Hollow; but Gunpowder, who seemed possessed with a demon, instead of keeping up it, made an opposite turn, and plunged headlong down hill to the left. This road leads through a sandy hollow, shaded by trees for about a quarter of a mile, where it crosses the bridge famous in goblin story, and just beyond swells the green knoll on which stands the whitewashed church.

As yet the panic of the steed had given his unskilful rider an apparent advantage in the chase; but just as he had got half way through the hollow, the girths of the saddle gave way, and he felt it slipping from under him. He seized it by the pommel, and endeavored to hold it firm, but in vain; and had just time to save himself by clasping old Gunpowder round the neck, when the saddle fell to the earth, and he heard it trampled under foot by his pursuer. For a moment the terror of Hans Van Ripper's wrath passed across his mind—for it was his Sunday saddle; but this was no time for petty fears; the goblin was hard on his haunches; and (unskilful rider that he was!) he had much ado to maintain his seat; sometimes slipping on one side, sometimes on another, and sometimes jolted on the high ridge of his horse's back-bone, with a violence that he verily feared would cleave him asunder.

An opening in the trees now cheered him with the hopes that the church bridge was at hand. The wavering reflection of a silver star in the bosom of the brook told him that he was not mistaken. He saw the walls of the church dimly glaring under the trees beyond. He recollected the place where Brom Bones's ghostly competitor had disappeared. "If I can but reach that bridge," thought Ichabod, "I am safe." Just then he heard the black steed panting and blowing close behind him; he even fancied that he felt his hot breath. Another convulsive kick in the ribs, and old Gunpowder sprang upon the bridge; he thundered over the resounding planks; he gained the opposite side; and now Ichabod cast a look behind to see if his pursuer should vanish, according to rule, in a flash of fire and brimstone. Just then he saw the goblin rising in his stirrups, and in the very act of hurling his head at him. Ichabod endeavored to dodge the horrible missile, but too late. It encountered his cranium with a tremendous crash—he was tumbled headlong into the dust, and Gunpowder, the black steed, and the goblin rider, passed by like a whirlwind.

The next morning the old horse was found without his saddle, and with the bridle under his feet, soberly cropping the grass at his master's gate. Ichabod did not make his appearance at breakfast—dinner-hour came, but no Ichabod. The boys assembled at the schoolhouse, and strolled idly about the banks of the brook; but no schoolmaster. Hans Van Ripper now began to feel some uneasiness about the fate of poor Ichabod, and his saddle. An inquiry was set on foot, and after diligent investigation they came upon his traces. In one part of the road leading to the church was found the saddle trampled in the dirt; the tracks of horses' hoofs deeply dented in the road, and evidently at furious speed, were traced to the bridge, beyond which, on the bank of a broad part of the brook, where the water ran deep and black, was found the hat of the unfortunate Ichabod, and close beside it a shattered pumpkin.

The brook was searched, but the body of the schoolmaster

was not to be discovered. Hans Van Ripper, as executor of his estate, examined the bundle which contained all his worldly effects. They consisted of two shirts and a half; two stocks for the neck; a pair or two of worsted stockings; an old pair of corduroy small-clothes; a rusty razor; a book of psalm tunes, full of dogs' ears; and a broken pitchpipe. As to the books and furniture of the school-house, they belonged to the community, excepting Cotton Mather's History of Witchcraft, a New England Almanac, and a book of dreams and fortune-telling; in which last was a sheet of foolscap much scribbled and blotted in several fruitless attempts to make a copy of verses in honor of the heiress of Van Tassel. These magic books and the poetic scrawl were forthwith consigned to the flames by Hans Van Ripper; who from that time forward determined to send his children no more to school; observing, that he never knew any good come of this same reading and writing. Whatever money the schoolmaster possessed, and he had received his quarter's pay but a day or two before, he must have had about his person at the time of his disappearance.

The mysterious event caused much speculation at the church on the following Sunday. Knots of gazers and gossips were collected in the churchyard, at the bridge, and at the spot where the hat and pumpkin had been found. The stories of Brouwer, of Bones, and a whole budget of others, were called to mind; and when they had diligently considered them all, and compared them with the symptoms of the present case, they shook their heads, and came to the conclusion that Ichabod had been carried off by the galloping Hessian. As he was a bachelor, and in nobody's debt, nobody troubled his head any more about him. The school was removed to a different quarter of the hollow, and another pedagogue reigned in his stead.

It is true, an old farmer, who had been down to New York on a visit several years after, and from whom this account of the ghostly adventure was received, brought home the intelligence that Ichabod Crane was still alive; that he had left the neighborhood, partly through fear of the goblin and Hans Van Ripper, and partly in mortification at having been suddenly dismissed by the heiress; that he had changed his quarters to a distant part of the country; had kept school and studied law at the same time, had been admitted to the bar, turned politician, electioneered, written for the newspapers, and finally had been made a justice of the Ten Pound Court. Brom Bones too, who shortly after his rival's disappearance conducted the blooming Katrina in triumph to the altar, was observed to look exceedingly knowing whenever the story of Ichabod was related, and always burst into a hearty laugh at the mention of the pumpkin; which led some to suspect that he knew more about the matter than he chose to tell.

The old country wives, however, who are the best judges of these matters, maintain to this day that Ichabod was spirited away by supernatural means; and it is a favorite story often told about the neighborhood round the winter evening fire. The bridge became more than ever an object of superstitious awe, and that may be the reason why the road has been altered of late years, so as to approach the church by the border of the mill-pond. The school-house being deserted, soon fell to decay, and was reported to be haunted by the ghost of the unfortunate pedagogue; and the ploughboy, loitering homeward of a still summer evening, has often fancied his voice at a distance, chanting a melancholy psalm tune among the tranquil solitudes of Sleepy Hollow.

POSTSCRIPT

FOUND IN THE HANDWRITING OF MR. KNICKERBOCKER

The preceding Tale is given, almost in the precise words in which I heard it related at a Corporation meeting of the ancient city of Manhattoes, at which were present many of its sagest and most illustrious burghers. The narrator was a pleasant, shabby, gentlemanly old fellow, in pepper-and-salt clothes, with a sadly humorous face; and one whom I strongly suspected of being poor—he made such efforts to be entertaining. When his story was concluded, there was much laughter and approbation, particularly from two or three deputy aldermen, who had been asleep a greater part of the time. There was, however, one tall, dry-looking old gentleman, with beetling eyebrows, who maintained a grave and rather severe face throughout: now and then folding his arms, inclining his head, and looking down upon the floor, as if turning a doubt over in his mind. He was one of your wary men, who never laugh, but upon good grounds—when they have reason and the law on their side. When the mirth of the rest of the company had subsided, and silence was restored, he leaned one arm on the elbow of his chair, and, sticking the other akimbo, demanded, with a slight but exceedingly sage motion of the head, and contraction of the brow, what was the moral of the story, and what it went to prove?

The story-teller, who was just putting a glass of wine to his lips, as a refreshment after his toils, paused for a moment, looked at his inquirer with an air of infinite deference, and, lowering the glass slowly to the table, observed, that the story was intended most logically to prove:—

"That there is no situation in life but has its advantages and pleasures—provided we will but take a joke as we find it:

"That, therefore, he that runs races with goblin troopers is likely to have rough riding of it.

"Ergo, for a country schoolmaster to be refused the hand of a Dutch heiress is a certain step to high preferment in the state."

The cautious old gentleman knit his brows tenfold closer after this explanation, being sorely puzzled by the ratiocination of the syllogism; while, methought, the one in pepper-and-salt eyed him with something of a triumphant leer. At length, he observed that all this was very well, but still he thought the story a little on the extravagant—there were one or two points on which he had his doubts.

"Faith, sir," replied the story-teller, "as to that matter, I don't believe one-half of it myself."

D. K.

The Spectre Bridegroom

A TRAVELLER'S TALE *

He that supper for is dight,
He lyes full cold, I trow, this night!
Yestreen to chamber I him led,
This night Gray-Steel has made his bed.

SIR EGER, SIR GRAHAME, AND SIR GRAY-STEEL

ON the summit of one of the heights of the Odenwald, a wild and romantic tract of Upper Germany, that lies not far from the confluence of the Main and the Rhine, there stood, many, many years since, the Castle of the Baron Von Landshort. It is now quite fallen to decay, and almost buried among beech trees and dark firs; above which, however, its old watchtower may still be seen, struggling, like the former possessor I have mentioned, to carry a high head, and look down upon the neighboring country.

The baron was a dry branch of the great family of Katzenellenbogen,† and inherited the relics of the property, and all the pride of his ancestors. Though the warlike disposition of his predecessors had much impaired the family possessions, yet the baron still endeavored to keep up some show of former state. The times were peaceable, and the German nobles, in general, had abandoned their inconvenient old castles, perched like eagles' nests among the mountains, and had built more convenient residences in the valleys: still the baron remained proudly drawn up in his little fortress, cherishing, with hereditary inveteracy, all the old family feuds; so that he was on ill terms with some of his nearest neighbors, on account of disputes that had happened between their great-great-grandfathers.

* The erudite reader, well versed in good-for-nothing lore, will perceive that the above Tale must have been suggested to the old Swiss by a little French anecdote, a circumstance said to have taken place at Paris.

† *i. e.,* CAT'S-ELBOW. The name of a family of those parts very powerful in former times. The appellation, we are told, was given in compliment to a peerless dame of the family, celebrated for her fine arm.

The baron had but one child, a daughter; but nature, when she grants but one child, always compensates by making it a prodigy; and so it was with the daughter of the baron. All the nurses, gossips, and country cousins, assured her father that she had not her equal for beauty in all Germany; and who should know better than they? She had, moreover, been brought up with great care under the superintendence of two maiden aunts, who had spent some years of their early life at one of the little German courts, and were skilled in all the branches of knowledge necessary to the education of a fine lady. Under their instructions she became a miracle of accomplishments. By the time she was eighteen, she could embroider to admiration, and had worked whole histories of the saints in tapestry, with such strength of expression in their countenances, that they looked like so many souls in purgatory. She could read without great difficulty, and had spelled her way through several church legends, and almost all the chivalric wonders of the Heldenbuch. She had even made considerable proficiency in writing; could sign her own name without missing a letter, and so legibly, that her aunts could read it without spectacles. She excelled in making little elegant good-for-nothing lady-like nicknacks of all kinds; was versed in the most abstruse dancing of the day; played a number of airs on the harp and guitar; and knew all the tender ballads of the Minnelieders by heart.

Her aunts, too, having been great flirts and coquettes in their younger days, were admirably calculated to be vigilant guardians and strict censors of the conduct of their niece; for there is no duenna so rigidly prudent, and inexorably decorous, as a superannuated coquette. She was rarely suffered out of their sight; never went beyond the domains of the castle, unless well attended, or rather well watched; had continual lectures read to her about strict decorum and implicit obedience; and, as to the men—pah!—she was taught to hold them at such a distance, and in such absolute distrust, that, unless properly authorized, she would not have cast a glance upon the handsomest cavalier in the world—no, not if he were even dying at her feet.

The good effects of this system were wonderfully apparent. The young lady was a pattern of docility and correctness. While others were wasting their sweetness in the glare of the world, and liable to be plucked and thrown aside by every hand, she was coyly blooming into fresh and lovely womanhood under the protection of those immaculate spinsters, like a rose-bud blushing forth among guardian thorns. Her aunts looked upon her with pride and exultation, and vaunted that though all the other young ladies in the world might go astray, yet, thank Heaven, nothing of the kind could happen to the heiress of Katzenellenbogen.

But, however scantily the Baron Von Landshort might be provided with children, his household was by no means a small one; for Providence had enriched him with abundance of poor relations. They, one and all, possessed the affectionate disposition common to humble relatives; were wonderfully attached to the baron, and took every possible occasion to come in swarms and enliven the castle. All family festivals were commemorated by these good people at the baron's expense; and when they were filled with good cheer, they would declare that there was nothing on earth so delightful as these family meetings, these jubilees of the heart.

The baron, though a small man, had a large soul, and it swelled with satisfaction at the consciousness of being the greatest man in the little world about him. He loved to tell long stories about the dark old warriors whose portraits looked grimly down from the walls around, and he found no listeners equal to those that fed at his expense. He was much given to the marvellous, and a firm believer in all those supernatural tales with which every mountain and valley in Germany abounds. The faith of his guests exceeded even his own: they listened to every tale of wonder with open eyes and mouth, and never failed to be astonished, even though repeated for the hundredth time. Thus lived the Baron Von Landshort, the oracle of his table, the absolute monarch of his little territory, and happy, above all things, in the persuasion that he was the wisest man of the age.

At the time of which my story treats, there was a great family gathering at the castle, on an affair of the utmost importance: it was to receive the destined bridegroom of the baron's daughter. A negotiation had been carried on between the father and an old nobleman of Bavaria, to unite the dignity of their houses by the marriage of their children. The preliminaries had been conducted with proper punctilio. The young people were betrothed without seeing each other; and the time was appointed for the marriage ceremony. The young Count Von Altenburg had been recalled from the army for the purpose, and was actually on his way to the baron's to receive his bride. Missives had even been received from him, from Wurtzburg, where he was accidentally detained, mentioning the day and hour when he might be expected to arrive.

The castle was in a tumult of preparation to give him a suitable welcome. The fair bride had been decked out with uncommon care. The two aunts had superintended her toilet, and quarrelled the whole morning about every article of her dress. The young lady had taken advantage of their contest to follow the bent of her own taste; and fortunately it was a good one. She looked as lovely as youthful bridegroom could desire; and the flutter of expectation heightened the lustre of her charms.

The suffusions that mantled her face and neck, the gentle heaving of the bosom, the eye now and then lost in reverie, all betrayed the soft tumult that was going on in her little heart. The aunts were continually hovering around her; for maiden aunts are apt to take great interest in affairs of this nature. They were giving her a world of staid counsel how to deport herself, what to say, and in what manner to receive the expected lover.

The baron was no less busied in preparations. He had, in truth, nothing exactly to do; but he was naturally a fuming bustling little man, and could not remain passive when all the world was in a hurry. He worried from top to bottom of the castle with an air of infinite anxiety; he continually called the servants from their work to exhort them to be diligent; and buzzed about every hall and chamber, as idly restless and importunate as a blue-bottle fly on a warm summer's day.

In the mean time the fatted calf had been killed; the forests had rung with the clamor of the huntsmen; the kitchen was crowded with good cheer; the cellars had yielded up whole oceans of *Rhein-wein* and *Ferne-wein;* and even the great Heidelburg tun had been laid under contribution. Every thing was ready to receive the distinguished guest with *Saus und Braus* in the true spirit of German hospitality—but the guest delayed to make his appearance. Hour rolled after hour. The sun, that had poured his downward rays upon the rich forest of the Odenwald, now just gleamed along the summits of the mountains. The baron mounted the highest tower, and strained his eyes in hope of catching a distant sight of the count and his attendants. Once he thought he beheld them; the sound of horns came floating from the valley, prolonged by the mountain echoes. A number of horsemen were seen far below, slowly advancing along the road; but when they had nearly reached the foot of the mountain, they suddenly struck off in a different direction. The last ray of sunshine departed—the bats began to flit by in the twilight—the road grew dimmer and dimmer to the view; and nothing appeared stirring in it but now and then a peasant lagging homeward from his labor.

While the old castle of Landshort was in this state of perplexity, a very interesting scene was transacting in a different part of the Odenwald.

The young Count Von Altenburg was tranquilly pursuing his route in that sober jog-trot way, in which a man travels toward matrimony when his friends have taken all the trouble and uncertainty of courtship off his hands, and a bride is waiting for him, as certainly as a dinner at the end of his journey. He had encountered at Wurtzburg, a youthful companion in arms, with whom he had seen some service on the frontiers; Herman Von Starkenfaust, one of the stoutest hands, and worthiest hearts, of German chivalry, who was now returning from the army. His father's castle was not far distant from the old fortress of Landshort, although an hereditary feud rendered the families hostile, and strangers to each other.

In the warm-hearted moment of recognition, the young friends related all their past adventures and fortunes, and the count gave the whole history of his intended nuptials with a young lady whom he had never seen, but of whose charms he had received the most enrapturing descriptions.

As the route of the friends lay in the same direction, they agreed to perform the rest of their journey together; and, that they might do it the more leisurely, set off from Wurtzburg at an early hour, the count having given directions for his retinue to follow and overtake him.

They beguiled their wayfaring with recollections of their

military scenes and adventures; but the count was apt to be a little tedious, now and then, about the reputed charms of his bride, and the felicity that awaited him.

In this way they had entered among the mountains of the Odenwald, and were traversing one of its most lonely and thickly-wooded passes. It is well known that the forests of Germany have always been as much infested by robbers as its castles by spectres; and, at this time, the former were particularly numerous, from the hordes of disbanded soldiers wandering about the country. It will not appear extraordinary, therefore, that the cavaliers were attacked by a gang of these stragglers, in the midst of the forest. They defended themselves with bravery, but were nearly overpowered, when the count's retinue arrived to their assistance. At sight of them the robbers fled, but not until the count had received a mortal wound. He was slowly and carefully conveyed back to the city of Wurtzburg, and a friar summoned from a neighboring convent, who was famous for his skill in administering to both soul and body; but half of his skill was superfluous; the moments of the unfortunate count were numbered.

With his dying breath he entreated his friend to repair instantly to the castle of Landshort, and explain the fatal cause of his not keeping his appointment with his bride. Though not the most ardent of lovers, he was one of the most punctilious of men, and appeared earnestly solicitous that his mission should be speedily and courteously executed. "Unless this is done," said he, "I shall not sleep quietly in my grave!" He repeated these last words with peculiar solemnity. A request, at a moment so impressive, admitted no hesitation. Starkenfaust endeavored to soothe him to calmness; promised faithfully to execute his wish, and gave him his hand in solemn pledge. The dying man pressed it in acknowledgment, but soon lapsed into delirium—raved about his bride—his engagements—his plighted word; ordered his horse, that he might ride to the castle of Landshort; and expired in the fancied act of vaulting into the saddle.

Starkenfaust bestowed a sigh and a soldier's tear on the untimely fate of his comrade; and then pondered on the awkward mission he had undertaken. His heart was heavy, and his head perplexed; for he was to present himself an unbidden guest among hostile people, and to damp their festivity with tidings fatal to their hopes. Still there were certain whisperings of curiosity in his bosom to see this far-famed beauty of Katzenellenbogen, so cautiously shut up from the world; for he was a passionate admirer of the sex, and there was a dash of eccentricity and enterprise in his character that made him fond of all singular adventure.

Previous to his departure he made all due arrangements with the holy fraternity of the convent for the funeral solemnities of his friend, who was to be buried in the cathedral of Wurtzburg, near some of his illustrious relatives; and the mourning retinue of the count took charge of his remains.

It is now high time that we should return to the ancient family of Katzenellenbogen, who were impatient for their guest, and still more for their dinner; and to the worthy little baron, whom we left airing himself on the watch-tower.

Night closed in, but still no guest arrived. The baron descended from the tower in despair. The banquet, which had been delayed from hour to hour, could no longer be postponed. The meats were already overdone; the cook in an agony; and the whole household had the look of a garrison that had been reduced by famine. The baron was obliged reluctantly to give orders for the feast without the presence of the guest. All were seated at table, and just on the point of commencing, when the sound of a horn from without the gate gave notice of the approach of a stranger. Another long blast filled the old courts of the castle with its echoes, and was answered by the warder from the walls. The baron hastened to receive his future son-in-law.

The drawbridge had been let down, and the stranger was before the gate. He was a tall, gallant cavalier, mounted on a black steed. His countenance was pale, but he had a beaming, romantic eye, and an air of stately melancholy. The baron was a little mortified that he should have come in this simple, solitary style. His dignity for a moment was ruffled, and he felt disposed to consider it a want of proper respect for the important occasion, and the important family with which he was to be connected. He pacified himself, however, with the conclusion, that it must have been youthful impatience which had induced him thus to spur on sooner than his attendants.

"I am sorry," said the stranger, "to break in upon you thus unseasonably——"

Here the baron interrupted him with a world of compliments and greetings; for, to tell the truth, he prided himself upon his courtesy and eloquence. The stranger attempted, once or twice, to stem the torrent of words, but in vain, so he bowed his head and suffered it to flow on. By the time the baron had come to a pause, they had reached the inner court of the castle; and the stranger was again about to speak, when he was once more interrupted by the appearance of the female part of the family, leading forth the shrinking and blushing bride. He gazed on her for a moment as one entranced; it seemed as if his whole soul beamed forth in the gaze, and rested upon that lovely form. One of the maiden aunts whispered something in her ear; she made an effort to speak; her moist blue eye was timidly raised; gave a shy glance of inquiry on the stranger; and was cast again to the ground. The words died away; but there was a sweet smile playing about her lips, and a soft dimpling of the cheek that showed her glance had not been unsatisfactory. It was impossible for a girl of the fond age of eighteen, highly predisposed for love and matrimony, not to be pleased with so gallant a cavalier.

The late hour at which the guest had arrived left no time for parley. The baron was peremptory, and deferred all particular conversation until the morning, and led the way to the untasted banquet.

It was served up in the great hall of the castle. Around the walls hung the hard-favored portraits of the heroes of the house of Katzenellenbogen, and the trophies which they had gained in the field and in the chase. Hacked corslets, splintered jousting spears, and tattered banners, were mingled with the spoils of sylvan warfare; the jaws of the wolf, and the tusks of the boar, grinned horribly among cross-bows and battle-axes, and a huge pair of antlers branched immediately over the head of the youthful bridegroom.

The cavalier took but little notice of the company or the entertainment. He scarcely tasted the banquet, but seemed absorbed in admiration of his bride. He conversed in a low tone that could not be overheard—for the language of love is never loud; but where is the female ear so dull that it cannot catch the softest whisper of the lover? There was a mingled tenderness and gravity in his manner, that appeared to have a powerful effect upon the young lady. Her color came and went as she listened with deep attention. Now and then she made some blushing reply, and when his eye was turned away, she would steal a sidelong glance at his romantic countenance, and heave a gentle sigh of tender happiness. It was evident that the young couple were completely enamored. The aunts, who were deeply versed in the mysteries of the heart, declared over and over again that they had fallen in love with each other at first sight.

The feast went on merrily, or at least noisily, for the guests were all blessed with those keen appetites that attend upon light purses and mountain air. The baron told his best and longest stories, and never had he told them so well, or with such great effect. If there was any thing marvellous, his auditors were lost in astonishment; and if any thing facetious, they were sure to laugh exactly in the right place. The baron, it is true, like most great men, was too dignified to utter any joke but a dull one; it was always enforced, however, by a bumper of excellent Hockheimer; and even a dull joke, at one's own table, served up with jolly old wine, is irresistible. Many good things were said by poorer and keener wits, that would not bear repeating, except on similar occasions; many sly speeches whispered in ladies' ears, that almost convulsed them with suppressed laughter; and a song or two roared out by a poor, but merry and broad-faced cousin of the baron, that absolutely made the maiden aunts hold up their fans.

Amidst all this revelry, the stranger guest maintained a most singular and unseasonable gravity. His countenance assumed a deeper cast of dejection as the evening advanced; and, strange as it may appear, even the baron's jokes seemed only to render him the more melancholy. At times he was lost in thought, and at times there was a perturbed and restless wandering of the eye that bespoke a mind but ill at ease. His conversations with the bride became more and more earnest and mysterious. Lowering clouds began to steal over the fair serenity of her brow, and tremors to run through her tender frame.

All this could not escape the notice of the company. Their gayety was chilled by the unaccountable gloom of the bridegroom; their spirits were infected; whispers and glances were interchanged, accompanied by shrugs and dubious shakes of the head. The song and the laugh grew less and less frequent; there were dreary pauses in the conversation, which were at length succeeded by wild tales and supernatural legends. One dismal story produced another still more dismal, and the baron nearly frightened some of the ladies into hysterics with the history of the goblin horseman that carried away the fair Leonora; a dreadful story, which has since been put into excellent verse, and is read and believed by all the world.

The bridegroom listened to this tale with profound attention. He kept his eyes steadily fixed on the baron, and, as the story drew to a close, began gradually to rise from his seat, growing taller and taller, until, in the baron's entranced eye, he seemed almost to tower into a giant. The moment the tale was finished, he heaved a deep sigh, and took a solemn farewell of the company. They were all amazement. The baron was perfectly thunder-struck.

"What! going to leave the castle at midnight? why, every thing was prepared for his reception; a chamber was ready for him if he wished to retire."

The stranger shook his head mournfully and mysteriously, and replied, "I must lay my head in a different chamber tonight!"

There was something in this reply, and the tone in which it was uttered, that made the baron's heart misgive him; but he rallied his forces, and repeated his hospitable entreaties.

The stranger shook his head silently, but positively, at every offer; and, waving his farewell to the company, stalked slowly out of the hall. The maiden aunts were absolutely petrified—the bride hung her head, and a tear stole to her eye.

The baron followed the stranger to the great court of the castle, where the black charger stood pawing the earth, and snorting with impatience. When they had reached the portal, whose deep archway was dimly lighted by a cresset, the stranger paused, and addressed the baron in a hollow tone of voice, which the vaulted roof rendered still more sepulchral.

"Now that we are alone," said he, "I will impart to you the reason of my going. I have a solemn, an indispensable engagement—"

"Why," said the baron, "cannot you send some one in your place?"

"It admits of no substitute—I must attend it in person—I must away to Wurtzburg cathedral—"

"Ay," said the baron, plucking up spirit, "but not until to-morrow—to-morrow you shall take your bride there."

"No! no!" replied the stranger, with tenfold solemnity, "my engagement is with no bride—the worms! the worms expect me! I am a dead man—I have been slain by robbers—my body lies at Wurtzburg—at midnight I am to be buried—the grave is waiting for me—I must keep my appointment!"

He sprang on his black charger, dashed over the drawbridge, and the clattering of his horse's hoofs was lost in the whistling of the night blast.

The baron returned to the hall in the utmost consternation, and related what had passed. Two ladies fainted outright, others sickened at the idea of having banqueted with a spectre. It was the opinion of some, that this might be the wild huntsman, famous in German legend. Some talked of mountain sprites, of wood-demons, and of other supernatural beings, with which the good people of Germany have been so grievously harassed since time immemorial. One of the poor relations ventured to suggest that it might be some sportive evasion of the young cavalier, and that the very gloominess of the caprice seemed to accord with so melancholy a personage. This, however, drew on him the indignation of the whole company, and especially of the baron, who looked upon him as little better than an infidel; so that he was fain to abjure his heresy as speedily as possible, and come into the faith of the true believers.

But whatever may have been the doubts entertained, they were completely put to an end by the arrival, next day, of regular missives, confirming the intelligence of the young count's murder, and his interment in Wurtzburg cathedral.

The dismay at the castle may well be imagined. The baron shut himself up in his chamber. The guests, who had come to rejoice with him, could not think of abandoning him in his distress. They wandered about the courts, or collected in groups in the hall, shaking their heads and shrugging their shoulders, at the troubles of so good a man; and sat longer than ever at table, and ate and drank more stoutly than ever, by way of keeping up their spirits. But the situation of the widowed bride was the most pitiable. To have lost a husband before she had even embraced him—and such a husband! if the very spectre could be so gracious and noble, what must have been the living man. She filled the house with lamentations.

On the night of the second day of her widowhood, she had retired to her chamber, accompanied by one of her aunts, who insisted on sleeping with her. The aunt, who was one of the best tellers of ghost stories in all Germany, had just been recounting one of her longest, and had fallen asleep in the very midst of it. The chamber was remote, and overlooked a small garden. The niece lay pensively gazing at the beams of the rising moon, as they trembled on the leaves of an aspen-tree before the lattice. The castle-clock had just tolled midnight, when a soft strain of music stole up from the garden. She rose hastily from her bed, and stepped lightly to the window. A tall figure stood among the shadows of the trees. As it raised its head, a beam of moonlight fell upon the countenance. Heaven and earth! she beheld the Spectre Bridegroom! A loud shriek at that moment burst upon her ear, and her aunt, who had been awakened by the music, and had followed her silently to the window, fell into her arms. When she looked again, the spectre had disappeared.

Of the two females, the aunt now required the most soothing, for she was perfectly beside herself with terror. As to the young lady, there was something, even in the spectre of her lover, that seemed endearing. There was still the semblance of manly beauty; and though the shadow of a man is but little calculated to satisfy the affections of a love-sick girl, yet, where the substance is not to be had, even that is consoling. The aunt declared she would never sleep in that chamber again; the niece, for once, was refractory, and declared as strongly that she would sleep in no other in the castle: the consequence was, that she had to sleep in it alone: but she drew a promise from her aunt not to relate the story of the spectre, lest she should be denied the only melancholy pleasure left her on earth—that of inhabiting the chamber over which the guardian shade of her lover kept its nightly vigils.

How long the good old lady would have observed this promise is uncertain, for she dearly loved to talk of the marvellous, and there is a triumph in being the first to tell a frightful story; it is, however, still quoted in the neighborhood, as a memorable instance of female secrecy, that she kept it to herself for a whole week; when she was suddenly absolved from all further restraint, by intelligence brought to the breakfast table one morning that the young lady was not to be found. Her room was empty—the bed had not been slept in—the window was open, and the bird had flown!

The astonishment and concern with which the intelligence was received can only be imagined by those who have witnessed the agitation which the mishaps of a great man cause among his friends. Even the poor relations paused for a moment from the indefatigable labors of the trencher; when the aunt, who had at first been struck speechless, wrung her hands, and shrieked out, "The goblin! the goblin! she's carried away by the goblin."

In a few words she related the fearful scene of the garden, and concluded that the spectre must have carried off his bride. Two of the domestics corroborated the opinion, for they had heard the clattering of a horse's hoofs down the mountain about midnight, and had no doubt that it was the spectre on his black charger, bearing her away to the tomb. All present were struck with the direful probability; for events of the kind are extremely common in Germany, as many well-authenticated histories bear witness.

What a lamentable situation was that of the poor baron! What a heart-rending dilemma for a fond father, and a member of the great family of Katzenellenbogen! His only daughter had either been rapt away to the grave, or he was to have some wood-demon for a son-in-law, and, perchance, a troop of goblin grandchildren. As usual, he was completely bewildered, and all the castle in an uproar. The men were ordered to take horse, and scour every road and path and glen of the Odenwald. The baron himself had just drawn on his jack-boots, girded on his sword, and was about to mount his steed to sally forth on the doubtful quest, when he was brought to a pause by a new apparition. A lady was seen approaching the castle, mounted on a palfrey, attended by a cavalier on horseback. She galloped up to the gate, sprang from her horse, and falling at the baron's feet, embraced his knees. It was his lost daughter, and her companion—the Spectre Bridegroom! The baron was astounded. He looked at his daughter, then at the spectre, and almost doubted the evidence of his senses. The latter, too, was wonderfully improved in his appearance since his visit to the world of spirits. His dress was splendid, and set off a noble figure of manly symmetry. He was no longer pale and melancholy. His fine countenance was flushed with the glow of youth, and joy rioted in his large dark eye.

The mystery was soon cleared up. The cavalier (for, in truth, as you must have known all the while, he was no goblin) announced himself as Sir Herman Von Starkenfaust. He related his adventure with the young count. He told how he had hastened to the castle to deliver the unwelcome tidings, but that the eloquence of the baron had interrupted him in every attempt to tell his tale. How the sight of the bride had completely captivated him, and that to pass a few hours near her, he had tacitly suffered the mistake to continue. How he had been sorely perplexed in what way to make a decent retreat, until the baron's goblin stories had suggested his eccentric exit. How, fearing the feudal hostility of the family, he had repeated his visits by stealth—had haunted the garden beneath the young lady's window—had wooed—had won—had borne away in triumph—and, in a word, had wedded the fair.

Under any other circumstances the baron would have been inflexible, for he was tenacious of paternal authority, and devoutly obstinate in all family feuds; but he loved his daughter; he had lamented her as lost; he rejoiced to find her still alive; and, though her husband was of a hostile house, yet, thank Heaven, he was not a goblin. There was something, it must be acknowledged, that did not exactly accord with his notions of strict veracity, in the joke the knight had passed upon him of his being a dead man; but several old friends present, who had served in the wars, assured him that every stratagem was excusable in love, and that the cavalier was entitled to especial privilege, having lately served as a trooper.

Matters, therefore, were happily arranged. The baron pardoned the young couple on the spot. The revels at the castle were resumed. The poor relations overwhelmed this new member of the family with loving kindness; he was so gallant, so generous—and so rich. The aunts, it is true, were somewhat scandalized that their system of strict seclusion and passive obedience should be so badly exemplified, but attributed it all to their negligence in not having the windows grated. One of them was particularly mortified at having her marvellous story marred, and that the only spectre she had ever seen should turn out a counterfeit; but the niece seemed perfectly happy at having found him substantial flesh and blood—and so the story ends.

The Broken Heart

I never heard
Of any true affection, but 'twas nipt
With care, that, like the caterpillar, eats
The leaves of the spring's sweetest book, the rose.

MIDDLETON

IT is a common practice with those who have outlived the susceptibility of early feeling, or have been brought up in the gay heartlessness of dissipated life, to laugh at all love stories, and to treat the tales of romantic passion as mere fictions of novelists and poets. My observations on human nature have induced me to think otherwise. They have convinced me, that however the surface of the character may be chilled and frozen by the cares of the world, or cultivated into mere smiles by the arts of society, still there are dormant fires lurking in the depths of the coldest bosom, which, when once enkindled, become impetuous, and are sometimes desolating in their effects. Indeed, I am a true believer in the blind deity, and go to the full extent of his doctrines. Shall I confess it?—I believe in broken hearts, and the possibility of dying of disappointed love. I do not, however, consider it a malady often fatal to my own sex; but I firmly believe that it withers down many a lovely woman into an early grave.

Man is the creature of interest and ambition. His nature leads him forth into the struggle and bustle of the world. Love is but the embellishment of his early life, or a song piped in the intervals of the acts. He seeks for fame, for fortune, for space in the world's thought, and dominion over his fellow-men. But a woman's whole life is a history of the affections. The heart is her world: it is there her ambition strives for empire; it is there her avarice seeks for hidden treasures. She sends forth her sympathies on adventure; she embarks her whole soul in the traffic of affection; and if shipwrecked, her case is hopeless—for it is a bankruptcy of the heart.

To a man the disappointment of love may occasion some bitter pangs: it wounds some feelings of tenderness—it blasts some prospects of felicity; but he is an active being—he may dissipate his thoughts in the whirl of varied occupation, or may plunge into the tide of pleasure; or, if the scene of disappointment be too full of painful associations, he can shift his abode at will, and taking as it were the wings of the morning, can "fly to the uttermost parts of the earth, and be at rest."

But woman's is comparatively a fixed, a secluded, and meditative life. She is more the companion of her own thoughts and feelings; and if they are turned to ministers of sorrow, where shall she look for consolation? Her lot is to be wooed and won; and if unhappy in her love, her heart is like some fortress that has been captured, and sacked, and abandoned, and left desolate.

How many bright eyes grow dim—how many soft cheeks grow pale—how many lovely forms fade away into the tomb, and none can tell the cause that blighted their loveliness! As the dove will clasp its wings to its side, and cover and conceal the arrow that is preying on its vitals, so is it the nature of woman to hide from the world the pangs of wounded affection. The love of a delicate female is always shy and silent. Even when fortunate, she scarcely breathes it to herself; but when otherwise, she buries it in the recesses of her bosom, and there lets it cower and brood among the ruins of her peace. With her the desire of the heart has failed. The great charm of existence is at an end. She neglects all the cheerful exercises which gladden the spirits, quicken the pulses, and send the tide of life in healthful currents through the veins. Her rest is broken—the sweet refreshment of sleep is poisoned by melancholy dreams—"dry sorrow drinks her blood," until her enfeebled frame sinks under the slightest external injury. Look for her, after a little while, and you find friendship weeping over her untimely grave, and wondering that one, who but lately glowed with all the radiance of health and beauty, should so speedily be brought down to "darkness and the worm." You will be told of some wintry chill, some casual indisposition, that laid her low—but no one knows of the mental malady which previously sapped her strength, and made her so easy a prey to the spoiler.

She is like some tender tree, the pride and beauty of the grove; graceful in its form, bright in its foliage, but with the worm preying at its heart. We find it suddenly withering, when it should be most fresh and luxuriant. We see it drooping its branches to the earth, and shedding leaf by leaf, until, wasted and perished away, it falls even in the stillness of the forest; and as we muse over the beautiful ruin, we strive in vain to recollect the blast or thunderbolt that could have smitten it with decay.

I have seen many instances of women running to waste and self-neglect, and disappearing gradually from the earth, almost as if they had been exhaled to heaven; and have repeatedly fancied that I could trace their death through the various declensions of consumption, cold, debility, languor, melancholy, until I reached the first symptom of disappointed love. But an instance of the kind was lately told to me; the circumstances are well known in the country where they happened, and I shall but give them in the manner in which they were related.

Every one must recollect the tragical story of young E——, the Irish patriot; it was too touching to be soon forgotten. During the troubles in Ireland, he was tried, condemned, and executed, on a charge of treason. His fate made a deep impression on public sympathy. He was so young—so intelligent—so generous—so brave—so every thing that we are apt to like in a young man. His conduct under trial, too, was so lofty and intrepid. The noble indignation with which he repelled the charge of treason against his country—the eloquent vindication of his name—and his pathetic appeal to posterity, in the hopeless hour of condemnation—all these entered deeply into every generous bosom, and even his enemies lamented the stern policy that dictated his execution.

But there was one heart, whose anguish it would be impossible to describe. In happier days and fairer fortunes, he had won the affections of a beautiful and interesting girl, the daughter of a late celebrated Irish barrister. She loved him with the disinterested fervor of a woman's first and early love. When every worldly maxim arrayed itself against him; when blasted in fortune, and disgrace and danger darkened around his name, she loved him the more ardently for his very sufferings. If, then, his fate could awaken the sympathy even of his foes, what must have been the agony of her, whose whole soul was occupied by his image! Let those tell who have had the portals of the tomb suddenly closed between them and the being they most loved on earth—who have sat at its threshold, as one shut out in a cold and lonely world, whence all that was most lovely and loving had departed.

But then the horrors of such a grave! so frightful, so dishonored! there was nothing for memory to dwell on that could soothe the pang of separation—none of those tender though melancholy circumstances, which endear the parting scene—nothing to melt sorrow into those blessed tears, sent like the dews of heaven to revive the heart in the parting hour of anguish.

To render her widowed situation more desolate, she had incurred her father's displeasure by her unfortunate attachment, and was an exile from the paternal roof. But could the sympathy and kind offices of friends have reached a spirit so shocked and driven in by horror, she would have experienced no want of consolation, for the Irish are a people of quick and generous sensibilities. The most delicate and cherishing attentions were paid her by families of wealth and distinction. She was led into society, and they tried by all kinds of occupation and amusement to dissipate her grief, and wean her from the tragical story of her loves. But it was all in vain. There are some strokes of calamity which scathe and scorch the soul—which penetrate to the vital seat of happiness—and blast it, never again to put forth bud or blossom. She never objected to frequent the haunts of pleasure, but was as much alone there as in the depths of solitude; walking about in a sad reverie, apparently unconscious of the world around her. She carried with her an inward woe that mocked at all the blandishments of friendship, and "heeded not the song of the charmer, charm he never so wisely."

The person who told me her story had seen her at a masquerade. There can be no exhibition of far-gone wretchedness more striking and painful than to meet it in such a scene. To find it wandering like a spectre, lonely and joyless, where all around is gay—to see it dressed out in the trappings of mirth, and looking so wan and woe-begone, as if it had tried in vain to cheat the poor heart into a momentary forgetfulness of sorrow. After strolling through the splendid rooms and giddy crowd with an air of utter abstraction, she sat herself down on the steps of an orchestra, and, looking about for some time with a vacant air, that showed her insensibility to the garish scene, she began, with the capriciousness of a sickly heart, to warble a little plaintive air. She had an exquisite voice; but on this occasion it was so simple, so touching, it breathed forth such a soul of wretchedness, that she drew a crowd mute and silent around her, and melted every one into tears.

The story of one so true and tender could not but excite great interest in a country remarkable for enthusiasm. It completely won the heart of a brave officer, who paid his addresses to her, and thought that one so true to the dead could not but prove affectionate to the living. She declined his attentions, for her thoughts were irrevocably engrossed by the memory of her former lover. He, however, persisted in his suit. He solicited not her tenderness, but her esteem. He was assisted by her conviction of his worth, and her sense of her own destitute and dependent situation, for she was existing on the kindness of friends. In a word, he at length succeeded in gaining her hand, though with the solemn assurance, that her heart was unalterably another's.

He took her with him to Sicily, hoping that a change of scene might wear out the remembrance of early woes. She was an amiable and exemplary wife, and made an effort to be a happy one; but nothing could cure the silent and devouring melancholy that had entered into her very soul. She wasted away in a slow, but hopeless decline, and at length sunk into the grave, the victim of a broken heart.

It was on her that Moore, the distinguished Irish poet, composed the following lines:

> She is far from the land where her young hero sleeps,
> And lovers around her are sighing;
> But coldly she turns from their gaze, and weeps,
> For her heart in his grave is lying.
>
> She sings the wild songs of her dear native plains,
> Every note which he loved awaking—
> Ah! little they think, who delight in her strains,
> How the heart of the minstrel is breaking!
>
> He had lived for his love—for his country he died,
> They were all that to life had entwined him—

Nor soon shall the tears of his country be dried,
Nor long will his love stay behind him!

Oh! make her a grave where the sunbeams rest,
When they promise a glorious morrow;
They'll shine o'er her sleep, like a smile from the west,
From her own loved island of sorrow!

The Boar's Head Tavern, Eastcheap

A SHAKSPEARIAN RESEARCH

"A tavern is the rendezvous, the exchange, the staple of good fellows. I have heard my great-grandfather tell, how his great-great-grandfather should say, that it was an old proverb when his great-grandfather was a child, that 'it was a good wind that blew a man to the wine.' "

MOTHER BOMBIE

IT is a pious custom, in some Catholic countries, to honor the memory of saints by votive lights burnt before their pictures. The popularity of a saint, therefore, may be known by the number of these offerings. One, perhaps, is left to moulder in the darkness of his little chapel; another may have a solitary lamp to throw its blinking rays athwart his effigy; while the whole blaze of adoration is lavished at the shrine of some beatified father of renown. The wealthy devotee brings his huge luminary of wax; the eager zealot his seven-branched candlestick, and even the mendicant pilgrim is by no means satisfied that sufficient light is thrown upon the deceased, unless he hangs up his little lamp of smoking oil. The consequence is, that in the eagerness to enlighten, they are often apt to obscure; and I have occasionally seen an unlucky saint almost smoked out of countenance by the officiousness of his followers.

In like manner has it fared with the immortal Shakspeare. Every writer considers it his bounden duty to light up some portion of his character or works, and to rescue some merit from oblivion. The commentator, opulent in words, produces vast tomes of dissertations; the common herd of editors send up mists of obscurity from their notes at the bottom of each page; and every casual scribbler brings his farthing rushlight of eulogy or research, to swell the cloud of incense and of smoke.

As I honor all established usages of my brethren of the quill, I thought it but proper to contribute my mite of homage to the memory of the illustrious bard. I was for some time, however, sorely puzzled in what way I should discharge this duty. I found myself anticipated in every attempt at a new reading; every doubtful line had been explained a dozen different ways, and perplexed beyond the reach of elucidation; and as to fine passages, they had all been amply praised by previous admirers; nay, so completely had the bard, of late, been overlarded with panegyric by a great German critic, that it was difficult now to find even a fault that had not been argued into a beauty.

In this perplexity, I was one morning turning over his pages, when I casually opened upon the comic scenes of Henry IV, and was, in a moment, completely lost in the madcap revelry of the Boar's Head Tavern. So vividly and naturally are these scenes of humor depicted, and with such force and consistency are the characters sustained, that they become mingled up in the mind with the facts and personages of real life. To few readers does it occur, that these are all ideal creations of a poet's brain, and that, in sober truth, no such knot of merry roysters ever enlivened the dull neighborhood of Eastcheap.

For my part I love to give myself up to the illusions of poetry. A hero of fiction that never existed is just as valuable to me as a hero of history that existed a thousand years since: and, if I may be excused such an insensibility to the common ties of human nature, I would not give up fat Jack for half the great men of ancient chronicle. What have the heroes of yore done for me, or men like me? They have conquered countries of which I do not enjoy an acre; or they have gained laurels of which I do not inherit a leaf; or they have furnished examples of hare-brained prowess, which I have neither the opportunity nor the inclination to follow. But, old Jack Falstaff!—kind Jack Falstaff!—sweet Jack Falstaff!—has enlarged the boundaries of human enjoyment: he has added vast regions of wit and good humor, in which the poorest man may revel; and has bequeathed a never-failing inheritance of jolly laughter, to make mankind merrier and better to the latest posterity.

A thought suddenly struck me: "I will make a pilgrimage to Eastcheap," said I, closing the book, "and see if the old Boar's Head Tavern still exists. Who knows but I may light upon some legendary traces of Dame Quickly and her guests; at any rate, there will be a kindred pleasure, in treading the halls once vocal with their mirth, to that the toper enjoys in smelling the empty cask once filled with generous wine."

The resoultion was no sooner formed than put in execution. I forbear to treat of the various adventures and wonders I encountered in my travels; of the haunted regions of Cock Lane; of the faded glories of Little Britain, and the parts adjacent; what perils I ran in Cateaton-street and old Jewry; of the renowned Guildhall and its two stunted giants, the pride and wonder of the city, and the terror of all unlucky urchins; and how I visited London Stone, and struck my staff upon it, in imitation of that arch rebel, Jack Cade.

Let it suffice to say, that I at length arrived in merry Eastcheap, that ancient region of wit and wassail, where the very names of the streets relished of good cheer, as Pudding Lane bears testimony even at the present day. For Eastcheap, says old Stowe, "was always famous for its convivial doings. The cookes cried hot ribbes of beef roasted, pies well baked, and other victuals: there was clattering of pewter pots, harpe, pipe, and sawtrie." Alas! how sadly is the scene changed since the roaring days of Falstaff and old Stowe! The madcap royster has given place to the plodding tradesman; the clattering of pots and the sound of "harpe and sawtrie," to the din of carts and the accursed dinging of the dustman's bell; and no song is heard, save, haply, the strain of some siren from Billingsgate, chanting the eulogy of deceased mackerel.

I sought, in vain, for the ancient abode of Dame Quickly. The only relic of it is a boar's head, carved in relief in stone, which formerly served as the sign, but at present is built into the parting line of two houses, which stand on the site of the renowned old tavern.

For the history of this little abode of good fellowship, I was referred to a tallow-chandler's widow, opposite, who had been born and brought up on the spot, and was looked up to as the indisputable chronicler of the neighborhood. I found her seated in a little back parlor, the window of which looked out upon a yard about eight feet square, laid out as a flower-garden; while a glass door opposite afforded a distant peep of the street, through a vista of soap and tallow candles: the two views, which comprised, in all probability, her prospects in life, and the little world in which she had lived, and moved, and had her being, for the better part of a century.

To be versed in the history of Eastcheap, great and little, from London Stone even unto the Monument, was doubtless, in her opinion, to be acquainted with the history of the universe. Yet, with all this, she possessed the simplicity of true wisdom, and that liberal communicative disposition, which I have generally remarked in intelligent old ladies, knowing in the concerns of their neighborhood.

Her information, however, did not extend far back into antiquity. She could throw no light upon the history of the Boar's Head, from the time that Dame Quickly espoused the valiant Pistol, until the great fire of London, when it was unfortunately burnt down. It was soon rebuilt, and continued to flourish under the old name and sign, until a dying landlord, struck with remorse for double scores, bad measures, and other iniquities, which are incident to the sinful race of publicans, endeavored to make his peace with heaven, by bequeathing the tavern to St. Michael's Church, Crooked Lane, towards the supporting of a chaplain. For some time the vestry meetings were regularly held there; but it was observed that the old Boar never held up his head under church government. He gradually declined, and finally gave his last gasp about thirty years since. The tavern was then turned into shops; but she informed me that a picture of it was still preserved in St. Michael's Church, which stood just in the rear. To get a sight of this picture was now my determination; so, having informed myself of the abode of the sexton, I took my leave of the venerable chronicler of Eastcheap, my visit having doubtless raised greatly her opinion of her legendary lore, and furnished an important incident in the history of her life.

It cost me some difficulty, and much curious inquiry, to ferret out the humble hanger-on to the church. I had to explore Crooked Lane, and diverse little alleys, and elbows, and dark passages, with which this old city is perforated, like an ancient cheese, or a worm-eaten chest of drawers. At length I traced him to a corner of a small court surrounded by lofty houses, where the inhabitants enjoy about as much of the face of heaven, as a community of frogs at the bottom of a well.

The sexton was a meek, acquiescing little man, of a bowing,

lowly habit: yet he had a pleasant twinkling in his eye, and, if encouraged, would now and then hazard a small pleasantry; such as a man of his low estate might venture to make in the company of high churchwardens, and other mighty men of the earth. I found him in company with the deputy organist, seated apart, like Milton's angels, discoursing, no doubt, on high doctrinal points, and settling the affairs of the church over a friendly pot of ale—for the lower classes of English seldom deliberate on any weighty matter without the assistance of a cool tankard to clear their understandings. I arrived at the moment when they had finished their ale and their argument, and were about to repair to the church to put it in order; so having made known my wishes, I received their gracious permission to accompany them.

The church of St. Michael's, Crooked Lane, standing a short distance from Billingsgate, is enriched with the tombs of many fishmongers of renown; and as every profession has its galaxy of glory, and its constellation of great men, I presume the monument of a mighty fishmonger of the olden time is regarded with as much reverence by succeeding generations of the craft, as poets feel on contemplating the tomb of Virgil, or soldiers the monument of a Marlborough or Turenne.

I cannot but turn aside, while thus speaking of illustrious men, to observe that St. Michael's, Crooked Lane, contains also the ashes of that doughty champion, William Walworth, knight, who so manfully clove down the sturdy wight, Wat Tyler, in Smithfield; a hero worthy of honorable blazon, as almost the only Lord Mayor on record famous for deeds of arms—the sovereigns of Cockney being generally renowned as the most pacific of all potentates.*

* The following was the ancient inscription on the monument of this worthy; which, unhappily, was destroyed in the great conflagration.

> Hereunder lyth a man of Fame,
> William Walworth callyd by name;
> Fishmonger he was in lyfftime here.
> And twise Lord Maior, as in books appere;
> Who, with courage stout and manly myght,
> Slew Jack Straw in Kyng Richard's sight.
> For which act done, and trew entent,
> The Kyng made him knyght incontinent;
> And gave him armes, as here you see,
> To declare his fact and chivaldrie.

Adjoining the church, in a small cemetery, immediately under the back window of what was once the Boar's Head, stands the tombstone of Robert Preston, whilom drawer at the tavern. It is now nearly a century since this trusty drawer of good liquor closed his bustling career, and was thus quietly deposited within call of his customers. As I was clearing away the weeds from his epitaph, the little sexton drew me on one side with a mysterious air, and informed me in a low voice, that once upon a time, on a dark wintry night, when the wind was unruly, howling, and whistling, banging about doors and windows, and twirling weathercocks, so that the living were frightened out of their beds, and even the dead could not sleep quietly in their graves, the ghost of honest Preston, which happened to be airing itself in the church-yard, was attracted by the well-known call of "waiter" from the Boar's Head, and made its sudden appearance in the midst of a roaring club, just as the parish clerk was singing a stave from the "mirre garland of Captain Death"; to the discomfiture of sundry train-band captains, and the conversion of an infidel attorney, who became a zealous Christian on the spot, and was never known to twist the truth afterwards, except in the way of business.

I beg it may be remembered, that I do not pledge myself for the authenticity of this anecdote; though it is well known that the church-yards and by-corners of this old metropolis are very much infested with perturbed spirits; and every one must have heard of the Cock Lane ghost, and the apparition that guards the regalia in the Tower, which has frightened so many bold sentinels almost out of their wits.

Be all this as it may, this Robert Preston seems to have been a worthy successor to the nimble-tongued Francis, who attended upon the revels of Prince Hal; to have been equally prompt with

He left this lyff the yere of our God
Thirteen hundred fourscore and three odd.

An error in the foregoing inscription has been corrected by the venerable Stowe. "Whereas," saith he, "it hath been far spread abroad by vulgar opinion, that the rebel smitten down so manfully by Sir William Walworth, the then worthy Lord Maior, was named Jack Straw, and not Wat Tyler, I thought good to reconcile this rash-conceived doubt by such testimony as I find in ancient and good records. The principal leaders, or captains, of the commons, were Wat Tyler, as the first man; the second was John, or Jack, Straw," etc., etc.

STOWE'S LONDON

his "anon, anon, sir;" and to have transcended his predecessor in honesty; for Falstaff, the veracity of whose taste no man will venture to impeach, flatly accuses Francis of putting lime in his sack; whereas honest Preston's epitaph lauds him for the sobriety of his conduct, the soundness of his wine, and the fairness of his measure.* The worthy dignitaries of the church, however, did not appear much captivated by the sober virtues of the tapster; the deputy organist, who had a moist look out of the eye, made some shrewd remark on the abstemiousness of a man brought up among full hogsheads; and the little sexton corroborated his opinion by a significant wink, and a dubious shake of the head.

Thus far my researches, though they threw much light on the history of tapsters, fishmongers, and Lord Mayors, yet disappointed me in the great object of my quest, the picture of the Boar's Head Tavern. No such painting was to be found in the church of St. Michael. "Marry and amen!" said I, "here endeth my research!" So I was giving the matter up, with the air of a baffled antiquary, when my friend the sexton, perceiving me to be curious in every thing relative to the old tavern, offered to show me the choice vessels of the vestry, which had been handed down from remote times, when the parish meetings were held at the Boar's Head. These were deposited in the parish clubroom, which had been transferred, on the decline of the ancient establishment, to a tavern in the neighborhood.

A few steps brought us to the house, which stands No. 12 Miles Lane, bearing the title of The Mason's Arms, and is kept by Master Edward Honeyball, the "bullyrock" of the establishment. It is one of those little taverns which abound in the heart

* As this inscription is rife with excellent morality, I transcribe it for the admonition of delinquent tapsters. It is, no doubt, the production of some choice spirit, who once frequented the Boar's Head.

> Bacchus, to give the toping world surprise,
> Produced one sober son, and here he lies.
> Though rear'd among full hogsheads, he defy'd
> The charms of wine, and every one beside.
> O reader, if to justice thou'rt inclined,
> Keep honest Preston daily in thy mind.
> He drew good wine, took care to fill his pots,
> Had sundry virtues that excused his faults.
> You that on Bacchus have the like dependence,
> Pray copy Bob in measure and attendance.

of the city, and form the centre of gossip and intelligence of the neighborhood. We entered the bar-room, which was narrow and darkling; for in these close lanes but few rays of reflected light are enabled to struggle down to the inhabitants, whose broad day is at best but a tolerable twilight. The room was partitioned into boxes, each containing a table spread with a clean white cloth, ready for dinner. This showed that the guests were of the good old stamp, and divided their day equally, for it was but just one o'clock. At the lower end of the room was a clear coal fire, before which a breast of lamb was roasting. A row of bright brass candlesticks and pewter mugs glistened along the mantelpiece, and an old-fashioned clock ticked in one corner. There was something primitive in this medley of kitchen, parlor, and hall, that carried me back to eariler times, and pleased me. The place, indeed, was humble, but every thing had that look of order and neatness, which bespeaks the superintendence of a notable English housewife. A group of amphibious-looking beings, who might be either fishermen or sailors, were regaling themselves in one of the boxes. As I was a visitor of rather higher pretensions, I was ushered into a little misshapen backroom, having at least nine corners. It was lighted by a skylight, furnished with antiquated leathern chairs, and ornamented with the portrait of a fat pig. It was evidently appropriated to particular customers, and I found a shabby gentleman, in a red nose and oil-cloth hat, seated in one corner, meditating on a half-empty pot of porter.

The old sexton had taken the landlady aside, and with an air of profound importance imparted to her my errand. Dame Honeyball was a likely, plump, bustling little woman, and no bad substitute for that paragon of hostesses, Dame Quickly. She seemed delighted with an opportunity to oblige; and hurrying up stairs to the archives of her house, where the precious vessels of the parish club were deposited, she returned, smiling and courtesying, with them in her hands.

The first she presented me was a japanned iron tobacco-box, of gigantic size, out of which, I was told, the vestry had smoked at their stated meetings, since time immemorial; and which was never suffered to be profaned by vulgar hands, or used on common occasions. I received it with becoming reverence; but what was my delight, at beholding on its cover the identical painting of which I was in quest! There was displayed the outside of the Boar's Head Tavern, and before the door was to be seen the whole convivial group, at table, in full revel; pictured with that wonderful fidelity and force, with which the portraits of renowned generals and commodores are illustrated on tobacco-boxes, for the benefit of posterity. Lest, however, there should be any mistake, the cunning limner had warily inscribed the names of Prince Hal and Falstaff on the bottoms of their chairs.

On the inside of the cover was an inscription, nearly obliterated, recording that this box was the gift of Sir Richard Gore, for the use of the vestry meetings at the Boar's Head Tavern, and that it was "repaired and beautified by his successor, Mr. John Packard, 1767." Such is a faithful description of this august and venerable relic; and I question whether the learned Scriblerius contemplated his Roman shield, or the Knights of the Round Table the long-sought san-greal, with more exultation.

While I was meditating on it with enraptured gaze, Dame Honeyball, who was highly gratified by the interest it excited, put in my hands a drinking cup or goblet, which also belonged to the vestry, and was descended from the old Boar's Head. It bore the inscription of having been the gift of Francis Wythers, knight, and was held, she told me, in exceeding great value, being considered very "antyke." This last opinion was strengthened by the shabby gentleman in the red nose and oil-cloth hat, and whom I strongly suspected of being a lineal descendant from the valiant Bardolph. He suddenly roused from his meditation on the pot of porter, and, casting a knowing look at the goblet, exclaimed, "Ay, ay! the head don't ache now that made that there article!"

The great importance attached to this memento of ancient revelry by modern churchwardens at first puzzled me; but there is nothing sharpens the apprehension so much as antiquarian research; for I immediately perceived that this could be no other than the identical "parcel-gilt goblet" on which Falstaff made his loving, but faithless vow to Dame Quickly; and which would, of course, be treasured up with care among the regalia of her domains, as a testimony of that solemn contract.*

* Thou didst swear to me upon a *parcel-gilt goblet,* sitting in my Dolphin chamber, at the round table, by a sea-coal fire, on Wednesday, in Whitsun-

Mine hostess, indeed, gave me a long history how the goblet had been handed down from generation to generation. She also entertained me with many particulars concerning the worthy vestrymen who have seated themselves thus quietly on the stools of the ancient roysters of Eastcheap, and, like so many commentators, utter clouds of smoke in honor of Shakspeare. These I forbear to relate, lest my readers should not be as curious in these matters as myself. Suffice it to say, the neighbors, one and all, about Eastcheap, believe that Falstaff and his merry crew actually lived and revelled there. Nay, there are several legendary anecdotes concerning him still extant among the oldest frequenters of the Mason's Arms, which they give as transmitted down from their forefathers; and Mr. M'Kash, an Irish hairdresser, whose shop stands on the site of the old Boar's Head, has several dry jokes of Fat Jack's, not laid down in the books, with which he makes his customers ready to die of laughter.

I now turned to my friend the sexton to make some further inquiries, but I found him sunk in pensive meditation. His head had declined a little on one side; a deep sigh heaved from the very bottom of his stomach; and, though I could not see a tear trembling in his eye, yet a moisture was evidently stealing from a corner of his mouth. I followed the direction of his eye through the door which stood open, and found it fixed wistfully on the savory breast of lamb, roasting in dripping richness before the fire.

I now called to mind that, in the eagerness of my recondite investigation, I was keeping the poor man from his dinner. My bowels yearned with sympathy, and, putting in his hand a small token of my gratitude and goodness, I departed, with a hearty benediction on him, Dame Honeyball, and the Parish Club of Crooked Lane; not forgetting my shabby, but sententious friend, in the oil-cloth hat and copper nose.

Thus have I given a "tedious brief" account of this interesting research, for which, if it prove too short and unsatisfactory, I can only plead my inexperience in this branch of literature, so

week, when the prince broke thy head for likening his father to a singing man at Windsor; thou didst swear to me then, as I was washing thy wound, to marry me, and make me my lady, thy wife. Canst thou deny it?—*Henry IV, Part 2.*

deservedly popular at the present day. I am aware that a more skilful illustrator of the immortal bard would have swelled the materials I have touched upon, to a good merchantable bulk; comprising the biographies of William Walworth, Jack Straw, and Robert Preston; some notice of the eminent fishmongers of St. Michael's; the history of Eastcheap, great and little; private anecdotes of Dame Honeyball, and her pretty daughter, whom I have not even mentioned; to say nothing of a damsel tending the breast of lamb (and whom, by the way, I remarked to be a comely lass, with a neat foot and ankle)—the whole enlivened by the riots of Wat Tyler, and illuminated by the great fire of London.

All this I leave, as a rich mine, to be worked by future commentators; nor do I despair of seeing the tobacco-box, and the "parcel-gilt goblet," which I have thus brought to light, the subjects of future engravings, and almost as fruitful of voluminous dissertations and disputes as the shield of Achilles, or the far-famed Portland vase.

Roscoe

— In the service of mankind to be
A guardian god below; still to employ
The mind's brave ardor in heroic aims,
Such as may raise us o'er the grovelling herd,
And make us shine forever — that is life.

THOMSON

ONE of the first places to which a stranger is taken in Liverpool is the Athenæum. It is established on a liberal and judicious plan; it contains a good library, and spacious reading-room, and is the great literary resort of the place. Go there at what hour you may, you are sure to find it filled with grave-looking personages, deeply absorbed in the study of newspapers.

As I was once visiting this haunt of the learned, my attention was attracted to a person just entering the room. He was advanced in life, tall, and of a form that might once have been commanding, but it was a little bowed by time—perhaps by care. He had a noble Roman style of countenance; a head that would have pleased a painter; and though some slight furrows on his brow showed that wasting thought had been busy there, yet his eye still beamed with the fire of a poetic soul. There was something in his whole appearance that indicated a being of a different order from the bustling race around him.

I inquired his name, and was informed that it was Roscoe. I drew back with an involuntary feeling of veneration. This, then, was an author of celebrity; this was one of those men, whose voices have gone forth to the ends of the earth; with whose minds I have communed even in the solitudes of America. Accustomed, as we are in our country, to know European writers only by their works, we cannot conceive of them, as of other men, engrossed by trivial or sordid pursuits, and jostling with the crowd of common minds in the dusty paths of life. They pass before our imaginations like superior beings, radiant with the emanations of their genius, and surrounded by a halo of literary glory.

To find, therefore, the elegant historian of the Medici, mingling among the busy sons of traffic, at first shocked my poetical ideas; but it is from the very circumstances and situation in which he has been placed, that Mr. Roscoe derives his highest claims to admiration. It is interesting to notice how some minds seem almost to create themselves, springing up under every disadvantage, and working their solitary but irresistible way through a thousand obstacles. Nature seems to delight in disappointing the assiduities of art, with which it would rear legitimate dulness to maturity; and to glory in the vigor and luxuriance of her chance productions. She scatters the seeds of genius to the winds, and though some may perish among the stony places of the world, and some be choked by the thorns and brambles of early adversity, yet others will now and then strike root even in the clefts of the rock, struggle bravely up into sunshine, and spread over their sterile birthplace all the beauties of vegetation.

Such has been the case with Mr. Roscoe. Born in a place apparently ungenial to the growth of literary talent; in the very market-place of trade; without fortune, family connections, or patronage; self-prompted, self-sustained, and almost self-taught, he has conquered every obstacle, achieved his way to eminence, and, having become one of the ornaments of the nation, has turned the whole force of his talents and influence to advance and embellish his native town.

Indeed, it is this last trait in his character which has given him the greatest interest in my eyes, and induced me particularly to point him out to my countrymen. Eminent as are his literary merits, he is but one among the many distinguished authors of this intellectual nation. They, however, in general, live but for their own fame, or their own pleasures. Their private history presents no lesson to the world, or, perhaps, a humiliating one of human frailty and inconsistency. At best, they are prone to steal away from the bustle and commonplace of busy existence; to indulge in the selfishness of lettered ease; and to revel in scenes of mental, but exclusive enjoyment.

Mr. Roscoe, on the contrary, has claimed none of the accorded privileges of talent. He has shut himself up in no garden of thought, nor elysium of fancy; but has gone forth into the highways and thoroughfares of life; he has planted bowers by the way-side, for the refreshment of the pilgrim and the sojourner, and has opened pure fountains, where the laboring man may turn aside from the dust and heat of the day, and drink of the living streams of knowledge. There is a "daily beauty in his life," on which mankind may meditate and grow better. It exhibits no lofty and almost useless, because inimitable, example of excellence; but presents a picture of active, yet simple and imitable virtues, which are within every man's reach, but which, unfortunately, are not exercised by many, or this world would be a paradise.

But his private life is peculiarly worthy the attention of the citizens of our young and busy country, where literature and the elegant arts must grow up side by side with the coarser plants of daily necessity; and must depend for their culture, not on the exclusive devotion of time and wealth, nor the quickening rays of titled patronage, but on hours and seasons snatched from the pursuit of worldly interests, by intelligent and public-spirited individuals.

He has shown how much may be done for a place in hours of leisure by one master spirit, and how completely it can give its own impress to surrounding objects. Like his own Lorenzo De' Medici, on whom he seems to have fixed his eye as on a pure model of antiquity, he has interwoven the history of his life with the history of his native town, and has made the foundations of its fame the monuments of his virtues. Wherever you go in Liverpool, you perceive traces of his footsteps in all that is elegant and liberal. He found the tide of wealth flowing merely in the channels of traffick; he has diverted from it invigorating rills to refresh the garden of literature. By his own example and constant exertions he has effected that union of commerce and the intellectual pursuits, so eloquently recommended in one of his latest writings: * and has practically proved how beautifully they may be brought to harmonize, and to benefit each other. The noble institutions for literary and scientific purposes, which reflect such credit on Liverpool, and are giving such an impulse to the public mind, have mostly been originated, and have all been

* Address on the opening of the Liverpool Institution.

effectively promoted, by Mr. Roscoe; and when we consider the rapidly increasing opulence and magnitude of that town, which promises to vie in commercial importance with the metropolis, it will be perceived that in awakening an ambition of mental improvement among its inhabitants, he has effected a great benefit to the cause of British literature.

In America, we know Mr. Roscoe only as the author—in Liverpool he is spoken of as the banker; and I was told of his having been unfortunate in business. I could not pity him, as I heard some rich men do. I considered him far above the reach of pity. Those who live only for the world, and in the world, may be cast down by the frowns of adversity; but a man like Roscoe is not to be overcome by the reverses of fortune. They do but drive him in upon the resources of his own mind; to the superior society of his own thoughts; which the best of men are apt sometimes to neglect, and to roam abroad in search of less worthy associates. He is independent of the world around him. He lives with antiquity and posterity; with antiquity, in the sweet communion of studious retirement; and with posterity, in the generous aspirings after future renown. The solitude of such a mind is its state of highest enjoyment. It is then visited by those elevated meditations which are the proper aliment of noble souls, and are, like manna, sent from heaven, in the wilderness of this world.

While my feelings were yet alive on the subject, it was my fortune to light on further traces of Mr. Roscoe. I was riding out with a gentleman, to view the environs of Liverpool, when he turned off, through a gate, into some ornamented grounds. After riding a short distance, we came to a spacious mansion of freestone, built in the Grecian style. It was not in the purest taste, yet it had an air of elegance, and the situation was delightful. A fine lawn sloped away from it, studded with clumps of trees, so disposed as to break a soft fertile country into a variety of landscapes. The Mersey was seen winding a broad quiet sheet of water through an expanse of green meadow-land; while the Welsh mountains, blended with clouds, and melting into distance, bordered the horizon.

This was Roscoe's favorite residence during the days of his prosperity. It had been the seat of elegant hospitality and literary retirement. The house was now silent and deserted. I saw the windows of the study, which looked out upon the soft scenery I have mentioned. The windows were closed—the library was gone. Two or three ill-favored beings were loitering about the place, whom my fancy pictured into retainers of the law. It was like visiting some classic fountain, that had once welled its pure waters in a sacred shade, but finding it dry and dusty, with the lizard and the toad brooding over the shattered marbles.

I inquired after the fate of Mr. Roscoe's library, which had consisted of scarce and foreign books, from many of which he had drawn the materials for his Italian histories. It had passed under the hammer of the auctioneer, and was dispersed about the country. The good people of the vicinity thronged like wreckers to get some part of the noble vessel that had been driven on shore. Did such a scene admit of ludicrous associations, we might imagine something whimsical in this strange irruption in the regions of learning. Pigmies rummaging the armory of a giant, and contending for the possession of weapons which they could not wield. We might picture to ourselves some knot of speculators, debating with calculating brow over the quaint binding and illuminated margin of an obsolete author; of the air of intense, but baffled sagacity, with which some successful purchaser attempted to dive into the black-letter bargain he had secured.

It is a beautiful incident in the story of Mr. Roscoe's misfortunes, and one which cannot fail to interest the studious mind, that the parting with his books seems to have touched upon his tenderest feelings, and to have been the only circumstance that could provoke the notice of his muse. The scholar only knows how dear these silent, yet eloquent, companions of pure thoughts and innocent hours become in the seasons of adversity. When all that is worldly turns to dross around us, these only retain their steady value. When friends grow cold, and the converse of intimates languishes into vapid civility and commonplace, these only continue the unaltered countenance of happier days, and cheer us with that true friendship which never deceived hope, nor deserted sorrow.

I do not wish to censure; but, surely, if the people of Liverpool had been properly sensible of what was due to Mr. Roscoe and themselves, his library would never have been sold. Good worldly reasons may, doubtless, be given for the circumstance, which it would be difficult to combat with others that might seem merely fanciful; but it certainly appears to me such an opportunity as seldom occurs, of cheering a noble mind struggling under misfortunes, by one of the most delicate, but most expressive tokens of public sympathy. It is difficult, however, to estimate a man of genius properly who is daily before our eyes. He becomes mingled and confounded with other men. His great qualities lose their novelty, we become too familiar with the common materials which form the basis even of the loftiest character. Some of Mr. Roscoe's townsmen may regard him merely as a man of business; others as a politician; all find him engaged like themselves in ordinary occupations, and surpassed, perhaps, by themselves on some points of worldly wisdom. Even that amiable and unostentatious simplicity of character, which gives the nameless grace to real excellence, may cause him to be undervalued by some coarse minds, who do not know that true worth is always void of glare and pretension. But the man of letters, who speaks of Liverpool, speaks of it as the residence of Roscoe. The intelligent traveller who visits it inquires where Roscoe is to be seen. He is the literary landmark of the place, indicating its existence to the distant scholar. He is, like Pompey's column at Alexandria, towering alone in classic dignity.

The following sonnet is addressed by Mr. Roscoe to his books on parting with them. If anything can add effect to the pure feeling and elevated thought here displayed, it is the conviction, that the whole is no effusion of fancy, but a faithful transcript from the writer's heart.

TO MY BOOKS

As one who, destined from his friends to part,
  Regrets his loss, but hopes again erewhile
  To share their converse and enjoy their smile,
And tempers as he may affliction's dart;

Thus, loved associates, chiefs of elder art,
  Teachers of wisdom, who could once beguile
  My tedious hours, and lighten every toil,
I now resign you; nor with fainting heart;

For pass a few short years, or days, or hours,
And happier seasons may their dawn unfold,
And all your sacred fellowship restore:
When, freed from earth, unlimited its powers,
Mind shall with mind direct communion hold,
And kindred spirits meet to part no more.

Traits of Indian Character

"I appeal to any white man if ever he entered Logan's cabin hungry, and he gave him not to eat; if ever he came cold and naked, and he clothed him not."

SPEECH OF AN INDIAN CHIEF

THERE is something in the character and habits of the North American savage, taken in connection with the scenery over which he is accustomed to range, its vast lakes, boundless forests, majestic rivers, and trackless plains, that is, to my mind, wonderfully striking and sublime. He is formed for the wilderness, as the Arab is for the desert. His nature is stern, simple, and enduring; fitted to grapple with difficulties, and to support privations. There seems but little soil in his heart for the support of the kindly virtues; and yet, if we would but take the trouble to penetrate through that proud stoicism and habitual taciturnity, which lock up his character from casual observation, we should find him linked to his fellow-man of civilized life by more of those sympathies and affections than are usually ascribed to him.

It has been the lot of the unfortunate aborigines of America, in the early periods of colonization, to be doubly wronged by the white men. They have been dispossessed of their hereditary possessions by mercenary and frequently wanton warfare: and their characters have been traduced by bigoted and interested writers. The colonist often treated them like beasts of the forest; and the author has endeavored to justify him in his outrages. The former found it easier to exterminate than to civilize; the latter to vilify than to discriminate. The appellations of savage and pagan were deemed sufficient to sanction the hostilities of both; and thus the poor wanderers of the forest were persecuted and defamed, not because they were guilty, but because they were ignorant.

The rights of the savage have seldom been properly appreciated or respected by the white man. In peace he has too often been the dupe of artful traffic; in war he has been regarded as a ferocious animal, whose life or death was a question of mere precaution and convenience. Man is cruelly wasteful of life when his own safety is endangered, and he is sheltered by impunity; and little mercy is to be expected from him, when he feels the sting of the reptile and is conscious of the power to destroy.

The same prejudices, which were indulged thus early, exist in common circulation at the present day. Certain learned societies have, it is true, with laudable diligence, endeavored to investigate and record the real characters and manners of the Indian tribes; the American government, too, has wisely and humanely exerted itself to inculcate a friendly and forbearing spirit towards them, and to protect them from fraud and injustice.* The current opinion of the Indian character, however, is too apt to be formed from the miserable hordes which infest the frontiers, and hang on the skirts of the settlements. These are too commonly composed of degenerate beings, corrupted and enfeebled by the vices of society, without being benefited by its civilization. That proud independence, which formed the main pillar of savage virtue, has been shaken down, and the whole moral fabric lies in ruins. Their spirits are humiliated and debased by a sense of inferiority, and their native courage cowed and daunted by the superior knowledge and power of their enlightened neighbors. Society has advanced upon them like one of those withering airs that will sometimes breed desolation over a whole region of fertility. It has enervated their strength, multiplied their diseases, and superinduced upon their original barbarity the low vices of artificial life. It has given them a thousand superfluous wants, whilst it has diminished their means of mere existence. It has driven before it the animals of the chase, who fly from the sound of the axe and the smoke of the settlement, and seek refuge in the depths of remoter forests and yet untrodden wilds. Thus do we too often find the Indians on our frontiers to be the mere wrecks and remnants of once powerful tribes, who have lingered in the vicinity of the settlements, and sunk

* The American government has been indefatigable in its exertions to ameliorate the situation of the Indians, and to introduce among them the arts of civilization, and civil and religious knowledge. To protect them from the frauds of the white traders, no purchase of land from them by individuals is permitted; nor is any person allowed to receive lands from them as a present, without the express sanction of government. These precautions are strictly enforced.

into precarious and vagabond existence. Poverty, repining and hopeless poverty, a canker of the mind unknown in savage life, corrodes their spirits, and blights every free and noble quality of their natures. They become drunken, indolent, feeble, thievish, and pusillanimous. They loiter like vagrants about the settlements, among spacious dwellings replete with elaborate comforts, which only render them sensible of the comparative wretchedness of their own condition. Luxury spreads its ample board before their eyes; but they are excluded from the banquet. Plenty revels over the fields; but they are starving in the midst of its abundance: the whole wilderness has blossomed into a garden; but they feel as reptiles that infest it.

How different was their state while yet the undisputed lords of the soil! Their wants were few, and the means of gratification within their reach. They saw every one around them sharing the same lot, enduring the same hardships, feeding on the same aliments, arrayed in the same rude garments. No roof then rose, but was open to the homeless stranger; no smoke curled among the trees, but he was welcome to sit down by its fire, and join the hunter in his repast. "For," says an old historian of New England, "their life is so void of care, and they are so loving also, that they make use of those things they enjoy as common goods, and are therein so compassionate, that rather than one should starve through want, they would starve all; thus they pass their time merrily, not regarding our pomp, but are better content with their own, which some men esteem so meanly of." Such were the Indians, whilst in the pride and energy of their primitive natures: they resembled those wild plants, which thrive best in the shades of the forest, but shrink from the hand of cultivation, and perish beneath the influence of the sun.

In discussing the savage character, writers have been too prone to indulge in vulgar prejudice and passionate exaggeration, instead of the candid temper of true philosophy. They have not sufficiently considered the peculiar circumstances in which the Indians have been placed, and the peculiar principles under which they have been educated. No being acts more rigidly from rule than the Indian. His whole conduct is regulated according to some general maxims early implanted in his mind. The moral laws that govern him are, to be sure, but few; but then he conforms to them all; the white man abounds in laws of religion, morals, and manners, but how many does he violate?

A frequent ground of accusation against the Indians is their disregard of treaties, and the treachery and wantonness with which, in time of apparent peace, they will suddenly fly to hostilities. The intercourse of the white men with the Indians, however, is too apt to be cold, distrustful, oppressive, and insulting. They seldom treat them with that confidence and frankness which are indispensable to real friendship; nor is sufficient caution observed not to offend against those feelings of pride or superstition, which often prompts the Indian to hostility quicker than mere considerations of interest. The solitary savage feels silently, but acutely. His sensibilities are not diffused over so wide a surface as those of the white man; but they run in steadier and deeper channels. His pride, his affections, his superstitions, are all directed towards fewer objects; but the wounds inflicted on them are proportionably severe, and furnish motives of hostility which we cannot sufficiently appreciate. Where a community is also limited in number, and forms one great patriarchal family, as in an Indian tribe, the injury of an individual is the injury of the whole; and the sentiment of vengeance is almost instantaneously diffused. One council fire is sufficient for the discussion and arrangement of a plan of hostilities. Here all the fighting men and sages assemble. Eloquence and superstition combine to inflame the minds of the warriors. The orator awakens their martial ardor, and they are wrought up to a kind of religious desperation, by the visions of the prophet and the dreamer.

An instance of one of those sudden exasperations, arising from a motive peculiar to the Indian character, is extant in an old record of the early settlement of Massachusetts. The planters of Plymouth had defaced the monuments of the dead at Passonagessit, and had plundered the grave of the Sachem's mother of some skins with which it had been decorated. The Indians are remarkable for the reverence which they entertain for the sepulchres of their kindred. Tribes that have passed generations exiled from the abodes of their ancestors, when by chance they have been travelling in the vicinity, have been known to turn aside from the highway, and, guided by wonderfully accurate tradition, have crossed the country for miles to some tumulus, buried perhaps in woods, where the bones of their tribe were anciently deposited; and there have passed hours in silent meditation. Influenced by this sublime and holy feeling, the Sachem, whose mother's tomb had been violated, gathered his men together, and addressed them in the following beautifully simple and pathetic harangue; a curious specimen of Indian eloquence, and an affecting instance of filial piety in a savage.

"When last the glorious light of all the sky was underneath this globe, and birds grew silent, I began to settle, as my custom is, to take repose. Before mine eyes were fast closed, methought I saw a vision, at which my spirit was much troubled; and trembling at that doleful sight, a spirit cried aloud, 'Behold, my son, whom I have cherished, see the breasts that gave thee suck, the hands that lapped thee warm, and fed thee oft. Canst thou forget to take revenge of those wild people who have defaced my monument in a despiteful manner, disdaining our antiquities and honorable customs? See, now, the Sachem's grave lies like the common people, defaced by an ignoble race. Thy mother doth complain, and implores thy aid against this thievish people, who have newly intruded on our land. If this be suffered, I shall not rest quiet in my everlasting habitation.' This said, the spirit vanished, and I, all in a sweat, not able scarce to speak, began to get some strength, and recollect my spirits that were fled, and determined to demand your counsel and assistance."

I have adduced this anecdote at some length, as it tends to show how these sudden acts of hostility, which have been attributed to caprice and perfidy, may often arise from deep and generous motives, which our inattention to Indian character and customs prevents our properly appreciating.

Another ground of violent outcry against the Indians is their barbarity to the vanquished. This had its origin partly in policy and partly in superstition. The tribes, though sometimes called nations, were never so formidable in their numbers, but that the loss of several warriors was sensibly felt; this was particularly the case when they had frequently been engaged in warfare; and many an instance occurs in Indian history, where a tribe, that had long been formidable to its neighbors, has been broken up and driven away, by the capture and massacre of its principal fighting men. There was a strong temptation, therefore, to the victor to be merciless; not so much to gratify any cruel revenge, as to provide for future security. The Indians had also the superstitious belief, frequent among barbarous nations, and prevalent also among the ancients, that the manes of their friends who had fallen in battle were soothed by the blood of the captives. The prisoners, however, who are not thus sacrificed, are adopted into their families in the place of the slain, and are treated with the confidence and affection of relatives and friends; nay, so hospitable and tender is their entertainment, that when the alternative is offered them, they will often prefer to remain with their adopted brethren, rather than return to the home and the friends of their youth.

The cruelty of the Indians towards their prisoners has been heightened since the colonization of the whites. What was formerly a compliance with policy and superstition, has been exasperated into a gratification of vengeance. They cannot but be sensible that the white men are the usurpers of their ancient dominion, the cause of their degradation, and the gradual destroyers of their race. They go forth to battle, smarting with injuries and indignities which they have individually suffered, and they are driven to madness and despair by the wide-spreading desolation, and the overwhelming ruin of European warfare. The whites have too frequently set them an example of violence, by burning their villages, and laying waste their slender means of subsistence: and yet they wonder that savages do not show moderation and magnanimity towards those who have left them nothing but mere existence and wretchedness.

We stigmatize the Indians, also, as cowardly and treacherous, because they use stratagem in warfare, in preference to open force; but in this they are fully justified by their rude code of honor. They are early taught that stratagem is praiseworthy; the bravest warrior thinks it no disgrace to lurk in silence, and take every advantage of his foe: he triumphs in the superior craft and sagacity by which he has been enabled to surprise and destroy an enemy. Indeed, man is naturally more prone to subtilty than open valor, owing to his physical weakness in comparison with other animals. They are endowed with natural weapons of defence: with horns, with tusks, with hoofs, and talons; but man has to depend on his superior sagacity. In all his encounters with these, his proper enemies, he resorts to stratagem; and when he perversely turns his hostility against his fellow-man, he at first continues the same subtle mode of warfare.

The natural principle of war is to do the most harm to our enemy with the least harm to ourselves; and this of course is to be effected by stratagem. That chivalrous courage which induces us to despise the suggestions of prudence, and to rush in the face of certain danger, is the offspring of society, and produced by education. It is honorable, because it is in fact the triumph of lofty sentiment over an instinctive repugnance to pain, and over those yearnings after personal ease and security, which society has condemned as ignoble. It is kept alive by pride and the fear of shame; and thus the dread of real evil is overcome by the superior dread of an evil which exists but in the imagination. It has been cherished and stimulated also by various means. It has been the theme of spirit-stirring song and chivalrous story. The poet and minstrel have delighted to shed round it the splendors of fiction; and even the historian has forgotten the sober gravity of narration, and broken forth into enthusiasm and rhapsody in its praise. Triumphs and gorgeous pageants have been its reward: monuments, on which art has exhausted its skill, and opulence its treasures, have been erected to perpetuate a nation's gratitude and admiration. Thus artificially excited, courage has risen to an extraordinary and factitious degree of heroism: and arrayed in all the glorious "pomp and circumstance of war," this turbulent quality has even been able to eclipse many of those quiet, but invaluable virtues, which silently ennoble the human character, and swell the tide of human happiness.

But if courage intrinsically consists in the defiance of danger and pain, the life of the Indian is a continual exhibition of it. He lives in a state of perpetual hostility and risk. Peril and adventure are congenial to his nature; or rather seem necessary to arouse his faculties and to give an interest to his existence. Surrounded by hostile tribes, whose mode of warfare is by ambush and surprisal, he is always prepared for fight, and lives with his weapons in his hands. As the ship careers in fearful singleness through the solitudes of ocean; as the bird mingles among clouds and storms, and wings its way, a mere speck, across the pathless fields of air; so the Indian holds his course, silent, solitary, but undaunted, through the boundless bosom of the wilderness. His expeditions may vie in distance and danger with the pilgrimage of the devotee, or the crusade of the knight-errant. He traverses vast forests, exposed to the hazards of lonely sickness, of lurking enemies, and pining famine. Stormy lakes, those great inland seas, are no obstacles to his wanderings: in his light canoe of bark he sports, like a feather, on their waves, and darts, with the swiftness of an arrow, down the roaring rapids of the rivers. His very subsistence is snatched from the midst of toil and peril. He gains his food by the hardships and dangers of the chase: he wraps himself in the spoils of the bear, the panther, and the buffalo, and sleeps among the thunders of the cataract.

No hero of ancient or modern days can surpass the Indian in his lofty contempt of death, and the fortitude with which he sustains its cruellest infliction. Indeed we here behold him rising superior to the white man, in consequence of his peculiar education. The latter rushes to glorious death at the cannon's mouth; the former calmly contemplates its approach, and triumphantly endures it, amidst the varied torments of surrounding foes and the protracted agonies of fire. He even takes a pride in taunting his persecutors, and provoking their ingenuity of torture; and as the devouring flames prey on his very vitals, and the flesh shrinks from the sinews, he raises his last song of triumph, breathing the defiance of an unconquered heart, and invoking the spirits of his fathers to witness that he dies without a groan.

Notwithstanding the obloquy with which the early historians have overshadowed the characters of the unfortunate natives, some bright gleams occasionally break through, which throw a degree of melancholy lustre on their memories. Facts are occasionally to be met with in the rude annals of the eastern provinces, which, though recorded with the coloring of prejudice and bigotry, yet speak for themselves; and will be dwelt on with applause and sympathy, when prejudice shall have passed away.

In one of the homely narratives of the Indian wars in New England, there is a touching account of the desolation carried into the tribe of the Pequod Indians. Humanity shrinks from the cold-blooded detail of indiscriminate butchery. In one place we read of the surprisal of an Indian fort in the night, when the wigwams were wrapped in flames, and the miserable inhabitants shot down and slain in attempting to escape, "all being despatched and ended in the course of an hour." After a series of similar transactions, "our soldiers," as the historian piously observes, "being resolved by God's assistance to make a final destruction of them," the unhappy savages being hunted from their homes and fortresses, and pursued with fire and sword, a scanty, but gallant band, the sad remnant of the Pequod warriors, with their wives and children, took refuge in a swamp.

Burning with indignation, and rendered sullen by despair; with hearts bursting with grief at the destruction of their tribe, and spirits galled and sore at the fancied ignominy of their defeat, they refused to ask their lives at the hands of an insulting foe, and preferred death to submission.

As the night drew on they were surrounded in their dismal retreat, so as to render escape impracticable. Thus situated, their enemy "plied them with shot all the time, by which means many were killed and buried in the mire." In the darkness and fog that preceded the dawn of day some few broke through the besiegers and escaped into the woods: "the rest were left to the conquerors, of which many were killed in the swamp, like sullen dogs who would rather, in their self-willedness and madness, sit still and be shot through, or cut to pieces," than implore for mercy. When the day broke upon this handful of forlorn but dauntless spirits, the soldiers, we are told, entering the swamp, "saw several heaps of them sitting close together, upon whom they discharged their pieces, laden with ten or twelve pistol bullets at a time, putting the muzzles of the pieces under the boughs, within a few yards of them; so as, besides those that were found dead, many more were killed and sunk into the mire, and never were minded more by friend or foe."

Can any one read this plain unvarnished tale, without admiring the stern resolution, the unbending pride, the loftiness of spirit, that seemed to nerve the hearts of these self-taught heroes, and to raise them above the instinctive feelings of human nature? When the Gauls laid waste the city of Rome, they found the senators clothed in their robes, and seated with stern tranquillity in their curule chairs; in this manner they suffered death without resistance or even supplication. Such conduct was, in them, applauded as noble and magnanimous; in the hapless Indian it was reviled as obstinate and sullen! How truly are we the dupes of show and circumstance! How different is virtue, clothed in purple and enthroned in state, from virtue, naked and destitute, and perishing obscurely in a wilderness!

But I forbear to dwell on these gloomy pictures. The eastern tribes have long since disappeared; the forests that sheltered them have been laid low, and scarce any traces remain of them in the thickly-settled states of New England, excepting here and there the Indian name of a village or a stream. And such must, sooner or later, be the fate of those other tribes which skirt the frontiers, and have occasionally been inveigled from their forests to mingle in the wars of white men. In a little while, and they will go the way that their brethren have gone before. The few hordes which still linger about the shores of Huron and Superior, and the tributary streams of the Mississippi, will share the fate of those tribes that once spread over Massachusetts and Connecticut, and lorded it along the proud banks of the Hudson; of that gigantic race said to have existed on the borders of the Susquehanna; and of those various nations that flourished about the Potomac and the Rappahannock, and that peopled the forests of the vast valley of Shenandoah. They will vanish like a vapor from the face of the earth; their very history will be lost in forgetfulness; and "the places that now know them will know them no more for ever." Or if, perchance, some dubious memorial of them should survive, it may be in the romantic dreams of the poet, to people in imagination his glades and groves, like the fauns and satyrs and sylvan deities of antiquity. But should he venture upon the dark story of their wrongs and wretchedness; should he tell how they were invaded, corrupted, despoiled, driven from their native abodes and the sepulchres of their fathers, hunted like wild beasts about the earth, and sent down with violence and butchery to the grave, posterity will either turn with horror and incredulity from the tale, or blush with indignation at the inhumanity of their forefathers. "We are driven back," said an old warrior, "until we can retreat no farther—our hatchets are broken, our bows are snapped, our fires are nearly extinguished: a little longer, and the white man will cease to persecute us—for we shall cease to exist!"

The Mutability of Literature

A COLLOQUY IN WESTMINSTER ABBEY

I know that all beneath the moon decays,
And what by mortals in this world is brought,
In time's great period shall return to nought.
I know that all the muse's heavenly lays,
With toil of sprite which are so dearly bought,
As idle sounds, of few or none are sought,
That there is nothing ligher than mere praise.

DRUMMOND OF HAWTHORNDEN

THERE are certain half-dreaming moods of mind, in which we naturally steal away from noise and glare, and seek some quiet haunt, where we may indulge our reveries and build our air castles undisturbed. In such a mood I was loitering about the old gray cloisters of Westminster Abbey, enjoying that luxury of wandering thought which one is apt to dignify with the name of reflection; when suddenly an interruption of madcap boys from Westminster School, playing at foot-ball, broke in upon the monastic stillness of the place, making the vaulted passages and mouldering tombs echo with their merriment. I sought to take refuge from their noise by penetrating still deeper into the solitudes of the pile, and applied to one of the vergers for admission to the library. He conducted me through a portal rich with the crumbling sculpture of former ages, which opened upon a gloomy passage leading to the chapter-house and the chamber in which doomsday book is deposited. Just within the passage is a small door on the left. To this the verger applied a key; it was double locked, and opened with some difficulty, as if seldom used. We now ascended a dark narrow staircase, and, passing through a second door, entered the library.

I found myself in a lofty antique hall, the roof supported by massive joists of old English oak. It was soberly lighted by a row of Gothic windows at a considerable height from the floor, and which apparently opened upon the roofs of the cloisters. An ancient picture of some reverend dignitary of the church in his robes hung over the fireplace. Around the hall and in a small gallery were the books, arranged in carved oaken cases. They consisted principally of old polemical writers, and were much more worn by time than use. In the centre of the library was a solitary table with two or three books on it, an inkstand without ink, and a few pens parched by long disuse. The place seemed fitted for quiet study and profound meditation. It was buried deep among the massive walls of the abbey, and shut up from the tumult of the world. I could only hear now and then the shouts of the schoolboys faintly swelling from the cloisters, and the sound of a bell tolling for prayers, echoing soberly along the roofs of the abbey. By degrees the shouts of merriment grew fainter and fainter, and at length died away; the bell ceased to toll, and a profound silence reigned through the dusky hall.

I had taken down a little thick quarto, curiously bound in parchment, with brass clasps, and seated myself at the table in a venerable elbow-chair. Instead of reading, however, I was beguiled by the solemn monastic air, and lifeless quiet of the place, into a train of musing. As I looked around upon the old volumes in their mouldering covers, thus ranged on the shelves, and apparently never disturbed in their repose, I could not but consider the library a kind of literary catacomb, where authors, like mummies, are piously entombed, and left to blacken and moulder in dusty oblivion.

How much, thought I, has each of these volumes, now thrust aside with such indifference, cost some aching head! how many weary days! how many sleepless nights! How have their authors buried themselves in the solitude of cells and cloisters; shut themselves up from the face of man, and the still more blessed face of nature; and devoted themselves to painful research and intense reflection! And all for what? to occupy an inch of dusty shelf—to have the title of their works read now and then in a future age, by some drowsy churchman or casual straggler like myself; and in another age to be lost, even to remembrance. Such is the amount of this boasted immortality. A mere temporary rumor, a local sound; like the tone of that bell which has just tolled among these towers, filling the ear for a moment—lingering transiently in echo—and then passing away like a thing that was not.

While I sat half murmuring, half meditating these unprofitable speculations with my head resting on my hand, I was thrumming with the other hand upon the quarto, until I accidentally loosened the clasps; when, to my utter astonishment, the little book gave two or three yawns, like one awaking from a deep sleep; then a husky hem; and at length began to talk. At first its voice was very hoarse and broken, being much troubled by a cobweb which some studious spider had woven across it; and having probably contracted a cold from long exposure to the chills and damps of the abbey. In a short time, however, it became more distinct, and I soon found it an exceedingly fluent conversable little tome. Its language, to be sure, was rather quaint and obsolete, and its pronunciation, what, in the present day, would be deemed barbarous; but I shall endeavor, as far as I am able, to render it in modern parlance.

It began with railings about the neglect of the world—about merit being suffered to languish in obscurity, and other such commonplace topics of literary repining, and complained bitterly that it had not been opened for more than two centuries. That the dean only looked now and then into the library, sometimes took down a volume or two, trifled with them for a few moments, and then returned them to their shelves. "What a plague do they mean," said the little quarto, which I began to perceive was somewhat choleric, "what a plague do they mean by keeping several thousand volumes of us shut up here, and watched by a set of old vergers, like so many beauties in a harem, merely to be looked at now and then by the dean? Books were written to give pleasure and to be enjoyed; and I would have a rule passed that the dean should pay each of us a visit at least once a year; or if he is not equal to the task, let them once in a while turn loose the whole school of Westminster among us, that at any rate we may now and then have an airing."

"Softly, my worthy friend," replied I, "you are not aware how much better you are off than most books of your generation. By being stored away in this ancient library, you are like the treasured remains of those saints and monarchs, which lie enshrined in the adjoining chapels; while the remains of your contemporary mortals, left to the ordinary course of nature, have long since returned to dust."

"Sir," said the little tome, ruffling his leaves and looking big, "I was written for all the world, not for the bookworms of an abbey. I was intended to circulate from hand to hand, like other great contemporary works; but here have I been clasped up for more than two centuries, and might have silently fallen a prey to these worms that are playing the very vengeance with my intestines, if you had not by chance given me an opportunity of uttering a few last words before I go to pieces."

"My good friend," rejoined I, "had you been left to the circulation of which you speak, you would long ere this have been no more. To judge from your physiognomy, you are now well stricken in years: very few of your contemporaries can be at present in existence; and those few owe their longevity to being immured like yourself in old libraries; which, suffer me to add, instead of likening to harems, you might more properly and gratefully have compared to those infirmaries attached to religious establishments, for the benefit of the old and decrepit, and where, by quiet fostering and no employment, they often endure to an amazingly good-for-nothing old age. You talk of your contemporaries as if in circulation—where do we meet with their works? what do we hear of Robert Groteste, of Lincoln? No one could have toiled harder than he for immortality. He is said to have written nearly two hundred volumes. He built, as it were, a pyramid of books to perpetuate his name: but, alas! the pyramid has long since fallen, and only a few fragments are scattered in various libraries, where they are scarcely disturbed even by the antiquarian. What do we hear of Giraldus Cambrensis, the historian, antiquary, philosopher, theologian, and poet? He declined two bishoprics, that he might shut himself up and write for posterity; but posterity never inquires after his labors. What of Henry of Huntingdon, who, besides a learned history of England, wrote a treatise on the contempt of the world, which the world has revenged by forgetting him? What is quoted of Joseph of Exeter, styled the miracle of his age in classical composition? Of his three great heroic poems one is lost forever, excepting a mere fragment; the others are known only to a few of the curious in literature; and as to his love verses and epigrams, they have entirely disappeared. What is in current use of John Wallis, the Franciscan, who acquired the name of the tree of life? Of William of Malmsbury; of Simeon of Durham; of Benedict of Peterborough; of John Hanvill of St. Albans; of——"

"Prithee, friend," cried the quarto, in a testy tone, "how old do you think me? You are talking of authors that lived long before my time, and wrote either in Latin or French, so that they in a manner expatriated themselves, and deserved to be forgotten; * but I, sir, was ushered into the world from the press of the renowned Wynkyn de Worde. I was written in my own native tongue, at a time when the language had become fixed; and indeed I was considered a model of pure and elegant English."

(I should observe that these remarks were couched in such intolerably antiquated terms, that I have had infinite difficulty in rendering them into modern phraseology.)

"I cry your mercy," said I, "for mistaking your age; but it matters little: almost all the writers of your time have likewise passed into forgetfulness; and De Worde's publications are mere literary rarities among book-collectors. The purity and stability of language, too, on which you found your claims to perpetuity, have been the fallacious dependence of authors of every age, even back to the times of the worthy Robert of Gloucester, who wrote his history in rhymes of mongrel Saxon.† Even now many talk of Spenser's 'well of pure English undefiled,' as if the language ever sprang from a well or fountain-head, and was not rather a mere confluence of various tongues, perpetually subject to changes and intermixtures. It is this which has made English literature so extremely mutable, and the reputation built upon it so fleeting. Unless thought can be committed to something more

* In Latin and French hath many soueraine wittes had great delyte to endite, and have many noble things fulfilde, but certes there ben some that speaken their poisye in French, of which speche the Frenchmen have as good a fantasye as we have in hearying of Frenchmen's Englishe.—*Chaucer's Testament of Love.*

† Holinshed, in his Chronicle, observes, "afterwards, also, by deligent travell of Geffry Chaucer and of John Gowre, in the time of Richard the Second, and after them of John Scogan and John Lydgate, monke of Berrie, our said toong was brought to an excellent passe, notwithstanding that it never came unto the type of perfection until the time of Queen Elizabeth, wherein John Jewell, Bishop of Sarum, John Fox, and sundrie learned and excellent writers, have fully accomplished the ornature of the same, to their great praise and immortal commendation."

permanent and unchangeable than such a medium, even thought must share the fate of every thing else, and fall into decay. This should serve as a check upon the vanity and exultation of the most popular writer. He finds the language in which he has embarked his fame gradually altering, and subject to the dilapidations of time and the caprice of fashion. He looks back and beholds the early authors of his country, once the favorites of their day, supplanted by modern writers. A few short ages have covered them with obscurity, and their merits can only be relished by the quaint taste of the bookworm. And such, he anticipates, will be the fate of his own work, which, however it may be admired in its day, and held up as a model of purity, will in the course of years grow antiquated and obsolete; until it shall become almost as unintelligible in its native land as an Egyptian obelisk, or one of those Runic inscriptions said to exist in the deserts of Tartary. I declare," added I, with some emotion, "when I contemplate a modern library, filled with new works, in all the bravery of rich gilding and binding, I feel disposed to sit down and weep; like the good Xerxes, when he surveyed his army, pranked out in all the splendor of military array, and reflected that in one hundred years not one of them would be in existence!"

"Ah," said the little quarto, with a heavy sigh, "I see how it is; these modern scribblers have superseded all the good old authors. I suppose nothing is read now-a-days but Sir Philip Sydney's Arcadia, Sackville's stately plays, and Mirror for Magistrates, or the fine-spun euphuisms of the 'unparalleled John Lyly.' "

"There you are again mistaken," said I; "the writers whom you suppose in vogue, because they happened to be so when you were last in circulation, have long since had their day. Sir Philip Sydney's Arcadia, the immortality of which was so fondly predicted by his admirers,* and which, in truth, is full of noble

* Live ever sweete booke; the simple image of his gentle witt, and the golden-pillar of his noble courage; and ever notify unto the world that thy writer was the secretary of eloquence, the breath of the muses, the honey-bee of the daintyest flowers of witt and arte, the pith of morale and intellectual virtues, the arme of Bellona in the field, the tonge of Suada in the chamber, the sprite of Practise in esse, and the paragon of excellency in print.—*Harvey Pierce's Supererogation.*

thoughts, delicate images, and graceful turns of language, is now scarcely ever mentioned. Sackville has strutted into obscurity; and even Lyly, though his writings were once the delight of a court, and apparently perpetuated by a proverb, is now scarcely known even by name. A whole crowd of authors who wrote and wrangled at the time, have likewise gone down, with all their writings and their controversies. Wave after wave of succeeding literature has rolled over them, until they are buried so deep, that it is only now and then that some industrious diver after fragments of antiquity brings up a specimen for the gratification of the curious.

"For my part," I continued, "I consider this mutability of language a wise precaution of Providence for the benefit of the world at large, and of authors in particular. To reason from analogy, we daily behold the varied and beautiful tribes of vegetables springing up, flourishing, adorning the fields for a short time, and then fading into dust, to make way for their successors. Were not this the case, the fecundity of nature would be a grievance instead of a blessing. The earth would groan with rank and excessive vegetation, and its surface become a tangled wilderness. In like manner the works of genius and learning decline, and make way for subsequent productions. Language gradually varies, and with it fade away the writings of authors who have flourished their allotted time; otherwise, the creative powers of genius would overstock the world, and the mind would be completely bewildered in the endless mazes of literature. Formerly there were some restraints on this excessive multiplication. Works had to be transcribed by hand, which was a slow and laborious operation; they were written either on parchment, which was expensive, so that one work was often erased to make way for another; or on papyrus, which was fragile and extremely perishable. Authorship was a limited and unprofitable craft, pursued chiefly by monks in the leisure and solitude of their cloisters. The accumulation of manuscripts was slow and costly, and confined almost entirely to monasteries. To these circumstances it may, in some measure, be owing that we have not been inundated by the intellect of antiquity; that the fountains of thought have not been broken up, and modern genius drowned in the deluge. But the inventions of paper and the press have put an end to all these restraints. They have made every one a writer, and enabled every mind to pour itself into print, and diffuse itself over the whole intellectual world. The consequences are alarming. The stream of literature has swollen into a torrent—augmented into a river—expanded into a sea. A few centuries since, five or six hundred manuscripts constituted a great library; but what would you say to libraries such as actually exist, containing three or four hundred thousand volumes; legions of authors at the same time busy; and the press going on with fearfully increasing activity, to double and quadruple the number? Unless some unforeseen mortality should break out among the progeny of the muse, now that she has become so prolific, I tremble for posterity. I fear the mere fluctuation of language will not be sufficient. Criticism may do much. It increases with the increase of literature, and resembles one of those salutary checks on population spoken of by economists. All possible encouragement, therefore, should be given to the growth of critics, good or bad. But I fear all will be in vain; let criticism do what it may, writers will write, printers will print, and the world will inevitably be overstocked with good books. It will soon be the employment of a lifetime merely to learn their names. Many a man of passable information, at the present day, reads scarcely anything but reviews; and before long a man of erudition will be little better than a mere walking catalogue."

"My very good sir," said the little quarto, yawning most drearily in my face, "excuse my interrupting you, but I perceive you are rather given to prose. I would ask the fate of an author who was making some noise just as I left the world. His reputation, however, was considered quite temporary. The learned shook their heads at him, for he was a poor half-educated varlet, that knew little of Latin, and nothing of Greek, and had been obliged to run the country for deer-stealing. I think his name was Shakspeare. I presume he soon sunk into oblivion."

"On the contrary," said I, "it is owing to that very man that the literature of his period has experienced a duration beyond the ordinary term of English literature. There rise authors now and then, who seem proof against the mutability of language, because they have rooted themselves in the unchanging principles of human nature. They are like gigantic trees that we sometimes see on the banks of a stream; which, by their vast and deep roots, penetrating through the mere surface, and laying hold on the very foundations of the earth, preserve the soil around them from being swept away by the ever-flowing current, and hold up many a neighboring plant, and, perhaps, worthless weed, to perpetuity. Such is the case with Shakspeare, whom we behold defying the encroachments of time, retaining in modern use the language and literature of his day, and giving duration to many an indifferent author, merely from having flourished in his vicinity. But even he, I grieve to say, is gradually assuming the tint of age, and his whole form is overrun by a profusion of commentators, who, like clambering vines and creepers, almost bury the noble plant that upholds them."

Here the little quarto began to heave his sides and chuckle, until at length he broke out in a plethoric fit of laughter that had well nigh choked him, by reason of his excessive corpulency. "Mighty well!" cried he, as soon as he could recover breath, "mighty well! and so you would persuade me that the literature of an age is to be perpetuated by a vagabond deer-stealer! by a man without learning; by a poet, forsooth—a poet!" And here he wheezed forth another fit of laughter.

I confess that I felt somewhat nettled at this rudeness, which, however, I pardoned on account of his having flourished in a less polished age. I determined, nevertheless, not to give up my point.

"Yes," resumed I, positively, "a poet; for of all writers he has the best chance for immortality. Others may write from the head, but he writes from the heart, and the heart will always understand him. He is the faithful portrayer of nature, whose features are always the same, and always interesting. Prose writers are voluminous and unwieldy; their pages are crowded with common-places, and their thoughts expanded into tediousness. But with the true poet every thing is terse, touching, or brilliant. He gives the choicest thoughts in the choicest language. He illustrates them by every thing that he sees most striking in nature and art. He enriches them by pictures of human life, such as it is passing before him. His writings, therefore, contain the spirit, the aroma, if I may use the phrase, of the age in which he lives. They are caskets which inclose within a small compass the wealth of the language—its family jewels, which are thus transmitted in a portable form to posterity. The setting may occasionally be antiquated, and require now and then to be renewed, as in the case of Chaucer; but the brilliancy and intrinsic value of the gems continue unaltered. Cast a look back over the long reach of literary history. What vast valleys of dulness, filled with monkish legends and academical controversies! what bogs of theological speculations! what dreary wastes of metaphysics! Here and there only do we behold the heaven-illuminated bards, elevated like beacons on their widely-separate heights, to transmit the pure light of poetical intelligence from age to age." *

I was just about to launch forth into eulogiums upon the poets of the day, when the sudden opening of the door caused me to turn my head. It was the verger, who came to inform me that it was time to close the library. I sought to have a parting word with the quarto, but the worthy little tome was silent; the clasps were closed: and it looked perfectly unconscious of all that had passed. I have been to the library two or three times since, and have endeavored to draw it into further conversation, but in vain; and whether all this rambling colloquy actually took place, or whether it was another of those odd day-dreams to which I am subject, I have never to this moment been able to discover.

* Thorow earth and waters deepe,
The pen by skill doth passe:
And featly nyps the worldes abuse,
And shoes us in a glasse,
The vertu and the vice
Of every wight alyve;
The honey comb that bee doth make
Is not so sweet in hyve,
As are the golden leves
That drop from poet's head!
Which doth surmount our common talke
As farre as dross doth lead.

CHURCHYARD

II. From *Bracebridge Hall*

The Stout Gentleman

A STAGE-COACH ROMANCE

I'll cross it though it blast me!

HAMLET

It was a rainy Sunday in the gloomy month of November. I had been detained, in the course of a journey, by a slight indisposition, from which I was recovering; but was still feverish, and obliged to keep within doors all day, in an inn of the small town of Derby. A wet Sunday in a country inn!—whoever has had the luck to experience one can alone judge of my situation. The rain pattered against the casements; the bells tolled for church with a melancholy sound. I went to the windows in quest of something to amuse the eye; but it seemed as if I had been placed completely out of the reach of all amusement. The windows of my bedroom looked out among tiled roofs and stacks of chimneys, while those of my sitting-room commanded a full view of the stable-yard. I know of nothing more calculated to make a man sick of this world than a stable-yard on a rainy day. The place was littered with wet straw that had been kicked about by travellers and stable-boys. In one corner was a stagnant pool of water, surrounding an island of muck; there were several half-drowned fowls crowded together under a cart, among which was a miserable, crestfallen cock, drenched out of all life and spirit; his drooping tail matted, as it were, into a single feather, along which the water trickled from his back; near the cart was a half-dozing cow, chewing the cud, and standing patiently to be rained on, with wreaths of vapor rising from her reeking hide; a wall-eyed horse, tired of the loneliness of the stable, was poking his spectral head out of a window, with the rain dripping on it from the eaves; an unhappy cur, chained to a dog-house hard by, uttered something, every now and then, between a bark and a yelp; a drab of a kitchen-wench tramped backwards and forwards through the yard in pattens, looking as sulky as the weather itself; everything, in short, was comfortless and forlorn, excepting a crew of hardened ducks, assembled like boon companions round a puddle, and making a riotous noise over their liquor.

I was lonely and listless, and wanted amusement. My room soon became insupportable. I abandoned it, and sought what is technically called the travellers'-room. This is a public room set apart at most inns for the accommodation of a class of wayfarers called travellers, or riders; a kind of commercial knights-errant, who are incessantly scouring the kingdom in gigs, on horseback, or by coach. They are the only successors that I know of at the present day to the knights-errant of yore. They lead the same kind of roving, adventurous life, only changing the lance for a driving-whip, the buckler for a pattern-card, and the coat of mail for an upper Benjamin. Instead of vindicating the charms of peerless beauty, they rove about, spreading the fame and standing of some substantial tradesman, or manufacturer, and are ready at any time to bargain in his name; it being the fashion nowadays to trade, instead of fight, with one another. As the room of the hostel, in the good old fighting-times, would be hung round at night with the armor of way-worn warriors, such as coats of mail, falchions, and yawning helmets, so the travellers'-room is garnished with the harnessing of their successors, with box-coats, whips of all kinds, spurs, gaiters, and oil-cloth covered hats.

I was in hopes of finding some of these worthies to talk with, but was disappointed. There were, indeed, two or three in the room; but I could make nothing of them. One was just finishing his breakfast, quarrelling with his bread and butter, and huffing the waiter; another buttoned on a pair of gaiters, with many execrations at Boots for not having cleaned his shoes well; a third sat drumming on the table with his fingers and looking at the rain as it streamed down the window-glass; they all appeared infected by the weather, and disappeared, one after the other, without exchanging a word.

I sauntered to the window, and stood gazing at the people, picking their way to church, with petticoats hoisted midleg high, and dripping umbrellas. The bell ceased to toll, and the streets became silent. I then amused myself with watching the daughters of a tradesman opposite; who, being confined to the house for fear of wetting their Sunday finery, played off their charms at the front windows, to fascinate the chance tenants of the inn. They at length were summoned away by a vigilant vinegar-faced mother, and I had nothing further from without to amuse me.

What was I to do to pass away the long-lived day? I was sadly nervous and lonely; and everything about an inn seems calculated to make a dull day ten times duller. Old newspapers, smelling of beer and tobacco-smoke, and which I had already read half a dozen times. Good-for-nothing books, that were worse than rainy weather. I bored myself to death with an old volume of the Lady's Magazine. I read all the commonplace names of ambitious travellers scrawled on the panes of glass; the eternal families of the Smiths, and the Browns, and the Jacksons, and the Johnsons, and all the other sons; and I deciphered several scraps of fatiguing inn-window poetry which I have met with in all parts of the world.

The day continued lowering and gloomy; the slovenly, ragged, spongy cloud drifted heavily along; there was no variety even in the rain: it was one dull, continued, monotonous patter —patter—patter, excepting that now and then I was enlivened by the idea of a brisk shower, from the rattling of the drops upon a passing umbrella.

It was quite *refreshing* (if I may be allowed a hackneyed phrase of the day) when, in the course of the morning, a horn blew, and a stage-coach whirled through the street, with outside passengers stuck all over it, cowering under cotton umbrellas, and seethed together, and reeking with the steams of wet box-coats and upper Benjamins.

The sound brought out from their lurking-places a crew of vagabond boys, and vagabond dogs, and the carroty-headed hostler, and that nondescript animal ycleped Boots, and all the other vagabond race that infest the purlieus of an inn; but the bustle was transient; the coach again whirled on its way; and boy and dog, and hostler and Boots, all slunk back again to their holes; the street again became silent, and the rain continued to rain on. In fact, there was no hope of its clearing up; the barometer pointed to rainy weather; mine hostess's tortoise-shell cat sat by the fire washing her face, and rubbing her paws over her ears; and, on referring to the Almanac, I found a direful prediction stretching from the top of the page to the bottom through the whole month, "expect—much—rain—about—this—time!"

I was dreadfully hipped. The hours seemed as if they would never creep by. The very ticking of the clock became irksome. At length the stillness of the house was interrupted by the ringing of a bell. Shortly after I heard the voice of a waiter at the bar: "The stout gentleman in No. 13 wants his breakfast. Tea and bread and butter, with ham and eggs; the eggs not to be too much done."

In such a situation as mine, every incident is of importance. Here was a subject of speculation presented to my mind, and ample exercise for my imagination. I am prone to paint pictures to myself, and on this occasion I had some materials to work upon. Had the guest upstairs been mentioned as Mr. Smith, or Mr. Brown, or Mr. Jackson, or Mr. Johnson, or merely as "the gentleman in No. 13," it would have been a perfect blank to me. I should have thought nothing of it; but "The stout gentleman!" —the very name had something in it of the picturesque. It at once gave the size; it embodied the personage to my mind's eye, and my fancy did the rest.

He was stout, or, as some term it, lusty; in all probability, therefore, he was advanced in life, some people expanding as they grow old. By his breakfasting rather late, and in his own room, he must be a man accustomed to live at his ease, and above the necessity of early rising; no doubt a round, rosy, lusty old gentleman.

There was another violent ringing. The stout gentleman was impatient for his breakfast. He was evidently a man of importance; "well to do in the world;" accustomed to be promptly waited upon; of a keen appetite, and a little cross when hungry; "perhaps," thought I, "he may be some London Alderman; or who knows but he may be a Member of Parliament?"

The breakfast was sent up, and there was a short interval of silence; he was, doubtless, making the tea. Presently there was a violent ringing; and before it could be answered, another ringing still more violent. "Bless me! what a choleric old gentleman!" The waiter came down in a huff. The butter was rancid, the eggs were overdone, the ham was too salt; the stout gentleman was evidently nice in his eating; one of those who eat and growl, and keep the waiter on the trot, and live in a state militant with the household.

The hostess got into a fume. I should observe that she was a brisk, coquettish woman; a little of a shrew, and something of a slammerkin, but very pretty withal; with a nincompoop for a husband, as shrews are apt to have. She rated the servants roundly for their negligence in sending up so bad a breakfast, but said not a word against the stout gentleman; by which I clearly perceived that he must be a man of consequence, entitled to make a noise and to give trouble at a country inn. Other eggs, and ham, and bread and butter were sent up. They appeared to be more graciously received; at least there was no further complaint.

I had not made many turns about the travellers'-room, when there was another ringing. Shortly afterwards there was a stir and an inquest about the house. The stout gentleman wanted the Times or the Chronicle newspaper. I set him down, therefore, for a Whig; or rather, from his being so absolute and lordly where he had a chance, I suspected him of being a Radical. Hunt, I had heard, was a large man; "who knows," thought I, "but it is Hunt himself!"

My curiosity began to be awakened. I inquired of the waiter who was this stout gentleman that was making all this stir; but I could get no information: nobody seemed to know his name. The landlords of bustling inns seldom trouble their heads about the names or occupations of their transient guests. The color of a coat, the shape or size of the person, is enough to suggest a travelling name. It is either the tall gentleman, or the short gentleman, or the gentleman in black, or the gentleman in snuff-color; or, as in the present instance, the stout gentleman. A designation of the kind once hit on, answers every purpose, and saves all further inquiry.

Rain—rain—rain! pitiless, ceaseless rain! No such thing as putting a foot out of doors, and no occupation nor amusement within. By and by I heard some one walking overhead. It was in the stout gentleman's room. He evidently was a large man by the heaviness of his tread; and an old man from his wearing such creaking soles. "He is doubtless," thought I, "some rich old square-toes of regular habits, and is now taking exercise after breakfast."

I now read all the advertisements of coaches and hotels that were stuck about the mantelpiece. The Lady's Magazine had become an abomination to me; it was as tedious as the day itself. I wandered out, not knowing what to do, and ascended again to my room. I had not been there long, when there was a squall from a neighboring bedroom. A door opened and slammed violently; a chamber-maid, that I had remarked for having a ruddy, good-humored face, went down stairs in a violent flurry. The stout gentleman had been rude to her!

This sent a whole host of my deductions to the deuce in a moment. This unknown personage could not be an old gentleman; for old gentlemen are not apt to be so obstreperous to chamber-maids. He could not be a young gentleman; for young gentlemen are not apt to inspire such indignation. He must be a middle-aged man, and confounded ugly into the bargain, or the girl would not have taken the matter in such terrible dudgeon. I confess I was sorely puzzled.

In a few minutes I heard the voice of my landlady. I caught a glance of her as she came tramping up-stairs,—her face glowing, her cap flaring, her tongue wagging the whole way. "She'd have no such doings in her house, she'd warrant. If gentlemen did spend money freely, it was no rule. She'd have no servant-maids of hers treated in that way, when they were about their work, that's what she wouldn't."

As I hate squabbles, particularly with women, and above all with pretty women, I slunk back into my room, and partly closed the door; but my curiosity was too much excited not to listen. The landlady marched intrepidly to the enemy's citadel, and entered it with a storm: the door closed after her. I heard her voice in high windy clamor for a moment or two. Then it gradually subsided, like a gust of wind in a garret; then there was a laugh; then I heard nothing more.

After a little while my landlady came out with an odd smile on her face, adjusting her cap, which was a little on one side. As she went down stairs, I heard the landlord ask her what was the matter; she said, "Nothing at all, only the girl's a fool." I was more than ever perplexed what to make of this unaccountable personage, who could put a good-natured chamber-maid in a passion, and send away a termagant landlady in smiles. He could not be so old, nor cross, nor ugly either.

I had to go to work at his picture again, and to paint him entirely different. I now set him down for one of those stout gentlemen that are frequently met with swaggering about the doors of country inns. Moist, merry fellows, in Belcher handkerchiefs, whose bulk is a little assisted by malt-liquors. Men who have seen the world, and been sworn at Highgate; who are used to tavern-life; up to all the tricks of tapsters, and knowing in the ways of sinful publicans. Free-livers on a small scale; who are prodigal within the compass of a guinea: who call all the waiters by name, tousle the maids, gossip with the landlady at the bar, and prose over a pint of port, or a glass of negus, after dinner.

The morning wore away in forming these and similar surmises. As fast as I wove one system of belief, some movement of the unknown would completely overturn it, and throw all my thoughts again into confusion. Such are the solitary operations of a feverish mind. I was, as I have said, extremely nervous; and the continual meditation on the concerns of this invisible personage began to have its effect: I was getting a fit of the fidgets.

Dinner-time came. I hoped the stout gentleman might dine in the travellers'-room, and that I might at length get a view of his person; but no—he had dinner served in his own room. What could be the meaning of this solitude and mystery? He could not be a radical; there was something too aristocratical in thus keeping himself apart from the rest of the world, and condemning himself to his own dull company throughout a rainy day. And then, too, he lived too well for a discontented politician. He seemed to expatiate on a variety of dishes, and to sit over his wine like a jolly friend of good living. Indeed, my doubts on this head were soon at an end; for he could not have finished his first bottle before I could faintly hear him humming a tune; and on listening I found it to be "God save the King." 'Twas plain, then, he was no radical, but a faithful subject; one who grew loyal over his bottle, and was ready to stand by king and constitution, when he could stand by nothing else. But who could he be? My conjectures began to run wild. Was he not some personage of distinction travelling incog.? "God knows!" said I, at my wit's end; "it may be one of the royal family for aught I know, for they are all stout gentlemen!"

The weather continued rainy. The mysterious unknown kept his room, and, as far as I could judge, his chair, for I did not hear him move. In the meantime, as the day advanced, the travellers'-room began to be frequented. Some, who had just arrived, came in buttoned up in box-coats; others came home who had been dispersed about the town; some took their dinners, and some their tea. Had I been in a different mood, I should have found entertainment in studying this peculiar class of men. There were two especially, who were regular wags of the road, and up to all the standing jokes of travellers. They had a thousand sly things to say to the waiting-maid, whom they called Louisa, and Ethelinda, and a dozen other fine names, changing the name every time, and chuckling amazingly at their own waggery. My mind, however, had been completely engrossed by the stout gentleman. He had kept my fancy in chase during a long day, and it was not now to be diverted from the scent.

The evening gradually wore away. The travellers read the papers two or three times over. Some drew round the fire and told long stories about their horses, about their adventures, their overturns, and breakings-down. They discussed the credit of different merchants and different inns; and the two wags told several choice anecdotes of pretty chamber-maids and kind landladies. All this passed as they were quietly taking what they called their night-caps, that is to say, strong glasses of brandy and water and sugar, or some other mixture of the kind; after which they one after another rang for "Boots" and the chamber-maid, and walked off to bed in old shoes cut down into marvellously uncomfortable slippers.

There was now only one man left: a short-legged, long-bodied, plethoric fellow, with a very large, sandy head. He sat by himself, with a glass of port-wine negus, and a spoon; sipping and stirring, and meditating and sipping, until nothing was left but the spoon. He gradually fell asleep bolt upright in his chair, with the empty glass standing before him; and the candle seemed to fall asleep too, for the wick grew long, and black, and cabbaged at the end, and dimmed the little light that remained in the chamber. The gloom that now prevailed was contagious. Around hung the shapeless, and almost spectral, box-coats of departed travellers, long since buried in deep sleep. I only heard the ticking of the clock, with the deep-drawn breathings of the sleeping topers, and the drippings of the rain, drop—drop—drop, from the eaves of the house. The church-bells chimed midnight. All at once the stout gentleman began to walk overhead, pacing slowly backwards and forwards. There was something extremely awful in all this, especially to one in my state of nerves. These ghastly great-coats, these guttural breathings, and the creaking footsteps of this mysterious being. His steps grew fainter and fainter, and at length died away. I could bear it no longer. I was wound up to the desperation of a hero of romance. "Be he who or what he may," said I to myself, "I'll have a sight of him!" I seized a chamber-candle, and hurried up to No. 13. The door stood ajar. I hesitated—I entered: the room was deserted. There stood a large, broad-bottomed elbow-chair at a table, on which was an empty tumbler, and a "Times," newspaper, and the room smelt powerfully of Stilton cheese.

The mysterious stranger had evidently but just retired. I turned off, sorely disappointed, to my room, which had been changed to the front of the house. As I went along the corridor, I saw a large pair of boots, with dirty, waxed tops, standing at the door of a bedchamber. They doubtless belonged to the unknown; but it would not do to disturb so redoubtable a personage in his den: he might discharge a pistol, or something worse, at my head. I went to bed, therefore, and lay awake half the night in a terribly nervous state; and even when I fell asleep, I was still haunted in my dreams by the idea of the stout gentleman and his wax-topped boots.

I slept rather late the next morning, and was awakened by some stir and bustle in the house, which I could not at first comprehend; until getting more awake, I found there was a mail-coach starting from the door. Suddenly there was a cry from below, "The gentleman has forgot his umbrella! Look for the gentleman's umbrella in No. 13!" I heard an immediate scampering of a chambermaid along the passage, and a shrill reply as she ran, "Here it is! here's the gentleman's umbrella!"

The mysterious stranger then was on the point of setting

off. This was the only chance I should ever have of knowing him. I sprang out of bed, scrambled to the window, snatched aside the curtains, and just caught a glimpse of the rear of a person getting in at the coach-door. The skirts of a brown coat parted behind, and gave me a full view of the broad disk of a pair of drab breeches. The door closed—"all right!" was the word—the coach whirled off;—and that was all I ever saw of the stout gentleman!

The Haunted House

FROM THE MSS. OF THE LATE DIEDRICH KNICKERBOCKER

Formerly almost every place had a house of this kind. If a house was seated on some melancholy place, or built in some old romantic manner, or if any particular accident had happened in it, such as murder, sudden death, or the like, to be sure that house had a mark set on it, and was afterwards esteemed the habitation of a ghost.

BOURNE'S ANTIQUITIES

IN the neighborhood of the ancient city of the Manhattoes there stood, not very many years since, an old mansion, which, when I was a boy, went by the name of the Haunted House. It was one of the very few remains of the architecture of the early Dutch settlers, and must have been a house of some consequence at the time when it was built. It consisted of a centre and two wings, the gable ends of which were shaped like stairs. It was built partly of wood, and partly of small Dutch bricks, such as the worthy colonists brought with them from Holland, before they discovered that bricks could be manufactured elsewhere. The house stood remote from the road, in the centre of a large field, with an avenue of old locust * trees leading up to it, several of which had been shivered by lightning, and two or three blown down. A few apple-trees grew straggling about the field; there were traces also of what had been a kitchen-garden; but the fences were broken down, the vegetables had disappeared, or had grown wild, and turned to little better than weeds, with here and there a ragged rose-bush, or a tall sunflower shooting up from among the brambles, and hanging its head sorrowfully, as if contemplating the surrounding desolation. Part of the roof of the old house had fallen in, the windows were shattered, the panels of the doors broken, and mended with rough boards, and two rusty weather-cocks at the ends of the house made a great

* Acacias.

jingling and whistling as they whirled about, but always pointed wrong. The appearance of the whole place was forlorn and desolate at the best of times; but, in unruly weather, the howling of the wind about the crazy old mansion, the screeching of the weather-cocks, and the slamming and banging of a few loose window-shutters, had altogether so wild and dreary an effect, that the neighborhood stood perfectly in awe of the place, and pronounced it the rendezvous of hobgoblins. I recollect the old building well; for many times, when an idle, unlucky urchin, I have prowled round its precinct, with some of my graceless companions, on holiday afternoons, when out on a freebooting cruise among the orchards. There was a tree standing near the house that bore the most beautiful and tempting fruit; but then it was on enchanted ground, for the place was so charmed by frightful stories that we dreaded to approach it. Sometimes we would venture in a body, and get near the Hesperian tree, keeping an eye upon the old mansion, and darting fearful glances into its shattered windows, when, just as we were about to seize upon our prize, an exclamation from some one of the gang, or an accidental noise, would throw us all into a panic, and we would scamper headlong from the place, nor stop until we had got quite into the road. Then there was sure to be a host of fearful anecdotes told of strange cries and groans, or of some hideous face suddenly seen staring out of one of the windows. By degrees we ceased to venture into these lonely grounds, but would stand at a distance, and throw stones at the building; and there was something fearfully pleasing in the sound as they rattled along the roof, or sometimes struck some jingling fragments of glass out of the windows.

The origin of this house was lost in the obscurity that covers the early period of the province, while under the government of their high mightinesses the states-general. Some reported it to have been a country residence of Wilhelmus Kieft, commonly called the Testy, one of the Dutch governors of New Amsterdam; others said it had been built by a naval commander who served under Van Tromp, and who, on being disappointed of preferment, retired from the service in disgust, became a philosopher through sheer spite, and brought over all his wealth to the province, that he might live according to his humor, and despise the world. The reason of its having fallen to decay was likewise a matter of dispute; some said it was in chancery, and had already cost more than its worth in legal expense; but the most current, and, of course, the most probable account, was that it was haunted, and that nobody could live quietly in it. There can, in fact, be very little doubt that this last was the case, there were so many corroborating stories to prove it—not an old woman in the neighborhood but could furnish at least a score. A gray-headed curmudgeon of a Negro who lived hard by had a whole budget of them to tell, many of which had happened to himself. I recollect many a time stopping with my schoolmates, and getting him to relate some. The old crone lived in a hovel, in the midst of a small patch of potatoes and Indian corn, which his master had given him on setting him free. He would come to us, with his hoe in his hand, and as we sat perched, like a row of swallows, on the rail of a fence, in the mellow twilight of a summer evening, would tell us such fearful stories, accompanied by such awful rollings of his white eyes, that we were almost afraid of our own footsteps as we returned home afterwards in the dark.

Poor old Pompey! many years are past since he died, and went to keep company with the ghosts he was so fond of talking about. He was buried in a corner of his own little potato patch; the plough soon passed over his grave, and levelled it with the rest of the field, and nobody thought any more of the grayheaded Negro. By singular chance I was strolling in that neighborhood, several years afterwards, when I had grown up to be a young man, and I found a knot of gossips speculating on a skull which had just been turned up by a ploughshare. They of course determined it to be the remains of some one who had been murdered, and they had raked up with it some of the traditionary tales of the haunted house. I knew it at once to be the relic of poor Pompey, but I held my tongue; for I am too considerate of other people's enjoyment even to mar a story of a ghost or a murder. I took care, however, to see the bones of my old friend once more buried in a place where they were not likely to be disturbed. As I sat on the turf and watched the interment, I fell into a long conversation with an old gentleman of the neighborhood, John Josse Vandermoere, a pleasant gossiping man, whose whole life was spent in hearing and telling the news of the province. He recollected old Pompey, and his stories about the Haunted House; but he assured me he could give me one still more strange than any that Pompey had related; and on my expressing a great curiosity to hear it, he sat down beside me on the turf, and told the following tale. I have endeavored to give it as nearly as possible in his words; but it is now many years since, and I am grown old, and my memory is not over-good. I cannot therefore vouch for the language, but I am always scrupulous as to facts.

D. K.

Dolph Heyliger

"I take the town of concord, where I dwell,
All Kilborn be my witness, if I were not
Begot in bashfulness, brought up in shamefacedness.
Let 'un bring a dog but to my vace that can
Zay I have beat 'un, and without a vault;
Or but a cat will swear upon a book,
I have as much as zet a vire her tail,
And I'll give him or her a crown for 'mends."

TALE OF A TUB

IN the early time of the province of New York, while it groaned under the tyranny of the English governor, Lord Cornbury, who carried his cruelties towards the Dutch inhabitants so far as to allow no Dominie, or schoolmaster, to officiate in their language without his special license; about this time there lived in the jolly little old city of the Manhattoes a kind motherly dame, known by the name of Dame Heyliger. She was the widow of a Dutch sea-captain, who died suddenly of a fever, in consequence of working too hard, and eating too heartily, at the time when all the inhabitants turned out in a panic, to fortify the place against the invasion of a small French privateer.* He left her with very little money, and one infant son, the only survivor of several children. The good woman had need of much management to make both ends meet, and keep up a decent appearance. However, as her husband had fallen a victim to his zeal for the public safety, it was universally agreed that "something ought to be done for the widow"; and on the hopes of this "something" she lived tolerably for some years; in the meantime everybody pitied and spoke well of her, and that helped along.

She lived in a small house, in a small street, called Garden Street, very probably from a garden which may have flourished there some time or other. As her necessities every year grew

* 1705.

greater, and the talk of the public about doing "something for her" grew less, she had to cast about for some mode of doing something for herself, by way of helping out her slender means, and maintaining her independence, of which she was somewhat tenacious.

Living in a mercantile town, she had caught something of the spirit, and determined to venture a little in the great lottery of commerce. On a sudden, therefore, to the great surprise of the street, there appeared at her window a grand array of gingerbread kings and queens, with their arms stuck akimbo, after the invariable royal manner. There were also several broken tumblers, some filled with sugar-plums, some with marbles; there were, moreover, cakes of various kinds, and barley-sugar, and Holland dolls, and wooden horses, with here and there gilt-covered picture-books, and now and then a skein of thread, or a dangling pound of candles. At the door of the house sat the good old dame's cat, a decent demure-looking personage, who seemed to scan everybody that passed, to criticize their dress, and now and then to stretch her neck, and to look out with sudden curiosity, to see what was going on at the other end of the street; but if by chance any idle vagabond dog came by, and offered to be uncivil—hoity-toity!—how she would bristle up, and growl, and spit, and strike out her paws! she was as indignant as ever was an ancient and ugly spinster on the approach of some graceless profligate.

But though the good woman had to come down to those humble means of subsistence, yet she still kept up a feeling of family pride, being descended from the Vanderspiegels, of Amsterdam; and she had the family arms painted and framed, and hung over her mantelpiece. She was, in truth, much respected by all the poorer people of the place; her house was quite a resort of the old wives of the neighborhood; they would drop in there of a winter's afternoon, as she sat knitting on one side of her fireplace, her cat purring on the other, and the teakettle singing before it; and they would gossip with her until late in the evening. There was always an arm-chair for Peter de Groodt, sometimes called Long Peter, and sometimes Peter Longlegs, the clerk and sexton of the little Lutheran church, who was her great crony, and indeed the oracle of her fireside.

Nay, the Dominie himself did not disdain, now and then, to step in, converse about the state of her mind, and take a glass of her special good cherry-brandy. Indeed, he never failed to call on New-Year's day, and wish her a happy New Year; and the good dame, who was a little vain on some points, always piqued herself on giving him as large a cake as any one in town.

I have said that she had one son. He was the child of her old age; but could hardly be called the comfort, for, of all unlucky urchins, Dolph Heyliger was the most mischievous. Not that the whipster was really vicious; he was only full of fun and frolic, and had that daring, gamesome spirit which is extolled in a rich man's child, but execrated in a poor man's. He was continually getting into scrapes; his mother was incessantly harassed with complaints of some waggish pranks which he had played off; bills were sent in for windows that he had broken; in a word, he had not reached his fourteenth year before he was pronounced, by all the neighborhood, to be a "wicked dog, the wickedest dog in the street!" Nay, one old gentleman, in a claret-colored coat, with a thin red face, and ferret eyes, went so far as to assure Dame Heyliger, that her son would, one day or other, come to the gallows!

Yet, notwithstanding all this, the poor old soul loved her boy. It seemed as though she loved him the better the worse he behaved, and that he grew more in her favor the more he grew out of favor with the world. Mothers are foolish, fond-hearted beings; there's no reasoning them out of their dotage; and, indeed, this poor woman's child was all that was left to love her in this world; so we must not think it hard that she turned a deaf ear to her good friends, who sought to prove to her that Dolph would come to a halter.

To do the varlet justice, too, he was strongly attached to his parent. He would not willingly have given her pain on any account; and when he had been doing wrong, it was but for him to catch his poor mother's eye fixed wistfully and sorrowfully upon him, to fill his heart with bitterness and contrition. But he was a heedless youngster, and could not, for the life of him, resist any new temptation to fun and mischief. Though quick at his learning, whenever he could be brought to apply himself, he was always prone to be led away by idle company, and would play truant to hunt after birds'-nests, to rob orchards, or to swim in the Hudson.

In this way he grew up, a tall, lubberly boy; and his mother began to be greatly perplexed what to do with him, or how to put him in a way to do for himself; for he had acquired such an unlucky reputation, that no one seemed willing to employ him.

Many were the consultations that she held with Peter de Groodt, the clerk and sexton, who was her prime counsellor. Peter was as much perplexed as herself, for he had no great opinion of the boy, and thought he would never come to good. He at once advised her to send him to sea: a piece of advice only given in the most desperate cases; but Dame Heyliger would not listen to such an idea; she could not think of letting Dolph go out of her sight. She was sitting one day knitting by her fireside, in great perplexity, when the sexton entered with an air of unusual vivacity and briskness. He had just come from a funeral. It had been that of a boy of Dolph's years, who had been apprentice to a famous German doctor, and had died of a consumption. It is true, there had been a whisper that the deceased had been brought to his end by being made the subject of the doctor's experiments, on which he was apt to try the effects of a new compound, or a quieting draught. This, however, it is likely, was a mere scandal; at any rate, Peter de Groodt did not think it worth mentioning; though, had we time to philosophize, it would be a curious matter for speculation, why a doctor's family is apt to be so lean and cadaverous, and a butcher's so jolly and rubicund.

Peter de Groodt, as I said before, entered the house of Dame Heyliger with unusual alacrity. A bright idea had popped into his head at the funeral, over which he had chuckled as he shovelled the earth into the grave of the doctor's disciple. It had occurred to him, that, as the situation of the deceased was vacant at the doctor's, it would be the very place for Dolph. The boy had parts, and could pound a pestle, and run an errand with any boy in the town; and what more was wanted in a student?

The suggestion of the sage Peter was a vision of glory to the mother. She already saw Dolph, in her mind's eye, with a cane at his nose, a knocker at his door, and an M.D. at the end of his name—one of the established dignitaries of the town.

The matter, once undertaken, was soon effected; the sexton had some influence with the doctor, they having had much dealing together in the way of their separate professions; and the very next morning he called and conducted the urchin, clad in his Sunday clothes, to undergo the inspection of Dr. Karl Lodovick Knipperhausen.

They found the doctor seated in an elbow-chair, in one corner of his study, or laboratory, with a large volume, in German print, before him. He was a short fat man, with a dark square face, rendered more dark by a black velvet cap. He had a little nobbed nose, not unlike the ace of spades, with a pair of spectacles gleaming on each side of his dusky countenance, like a couple of bow-windows.

Dolph felt struck with awe on entering into the presence of this learned man; and gazed about him with boyish wonder at the furniture of this chamber of knowledge; which appeared to him almost as the den of a magician. In the centre stood a claw-footed table, with pestle and mortar, phials and gallipots, and a pair of small burnished scales. At one end was a heavy clothespress, turned into a receptacle for drugs and compounds; against which hung the doctor's hat and cloak, and gold-headed cane, and on the top grinned a human skull. Along the mantelpiece were glass vessels, in which were snakes and lizards, and a human fœtus preserved in spirits. A closet, the doors of which were taken off, contained three whole shelves of books, and some, too, of mighty folio dimensions—a collection the like of which Dolph had never before beheld. As, however, the library did not take up the whole of the closet, the doctor's thrifty housekeeper had occupied the rest with pots of pickles and preserves; and had hung about the room, among awful implements of the healing art, strings of red pepper and corpulent cucumbers, carefully preserved for seed.

Peter de Groodt and his protégé were received with great gravity and stateliness by the doctor, who was a very wise, dignified little man, and never smiled. He surveyed Dolph from head to foot, above, and under, and through his spectacles, and the poor lad's heart quailed as these great glasses glared on him like two full moons. The doctor heard all that Peter de Groodt had to say in favor of the youthful candidate; and then wetting his thumb with the end of his tongue, he began deliberately to turn over page after page of the great black volume before him. At length, after many hums and haws, and strokings of the chin, and all that hesitation and deliberation with which a wise man proceeds to do what he intended to do from the very first, the doctor agreed to take the lad as a disciple; to give him bed, board, and clothing, and to instruct him in the healing art; in return for which he was to have his services until his twenty-first year.

Behold, then, our hero, all at once transformed from an unlucky urchin running wild about the streets, to a student of medicine, diligently pounding a pestle, under the auspices of the learned Doctor Karl Lodovick Knipperhausen. It was a happy transition for his fond old mother. She was delighted with the idea of her boy's being brought up worthy of his ancestors; and anticipated the day when he would be able to hold up his head with the lawyer, that lived in the large house opposite; or, peradventure, with the Dominie himself.

Doctor Knipperhausen was a native of the Palatinate in Germany; whence, in company with many of his countrymen, he had taken refuge in England, on account of religious persecution. He was one of nearly three thousand Palatines, who came over from England in 1710, under the protection of Governor Hunter. Where the doctor had studied, how he had acquired his medical knowledge, and where he had received his diploma, it is hard at present to say, for nobody knew at the time; yet it is certain that his profound skill and abstruse knowledge were the talk and wonder of the common people, far and near.

His practice was totally different from that of any other physician—consisting in mysterious compounds, known only to himself, in the preparing and administering of which, it was said, he always consulted the stars. So high an opinion was entertained of his skill, particularly by the German and Dutch inhabitants, that they always resorted to him in desperate cases. He was one of those infallible doctors that are always effecting sudden and surprising cures, when the patient has been given up by all the regular physicians; unless, as is shrewdly observed, the case has been left too long before it was put into their hands. The doctor's library was the talk and marvel of the neighborhood, I might almost say of the entire burgh. The good people looked with reverence at a man who had read three whole shelves full of books, and some of them, too, as large as a family Bible. There were many disputes among the members of the little Lutheran church, as to which was the wisest man, the doctor or the Dominie. Some of his admirers even went so far as to say, that he knew more than the governor himself—in a word, it was thought that there was no end to his knowledge!

No sooner was Dolph received into the doctor's family, than he was put in possession of the lodging of his predecessor. It was a garret-room of a steep-roofed Dutch house, where the rain had pattered on the shingles, and the lightning gleamed, and the wind piped through the crannies in stormy weather; and where whole troops of hungry rats, like Don Cossacks, galloped about, in defiance of traps and ratsbane.

He was soon up to his ears in medical studies, being employed, morning, noon, and night, in rolling pills, filtering tinctures, or pounding the pestle and mortar in one corner of the laboratory; while the doctor would take his seat in another corner, when he had nothing else to do, or expected visitors, and arrayed in his morning-gown and velvet cap, would pore over the contents of some folio volume. It is true, that the regular thumping of Dolph's pestle, or, perhaps, the drowsy buzzing of the summer-flies, would now and then lull the little man into a slumber; but then his spectacles were always wide awake, and studiously regarding the book.

There was another personage in the house, however, to whom Dolph was obliged to pay allegiance. Though a bachelor, and a man of such great dignity and importance, the doctor was, like many other wise men, subject to petticoat government. He was completely under the sway of his housekeeper—a spare, busy, fretting housewife, in a little, round, quilted German cap, with a huge bunch of keys jingling at the girdle of an exceedingly long waist. Frau Ilsé (or Frow Ilsy, as it was pronounced) had accompanied him in his various migrations from Germany to England, and from England to the province; managing his establishment and himself too: ruling him, it is true, with a gentle hand, but carrying a high hand with all the world beside. How she had acquired such ascendency I do not pretend to say. People, it is true, did talk—but have not people been prone to talk ever since the world began? Who can tell how women generally contrive to get the upper hand? A husband, it is true, may now and then be master in his own house; but who ever knew a bachelor that was not managed by his housekeeper?

Indeed, Frau Ilsy's power was not confined to the doctor's household. She was one of those prying gossips who know every one's business better than they do themselves; and whose all-seeing eyes, and all-telling tongues, are terrors throughout a neighborhood.

Nothing of any moment transpired in the world of scandal of this little burgh, but it was known to Frau Ilsy. She had her crew of cronies, that were perpetually hurrying to her little parlor with some precious bit of news; nay, she would sometimes discuss a whole volume of secret history, as she held the street-door ajar, and gossiped with one of these garrulous cronies in the very teeth of a December blast.

Between the doctor and the housekeeper it may easily be supposed that Dolph had a busy life of it. As Frau Ilsy kept the keys, and literally ruled the roast, it was starvation to offend her, though he found the study of her temper more perplexing even than that of medicine. When not busy in the laboratory, she kept him running hither and thither on her errands; and on Sundays he was obliged to accompany her to and from church, and carry her Bible. Many a time has the poor varlet stood shivering and blowing his fingers, or holding his frost-bitten nose, in the church-yard, while Ilsy and her cronies were huddled together, wagging their heads, and tearing some unlucky character to pieces.

With all his advantages, however, Dolph made very slow progress in his art. This was no fault of the doctor's, certainly, for he took unwearied pains with the lad, keeping him close to the pestle and mortar, or on the trot about town with phials and pill-boxes; and if he ever flagged in his industry, which he was rather apt to do, the doctor would fly into a passion, and ask him if he ever expected to learn his profession, unless he applied himself closer to the study. The fact is, he still retained the fondness for sport and mischief that had marked his childhood; the habit, indeed, had strengthened with his years, and gained force from being thwarted and constrained. He daily grew more and more untractable, and lost favor in the eyes, both of the doctor and the housekeeper.

In the meantime the doctor went on, waxing wealthy and renowned. He was famous for his skill in managing cases not laid down in the books. He had cured several old women and young girls of witchcraft—a terrible complaint, and nearly as prevalent in the province in those days as hydrophobia is at present. He had even restored one strapping country-girl to perfect health, who had gone so far as to vomit crooked pins and needles; which is considered a desperate stage of the malady. It was whispered, also, that he was possessed of the art of preparing love-powders; and many applications had he in consequence from love-sick patients of both sexes. But all these cases formed the mysterious part of his practice, in which, according to the cant phrase, "secrecy and honor might be depended on." Dolph, therefore, was obliged to turn out of the study whenever such consultations occurred, though it is said he learnt more of the secrets of the art at the key-hole than by all the rest of his studies put together.

As the doctor increased in wealth, he began to extend his possessions, and to look forward, like other great men, to the time when he should retire to the repose of a country-seat. For this purpose he had purchased a farm, or, as the Dutch settlers called it, a *bowerie*, a few miles from town. It had been the residence of a wealthy family, that had returned some time since to Holland. A large mansion-house stood in the centre of it, very much out of repair, and which, in consequence of certain reports, had received the appellation of the Haunted House. Either from these reports, or from its actual dreariness, the doctor found it impossible to get a tenant; and that the place might not fall to ruin before he could reside in it himself, he placed a country boor, with his family, in one wing, with the privilege of cultivating the farm on shares.

The doctor now felt all the dignity of a landholder rising within him. He had a little of the German pride of territory in his composition, and almost looked upon himself as owner of a principality. He began to complain of the fatigue of business; and was fond of riding out "to look at his estate." His little expeditions to his lands were attended with a bustle and parade that created a sensation throughout the neighborhood. His wall-eyed horse stood, stamping and whisking off the flies, for a full hour before the house. Then the doctor's saddlebags would be brought out and adjusted; then, after a little while, his cloak would be rolled up and strapped to the saddle; then his umbrella would be buttoned to the cloak; while, in the meantime, a group of ragged boys, that observant class of beings, would gather before the door. At length the doctor would issue forth, in a pair of jack-boots that reached above his knees, and a cocked hat flapped down in front. As he was a short, fat man, he took some time to mount into the saddle; and when there, he took some time to have the saddle and stirrups properly adjusted, enjoying the wonder and admiration of the urchin crowd. Even after he had set off, he would pause in the middle of the street, or trot back two or three times to give some parting orders; which were answered by the housekeeper from the door, or Dolph from the study, or the black cook from the cellar, or the chambermaid from the garret-window; and there were generally some last words bawled after him, just as he was turning the corner.

The whole neighborhood would be aroused by this pomp and circumstance. The cobbler would leave his last; the barber would thrust out his frizzled head, with a comb sticking in it; a knot would collect at the grocer's door, and the word would be buzzed from one end of the street to the other, "The doctor's riding out to his country-seat!"

These were golden moments for Dolph. No sooner was the doctor out of sight, than pestle and mortar were abandoned; the laboratory was left to take care of itself, and the student was off on some madcap frolic.

Indeed, it must be confessed, the youngster, as he grew up, seemed in a fair way to fulfil the prediction of the old claret-colored gentleman. He was the ringleader of all holiday sports and midnight gambols; ready for all kinds of mischievous pranks and hare-brained adventures.

There is nothing so troublesome as a hero on a small scale, or, rather, a hero in a small town. Dolph soon became the abhorrence of all drowsy, housekeeping old citizens, who hated noise, and had no relish for waggery. The good dames, too, considered him as little better than a reprobate, gathered their daughters under their wings whenever he approached, and pointed him out as a warning to their sons. No one seemed to hold him in much regard except the wild striplings of the place, who were captivated by his open-hearted, daring manners—and the Negroes, who always looked upon every idle, do-nothing youngster as a kind of gentleman. Even the good Peter de Groodt, who had considered himself a kind of patron of the lad, began to despair of him; and would shake his head dubiously, as he listened to a long complaint from the housekeeper, and sipped a glass of her raspberry brandy.

Still his mother was not to be wearied out of her affection by all the waywardness of her boy; nor disheartened by the stories of his misdeeds, with which her good friends were continually regaling her. She had, it is true, very little of the pleasure which rich people enjoy, in always hearing their children praised; but she considered all this ill-will as a kind of persecution which he suffered, and she liked him the better on that account. She saw him growing up a fine, tall, good-looking youngster, and she looked at him with the secret pride of a mother's heart. It was her great desire that Dolph should appear like a gentleman, and all the money she could save went towards helping out his pocket and his wardrobe. She would look out of the window after him, as he sallied forth in his best array, and her heart would yearn with delight; and once, when Peter de Groodt, struck with the youngster's gallant appearance on a bright Sunday morning, observed, "Well, after all, Dolph does grow a comely fellow!" the tear of pride started into the mother's eye. "Ah, neighbor! neighbor!" exclaimed she, "they may say what they please; poor Dolph will yet hold up his head with the best of them!"

Dolph Heyliger had now nearly attained his one-and-twentieth year, and the term of his medical studies was just expiring; yet it must be confessed that he knew little more of the profession than when he first entered the doctor's doors. This, however, could not be from any want of quickness of parts, for he showed amazing aptness in mastering other branches of knowledge, which he could only have studied at intervals. He was, for instance, a sure marksman, and won all the geese and turkeys at Christmas holidays. He was a bold rider; he was famous for leaping and wrestling; he played tolerably on the fiddle; could swim like a fish; and was the best hand in the whole place at fives and nine-pins.

All these accomplishments, however, procured him no favor in the eyes of the doctor, who grew more and more crabbed and intolerant the nearer the term of apprenticeship approached. Frau Ilsy, too, was forever finding some occasion to raise a windy tempest about his ears, and seldom encountered him about the house without a clatter of the tongue; so that at length the jingling of her keys, as she approached, was to Dolph like the ringing of the prompter's bell, that gives notice of a theatrical thunderstorm. Nothing but the infinite good-humor of the heedless youngster enabled him to bear all this domestic tyranny without open rebellion. It was evident that the doctor and his housekeeper were preparing to beat the poor youth out of the nest, the moment his term should have expired—a short-hand mode which the doctor had of providing for useless disciples.

Indeed the little man had been rendered more than usually irritable lately in consequence of various cares and vexations which his country estate had brought upon him. The doctor had been repeatedly annoyed by the rumors and tales which prevailed concerning the old mansion, and found it difficult to prevail even upon the country-man and his family to remain there rent-free. Every time he rode out to the farm he was teased by some fresh complaint of strange noises and fearful sights, with which the tenants were disturbed at night; and the doctor would come home fretting and fuming, and vent his spleen upon the whole household. It was indeed a sore grievance that affected him both in pride and purse. He was threatened with an absolute loss of the profits of his property; and then, what a blow to his territorial consequence, to be the landlord of a haunted house!

It was observed, however, that with all his vexation, the doctor never proposed to sleep in the house himself; nay, he could never be prevailed upon to remain on the premises after dark, but made the best of his way for town as soon as the bats began to flit about in the twilight. The fact was, the doctor had a secret belief in ghosts, having passed the early part of his life in a country where they particularly abound; and indeed the story went, that, when a boy, he had once seen the devil upon the Hartz Mountains in Germany.

At length the doctor's vexations on this head were brought to a crisis. One morning as he sat dozing over a volume in his study, he was suddenly startled from his slumbers by the bustling in of the housekeeper.

"Here's a fine to do!" cried she, as she entered the room. "Here's Claus Hopper come in, bag and baggage, from the farm, and swears he'll have nothing more to do with it. The whole family have been frightened out of their wits; for there's such racketing and rummaging about the old house, that they can't sleep quiet in their beds!"

"Donner and blitzen!" cried the doctor, impatiently; "will they never have done chattering about that house? What a pack of fools, to let a few rats and mice frighten them out of good quarters!"

"Nay, nay," said the housekeeper, wagging her head knowingly, and piqued at having a good ghost-story doubted, "there's more in it than rats and mice. All the neighborhood talks about the house; and then such sights as have been seen in it! Peter de Groodt tells me, that the family that sold you the house, and went to Holland, dropped several strange hints about it, and said, 'they wished you joy of your bargain;' and you know yourself there's no getting any family to live in it."

"Peter de Groodt's a ninny—an old woman," said the doctor, peevishly; "I'll warrant he's been filling these people's heads full of stories. It's just like his nonsense about the ghost that haunted the church-belfry, as an excuse for not ringing the bell that cold night when Harmanus Brinkerhoff's house was on fire. Send Claus to me."

Claus Hopper now made his appearance: a simple country lout, full of awe at finding himself in the very study of Dr. Knipperhausen, and too much embarrassed to enter in much detail of the matters that had caused his alarm. He stood twirling his hat in one hand, resting sometimes on one leg, sometimes on the other, looking occasionally at the doctor, and now and then stealing a fearful glance at the death's-head that seemed ogling him from the top of the clothes-press.

The doctor tried every means to persuade him to return to the farm, but all in vain; he maintained a dogged determination on the subject; and at the close of every argument or solicitation would make the same brief, inflexible reply, "Ich kan nicht, mynheer." The doctor was a "little pot, and soon hot;" his patience was exhausted by these continual vexations about his estate. The stubborn refusal of Claus Hopper seemed to him like flat rebellion; his temper suddenly boiled over, and Claus was glad to make a rapid retreat to escape scalding.

When the bumpkin got to the housekeeper's room, he found Peter de Groodt, and several other true believers, ready to receive him. Here he indemnified himself for the restraint he had suffered in the study, and opened a budget of stories about the haunted house that astonished all his hearers. The housekeeper believed them all, if it was only to spite the doctor for having received her intelligence so uncourteously. Peter de Groodt matched them with many a wonderful legend of the times of the Dutch dynasty, and of the Devil's Stepping-stones; and of the pirate hanged at Gibbet Island, that continued to swing there at night long after the gallows was taken down; and of the ghost of the unfortunate Governor Leisler, hanged for treason, which haunted the old fort and the government-house. The gossiping knot dispersed, each charged with direful intelligence. The sexton disburdened himself at a vestry meeting that was held that very day, and the black cook forsook her kitchen, and spent half the day at the street-pump, that gossiping-place of servants, dealing forth the news to all that came for water. In a little time the whole town was in a buzz with tales about the haunted house. Some said that Claus Hopper had seen the devil, while others hinted that the house was haunted by the ghosts of some of the patients whom the doctor had physicked out of the world, and that was the reason why he did not venture to live in it himself.

All this put the little doctor in a terrible fume. He threatened vengeance on any one who should affect the value of his property by exciting popular prejudices. He complained loudly of thus being in a manner dispossessed of his territories by mere bugbears; but he secretly determined to have the house exorcised by the Dominie. Great was his relief, therefore, when in the midst of his perplexities, Dolph stepped forward and undertook to garrison the haunted house. The youngster had been listening to all the stories of Claus Hopper and Peter de Groodt: he was fond of adventure, he loved the marvellous, and his imagination had become quite excited by these tales of wonder. Besides, he had led such an uncomfortable life at the doctor's, being subjected to the intolerable thraldom of early hours, that he was delighted at the prospect of having a house to himself, even though it should be a haunted one. His offer was eagerly accepted, and it was determined he should mount guard that very night. His only stipulation was, that the enterprise should be kept secret from his mother; for he knew the poor soul would not sleep a wink if she knew her son was waging war with the powers of darkness.

When night came on he set out on this perilous expedition. The old black cook, his only friend in the household, had provided him with a little mess for supper, and a rush-light; and she tied round his neck an amulet, given her by an African conjurer, as a charm against evil spirits. Dolph was escorted on his way by the doctor and Peter de Groodt, who had agreed to accompany him to the house, and to see him safe lodged. The night was overcast, and it was very dark when they arrived at the grounds which surrounded the mansion. The sexton led the way with the lantern. As they walked along the avenue of acacias, the fitful light, catching from bush to bush, and tree to tree, often startled the doughty Peter, and made him fall back upon his followers; and the doctor grappled still closer hold of Dolph's arm, observing that the ground was very slippery and uneven. At one time they were nearly put to total rout by a bat, which came flitting about the lantern; and the notes of the insects from the trees, and the frogs from a neighboring pond, formed a most drowsy and doleful concert. The front door of the mansion opened with a grating sound, that made the doctor turn pale. They entered a tolerably large hall, such as is common in American country-houses, and which serves for a sitting-room in warm weather. From this they went up a wide staircase, that groaned and creaked as they trod, every step making its particular note, like the key of a harpsichord. This led to another hall on the second story, whence they entered the room where Dolph was to sleep. It was large, and scantily furnished; the shutters were closed; but as they were much broken, there was no want of a circulation of air. It appeared to have been that sacred chamber, known among Dutch housewives by the name of "the best bedroom," which is the best furnished room in the house, but in which scarce anybody is ever permitted to sleep. Its splendor, however, was all at an end. There were a few broken articles of furniture about the room, and in the centre stood a heavy deal table and a large arm-chair, both of which had the look of being coeval with the mansion. The fireplace was wide, and had been faced with Dutch tiles, representing Scripture stories; but some of them had fallen out of their places, and lay scattered about the hearth. The sexton lit the rush-light; and the doctor, looking fearfully about the room, was just exhorting Dolph to be of good cheer, and to pluck up a stout heart, when a noise in the chimney, like voices and struggling, struck a sudden panic into the sexton. He took to his heels with the lantern; the doctor followed hard after him; the stairs groaned and creaked as they hurried down, increasing their agitation and speed by its noise. The front door slammed after them; and Dolph heard them scrabbling down the avenue, till the sound of their feet was lost in the distance. That he did not join in this precipitate retreat might have been owing to his possessing a little more courage than his companions, or perhaps that he had caught a glimpse of the cause of their dismay, in a nest of chimney-swallows, that came tumbling down into the fireplace.

Being now left to himself, he secured the front door by a strong bolt and bar; and having seen that the other entrances were fastened, returned to his desolate chamber. Having made his supper from the basket which the good old cook had provided, he locked the chamber-door, and retired to rest on a mattress in one corner. The night was calm and still; and nothing broke upon the profound quiet but the lonely chirping of a cricket from the chimney of a distant chamber. The rush-light, which stood in the centre of the deal table, shed a feeble yellow ray, dimly illumining the chamber, and making uncouth shapes and shadows on the walls, from the clothes which Dolph had thrown over a chair.

With all his boldness of heart, there was something subduing in this desolate scene; and he felt his spirits flag within him, as he lay on his hard bed and gazed about the room. He was turning over in his mind his idle habits, his doubtful prospects, and now and then heaving a heavy sigh as he thought on his poor old mother; for there is nothing like the silence and loneliness of night to bring dark shadows over the brightest mind. By and by he thought he heard a sound as of some one walking below stairs. He listened, and distinctly heard a step on the great staircase. It approached solemnly and slowly, tramp—tramp—tramp! It was evidently the tread of some heavy personage; and yet how could he have got into the house without making a noise? He had examined all the fastenings, and was certain that every entrance was secure. Still the steps advanced, tramp—tramp—tramp! It was evident that the person approaching could not be a robber, the step was too loud and deliberate; a robber would either be stealthy or precipitate. And now the footsteps had ascended the staircase; they were slowly advancing along the passage, resounding through the silent and empty apartments. The very cricket had ceased its melancholy note, and nothing interrupted their awful distinctness. The door, which had been locked on the inside, slowly swung open, as if self-moved. The footsteps entered the room; but no one was to be seen. They passed slowly and audibly across it, tramp—tramp—tramp! but whatever made the sound was invisible. Dolph rubbed his eyes, and stared about him; he could see to every part of the dimly-lighted chamber; all was vacant; yet still he heard those mysterious footsteps, solemnly walking about the chamber. They ceased, and all was dead silence. There was something more appalling in this invisible visitation than there would have been in anything that addressed itself to the eye-sight. It was awfully vague and indefinite. He felt his heart beat against his ribs; a cold sweat broke out upon his forehead; he lay for some time in a state of violent agitation: nothing, however, occurred to increase his alarm. His light gradually burnt down into the socket, and he fell asleep. When he awoke it was broad daylight; the sun was peering through the cracks of the window-shutters, and the birds were merrily singing about the house. The bright cheery day soon put to flight all the terrors of the preceding night. Dolph laughed, or rather tried to laugh, at all that had passed, and endeavored to persuade himself that it was a mere freak of the imagination, conjured up by the stories he had heard; but he was a little puzzled to find the door of his room locked on the inside, notwithstanding that he had positively seen it swing open as the footsteps had entered. He returned to town in a state of considerable perplexity; but he determined to say nothing on the subject, until his doubts were either confirmed or removed by another night's watching. His silence was a grievous disappointment to the gossips who had gathered at the doctor's mansion. They had prepared their minds to hear direful tales, and were almost in a rage at being assured he had nothing to relate.

The next night, then, Dolph repeated his vigil. He now entered the house with some trepidation. He was particular in examining the fastenings of all the doors, and securing them well. He locked the door of his chamber, and placed a chair against it; then having dispatched his supper, he threw himself on his mattress and endeavored to sleep. It was all in vain; a thousand crowding fancies kept him waking. The time slowly dragged on, as if minutes were spinning themselves out into hours. As the night advanced, he grew more and more nervous; and he almost started from his couch when he heard the mysterious footstep again on the staircase. Up it came, as before, solemnly and slowly, tramp—tramp—tramp! It approached along the passage; the door again swung open, as if there had been neither lock nor impediment, and a strange-looking figure stalked into the room. It was an elderly man, large and robust, clothed in the old Flemish fashion. He had on a kind of short cloak, with a garment under it, belted round the waist; trunk-hose, with great bunches or bows at the knees; and a pair of russet boots, very large at top, and standing widely from his legs. His hat was broad and slouched, with a feather trailing over one side. His iron-grey hair hung in thick masses on his neck; and he had a short grizzled beard. He walked slowly round the room, as if examining that all was safe; then, hanging his hat on a peg beside the door, he sat down in the elbow-chair, and, leaning his elbow on the table, fixed his eyes on Dolph with an unmoving and deadening stare.

Dolph was not naturally a coward; but he had been brought up in an implicit belief in ghosts and goblins. A thousand stories came swarming to his mind that he had heard about this building; and as he looked at this strange personage, with his uncouth garb, his pale visage, his grizzly beard, and his fixed, staring, fish-like eye, his teeth began to chatter, his hair to rise on his head, and a cold sweat to break out all over his body. How long he remained in this situation he could not tell, for he was like one fascinated. He could not take his gaze off from the spectre; but lay staring at him, with his whole intellect absorbed in the contemplation. The old man remained seated behind the table, without stirring, or turning an eye, always keeping a dead steady glare upon Dolph. At length the household cock, from a neighboring farm, clapped his wings, and gave a loud cheerful crow that rung over the fields. At the sound the old man slowly rose, and took down his hat from the peg; the door opened, and closed after him; he was heard to go slowly down the staircase, tramp—tramp—tramp!—and when he had got to the bottom, all was again silent. Dolph lay and listened earnestly; counted every foot-fall; listened, and listened, if the steps should return, until, exhausted by watching and agitation, he fell into a troubled sleep.

Daylight again brought fresh courage and assurance. He would fain have considered all that had passed as a mere dream; yet there stood the chair in which the unknown had seated himself; there was the table on which he had leaned; there was the peg on which he had hung his hat; and there was the door, locked precisely as he himself had locked it, with the chair placed against it. He hastened down-stairs, and examined the doors and windows; all were exactly in the same state in which he had left them, and there was no apparent way by which any being could have entered and left the house, without leaving some trace behind. "Pooh!" said Dolph to himself, "it was all a dream:"—but it would not do; the more he endeavored to shake the scene off from his mind, the more it haunted him.

Though he persisted in a strict silence as to all that he had seen or heard, yet his looks betrayed the uncomfortable night that he had passed. It was evident that there was something wonderful hidden under this mysterious reserve. The doctor took him into the study, locked the door, and sought to have a full and confidential communication; but he could get nothing out of him. Frau Ilsy took him aside into the pantry, but to as little purpose; and Peter de Groodt held him by the button for a full hour, in the church-yard, the very place to get at the bottom of a ghost-story, but came off not a whit wiser than the rest. It is always the case, however, that one truth concealed makes a dozen current lies. It is like a guinea locked up in a bank, that has a dozen paper representatives. Before the day was over, the neighborhood was full of reports. Some said that Dolph Heyliger watched in the haunted house, with pistols loaded with silver bullets; others, that he had a long talk with a spectre without a head; others, that Doctor Knipperhausen and the sexton had been hunted down the Bowery lane, and quite into town, by a legion of ghosts of their customers. Some shook their heads, and thought it a shame the doctor should put Dolph to pass the night alone in that dismal house, where he might be spirited away no one knew whither; while others observed, with a shrug, that if the devil did carry off the youngster, it would be but taking his own.

These rumors at length reached the ears of the good Dame Heyliger, and, as may be supposed, threw her into a terrible alarm. For her son to have opposed himself to danger from living foes, would have been nothing so dreadful in her eyes, as to dare alone the terrors of the haunted house. She hastened to the doctor's, and passed a great part of the day in attempting to dissuade Dolph from repeating his vigil; she told him a score of tales, which her gossiping friends had just related to her, of persons who had been carried off, when watching alone in old ruinous houses. It was all to no effect. Dolph's pride, as well as curiosity, was piqued. He endeavored to calm the apprehensions of his mother, and to assure her that there was no truth in all the rumors she had heard; she looked at him dubiously and shook her head; but finding his determination was not to be shaken, she brought him a little thick Dutch Bible, with brass clasps, to take with him, as a sword wherewith to fight the powers of darkness; and, lest that might not be sufficient, the housekeeper gave him the Heidelberg catechism by way of dagger.

The next night, therefore, Dolph took up his quarters for the third time in the old mansion. Whether dream or not, the same thing was repeated. Towards midnight, when everything was still, the same sound echoed through the empty halls, tramp—tramp—tramp! The stairs were again ascended; the door again swung open: the old man entered; walked round the room; hung up his hat, and seated himself by the table. The same fear and trembling came over poor Dolph, though not in so violent a degree. He lay in the same way, motionless and fascinated, staring at the figure, which regarded him as before with a dead, fixed, chilling gaze. In this way they remained for a long time, till, by degrees, Dolph's courage began gradually to revive. Whether alive or dead, this being had certainly some object in his visitation; and he recollected to have heard it said, spirits have no power to speak until spoken to. Summoning up resolution, therefore, and making two or three attempts, before he could get his parched tongue in motion, he addressed the unknown in the most solemn form of adjuration, and demanded to know what was the motive of his visit.

No sooner had he finished, than the old man rose, took down his hat, the door opened, and he went out, looking back upon Dolph just as he crossed the threshold, as if expecting him to follow. The youngster did not hesitate an instant. He took the candle in his hand, and the Bible under his arm, and obeyed the tacit invitation. The candle emitted a feeble, uncertain ray, but still he could see the figure before him slowly descend the stairs. He followed trembling. When it had reached the bottom of the stairs, it turned through the hall towards the back door of the mansion. Dolph held the light over the balustrades; but, in his eagerness to catch a sight of the unknown, he flared his feeble taper so suddenly, that it went out. Still there was sufficient light from the pale moonbeams, that fell through a narrow window, to give him an indistinct view of the figure, near the door. He followed, therefore, down stairs, and turned towards the place; but when he arrived there, the unknown had disappeared. The door remained fast barred and bolted; there was no other mode of exit; yet the being, whatever he might be, was gone. He unfastened the door, and looked out into the fields. It was a hazy, moonlight night, so that the eye could distinguish objects at some distance. He thought he saw the unknown in a footpath which led from the door. He was not mistaken; but how had he got out of the house? He did not pause to think, but followed on. The old man proceeded at a measured pace, without looking about him, his footsteps sounding on the hard ground. He passed through the orchard of apple-trees, always keeping the footpath.

It led to a well, situated in a little hollow, which had supplied the farm with water. Just at this well Dolph lost sight of him. He rubbed his eyes and looked again; but nothing was to be seen of the unknown. He reached the well, but nobody was there. All the surrounding ground was open and clear; there was no bush nor hiding-place. He looked down the well, and saw, at a great depth, the reflection of the sky in the still water. After remaining here for some time, without seeing or hearing anything more of his mysterious conductor, he returned to the house, full of awe and wonder. He bolted the door, groped his way back to bed, and it was long before he could compose himself to sleep.

His dreams were strange and troubled. He thought he was following the old man along the side of a great river, until they came to a vessel on the point of sailing; and that his conductor led him on board and vanished. He remembered the commander of the vessel, a short swarthy man, with crisped black hair, blind of one eye, and lame of one leg; but the rest of his dream was very confused. Sometimes he was sailing; sometimes on shore; now amidst storms and tempests, and now wandering quietly in unknown streets. The figure of the old man was strangely mingled up with the incidents of the dream, and the whole distinctly wound up by his finding himself on board of the vessel again, returning home, with a great bag of money!

When he woke, the gray, cool light of dawn was streaking the horizon, and the cocks passing the reveille from farm to farm throughout the country. He rose more harassed and perplexed than ever. He was singularly confounded by all that he had seen and dreamt, and began to doubt whether his mind was not affected, and whether all that passing in his thoughts might not be mere feverish fantasy. In his present state of mind, he did not feel disposed to return immediately to the doctor's, and undergo the cross-questioning of the household. He made a scanty breakfast, therefore, on the remains of the last night's provisions, and then wandered out into the fields to meditate on all that had befallen him. Lost in thought, he rambled about, gradually approaching the town, until the morning was far advanced, when he was aroused by a hurry and bustle around him. He found himself near the water's edge, in a throng of people, hurrying to a pier, where was a vessel ready to make sail. He was unconsciously carried along by the impulse of the crowd, and found that it was a sloop, on the point of sailing up the Hudson to Albany. There was much leave-taking, and kissing of old women and children, and great activity in carrying on board baskets of bread and cakes, and provisions of all kinds, notwithstanding the mighty joints of meat that dangled over the stern; for a voyage to Albany was an expedition of great moment in those days. The commander of the sloop was hurrying about, and giving a world of orders, which were not very strictly attended to; one man being busy in lighting his pipe, and another in sharpening his snickersnee.

The appearance of the commander suddenly caught Dolph's attention. He was short and swarthy, with crisped black hair; blind of one eye and lame of one leg—the very commander that he had seen in his dream! Surprised and aroused, he considered the scene more attentively, and recalled still further traces of his dream: the appearance of the vessel, of the river, and of images, a variety of other objects accorded with the imperfect vaguely rising to recollection.

As he stood musing on these circumstances, the captain suddenly called out to him in Dutch, "Step on board, young man, or you'll be left behind!" he was startled by the summons; he saw that the sloop was cast loose, and was actually moving from the pier; it seemed as if he was actuated by some irresistible impulse; he sprang upon the deck, and the next moment the sloop was hurried off by the wind and tide. Dolph's thoughts and feelings were all in tumult and confusion. He had been strongly worked upon by the events which had recently befallen him, and could not but think there was some connection between his present situation and his last night's dream. He felt as if under supernatural influence; and tried to assure himself with an old and favorite maxim of his, that "one way or other all would turn out for the best." For a moment, the indignation of the doctor at his departure, without leave, passed across his mind, but that was matter of little moment; then he thought of the distress of his mother at his strange disappearance, and the idea gave him a sudden pang; he would have entreated to be put on shore; but he knew with such wind and tide the entreaty would have been in vain. Then the inspiring love of novelty and adventure came rushing in full tide through his bosom; he felt himself launched strangely and suddenly on the world, and under full way to explore the regions of wonder that lay up this mighty river, and beyond those blue mountains which had bounded his horizon since childhood. While he was lost in this whirl of thought, the sails strained to the breeze; the shores seemed to hurry away behind him; and before he perfectly recovered his self-possession, the sloop was ploughing her way past Spiking-devil and Yonkers, and the tallest chimney of the Manhattoes had faded from his sight.

I have said that a voyage up the Hudson in those days was an undertaking of some moment; indeed, it was as much thought of as a voyage to Europe is at present. The sloops were often many days on the way; the cautious navigators taking in sail when it blew fresh, and coming to anchor at night; and stopping to send the boat ashore for milk for tea; without which it was impossible for the worthy old lady passengers to subsist. And there were the much-talked-of perils of the Tappaan Zee, and the highlands. In short, a prudent Dutch burgher would talk of such a voyage for months, and even years, beforehand; and never undertook it without putting his affairs in order, making his will, and having prayers said for him in the Low Dutch churches.

In the course of such a voyage, therefore, Dolph was satisfied he would have time enough to reflect, and to make up his mind as to what he should do when he arrived at Albany. The captain, with his blind eye, and lame leg, would, it is true, bring his strange dream to mind, and perplex him sadly for a few moments; but of late his life had been made up so much of dreams and realities, his nights and days had been so jumbled together, that he seemed to be moving continually in a delusion. There is always, however, a kind of vagabond consolation in a man's having nothing in this world to lose; with this Dolph comforted his heart, and determined to make the most of the present enjoyment.

In the second day of the voyage they came to the highlands. It was the latter part of a calm, sultry day, that they floated gently with the tide between these stern mountains. There was that perfect quiet which prevails over nature in the languor of summer heat; the turning of a plank, or the accidental falling of an oar on deck, was echoed from the mountain-side, and reverberated along the shores; and if by chance the captain gave a shout of command, there were airy tongues which mocked it from every cliff.

Dolph gazed about him in mute delight and wonder at these scenes of nature's magnificence. To the left the Dunderberg reared its woody precipices, height over height, forest over forest, away into the deep summer sky. To the right, strutted forth the bold promontory of Antony's Nose, with a solitary eagle wheeling about it; while beyond, mountain succeeded to mountain, until they seemed to lock their arms together, and confine this mighty river in their embraces. There was a feeling of quiet luxury in gazing at the broad, green bosoms here and there scooped out among the precipices; or at woodlands high in air, nodding over the edge of some beetling bluff, and their foliage all transparent in the yellow sunshine.

In the midst of his admiration, Dolph remarked a pile of bright, snowy clouds, peering above the western heights. It was succeeded by another, and another, each seemingly pushing onwards its predecessor, and towering, with dazzling brilliancy, in the deep-blue atmosphere; and now muttering peals of thunder were faintly heard rolling behind the mountains. The river, hitherto still and glassy, reflecting pictures of the sky and land, now showed a dark ripple at a distance, as the breeze came creeping up it. The fish-hawks wheeled and screamed, and sought their nests on the high dry trees; the crows flew clamorously to the crevices of the rocks, and all nature seemed conscious of the approaching thunder-gust.

The clouds now rolled in volumes over the mountain-tops; their summits still bright and snowy, but the lower parts of an inky blackness. The rain began to patter down in broad and scattered drops; the wind freshened, and curled up the waves; at length it seemed as if the bellying clouds were torn open by the mountain-tops, and complete torrents of rain came rattling down. The lightning leaped from cloud to cloud, and streamed quivering against the rocks, splitting and rending the stoutest forest-trees. The thunder burst in tremendous explosions; the peals were echoed from mountain to mountain; they crashed upon

Dunderberg, and rolled up the long defile of the highlands, each headland making a new echo, until old Bull Hill seemed to bellow back the storm.

For a time the scudding rack and mist, and the sheeted rain, almost hid the landscape from the sight. There was a fearful gloom, illumined still more fearfully by the streams of lightning which glittered among the raindrops. Never had Dolph beheld such an absolute warring of the elements; it seemed as if the storm was tearing and rending its way through this mountain defile, and had brought all the artillery of heaven into action.

The vessel was hurried on by the increasing wind, until she came to where the river makes a sudden bend, the only one in the whole course of its majestic career.* Just as they turned the point, a violent flaw of wind came sweeping down a mountain gully, bending the forest before it, and, in a moment, lashing up the river into white froth and foam. The captain saw the danger, and cried out to lower the sail. Before the order could be obeyed, the flaw struck the sloop, and threw her on her beam ends. Everything now was fright and confusion: the flapping of the sails, the whistling and rushing of the wind, the bawling of the captain and crew, the shrieking of the passengers, all mingled with the rolling and bellowing of the thunder. In the midst of the uproar the sloop righted; at the same time the mainsail shifted, the boom came sweeping the quarter-deck, and Dolph, who was gazing unguardedly at the clouds, found himself, in a moment, floundering in the river.

For once in his life one of his idle accomplishments was of use to him. The many truant hours he had devoted to sporting in the Hudson had made him an expert swimmer; yet with all his strength and skill he found great difficulty in reaching the shore. His disappearance from the deck had not been noticed by the crew, who were all occupied by their own danger. The sloop was driven along with inconceivable rapidity. She had hard work to weather a long promontory on the eastern shore, round which the river turned, and which completely shut her from Dolph's view.

It was on a point of the western shore that he landed, and, scrambling up the rocks, threw himself, faint and exhausted, at

* This must have been the bend at West Point.

the foot of a tree. By degrees the thundergust passed over. The clouds rolled away to the east, where they lay piled in feathery masses, tinted with the last rosy rays of the sun. The distant play of the lightning might be seen about the dark bases, and now and then might be heard the faint muttering of the thunder. Dolph rose, and sought about to see if any path led from the shore, but all was savage and trackless. The rocks were piled upon each other; great trunks of trees lay shattered about, as they had been blown down by the strong winds which draw through these mountains, or had fallen through age. The rocks, too, were overhung with wild vines and briers, which completely matted themselves together, and opposed a barrier to all ingress; every movement that he made shook down a shower from the dripping foliage. He attempted to scale one of these almost perpendicular heights; but, though strong and agile, he found it an Herculean undertaking. Often he was supported merely by crumbling projections of the rock, and sometimes he clung to roots and branches of trees, and hung almost suspended in the air. The wood-pigeon came cleaving his whistling flight by him, and the eagle screamed from the brow of the impending cliff. As he was thus clambering, he was on the point of seizing hold of a shrub to aid his ascent, when something rustled among the leaves, and he saw a snake quivering along like lightning, almost from under his hand. It coiled itself up immediately, in an attitude of defiance, with flattened head, distended jaws, and quickly vibrating tongue, that played like a little flame about its mouth. Dolph's heart turned faint within him, and he had well-nigh let go his hold and tumbled down the precipice. The serpent stood on the defensive but for an instant; and finding there was no attack, glided away into a cleft of the rock. Dolph's eye followed it with fearful intensity, and saw a nest of adders, knotted, and writhing, and hissing in the chasm. He hastened with all speed from so frightful a neighborhood. His imagination, full of this new horror, saw an adder in every curling vine, and heard the tail of a rattlesnake in every dry leaf that rustled.

At length he succeeded in scrambling to the summit of a precipice; but it was covered by a dense forest. Wherever he could gain a lookout between trees, he beheld heights and cliffs, one rising beyond another, until huge mountains overtopped the whole. There were no signs of cultivation; no smoke curling among the trees to indicate a human residence. Everything was wild and solitary. As he was standing on the edge of a precipice overlooking a deep ravine fringed with trees, his feet detached a great fragment of rock; it fell, crashing its way through the tree-tops, down into the chasm. A loud whoop, or rather yell, issued from the bottom of the glen; the moment after there was a report of a gun; and a ball came whistling over his head, cutting the twigs and leaves, and burying itself deep in the bark of a chestnut-tree.

Dolph did not wait for a second shot, but made a precipitate retreat; fearing every moment to hear the enemy in pursuit. He succeeded, however, in returning unmolested to the shore, and determined to penetrate no farther into a country so beset with savage perils.

He sat himself down, dripping, disconsolately, on a stone. What was to be done? where was he to shelter himself? The hour of repose was approaching: the birds were seeking their nests, the bat began to flit about in the twilight, and the night-hawk, soaring high in the heaven, seemed to be calling out the stars. Night gradually closed in, and wrapped everything in gloom; and though it was the latter part of summer, the breeze stealing along the river, and among these dripping forests, was chilly and penetrating, especially to a half-drowned man.

As he sat drooping and despondent in this comfortless condition, he perceived a light gleaming through the trees near the shore, where the winding of the river made a deep bay. It cheered him with the hope of a human habitation, where he might get something to appease the clamorous cravings of his stomach, and what was equally necessary in his shipwrecked condition, a comfortable shelter for the night. With extreme difficulty he made his way toward the light, along ledges of rocks, down which he was in danger of sliding into the river, and over great trunks of fallen trees; some of which had been blown down in the late storm, and lay so thickly together that he had to struggle through their branches. At length he came to the brow of a rock overhanging a small dell, whence the light proceeded. It was from a fire at the foot of a great tree in the midst of a grassy interval or plat among the rocks. The fire cast up a red glare among the gray crags, and impending trees; leaving chasms of deep gloom, that resembled entrances to caverns. A small brook rippled close by, betrayed by the quivering reflection of the flame. There were two figures moving about the fire, and others squatted before it. As they were between him and the light, they were in complete shadow: but one of them happening to move round to the opposite side. Dolph was startled at perceiving, by the glare falling on painted features, and glittering on silver ornaments, that he was an Indian. He now looked more narrowly, and saw guns leaning against a tree, and a dead body lying on the ground. Here was the very foe that had fired at him from the glen. He endeavored to retreat quietly, not caring to intrust himself to these half-human beings in so savage and lonely a place. It was too late: the Indian, with that eagle quickness of eye so remarkable in his race, perceived something stirring among the bushes on the rock: he seized one of the guns that leaned against the tree; one moment more, and Dolph might have had his passion for adventure cured by a bullet. He halloed loudly, with the Indian salutation of friendship; the whole party sprang upon their feet; the salutation was returned, and the straggler was invited to join them at the fire.

On approaching, he found, to his consolation, the party was composed of white men as well as Indians. One, evidently the principal personage, or commander, was seated on a trunk of a tree before the fire. He was a large, stout man, somewhat advanced in life, but hale and hearty. His face was bronzed almost to the color of an Indian's; he had strong but rather jovial features, an aquiline nose, and a mouth shaped like a mastiff's. His face was half thrown in shade by a broad hat, with a buck's tail in it. His gray hair hung short in his neck. He wore a hunting-frock, with Indian leggins, and moccasins, and a tomahawk in the broad wampum-belt round his waist. As Dolph caught a distinct view of his person and features, something reminded him of the old man of the haunted house. The man before him, however, was different in dress and age; he was more cheery too in aspect, and it was hard to find where the vague resemblance lay; but a resemblance there certainly was. Dolph felt some degree of awe in approaching him; but was assured by a frank, hearty welcome. He was still further encouraged by perceiving that the dead body, which had caused him some alarm, was that of a deer; and his satisfaction was complete in discerning, by savory steams from a kettle, suspended by a hooked stick over the fire, that there was a part cooking for the evening's repast.

He had, in fact, fallen in with a rambling hunting-party, such as often took place in those days among the settlers along the river. The hunter is always hospitable; and nothing makes men more social and unceremonious than meeting in the wilderness. The commander of the party poured out a dram of cheering liquor, which he gave him with a merry leer, to warm his heart; and ordered one of his followers to fetch some garments from a pinnace, moored in a cove close by, while those in which our hero was dripping might be dried before the fire.

Dolph found, as he had suspected, that the shot from the glen, which had come so near giving him his quietus when on the precipice, was from the party before him. He had nearly crushed one of them by the fragments of rock which he had detached; and the jovial old hunter, in the broad hat and buck-tail, had fired at the place where he saw the bushes move, supposing it to be the sound of some wild animal. He laughed heartily at the blunder, it being what is considered an exceeding good joke among hunters: "But faith, my lad," said he, "if I had but caught a glimpse of you to take sight at, you would have followed the rock. Antony Vander Heyden is seldom known to miss his aim." These last words were at once a clue to Dolph's curiosity: and a few questions let him completely into the character of the man before him, and of his band of woodland rangers. The commander in the broad hat and hunting-frock was no less a personage than the Heer Antony Vander Heyden, of Albany, of whom Dolph had many a time heard. He was, in fact, the hero of many a story, his singular humors and whimsical habits being matters of wonder to his quiet Dutch neighbors. As he was a man of property, having had a father before him from whom he inherited large tracts of wild land, and whole barrels full of wampum, he could indulge his humors without control. Instead of staying quietly at home, eating and drinking at regular mealtimes, amusing himself by smoking his pipe on the bench before the door, and then turning into a comfortable bed at night, he delighted in all kinds of rough, wild expeditions: never so happy as when on a hunting-party in the wilderness, sleeping under trees or bark sheds, or cruising down the river, or on some woodland lake, fishing and fowling, and living the Lord knows how.

He was a great friend to Indians, and to an Indian mode of life; which he considered true natural liberty and manly enjoyment. When at home he had always several Indian hangers-on who loitered about his house, sleeping like hounds in the sunshine; or preparing hunting and fishing tackle for some new expedition; or shooting at marks with bows and arrows.

Over these vagrant beings Heer Antony had as perfect command as a huntsman over his pack; though they were great nuisances to the regular people of his neighborhood. As he was a rich man, no one ventured to thwart his humors; indeed, his hearty, joyous manner made him universally popular. He would troll a Dutch song as he tramped along the street; hail every one a mile off, and when he entered a house, would slap the good man familiarly on the back, shake him by the hand till he roared, and kiss his wife and daughter before his face—in short, there was no pride nor ill humor about Heer Antony.

Besides his Indian hangers-on, he had three or four humble friends among the white men, who looked up to him as a patron, and had the run of his kitchen, and the favor of being taken with him occasionally on his expeditions. With a medley of such retainers he was at present on a cruise along the shores of the Hudson, in a pinnace kept for his own recreation. There were two white men with him, dressed partly in the Indian style, with moccasins and hunting-shirts; the rest of his crew consisted of four favorite Indians. They had been prowling about the river, without any definite object, until they found themselves in the highlands; where they had passed two or three days, hunting the deer which still lingered among these mountains.

"It is lucky for you, young man," said Antony Vander Heyden, "that you happened to be knocked overboard to-day, as to-morrow morning we start early on our return homewards; and you might then have looked in vain for a meal among the mountains—but come, lads, stir about! stir about! Let's see what prog we have for supper; the kettle has boiled long enough; my stomach cries cupboard; and I'll warrant our guest is in no mood to dally with his trencher."

There was a bustle now in the little encampment; one took off the kettle and turned a part of the contents into a huge wooden bowl. Another prepared a flat rock for a table; while a third brought various utensils from the pinnace; Heer Antony himself brought a flask or two of precious liquor from his own private locker; knowing his boon companions too well to trust any of them with the key.

A rude but hearty repast was soon spread; consisting of venison smoking from the kettle, with cold bacon, boiled Indian corn, and mighty loaves of good brown household bread. Never had Dolph made a more delicious repast; and when he had washed it down with two or three draughts from the Heer Antony's flask, and felt the jolly liquor sending its warmth through his veins, and glowing round his very heart, he would not have changed his situation, no, not with the governor of the province.

The Heer Antony, too, grew chirping and joyous; told half a dozen fat stories, at which his white followers laughed immoderately, though the Indians, as usual, maintained an invincible gravity.

"This is your true life, my boy!" said he, slapping Dolph on the shoulder; "a man is never a man till he can defy wind and weather, range woods and wilds, sleep under a tree, and live on bass-wood leaves!"

And then would he sing a stave or two of a Dutch drinking-song, swaying a short swab Dutch bottle in his hand, while his myrmidons would join in the chorus, until the woods echoed again—as the good old song has it,

> "They all with a shout made the elements ring
> So soon as the office was o'er,
> To feasting they went, with true merriment,
> And tippled strong liquor gillore."

In the midst of his joviality, however, Heer Antony did not lose sight of discretion. Though he pushed the bottle without reserve to Dolph, he always took care to help his followers himself, knowing the beings he had to deal with; and was particular in granting but a moderate allowance to the Indians. The repast being ended, the Indians having drunk their liquor, and smoked their pipes, now wrapped themselves in their blankets, stretched themselves on the ground, with their feet to the fire, and soon fell asleep, like so many tired hounds. The rest of the party remained chatting before the fire, which the gloom of the forest, and the dampness of the air from the late storm, rendered extremely grateful and comforting. The conversation gradually moderated from the hilarity of supper-time, and turned upon hunting-adventures, and exploits and perils in the wilderness, many of which were so strange and improbable, that I will not venture to repeat them, lest the veracity of Antony Vander Heyden and his comrades should be brought into question. There were many legendary tales told, also, about the river, and the settlements on its borders; in which valuable kind of lore the Heer Antony seemed deeply versed. As the sturdy bush-beater sat in a twisted root of a tree, that served him for an arm-chair, dealing forth these wild stories, with the fire gleaming on his strongly marked visage, Dolph was again repeatedly perplexed by something that reminded him of the phantom of the haunted house; some vague resemblance not to be fixed upon any precise feature or lineament, but pervading the general air of his countenance and figure.

The circumstance of Dolph's falling overboard led to the relation of divers disasters and singular mishaps that had befallen voyagers on this great river, particularly in the earlier periods of colonial history; most of which the Heer deliberately attributed to supernatural causes. Dolph stared at this suggestion; but the old gentleman assured him it was very currently believed by the settlers along the river, that these highlands were under the dominion of supernatural and mischievous beings, which seemed to have taken some pique against the Dutch colonists in the early time of the settlement. In consequence of this, they have ever taken particular delight in venting their spleen, and indulging their humors, upon the Dutch skippers; bothering them with flaws, head-winds, counter-currents, and all kinds of impediments; insomuch, that a Dutch navigator was always obliged to be exceedingly wary and deliberate in his proceedings; to come to anchor at dusk; to drop his peak, or take in sail, whenever he saw a swag-bellied cloud rolling over the mountains; in short, to take so many precautions, that he was often apt to be an incredible time in toiling up the river.

Some, he said, believed these mischievous powers of the air to be the evil spirits conjured up by the Indian wizards, in the early times of the province, to revenge themselves on the strangers who had dispossessed them of their country. They even attributed to their incantations the misadventure which befell the renowned Hendrick Hudson, when he sailed so gallantly up this river in quest of a northwest passage, and, as he thought, ran his ship aground; which they affirm was nothing more nor less than a spell of these same wizards, to prevent his getting to China in this direction.

The greater part, however, Heer Antony observed, accounted for all the extraordinary circumstances attending this river, and the perplexities of the skippers who navigated it, by the old legend of the Storm-ship which haunted Point-no-point. On finding Dolph to be utterly ignorant of this tradition, the Heer stared at him for a moment with surprise, and wondered where he had passed his life, to be uninformed on so important a point of history. To pass away the remainder of the evening, therefore, he undertook the tale, as far as his memory would serve, in the very words in which it had been written out by Mynheer Selyne, an early poet of the New Netherlandts. Giving, then, a stir to the fire, that sent up its sparks among the trees like a little volcano, he adjusted himself comfortably in his root of a tree, and throwing back his head, and closing his eyes for a few moments, to summon up his recollection, he related the following legend.

THE STORM-SHIP

In the golden age of the province of the New Netherlands, when under the sway of Wouter Van Twiller, otherwise called the Doubter, the people of the Manhattoes were alarmed one sultry afternoon, just about the time of the summer solstice, by a tremendous storm of thunder and lightning. The rain fell in such torrents as absolutely to spatter up and smoke along the ground. It seemed as if the thunder rattled and rolled over the very roofs of the houses; the lightning was seen to play about the church of St. Nicholas, and to strive three times, in vain, to strike its weather-cock. Garret Van Horne's new chimney was split almost from top to bottom; and Doffue Mildeberger was struck speechless from his bald-faced mare, just as he was riding into town. In a word, it was one of those unparalleled storms which only happen once within the memory of that venerable personage known in all towns by the appellation of "the oldest inhabitant."

Great was the terror of the good old women of the Manhattoes. They gathered their children together, and took refuge in the cellars; after having hung a shoe on the iron point of every bedpost, lest it should attract the lightning. At length the storm abated; the thunder sank into a growl, and the setting sun, breaking from under the fringed borders of the clouds, made the broad bosom of the bay to gleam like a sea of molten gold.

The word was given from the fort that a ship was standing up the bay. It passed from mouth to mouth, and street to street, and soon put the little capital in a bustle. The arrival of a ship, in those early times of the settlement, was an event of vast importance to the inhabitants. It brought them news from the old world, from the land of their birth, from which they were so completely severed: to the yearly ship, too, they looked for their supply of luxuries, of finery, of comforts, and almost of necessaries. The good vrouw could not have her new cap nor new gown until the arrival of the ship; the artist waited for it for his tools, the burgomaster for his pipe and his supply of Hollands, the schoolboy for his top and marbles, and the lordly landholder for the bricks with which he was to build his new mansion. Thus every one, rich and poor, great and small, looked out for the arrival of the ship. It was the great yearly event of the town of New Amsterdam; and from one end of the year to the other, the ship—the ship—the ship—was the continual topic of conversation.

The news from the fort, therefore, brought all the populace down to the Battery, to behold the wished-for sight. It was not exactly the time when she had been expected to arrive, and the circumstance was a matter of some speculation. Many were the groups collected about the Battery. Here and there might be seen a burgomaster, of slow and pompous gravity, giving his opinion with great confidence to a crowd of old women and idle boys. At another place was a knot of old weather-beaten fellows, who had been seamen or fishermen in their times, and were great authorities on such occasions; these gave different opinions, and caused great disputes among their several adherents: but the man most looked up to, and followed and watched by the crowd, was Hans Van Pelt, an old Dutch sea-captain retired from service, the nautical oracle of the place. He reconnoitred the ship through an ancient telescope, covered with tarry canvas, hummed a Dutch tune to himself, and said nothing. A hum, however, from Hans Van Pelt, had always more weight with the public than a speech from another man.

In the meantime the ship became more distinct to the naked eye: she was a stout, round, Dutch-built vessel, with high bow and poop, and bearing Dutch colors. The evening sun gilded her bellying canvas, as she came riding over the long waving billows. The sentinel who had given notice of her approach, declared, that he first got sight of her when she was in the centre of the bay; and that she broke suddenly on his sight, just as if she had come out of the bosom of the black thunder-cloud. The bystanders looked at Hans Van Pelt, to see what he would say to this report: Hans Van Pelt screwed his mouth closer together, and said nothing; upon which some shook their heads, and others shrugged their shoulders.

The ship was now repeatedly hailed, but made no reply, and passing by the fort, stood on up the Hudson. A gun was brought to bear on her, and, with some difficulty, loaded and fired by Hans Van Pelt, the garrison not being expert in artillery. The shot seemed absolutely to pass through the ship, and to skip along the water on the other side, but no notice was taken of it! What was strange, she had all her sails set, and sailed right against wind and tide, which were both down the river. Upon this Hans Van Pelt, who was likewise harbor-master, ordered his boat, and set off to board her; but after rowing two or three hours, he returned without success. Sometimes he would get within one or two hundred yards of her, and then, in a twinkling, she would be half a mile off. Some said it was because his oarsmen, who were rather pursy and short-winded, stopped every now and then to take breath, and spit on their hands; but this it is probable was a mere scandal. He got near enough, however, to see the crew; who were all dressed in the Dutch style, the officers in doublets and high hats and feathers; not a word was spoken by any one on board; they stood as motionless as so many statues, and the ship seemed as if left to her own government. Thus she kept on, away up the river, lessening and lessening in the evening sunshine, until she faded from sight, like a little white cloud melting away in the summer sky.

The appearance of this ship threw the governor into one of the deepest doubts that ever beset him in the whole course of his administration. Fears were entertained for the security of the infant settlements on the river, lest this might be an enemy's ship in disguise, sent to take possession. The governor called together his council repeatedly to assist him with their conjectures. He sat in his chair of state, built of timber from the sacred forest of the Hague, smoking his long jasmin pipe, and listening to all that his counsellors had to say on a subject about which they knew nothing; but in spite of all the conjecturing of the sagest and oldest heads, the governor still continued to doubt.

Messengers were dispatched to different places on the river; but they returned without any tidings—the ship had made no port. Day after day, and week after week, elapsed, but she never returned down the Hudson. As, however, the council seemed solicitous for intelligence, they had it in abundance. The captains of the sloops seldom arrived without bringing some report of having seen the strange ship at different parts of the river; sometimes near the Pallisadoes, sometimes off Croton Point, and sometimes in the highlands; but she never was reported as having been seen above the highlands. The crews of the sloops, it is true, generally differed among themselves in their accounts of these apparitions; but that may have arisen from the uncertain situations in which they saw her. Sometimes it was by the flashes of the thunder-storm lighting up a pitchy night, and giving glimpses of her careering across Tappaan Zee, or the wide waste of Haverstraw Bay. At one moment she would appear close upon them, as if likely to run them down, and would throw them into great bustle and alarm; but the next flash would show her far off, always sailing against the wind. Sometimes, in quiet moonlight nights, she would be seen under some high bluff of the highlands, all in deep shadow, excepting her topsails glittering in the moonbeams; by the time, however, that the voyagers reached the place, no ship was to be seen; and when they had passed on for some distance, and looked back, behold! there she was again, with her topsails in the moonshine! Her appearance was always just after, or just before, or just in the midst of unruly weather; and she was known among the skippers and voyagers of the Hudson by the name of "the storm-ship."

These reports perplexed the governor and his council more than ever; and it would be endless to repeat the conjectures and opinions uttered on the subject. Some quoted cases in point, of ships seen off the coast of New England, navigated by witches and goblins. Old Hans Van Pelt, who had been more than once to the Dutch colony at the Cape of Good Hope, insisted that this must be the flying Dutchman, which had so long haunted Table Bay; but being unable to make port, had now sought another harbor. Others suggested, that, if it really was a supernatural apparition, as there was every natural reason to believe, it might be Hendrick Hudson, and his crew of the Halfmoon; who, it was well known, had once run aground in the upper part of the river in seeking a northwest passage to China. This opinion had very little weight with the governor, but it passed current out of doors; for indeed it had already been reported, that Hendrick Hudson and his crew haunted the Kaatskill Mountains; and it appeared very reasonable to suppose, that his ship might infest the river where the enterprise was baffled, or that it might bear the shadowy crew to their periodical revels in the mountain.

Other events occurred to occupy the thoughts and doubts of the sage Wouter and his council, and the storm-ship ceased to be a subject of deliberation at the board. It continued, however, a matter of popular belief and marvellous anecdote through the whole time of the Dutch government, and particularly just before the capture of New Amsterdam, and the subjugation of the province by the English squadron. About that time the storm-ship was repeatedly seen in the Tappaan Zee, and about Weehawk, and even down as far as Hoboken; and her appearance was supposed to be ominous of the approaching squall in public affairs, and the downfall of Dutch domination.

Since that time we have no authentic accounts of her; though it is said she still haunts the highlands, and cruises about Point-no-point. People who live along the river insist that they sometimes see her in summer moonlight; and that in a deep still midnight they have heard the chant of her crew, as if heaving the lead; but sights and sounds are so deceptive along the mountainous shores, and about the wide bays and long reaches of this great river, that I confess I have very strong doubts upon the subject.

It is certain, nevertheless, that strange things have been seen in these highlands in storms, which are considered as connected with the old story of the ship. The captains of the river craft talk of a little bulbous-bottomed Dutch goblin, in trunk-hose and sugar-loafed hat, with a speaking-trumpet in his hand, which they say keeps about the Dunderberg.* They declare that they have heard him, in stormy weather, in the midst of the turmoil, giving orders in Low Dutch for the piping up of a fresh gust of wind, or the rattling off of another thunder-clap. That sometimes he has been seen surrounded by a crew of little imps in broad breeches and short doublets; tumbling head-over-heels in the rack and mist, and playing a thousand gambols in the air; or buzzing like a swarm of flies about Antony's Nose; and that, at such times, the hurry-scurry of the storm was always greatest. One time a sloop, in passing by the Dunderberg, was overtaken by a thunder-gust, that came scouring round the mountain, and seemed to burst just over the vessel. Though tight and well ballasted, she labored dreadfully, and the water came over the gunwale. All the crew were amazed when it was discovered that there was a little white sugar-loaf hat on the mast-head, known at once to be the hat of the Heer of the Dunderberg. Nobody, however, dared to climb to the mast-head, and get rid of this terrible hat. The sloop continued laboring and rocking, as if she would have rolled her mast overboard, and seemed in continual danger either of upsetting or of running on shore. In this way she drove quite through the highlands, until she had passed Pollopol's Island, where, it is said, the jurisdiction of the Dunderberg potentate ceases. No sooner had she passed this bourn, than the little hat spun up into the air like a top, whirled up all the clouds into a vortex, and hurried them back to the summit of the Dunderberg; while the sloop righted herself, and sailed on as quietly as if in a millpond. Nothing saved her from utter wreck

* *i. e.,* The "Thunder-Mountain," so called from its echoes.

but the fortunate circumstance of having a horse-shoe nailed against the mast—a wise precaution against evil spirits, since adopted by all the Dutch captains that navigate this haunted river.

There is another story told of this foul-weather urchin, by Skipper Daniel Ouselsticker, of Fishkill, who was never known to tell a lie. He declared, that, in a severe squall, he saw him seated astride of his bowsprit, riding the sloop ashore, full butt against Antony's Nose, and that he was exorcised by Dominie Van Gieson, of Esopus, who happened to be on board, and who sang the hymn of St. Nicholas; whereupon the goblin threw himself up in the air like a ball, and went off in a whirlwind, carrying away with him the nightcap of the Dominie's wife; which was discovered the next Sunday morning hanging on the weather-cock of Esopus church-steeple, at least forty miles off! Several events of this kind having taken place, the regular skippers of the river, for a long time, did not venture to pass the Dunderberg without lowering their peaks, out of homage to the Heer of the mountain; and it was observed that all such as paid this tribute of respect were suffered to pass unmolested.*

"Such," said Antony Vander Heyden, "are a few of the stories written down by Selyne, the poet, concerning the storm-ship—which he affirms to have brought a crew of mischievous imps into the province, from some old ghost-ridden country of

* Among the superstitions which prevailed in the colonies, during the early times of the settlements, there seems to have been a singular one about phantom ships. The superstitious fancies of men are always apt to turn upon those objects which concern their daily occupations. The solitary ship, which, from year to year, came like a raven in the wilderness, bringing to the inhabitants of a settlement the comforts of life from the world from which they were cut off, was apt to be present to their dreams, whether sleeping or waking. The accidental sight from shore of a sail gliding along the horizon in those as yet lonely seas, was apt to be a matter of much talk and speculation. There is mention made in one of the early New England writers of a ship navigated by witches, with a great horse that stood by the mainmast. I have met with another story, somewhere, of a ship that drove on shore, in fair, sunny, tranquil weather, with sails all set, and a table spread in the cabin, as if to regale a number of guests, yet not a living being on board. These phantom ships always sailed in the eye of the wind; or ploughed their way with great velocity, making the smooth sea foam before their bows, when not a breath of air was stirring.

Moore has finely wrought up one of these legends of the sea into a little tale, which, within a small compass, contains the very essence of this species of supernatural fiction. I allude to his Spectre Ship, bound to Deadman's Isle.

Europe. I could give a host more, if necessary; for all the accidents that so often befall the river craft in the highlands are said to be tricks played off by these imps of the Dunderberg; but I see that you are nodding, so let us turn in for the night."

The moon had just raised her silver horns above the round back of Old Bull Hill, and lit up the gray rocks and shagged forests, and glittered on the waving bosom of the river. The night-dew was falling, and the late gloomy mountains began to soften and put on a gray aërial tint in the dewy light. The hunters stirred the fire, and threw on fresh fuel to qualify the damp of the night-air. They then prepared a bed of branches and dry leaves under a ledge of rocks for Dolph; while Antony Vander Heyden, wrapping himself in a huge coat of skins, stretched himself before the fire. It was some time, however, before Dolph could close his eyes. He lay contemplating the strange scene before him: the wild woods and rocks around; the fire throwing fitful gleams on the faces of the sleeping savages; and the Heer Antony, too, who so singularly, yet vaguely, reminded him of the nightly visitant to the haunted house. Now and then he heard the cry of some wild animal from the forest; or the hooting of the owl; or the notes of the whippoorwill, which seemed to abound among these solitudes; or the splash of a sturgeon, leaping out of the river and falling back full-length on its placid surface. He contrasted all this with his accustomed nest in the garret-room of the doctor's mansion—where the only sounds at night were the church-clock telling the hour; the drowsy voice of the watchman, drawling out all was well; the deep snoring of the doctor's clubbed nose from below-stairs; or the cautious labors of some carpenter rat gnawing in the wainscot. His thoughts then wandered to his poor old mother: what would she think of his mysterious disappearance—what anxiety and distress would she not suffer? This thought would continually intrude itself to mar his present enjoyment. It brought with it a feeling of pain and compunction, and he fell asleep with the tears yet standing in his eyes.

Were this a mere tale of fancy, here would be a fine opportunity for weaving in strange adventures among these wild mountains, and roving hunters; and, after involving my hero in a variety of perils and difficulties, rescuing him from them all by some miraculous contrivance; but as this is absolutely a true story, I must content myself with simple facts, and keep to probabilities.

At an early hour of the next day, therefore, after a hearty morning's meal, the encampment broke up, and our adventurers embarked in the pinnace of Antony Vander Heyden. There being no wind for the sails, the Indians rowed her gently along, keeping time to a kind of chant of one of the white men. The day was serene and beautiful; the river without a wave; and as the vessel cleft the glassy water, it left a long, undulating track behind. The crows, who had scented the hunters' banquet, were already gathering and hovering in the air, just where a column of thin, blue smoke, rising from among the trees showed the place of their last night's quarters. As they coasted along the bases of the mountains, the Heer Antony pointed out to Dolph a bald eagle, the sovereign of these regions, who sat perched on a dry tree that projected over the river, and, with eye turned upwards, seemed to be drinking in the splendor of the morning sun. Their approach disturbed the monarch's meditations. He first spread one wing, and then the other; balanced himself for a moment; and then, quitting his perch with dignified composure, wheeled slowly over their heads. Dolph snatched up a gun, and sent a whistling ball after him, that cut some of the feathers from his wing; the report of the gun leaped sharply from rock to rock, and awakened a thousand echoes; but the monarch of the air sailed calmly on, ascending higher and higher, and wheeling widely as he ascended, soaring up the green bosom of the woody mountain, until he disappeared over the brow of a beetling precipice. Dolph felt in a manner rebuked by this proud tranquillity, and almost reproached himself for having so wantonly insulted this majestic bird. Heer Antony told him, laughing, to remember that he was not yet out of the territories of the lord of the Dunderberg; and an old Indian shook his head, and observed, that there was bad luck in killing an eagle; the hunter, on the contrary, should always leave him a portion of his spoils.

Nothing, however, occurred to molest them on their voyage. They passed pleasantly through magnificent and lonely scenes, until they came to where Pollopol's Island lay, like a floating bower at the extremity of the highlands. Here they landed, until the heat of the day should abate, or a breeze spring up that might supersede the labor of the oar. Some prepared the mid-day meal, while others reposed under the shade of the trees, in luxurious summer indolence, looking drowsily forth upon the beauty of the scene. On the one side were the highlands, vast and cragged, feathered to the top with forests, and throwing their shadows on the glassy water that dimpled at their feet. On the other side was a wide expanse of the river, like a broad lake, with long sunny reaches, and green headlands; and the distant line of Shawangunk mountains waving along a clear horizon, or checkered by a fleecy cloud.

But I forbear to dwell on the particulars of their cruise along the river; this vagrant, amphibious life, careering across silver sheets of water; coasting wild woodland shores; banqueting on shady promontories, with the spreading tree overhead, the river curling its light foam to one's feet, and distant mountain, and rock, and tree, and snowy cloud, and deep-blue sky, all mingling in summer beauty before one; all this, though never cloying in the enjoyment, would be but tedious in narration.

When encamped by the water-side, some of the party would go into the woods and hunt; others would fish: sometimes they would amuse themselves by shooting at a mark, by leaping, by running, by wrestling; and Dolph gained great favor in the eyes of Antony Vander Heyden, by his skill and adroitness in all these exercises; which the Heer considered as the highest of manly accomplishments.

Thus did they coast jollily on, choosing only the pleasant hours for voyaging; sometimes in the cool morning dawn, sometimes in the sober evening twilight, and sometimes when the moonshine spangled the crisp curling waves that whispered along the sides of their little bark. Never had Dolph felt so completely in his element; never had he met with anything so completely to his taste as this wild hap-hazard life. He was the very man to second Antony Vander Heyden in his rambling humors, and gained continually on his affections. The heart of the old bush-whacker yearned toward the young man, who seemed thus growing up in his own likeness; and as they approached to the end of their voyage, he could not help inquiring a little into his history. Dolph frankly told him his course of life, his severe medical studies, his little proficiency, and his very dubious prospects. The Heer was shocked to find that such amazing talents and accomplishments were to be cramped and buried under a doctor's wig. He had a sovereign contempt for the healing art, having never had any other physician than the butcher. He bore a mortal grudge to all kinds of study also, ever since he had been flogged about an unintelligible book when he was a boy. But to think that a young fellow like Dolph, of such wonderful abilities, who could shoot, fish, run, jump, ride, and wrestle, should be obliged to roll pills, and administer juleps for a living—'twas monstrous! He told Dolph never to despair, but to "throw physic to the dogs"; for a young fellow of his prodigious talents could never fail to make his way. "As you seem to have no aquaintance in Albany," said Heer Antony, "you shall go home with me, and remain under my roof until you can look about you; and in the meantime we can take an occasional bout at shooting and fishing, for it is a pity that such talents should lie idle."

Dolph, who was at the mercy of chance, was not hard to be persuaded. Indeed, on turning over matters in his mind, which he did very sagely and deliberately, he could not but think that Antony Vander Heyden was, "somehow or other," connected with the story of the Haunted House; that the misadventure in the highlands, which had thrown them so strangely together, was, "somehow or other," to work out something good: in short, there is nothing so convenient as this "somehow-or-other" way of accommodating one's self to circumstances; it is the mainstay of a heedless actor, and tardy reasoner, like Dolph Heyliger; and he who can, in this loose, easy way, link foregone evil to anticipated good, possesses a secret of happiness almost equal to the philosopher's stone.

On their arrival at Albany, the sight of Dolph's companion seemed to cause universal satisfaction. Many were the greetings at the river-side, and the salutations in the streets; the dogs bounded before him; the boys whooped as he passed; everybody seemed to know Antony Vander Heyden. Dolph followed on in silence, admiring the neatness of this worthy burgh; for in those days Albany was in all its glory, and inhabited almost exclusively by the descendants of the original Dutch settlers, not having as yet been discovered and colonized by the restless people of New

England. Everything was quiet and orderly; everything was con ducted calmly and leisurely; no hurry, no bustle, no struggling and scrambling for existence. The grass grew about the unpaved streets, and relieved the eye by its refreshing verdure. Tall sycamores or pendent willows shaded the houses, with caterpillars swinging, in long silken strings, from their branches; or moths, fluttering about like coxcombs, in joy at their gay transformation. The houses were built in the old Dutch style, with the gable-ends towards the street. The thrifty housewife was seated on a bench before her door, in close-crimped cap, bright-flowered gown, and white apron, busily employed in knitting. The husband smoked his pipe on the opposite bench; and the little pet Negro girl, seated on the step at her mistress's feet, was industriously plying her needle. The swallows sported about the eaves, or skimmed along the streets, and brought back some rich booty for their clamorous young; and the little housekeeping wren flew in and out of a Liliputian house, or an old hat nailed against the wall. The cows were coming home, lowing through the streets, to be milked at their owner's door; and if, perchance, there were any loiterers, some Negro urchin, with a long goad, was gently urging them homewards.

As Dolph's companion passed on, he received a tranquil nod from the burghers, and a friendly word from their wives; all calling him familiarly by the name of Antony; for it was the custom in this stronghold of the patriarchs, where they had all grown up together from childhood, to call each other by the Christian name. The Heer did not pause to have his usual jokes with them, for he was impatient to reach his home. At length they arrived at his mansion. It was of some magnitude, in the Dutch style, with large iron figures on the gables, that gave the date of its erection, and showed that it had been built in the earliest times of the settlement.

The news of Heer Antony's arrival had preceded him, and the whole household was on the look-out. A crew of Negroes, large and small, had collected in front of the house to receive him. The old, white-headed ones, who had grown gray in his service, grinned for joy, and made many awkward bows and grimaces, and the little ones capered about his knees. But the most happy being in the household was a little, plump, blooming lass, his only child, and the darling of his heart. She came bounding out of the house; but the sight of a strange young man with her father called up, for a moment, all the bashfulness of a home-bred damsel. Dolph gazed at her with wonder and delight; never had he seen, as he thought, anything so comely in the shape of a woman. She was dressed in the good old Dutch taste, with long stays, and full, short petticoats, so admirably adapted to show and set off the female form. Her hair, turned up under a small round cap, displayed the fairness of her forehead; she had fine, blue, laughing eyes, a trim, slender waist, and soft swell—but, in a word, she was a little Dutch divinity; and Dolph, who never stopped half-way in a new impulse, fell desperately in love with her.

Dolph was now ushered into the house with a hearty welcome. In the interior was a mingled display of Heer Antony's taste and habits, and of the opulence of his predecessors. The chambers were furnished with good old mahogany; the beaufets and cupboards glittered with embossed silver and painted china. Over the parlor fireplace was, as usual, the family coat of arms, painted and framed; above which was a long duck fowling-piece, flanked by an Indian pouch, and a powder-horn. The room was decorated with many Indian articles, such as pipes of peace, tomahawks, scalping-knives, hunting-pouches, and belts of wampum; and there were various kinds of fishing-tackle, and two or three fowling-pieces in the corners. The household affairs seemed to be conducted, in some measure, after the master's humors; corrected, perhaps, by a little quiet management of the daughter's. There was a great degree of patriarchal simplicity, and good-humored indulgence. The Negroes came into the room without being called, merely to look at their master, and hear of his adventures; they would stand listening at the door until he had finished a story, and then go off on a broad grin, to repeat it in the kitchen. A couple of pet Negro children were playing about the floor with the dogs, and sharing with them their bread and butter. All the domestics looked hearty and happy; and when the table was set for the evening repast, the variety and abundance of good household luxuries bore testimony to the open-handed liberality of the Heer, and the notable housewifery of his daughter.

In the evening there dropped in several of the worthies of the place, the Van Rensselaers, and the Gansevoorts, and the Rosebooms, and others of Antony Vander Heyden's intimates, to hear an account of his expedition; for he was the Sinbad of Albany, and his exploits and adventures were favorite topics of conversation among the inhabitants. While these sat gossiping together about the door of the hall, and telling long twilight stories, Dolph was cosily seated, entertaining the daughter, on a window-bench. He had already got on intimate terms; for those were not times of false reserve and idle ceremony; and, besides, there is something wonderfully propitious to a lover's suit in the delightful dusk of a long summer evening; it gives courage to the most timid tongue, and hides the blushes of the bashful. The stars alone twinkled brightly; and now and then a fire-fly streamed his transient light before the window, or, wandering into the room, flew gleaming about the ceiling.

What Dolph whispered in her ear that long summer evening, it is impossible to say; his words were so low and indistinct, that they never reached the ear of the historian. It is probable, however, that they were to the purpose; for he had a natural talent at pleasing the sex, and was never long in company with a petticoat without paying proper court to it. In the meantime the visitors, one by one, departed; Antony Vander Heyden, who had fairly talked himself silent, sat nodding alone in his chair by the door, when he was suddenly aroused by a hearty salute with which Dolph Heyliger had unguardedly rounded off one of his periods, and which echoed through the still chamber like the report of a pistol. The Heer started up, rubbed his eyes, called for lights, and observed that it was high time to go to bed; though, on parting for the night, he squeezed Dolph heartily by the hand, looked kindly in his face, and shook his head knowingly; for the Heer well remembered what he himself had been at the youngster's age.

The chamber in which our hero was lodged was spacious, and panelled with oak. It was furnished with clothes-presses, and mighty chests of drawers, well waxed, and glittering with brass ornaments. These contained ample stock of family linen; for the Dutch housewives had always a laudable pride in showing off their household treasures to strangers.

Dolph's mind, however, was too full to take particular note of the objects around him; yet he could not help continually comparing the free open-hearted cheeriness of this establishment with the starveling, sordid, joyless housekeeping at Doctor Knipperhausen's. Still something marred the enjoyment: the idea that he must take leave of his hearty host, and pretty hostess, and cast himself once more adrift upon the world. To linger here would be folly: he should only get deeper in love; and for a poor varlet, like himself, to aspire to the daughter of the great Heer Vander Heyden—it was madness to think of such a thing! The very kindness that the girl had shown towards him prompted him, on reflection, to hasten his departure; it would be a poor return for the frank hospitality of his host to entangle his daughter's heart in an injudicious attachment. In a word, Dolph was like many other young reasoners of exceeding good hearts and giddy heads—who think after they act, and act differently from what they think—who make excellent determinations overnight, and forget to keep them the next morning.

"This is a fine conclusion, truly, of my voyage," said he, as he almost buried himself in a sumptuous feather-bed, and drew the fresh white sheets up to his chin. "Here am I, instead of finding a bag of money to carry home, launched in a strange place, with scarcely a stiver in my pocket; and, what is worse, have jumped ashore up to my very ears in love into the bargain. However," added he, after some pause, stretching himself, and turning himself in bed, "I'm in good quarters for the present, at least; so I'll e'en enjoy the present moment, and let the next take care of itself; I dare say all will work out, 'somehow or other,' for the best."

As he said these words, he reached out his hand to extinguish the candle, when he was suddenly struck with astonishment and dismay, for he thought he beheld the phantom of the haunted house, staring on him from a dusky part of the chamber. A second look reassured him, as he perceived that what he had taken for the spectre was, in fact, nothing but a Flemish portrait, hanging in a shadowy corner, just behind a clothes-press. It was, however, the precise representation of his nightly visitor. The same cloak and belted jerkin, the same grizzled beard and fixed eye, the same broad slouched hat, with a feather hanging over one side. Dolph now called to mind the resemblance he had frequently remarked between his host and the old man of the haunted house; and was fully convinced they were in some way connected, and that some especial destiny had governed his voyage. He lay gazing on the portrait with almost as much awe as he had gazed on the ghostly original, until the shrill house-clock warned him of the lateness of the hour. He put out the light; but remained for a long time turning over these curious circumstances and coincidences in his mind, until he fell asleep. His dreams partook of the nature of his waking thoughts. He fancied that he still lay gazing on the picture, until, by degrees, it became animated; that the figure descended from the wall, and walked out of the room; that he followed it, and found himself by the well to which the old man pointed, smiled on him, and disappeared.

In the morning, when he waked, he found his host standing by his bedside, who gave him a hearty morning's salutation, and asked him how he had slept. Dolph answered cheerily; but took occasion to inquire about the portrait that hung against the wall. "Ah," said Heer Antony, "that's a portrait of old Killian Vander Spiegel, once a burgomaster of Amsterdam, who, on some popular troubles, abandoned Holland, and came over to the province during the government of Peter Stuyvesant. He was my ancestor by the mother's side, and an old miserly curmudgeon he was. When the English took possession of New Amsterdam, in 1664, he retired into the country. He fell into a melancholy, apprehending that his wealth would be taken from him and he come to beggary. He turned all his property into cash, and used to hide it away. He was for a year or two concealed in various places, fancying himself sought after by the English, to strip him of his wealth; and finally he was found dead in his bed one morning, without any one being able to discover where he had concealed the greater part of his money."

When his host had left the room, Dolph remained for some time lost in thought. His whole mind was occupied by what he had heard. Vander Spiegel was his mother's family name; and he recollected to have heard her speak of this very Killian Vander Spiegel as one of her ancestors. He had heard her say, too, that her father was Killian's rightful heir, only that the old man died without leaving anything to be inherited. It now appeared that Heer Antony was likewise a descendant, and perhaps an heir also, of this poor rich man; and that thus the Heyligers and the Vander Heydens were remotely connected. "What," thought he, "if, after all, this is the interpretation of my dream, that this is the way I am to make my fortune by this voyage to Albany, and that I am to find the old man's hidden wealth in the bottom of that well? But what an odd roundabout mode of communicating the matter! Why the plague could not the old goblin have told me about the well at once, without sending me all the way to Albany, to hear a story that was to send me all the way back again?"

These thoughts passed through his mind while he was dressing. He descended the stairs, full of perplexity, when the bright face of Marie Vander Heyden suddenly beamed in smiles upon him, and seemed to give him a clue to the whole mystery. "After all," thought he, "the old goblin is in the right. If I am to get his wealth, he means that I shall marry his pretty descendant; thus both branches of the family will again be united, and the property go on in the proper channel."

No sooner did this idea enter his head, than it carried conviction with it. He was now all impatience to hurry back and secure the treasure, which, he did not doubt, lay at the bottom of the well, and which he feared every moment might be discovered by some other person. "Who knows," thought he, "but this night-walking old fellow of the haunted house may be in the habit of haunting every visitor, and may give a hint to some shrewder fellow than myself, who will take a shorter cut to the well than by the way of Albany?" He wished a thousand times that the babbling old ghost was laid in the Red Sea, and his rambling portrait with him. He was in a perfect fever to depart. Two or three days elapsed before any opportunity presented for returning down the river. They were ages to Dolph, notwithstanding that he was basking in the smiles of the pretty Marie, and daily getting more and more enamoured.

At length the very sloop from which he had been knocked overboard prepared to make sail. Dolph made an awkward apology to his host for his sudden departure. Antony Vander Heyden was sorely astonished. He had concerted half a dozen excursions into the wilderness; and his Indians were actually preparing for a grand expedition to one of the lakes. He took Dolph aside, and exerted his eloquence to get him to abandon all thoughts of business and to remain with him, but in vain; and he at length gave up the attempt, observing, "that it was a thousand pities so fine a young man should throw himself away." Heer Antony, however, gave him a hearty shake by the hand at parting, with a favorite fowling-piece, and an invitation to come to his house whenever he revisited Albany. The pretty little Marie said nothing; but as he gave her a farewell kiss, her dimpled cheek turned pale, and a tear stood in her eye.

Dolph sprang lightly on board of the vessel. They hoisted sail; the wind was fair; they soon lost sight of Albany, its green hills and embowered islands. They were wafted gayly past the Kaatskill Mountains, whose fairy heights were bright and cloudless. They passed prosperously through the highlands, without any molestation from the Dunderberg goblin and his crew; they swept on across Haverstraw Bay, and by Croton Point, and through the Tappaan Zee, and under the Palisadoes, until, in the afternoon of the third day, they saw the promontory of Hoboken hanging like a cloud in the air; and, shortly after, the roofs of the Manhattoes rising out of the water.

Dolph's first care was to repair to his mother's house; for he was continually goaded by the idea of the uneasiness she must experience on his account. He was puzzling his brains, as he went along, to think how he should account for his absence without betraying the secrets of the haunted house. In the midst of these cogitations he entered the street in which his mother's house was situated, when he was thunderstruck at beholding it a heap of ruins.

There had evidently been a great fire, which had destroyed several large houses, and the humble dwelling of poor Dame Heyliger had been involved in the conflagration. The walls were not so completely destroyed, but that Dolph could distinguish some traces of the scene of his childhood. The fireplace, about which he had often played, still remained, ornamented with Dutch tiles, illustrating passages in Bible history, on which he had many a time gazed with admiration. Among the rubbish lay the wreck of the good dame's elbow-chair, from which she had given him so many a wholesale precept; and hard by it was the family Bible, with brass clasps; now, alas! reduced almost to a cinder.

For a moment Dolph was overcome by this dismal sight, for he was seized with the fear that his mother had perished in the flames. He was relieved, however, from his horrible apprehension by one of the neighbors, who happened to come by and informed him that his mother was yet alive.

The good woman had, indeed, lost everything by this unlooked-for calamity; for the populace had been so intent upon saving the fine furniture of her rich neighbors, that the little tenement, and the little all of poor Dame Heyliger, had been suffered to consume without interruption; nay, had it not been for the gallant assistance of her old crony, Peter de Groodt, the worthy dame and her cat might have shared the fate of their habitation.

As it was, she had been overcome with fright and affliction, and lay ill in body and sick at heart. The public, however, had showed her its wonted kindness. The furniture of her rich neighbors being, as far as possible rescued from the flames; themselves duly and ceremoniously visited and condoled with on the injury of their property, and their ladies commiserated on the agitation of their nerves; the public, at length, began to recollect something about poor Dame Heyliger. She forthwith became again a subject of universal sympathy; everybody pitied her more than ever; and if pity could but have been coined into cash—good Lord! how rich she would have been!

It was now determined, in good earnest, that something ought to be done for her without delay. The Dominie, therefore, put up prayers for her on Sunday, in which all the congregation joined most heartily. Even Cobus Groesbeek, the alderman, and Mynheer Milledollar, the great Dutch merchant, stood up in their pews, and did not spare their voices on the occasion; and it was thought the prayers of such great men could not but have their due weight. Doctor Knipperhausen, too, visited her professionally, and gave her abundance of advice gratis, and was universally lauded for his charity. As to her old friend, Peter de Groodt, he was a poor man, whose pity, and prayers, and advice could be of but little avail, so he gave her all that was in his power—he gave her shelter.

To the humble dwelling of Peter de Groodt, then, did Dolph turn his steps. On his way thither he recalled all the tenderness and kindness of his simple-hearted parent, her indulgence of his errors, her blindness to his faults; and then he bethought himself of his own idle, harum-scarum life. "I've been a sad scapegrace," said Dolph, shaking his head sorrowfully. "I've been a complete sink-pocket, that's the truth of it. But," added he briskly, and clasping his hands, "only let her live—only let her live—and I will show myself indeed a son!"

As Dolph approached the house he met Peter de Groodt coming out of it. The old man started back aghast, doubting whether it was not a ghost that stood before him. It being bright daylight, however, Peter soon plucked up heart, satisfied that no ghost dare show his face in such clear sunshine. Dolph now learned from the worthy sexton the consternation and rumor to which his mysterious disappearance had given rise. It had been universally believed that he had been spirited away by those hobgoblin gentry that infested the haunted house; and old Abraham Vandozer, who lived by the great buttonwood-trees, near the three-mile stone, affirmed that he had heard a terrible noise in the air, as he was going home late at night, which seemed just as if a flock of wild geese were overhead, passing off towards the northward. The haunted house was, in consequence, looked upon with ten times more awe than ever; nobody would venture to pass a night in it for the world, and even the doctor had ceased to make his expeditions to it in the daytime.

It required some preparation before Dolph's return could be made known to his mother, the poor soul having bewailed him as lost; and her spirits having been sorely broken down by a number of comforters, who daily cheered her with stories of ghosts, and of people carried away by the devil. He found her confined to her bed, with the other member of the Heyliger family, the good dame's cat, purring beside her, but sadly singed, and utterly despoiled of those whiskers which were the glory of her physiognomy. The poor woman threw her arms about

Dolph's neck. "My boy! my boy! art thou still alive?" For a time she seemed to have forgotten all her losses and troubles in her joy at his return. Even the sage grimalkin showed indubitable signs of joy at the return of the youngster. She saw, perhaps, that they were a forlorn and undone family, and felt a touch of that kindliness which fellow-sufferers only know. But, in truth, cats are a slandered people; they have more affection in them than the world commonly gives them credit for.

The good dame's eyes glistened as she saw one being at least, besides herself, rejoiced at her son's return. "Tib knows thee! poor dumb beast!" said she, smoothing down the mottled coat of her favorite; then recollecting herself, with a melancholy shake of the head, "Ah, my poor Dolph!" exclaimed she, "thy mother can help thee no longer! She can no longer help herself! What will become of thee, my poor boy!"

"Mother," said Dolph, "don't talk in that strain; I've been too long a charge upon you; it's now my part to take care of you in your old days. Come! be of good cheer! you, and I, and Tib will all see better days. I'm here, you see, young, and sound, and hearty; then don't let us despair; I dare say things will all, somehow or other, turn out for the best."

While this scene was going on with the Heyliger family, the news was carried to Doctor Knipperhausen of the safe return of his disciple. The little doctor scarce knew whether to rejoice or be sorry at the tidings. He was happy at having the foul reports which had prevailed concerning his country mansion thus disproved; but he grieved at having his disciple, of whom he had supposed himself fairly disencumbered, thus drifting back, a heavy charge upon his hands. While balancing between these two feelings, he was determined by the counsels of Frau Ilsy, who advised him to take advantage of the truant absence of the youngster, and shut the door upon him forever.

At the hour of bedtime, therefore, when it was supposed the recreant disciple would seek his old quarters, everything was prepared for his reception. Dolph, having talked his mother into a state of tranquillity, sought the mansion of his quondam master, and raised the knocker with a faltering hand. Scarcely, however, had it given a dubious rap, when the doctor's head, in a red nightcap, popped out of one window, and the housekeeper's, in a white nightcap, out of another. He was now greeted with a tremendous volley of hard names and hard language, mingled with invaluable pieces of advice, such as are seldom ventured to be given excepting to a friend in distress, or a culprit at the bar. In a few moments, not a window in the street but had its particular nightcap, listening to the shrill treble of Frau Ilsy, and the guttural croaking of Dr. Knipperhausen; and the word went from window to window, "Ah! here's Dolph Heyliger come back, and at his old pranks again." In short, poor Dolph found he was likely to get nothing from the doctor but good advice; a commodity so abundant as even to be thrown out of the window; so he was fain to beat a retreat, and take up his quarters for the night under the lowly roof of honest Peter de Groodt.

The next morning, bright and early, Dolph was out at the haunted house. Everything looked just as he had left it. The fields were grass-grown and matted, and appeared as if nobody had traversed them since his departure. With palpitating heart he hastened to the well. He looked down into it, and saw that it was of great depth, with water at the bottom. He had provided himself with a strong line, such as the fishermen use on the banks of Newfoundland. At the end was a heavy plummet and a large fish-hook. With this he began to sound the bottom of the well, and to angle about in the water. The water was of some depth; there was also much rubbish, stones from the top having fallen in. Several times his hook got entangled, and he came near breaking his line. Now and then, too, he hauled up mere trash, such as the skull of a horse, an iron hoop, and a shattered iron-bound bucket. He had now been several hours employed without finding anything to repay his trouble, or to encourage him to proceed. He began to think himself a great fool, to be thus decoyed into a wild-goose chase by mere dreams, and was on the point of throwing line and all into the well, and giving up all further angling.

"One more cast of the line," said he, "and that shall be the last." As he sounded, he felt the plummet slip, as it were, through the interstices of loose stones; and as he drew back the line, he felt that the hook had taken hold of something heavy. He had to manage his line with great caution, lest it should be broken by the strain upon it. By degrees the rubbish which lay upon the article he had hooked gave way; he drew it to the surface of the water, and what was his rapture at seeing something like silver glittering at the end of his line! Almost breathless with anxiety, he drew it up to the mouth of the well, surprised at its great weight, and fearing every instant that his hook would slip from its hold, and his prize tumble again to the bottom. At length he landed it safe beside the well. It was a great silver porringer, of an ancient form, richly embossed, and with armorial bearings engraved on its side, similar to those over his mother's mantelpiece. The lid was fastened down by several twists of wire; Dolph loosened them with a trembling hand, and, on lifting the lid, behold! the vessel was filled with broad golden pieces, of a coinage which he had never seen before! It was evident he had lit on the place where Killian Vander Spiegel had concealed his treasure.

Fearful of being seen by some straggler, he cautiously retired, and buried his pot of money in a secret place. He now spread terrible stories about the haunted house, and deterred every one from approaching it, while he made frequent visits to it in stormy days, when no one was stirring in the neighboring fields; though, to tell the truth, he did not care to venture there in the dark. For once in his life he was diligent and industrious, and followed up his new trade of angling with such perseverance and success, that in a little while he had hooked up wealth enough to make him, in those moderate days, a rich burgher for life.

It would be tedious to detail minutely the rest of this story. To tell how he gradually managed to bring his property into use without exciting surprise and inquiry—how he satisfied all scruples with regard to retaining the property, and at the same time gratified his own feelings by marrying the pretty Marie Vander Heyden—and how he and Heer Antony had many a merry and roving expedition together.

I must not omit to say, however, that Dolph took his mother home to live with him, and cherished her in her old days. The good dame, too, had the satisfaction of no longer hearing her son made the theme of censure; on the contrary, he grew daily in public esteem; everybody spoke well of him and his wines;

and the lordliest burgomaster was never known to decline his invitation to dinner. Dolph often related, at his own table, the wicked pranks which had once been the abhorrence of the town; but they were now considered excellent jokes, and the gravest dignitary was fain to hold his sides when listening to them. No one was more struck with Dolph's increasing merit than his old master the doctor; and so forgiving was Dolph, that he absolutely employed the doctor as his family physician, only taking care that his prescriptions should be always thrown out of the window. His mother had often her junto of old cronies to take a snug cup of tea with her in her comfortable little parlor; and Peter de Groodt, as he sat by the fireside, with one of her grandchildren on his knee, would many a time congratulate her upon her son turning out so great a man; upon which the good old soul would wag her head with exultation, and exclaim, "Ah, neighbor, neighbor! did I not say that Dolph would one day or other hold up his head with the best of them?"

Thus did Dolph Heyliger go on, cheerily and prosperously, growing merrier as he grew older and wiser, and completely falsifying the old proverb about money got over the devil's back; for he made good use of his wealth, and became a distinguished citizen, and a valuable member of the community. He was a great promoter of public institutions, such as beef-steak societies and catch-clubs. He presided at all public dinners, and was the first that introduced turtle from the West Indies. He improved the breed of race-horses and game-cocks, and was so great a patron of modest merit, that any one who could sing a good song, or tell a good story, was sure to find a place at his table.

He was a member, too, of the corporation, made several laws for the protection of game and oysters, and bequeathed to the board a large silver punch-bowl, made out of the identical porringer before mentioned, and which is in the possession of the corporation to this very day.

Finally, he died, in a florid old age, of an apoplexy at a corporation feast, and was buried with great honors in the yard of the little Dutch church in Garden Street, where his tombstone may still be seen with a modest epitaph in Dutch, by his friend Mynheer Justus Benson, an ancient and excellent poet of the province.

The foregoing tale rests on better authority than most tales of the kind, as I have it at second-hand from the lips of Dolph Heyliger himself. He never related it till towards the latter part of his life, and then in great confidence (for he was very discreet) to a few of his particular cronies at his own table, over a supernumerary bowl of punch; and, strange as the hobgoblin parts of the story may seem, there never was a single doubt expressed on the subject by any of his guests. It may not be amiss, before concluding, to observe that, in addition to his other accomplishments, Dolph Heyliger was noted for being the ablest drawer of the long-bow in the whole province.

III. From *Tales of a Traveller*

The Bold Dragoon

OR

THE ADVENTURE OF MY GRANDFATHER*

MY grandfather was a bold dragoon, for it's a profession, d'ye see, that has run in the family. All my forefathers have been dragoons, and died on the field of honor, except myself, and I hope my posterity may be able to say the same; however, I don't mean to be vainglorious. Well, my grandfather, as I said, was a bold dragoon, and had served in the Low Countries. In fact, he was one of that very army, which, according to my uncle Toby, swore so terribly in Flanders. He could swear a good stick himself; and moreover was the very man that introduced the doctrine Corporal Trim mentions of radical heat and radical moisture, or, in other words, the mode of keeping out the damps of ditch-water by burnt brandy. Be that as it may, it's nothing to the purport of my story. I only tell it to show you that my grandfather was a man not easily to be humbugged. He had seen service, or, according to his own phrase, he had seen the devil—and that's saying everything.

Well, gentlemen, my grandfather was on his way to England, for which he intended to embark from Ostend—bad luck to the place! for one where I was kept by storms and head-winds for three long days, and the devil of a jolly companion or pretty girl to comfort me. Well, as I was saying, my grandfather was on his way to England, or rather to Ostend—no matter which, it's all the same. So one evening, towards nightfall, he rode jollily into Bruges. Very like you all know Bruges, gentlemen; a queer, old-fashioned Flemish town, once, they say, a great place for trade and money-making in old times, when the Mynheers were in their glory; but almost as large and as empty as an Irishman's pocket at the present day. Well, gentlemen, it was at the time of the annual fair. All Bruges was crowded; and the canals swarmed with Dutch boats, and the streets swarmed with

* The narrator of this tale is a jovial Irish captain of dragoons, a member of a group gathered to exchange fabulous stories.—Ed.

Dutch merchants; and there was hardly any getting along for goods, wares, and merchandises, and peasants in big breeches, and women in half a score of petticoats.

My grandfather rode jollily along, in his easy, slashing way, for he was a saucy, sunshiny fellow—staring about him at the motley crowd, and the old houses with gable ends to the street, and storks' nests in the chimneys; winking at the yafrows who showed their faces at the windows, and joking the women right and left in the street; all of whom laughed, and took it in amazing good part; for though he did not know a word of the language, yet he had always a knack of making himself understood among the women.

Well, gentlemen, it being the time of the annual fair, all the town was crowded, every inn and tavern full, and my grandfather applied in vain from one to the other for admittance. At length he rode up to an old rickety inn, that looked ready to fall to pieces, and which all the rats would have run away from, if they could have found room in any other house to put their heads. It was just such a queer building as you see in Dutch pictures, with a tall roof that reached up into the clouds, and as many garrets, one over the other, as the seven heavens of Mahomet. Nothing had saved it from tumbling down but a stork's nest on the chimney, which always brings good luck to a house in the Low Countries; and at the very time of my grandfather's arrival, there were two of these long-legged birds of grace standing like ghosts on the chimney-top. Faith, but they've kept the house on its legs to this very day, for you may see it any time you pass through Bruges, as it stands there yet, only it is turned into a brewery of strong Flemish beer—at least it was so when I came that way after the battle of Waterloo.

My grandfather eyed the house curiously as he approached. It might not have altogether struck his fancy, had he not seen in large letters over the door,

HEER VERKOOPT MAN GOEDEN DRANK.

My grandfather had learnt enough of the language to know that the sign promised good liquor. "This is the house for me," said he, stopping short before the door.

The sudden appearance of a dashing dragoon was an event

in an old inn frequented only by the peaceful sons of traffic. A rich burgher of Antwerp, a stately ample man in a broad Flemish hat, and who was the great man and great patron of the establishment, sat smoking a clean long pipe on one side of the door; a fat little distiller of Geneva, from Schiedam, sat smoking on the other; and the bottle-nosed host stood in the door, and the comely hostess, in crimped cap, beside him; and the hostess's daughter, a plump Flanders lass, with long gold pendants in her ears, was at a side-window.

"Humph!" said the rich burgher of Antwerp, with a sulky glance at the stranger.

"De duyvel!" said the fat little distiller of Schiedam.

The landlord saw, with the quick glance of a publican, that the new guest was not at all to the taste of the old ones; and, to tell the truth, he did not like my grandfather's saucy eye. He shook his head. "Not a garret in the house but was full."

"Not a garret!" echoed the landlady.

"Not a garret!" echoed the daughter.

The burgher of Antwerp, and the little distiller of Schiedam, continued to smoke their pipes sullenly, eyeing the enemy askance from under their broad hats, but said nothing.

My grandfather was not a man to be browbeaten. He threw the reins on his horse's neck, cocked his head on one side, stuck one arm akimbo—"Faith and troth!" said he, "but I'll sleep in this house this very night." As he said this he gave a slap on his thigh, by way of emphasis—the slap went to the landlady's heart.

He followed up the vow by jumping off his horse, and making his way past the staring Mynheers into the public room. Maybe you've been in the bar-room of an old Flemish inn—faith, but a handsome chamber it was as you'd wish to see; with a brick floor, and a great fireplace, with the whole Bible history in glazed tiles, and then the mantelpiece, pitching itself head foremost out of the wall, with a whole regiment of cracked teapots and earthen jugs paraded on it; not to mention half a dozen great Delft platters, hung about the room by way of pictures; and the little bar in one corner, and the bouncing barmaid inside of it, with a red calico cap, and yellow ear-drops.

My grandfather snapped his fingers over his head, as he

cast an eye round the room—"Faith, this is the very house I've been looking after," said he.

There was some further show of resistance on the part of the garrison; but my grandfather was an old soldier, and an Irishman to boot, and not easily repulsed, especially after he had got into the fortress. So he blarneyed the landlord, kissed the landlord's wife, tickled the landlord's daughter, chucked the bar-maid under the chin; and it was agreed on all hands that it would be a thousand pities, and a burning shame into the bargain, to turn such a bold dragoon into the streets. So they laid their heads together, that is to say, my grandfather and the landlady, and it was at length agreed to accommodate him with an old chamber that had been for some time shut up.

"Some say it's haunted," whispered the landlord's daughter; "but you are a bold dragoon, and I dare say don't fear ghosts."

"The devil a bit!" said my grandfather, pinching her plump cheek. "But if I should be troubled by ghosts, I've been to the Red Sea in my time, and have a pleasant way of laying them, my darling."

And then he whispered something to the girl which made her laugh, and give him a good-humored box on the ear. In short, there was nobody knew better how to make his way among the petticoats than my grandfather.

In a little while, as was his usual way, he took complete possession of the house, swaggering all over it; into the stable to look after his horse, into the kitchen to look after his supper. He had something to say or do with every one; smoked with the Dutchmen, drank with the Germans, slapped the landlord on the shoulder, romped with his daughter and the bar-maid; never, since the days of Alley Croaker, had such a rattling blade been seen. The landlord stared at him with astonishment; the landlord's daughter hung her head and giggled whenever he came near; and as he swaggered along the corridor, with his sword trailing by his side, the maids looked after him, and whispered to one another, "What a proper man!"

At supper, my grandfather took command of the table-d'hôte as though he had been at home; helped everybody, not forgetting himself; talked with every one, whether he understood their language or not; and made his way into the intimacy of the rich burgher of Antwerp, who had never been known to be sociable with any one during his life. In fact, he revolutionized the whole establishment, and gave it such a rouse, that the very house reeled with it. He outsat every one at table, excepting the little fat distiller of Schiedam, who sat soaking a long time before he broke forth; but when he did, he was a very devil incarnate. He took a violent affection for my grandfather; so they sat drinking and smoking, and telling stories, and singing Dutch and Irish songs, without understanding a word each other said, until the little Hollander was fairly swamped with his own gin and water, and carried off to bed, whooping and hickuping, and trolling the burden of a Low Dutch love-song.

Well, gentlemen, my grandfather was shown to his quarters up a large staircase, composed of loads of hewn timber; and through long rigmarole passages, hung with blackened paintings of fish, and fruit, and game, and country frolics, and huge kitchens, and portly burgomasters, such as you see about old-fashioned Flemish inns, till at length he arrived at his room.

An old-times chamber it was, sure enough, and crowded with all kinds of trumpery. It looked like an infirmary for decayed and superannuated furniture, where everything diseased or disabled was sent to nurse or to be forgotten. Or rather it might be taken for a general congress of old legitimate movables, where every kind and country had a representative. No two chairs were alike. Such high backs and low backs, and leather bottoms, and worsted bottoms, and straw bottoms, and no bottoms; and cracked marble tables with curiously carved legs, holding balls in their claws, as though they were going to play at ninepins.

My grandfather made a bow to the motley assemblage as he entered, and, having undressed himself, placed his light in the fireplace, asking pardon of the tongs, which seemed to be making love to the shovel in the chimney-corner, and whispering soft nonsense in its ear.

The rest of the guests were by this time sound asleep, for your Mynheers are huge sleepers. The housemaids crept up yawning to their attics; and not a female head in the inn was laid on a pillow that night without dreaming of the bold dragoon.

My grandfather, for his part, got into bed, and drew over him one of those great bags of down, under which they smother a man in the Low Countries; and there he lay, melting between two feather beds, like an anchovy sandwich between two slices of toast and butter. He was a warm-complexioned man, and this smothering played the very deuce with him. So, sure enough, in a little time it seemed as if a legion of imps were twitching at him, and all the blood in his veins was in a fever-heat.

He lay still, however, until all the house was quiet, excepting the snoring of the Mynheers from the different chambers; who answered one another in all kinds of tones and cadences, like so many bull-frogs in a swamp. The quieter the house became the more unquiet became my grandfather. He waxed warmer and warmer, until at length the bed became too hot to hold him.

"Maybe the maid had warmed it too much?" said the curious gentleman, inquiringly.

"I rather think the contrary," replied the Irishman. "But, be that as it may, it grew too hot for my grandfather."

"Faith, there's no standing this any longer," says he. So he jumped out of bed, and went strolling about the house.

"What for?" said the inquisitive gentleman.

"Why, to cool himself, to be sure—or perhaps to find a more comfortable bed—or perhaps— But no matter what he went for—he never mentioned—and there's no use in taking up our time in conjecturing."

Well, my grandfather had been for some time absent from his room, and was returning, perfectly cool, when just as he reached the door, he heard a strange noise within. He paused and listened. It seemed as if some one were trying to hum a tune in defiance of the asthma. He recollected the report of the room being haunted; but he was no believer in ghosts, so he pushed the door gently open and peeped in.

Egad, gentlemen, there was a gambol carrying on within enough to have astonished St. Anthony himself. By the light of the fire he saw a pale weazen-faced fellow, in a long flannel gown and a tall white night-cap with a tassel to it, who sat by the fire with a bellows under his arm by way of bagpipe, from which he forced the asthmatical music that had bothered my grandfather. As he played, too, he kept twitching about with a thousand queer contortions, nodding his head, and bobbing about his tasselled night-cap.

My grandfather thought this very odd and mighty presumptuous, and was about to demand what business he had to play his wind-instrument in another gentleman's quarters, when a new cause of astonishment met his eye. From the opposite side of the room a long-backed, bandy-legged chair, covered with leather, and studded all over in a coxcombical fashion with little brass nails, got suddenly into motion, thrust out first a claw-foot, then a crooked arm, and at length, making a leg, slided gracefully up to an easy-chair of tarnished brocade, with a hole in its bottom, and led it gallantly out in a ghostly minuet about the floor.

The musician now played fiercer and fiercer, and bobbed his head and his night-cap about like mad. By degrees the dancing mania seemed to seize upon all other pieces of furniture. The antique, long-bodied chairs paired off in couples and led down a country-dance; a three-legged stool danced a hornpipe, though horribly puzzled by its supernumerary limb; while the amorous tongs seized the shovel round the waist, and whirled it about the room in a German waltz. In short, all the movables got in motion: pirouetting hands across, right and left, like so many devils; all except a great clothes-press, which kept courtesying and courtesying in a corner, like a dowager, in exquisite time to the music; being rather too corpulent to dance, or perhaps at a loss for a partner.

My grandfather concluded the latter to be the reason; so being, like a true Irishman, devoted to the sex, and at all times ready for a frolic, he bounced into the room, called to the musician to strike up Paddy O'Rafferty, capered up to the clothes-press, and seized upon the two handles to lead her out——when —whirr! the whole revel was at an end. The chairs, tables, tongs and shovel, slunk in an instant as quietly into their places as if nothing had happened, and the musician vanished up the chimney, leaving the bellows behind him in his hurry. My grandfather found himself seated in the middle of the floor with the clothes-press sprawling before him, and the two handles jerked off, and in his hands.

"Then, after all, this was a mere dream!" said the inquisitive gentleman.

"The divil a bit of a dream!" replied the Irishman. "There

never was a truer fact in this world. Faith, I should have liked to see any man tell my grandfather it was a dream."

Well, gentlemen, as the clothes-press was a mighty heavy body, and my grandfather likewise, particularly in rear, you may easily suppose that two such heavy bodies coming to the ground would make a bit of a noise. Faith, the old mansion shook as though it had mistaken it for an earthquake. The whole garrison was alarmed. The landlord, who slept below, hurried up with a candle to inquire the cause, but with all his haste his daughter had arrived at the scene of uproar before him. The landlord was followed by the landlady, who was followed by the bouncing barmaid, who was followed by the simpering chambermaids, all holding together, as well as they could, such garments as they first laid hands on; but all in a terrible hurry to see what the deuce was to pay in the chamber of the bold dragoon.

My grandfather related the marvellous scene he had witnessed, and the broken handles of the prostrate clothes-press bore testimony to the fact. There was no contesting such evidence; particularly with a lad of my grandfather's complexion, who seemed able to make good every word either with sword or shillelah. So the landlord scratched his head and looked silly, as he was apt to do when puzzled. The landlady scratched—no, she did not scratch her head, but she knit her brow, and did not seem half pleased with the explanation. But the landlady's daughter corroborated it by recollecting that the last person who had dwelt in that chamber was a famous juggler who died of St. Vitus's dance, and had no doubt infected all the furniture.

This set all things to rights, particularly when the chambermaids declared that they had all witnessed strange carryings on in that room; and as they declared this "upon their honors," there could not remain a doubt upon this subject.

"And did your grandfather go to bed again in that room?" said the inquisitive gentleman.

"That's more than I can tell. Where he passed the rest of the night was a secret he never disclosed. In fact, though he had seen much service, he was but indifferently acquainted with geography, and apt to make blunders in his travels about inns at night, which it would have puzzled him sadly to account for in the morning."

Literary Life

AMONG other subjects of a traveller's curiosity, I had at one time a great craving after anecdotes of literary life; and being at London, one of the most noted places for the production of books, I was excessively anxious to know something of the animals which produced them. Chance fortunately threw me in the way of a literary man by the name of Buckthorne, an eccentric personage, who had lived much in the metropolis, and could give me the natural history of every odd animal to be met with in that wilderness of men. He readily imparted to me some useful hints upon the subject of my inquiry.

"The literary world," said he, "is made up of little confederacies, each looking upon its own members as the lights of the universe; and considering all others as mere transient meteors, doomed soon to fall and be forgotten, while its own luminaries are to shine steadily on to immortality."

"And pray," said I, "how is a man to get a peep into those confederacies you speak of? I presume an intercourse with authors is a kind of intellectual exchange, where one must bring his commodities to barter, and always give a *quid pro quo*."

"Pooh, pooh! how you mistake," said Buckthorne, smiling; "you must never think to become popular among wits by shining. They go into society to shine themselves, not to admire the brilliancy of others. I once thought as you do, and never went into literary society without studying my part beforehand; the consequence was, that I soon got the name of an intolerable proser, and should in a little while have been completely excommunicated, had I not changed my plan of operations. No, sir, no character succeeds so well among wits as that of a good listener; or if ever you are eloquent, let it be when tête-à-tête with an author, and then in praise of his own works, or, what is nearly as acceptable, in disparagement of the works of his contemporaries. If ever he speaks favorably of the productions of a particular friend, dissent boldly from him; pronounce his friend to be a blockhead; never fear his being vexed. Much as people speak of the irritability of authors, I never found one to take offence at such contradictions. No, no, sir, authors are particularly candid in admitting the faults of their friends.

"Indeed, I would advise you to be exceedingly sparing of remarks on all modern works, except to make sarcastic observations on the most distinguished writers of the day."

"I'll praise none that have not been dead at least half a century."

"Even then," observed Mr. Buckthorne, "I would advise you to be rather cautious; for you must know that many old writers have been enlisted under the banners of different sects, and their merits have become as completely topics of party discussion as the merits of living statesmen and politicians. Nay, there have been whole periods of literature absolutely taboo'd, to use a South Sea phrase. It is, for example, as much as a man's critical reputation is worth in some circles, to say a word in praise of any of the writers of the reign of Charles the Second, or even of Queen Anne, they being all declared Frenchmen in disguise."

"And pray," said I, "when am I then to know that I am on safe grounds, being totally unacquainted with the literary landmarks, and the boundary-line of fashionable taste?"

"Oh!" replied he, "there is fortunately one tract of literature which forms a kind of neutral ground, on which all the literary meet amicably, and run riot in the excess of their good-humor; and this is in the reigns of Elizabeth and James. Here you may praise away at random. Here it is 'cut and come again;' and the more obscure the author, and the more quaint and crabbed his style, the more your admiration will smack of the real relish of the connoisseur; whose taste, like that of an epicure, is always for game that has an antiquated flavor.

"But," continued he, "as you seem anxious to know something of literary society, I will take an opportunity to introduce you to some coterie, where the talents of the day are assembled. I cannot promise you, however, that they will all be of the first order. Somehow or other, our great geniuses are not gregarious; they do not go in flocks, but fly singly in general society. They prefer mingling like common men with the multitude, and are apt to carry nothing of the author about them but the reputation. It is only the inferior orders that herd together, acquire strength and importance by their confederacies, and bear all the distinctive characteristics of their species."

A Literary Dinner

A FEW days after this conversation with Mr. Buckthorne, he called upon me, and took me with him to a regular literary dinner. It was given by a great bookseller, or rather a company of booksellers, whose firm surpassed in length that of Shadrach, Meshech, and Abednego.

I was surprised to find between twenty and thirty guests assembled, most of whom I had never seen before. Mr. Buckthorne explained this to me, by informing me that this was a business-dinner, or kind of field-day which the house gave about twice a year to its authors. It is true they did occasionally give snug dinners to three or four literary men at a time; but then these were generally select authors, favorites of the public, such as had arrived at their sixth or seventh editions. "There are," said he, "certain geographical boundaries in the land of literature, and you may judge tolerably well of an author's popularity by the wine his bookseller gives him. An author crosses the port line about the third edition, and gets into claret; and when he has reached the sixth or seventh, he may revel in champagne and burgundy."

"And pray," said I, "how far may these gentlemen have reached that I see around me? are any of these claret-drinkers?"

"Not exactly, not exactly. You find at these great dinners the common steady run of authors, one- or two-edition men; or if any others are invited, they are aware that it is a kind of republican meeting—you understand me—a meeting of the republic of letters; and that they must expect nothing but plain, substantial fare."

These hints enabled me to comprehend more fully the arrangement of the table. The two ends were occupied by two partners of the house; and the host seemed to have adopted Addison's idea as to the literary precedence of his guests. A popular poet had the post of honor; opposite to whom was a hot-pressed traveller in quarto with plates. A grave-looking antiquarian, who had produced several solid works, that were much quoted and little read, was treated with great respect, and seated next to a neat, dressy gentleman in black, who had written a thin, genteel, hot-pressed octavo on political economy, that was getting into fashion. Several three-volumed duodecimo men, of fair currency, were placed about the centre of the table; while the lower end was taken up with small poets, translators, and authors who had not as yet risen into much notoriety.

The conversation during dinner was by fits and starts; breaking out here and there in various parts of the table in small flashes, and ending in smoke. The poet, who had the confidence of a man on good terms with the world, and independent of his bookseller, was very gay and brilliant, and said many clever things which set the partner next him in a roar, and delighted all the company. The other partner, however, maintained his sedateness, and kept carving on, with the air of a thorough man of business, intent upon the occupation of the moment. His gravity was explained to me by my friend Buckthorne. He informed me that the concerns of the house were admirably distributed among the partners. "Thus, for instance," said he, "the grave gentleman is the carving partner, who attends to the joints; and the other is the laughing partner, who attends to the jokes."

The general conversation was chiefly carried on at the upper end of the table, as the authors there seemed to possess the greatest courage of the tongue. As to the crew at the lower end, if they did not make much figure in talking, they did in eating. Never was there a more determined, inveterate, thoroughly sustained attack on the trencher than by this phalanx of masticators. When the cloth was removed, and the wine began to circulate, they grew very merry and jocose among themselves. Their jokes, however, if by chance any of them reached the upper end of the table, seldom produced much effect. Even the laughing partner did not think it necessary to honor them with a smile; which my neighbor Buckthorne accounted for, by informing me that there was a certain degree of popularity to be obtained before a bookseller could afford to laugh at an author's jokes.

Among this crew of questionable gentlemen thus seated below the salt, my eye singled out one in particular. He was rather shabbily dressed; though he had evidently made the most of a rusty black coat, and wore his shirt-frill plaited and puffed out voluminously at the bosom. His face was dusky, but florid, perhaps a little too florid, particularly about the nose; though the rosy hue gave the greater lustre to a twinkling black eye. He had a little the look of a boon companion, with that dash of the poor devil in it which gives an inexpressible mellow tone to a man's humor. I had seldom seen a face of richer promise; but never was promise so ill kept. He said nothing, ate and drank with the keen appetite of a garreteer, and scarcely stopped to laugh, even at the good jokes from the upper end of the table. I inquired who he was. Buckthorne looked at him attentively: "Gad," said he, "I have seen that face before, but where I cannnot recollect. He cannot be an author of any note. I suppose some writer of sermons, or grinder of foreign travels."

After dinner we retired to another room to take tea and coffee, where we were reinforced by a cloud of inferior guests—authors of small volumes in boards, and pamphlets stitched in blue paper. These had not as yet arrived to the importance of a dinner-invitation, but were invited occasionally to pass the evening in a friendly way. They were very respectful to the partners, and, indeed, seemed to stand a little in awe of them; but they paid devoted court to the lady of the house, and were extravagantly fond of the children. Some few, who did not feel confidence enough to make such advances, stood shyly off in corners, talking to one another; or turned over portfolios of prints which they had not seen above five thousand times, or moused over the music on the forte-piano.

The poet and the thin octavo gentleman were the persons most current and at their ease in the drawing-room; being men evidently of circulation in the West End. They got on each side of the lady of the house, and paid her a thousand compliments and civilities, at some of which I thought she would have expired with delight. Everything they said and did had the odor of fashionable life. I looked round in vain for the poor-devil author in the rusty black coat; he had disappeared immediately after leaving the table, having a dread, no doubt, of the glaring light of a drawing-room. Finding nothing further to interest my attention, I took my departure soon after coffee had been served, leaving the poet, and the thin, genteel, hot-pressed octavo gentleman, masters of the field.

The Club of Queer Fellows

I THINK it was the very next evening that, in coming out of Covent Garden Theatre with my eccentric friend Buckthorne, he proposed to give me another peep at life and character. Finding me willing for any research of the kind, he took me through a variety of the narrow courts and lanes about Covent Garden, until we stopped before a tavern, from which we heard the bursts of merriment of a jovial party. There would be a loud peal of laughter, then an interval, then another peal, as if a prime wag were telling a story. After a little while there was a song, and at the close of each stanza a hearty roar, and a vehement thumping on the table.

"This is the place," whispered Buckthorne; "it is the club of queer fellows, a great resort of the small wits, third-rate actors, and newspaper critics of the theatres. Any one can go in on paying a sixpence at the bar for the use of the club."

We entered, therefore, without ceremony, and took our seats at a lone table, in a dusky corner of the room. The club was assembled round a table, on which stood beverages of various kinds, according to the tastes of the individuals. The members were a set of queer fellows indeed; but what was my surprise on recognizing, in the prime wit of the meeting, the poor-devil author whom I had remarked at the booksellers' dinner for his promising face and his complete taciturnity. Matters, however, were entirely changed with him. There he was a mere cipher; here he was lord of the ascendant, the choice spirit, the dominant genius. He sat at the head of the table with his hat on, and an eye beaming even more luminously than his nose. He had a quip and a fillip for every one, and a good thing on every occasion. Nothing could be said or done without eliciting a spark from him: and I solemnly declare I have heard much worse wit even from noblemen. His jokes, it must be confessed, were rather wet, but they suited the circle over which he presided. The company were in that maudlin mood, when a little wit goes a great way. Every time he opened his lips there was sure to be a roar; and even sometimes before he had time to speak.

We were fortunate enough to enter in time for a glee composed by him expressly for the club, and which he sung with two boon companions, who would have been worthy subjects for Hogarth's pencil. As they were each provided with a written copy, I was enabled to procure the reading of it.

> "Merrily, merrily push round the glass,
> And merrily troll the glee,
> For he who won't drink till he wink, is an ass,
> So, neighbor, I drink to thee.
>
> "Merrily, merrily fuddle thy nose,
> Until it right rosy shall be;
> For a jolly red nose, I speak under the rose,
> Is a sign of good company."

We waited until the party broke up, and no one but the wit remained. He sat at the table with his legs stretched under it, and wide apart; his hands in his breeches-pockets; his head drooped upon his breast; and gazing with lack-lustre countenance on an empty tankard. His gayety was gone, his fire completely quenched.

My companion approached, and startled him from his fit of brown study, introducing himself on the strength of their having dined together at the booksellers'.

"By the way," said he, "it seems to me I have seen you before; your face is surely that of an old acquaintance, though for the life of me I cannot tell where I have known you."

"Very likely," replied he, with a smile; "many of my old friends have forgotten me. Though, to tell the truth, my memory in this instance is as bad as your own. If, however, it will assist your recollection in any way, my name is Thomas Dribble, at your service."

"What! Tom Dribble, who was at old Birchell's school in Warwickshire?"

"The same," said the other, coolly.

"Why, then, we are old schoolmates, though it's no wonder you don't recollect me. I was your junior by several years; don't you recollect little Jack Buckthorne?"

Here there ensued a scene of school-fellow recognition, and a world of talk about old school-times and school-pranks. Mr. Dribble ended by observing, with a heavy sigh, "that times were sadly changed since those days."

"Faith, Mr. Dribble," said I, "you seem quite a different man here from what you were at dinner. I had no idea that you had so much stuff in you. There you were all silence, but here you absolutely keep the table in a roar."

"Ah! my dear sir," replied he, with a shake of the head, and a shrug of the shoulder, "I am a mere glowworm. I never shine by daylight. Besides, it's a hard thing for a poor devil of an author to shine at the table of a rich bookseller. Who do you think would laugh at anything I could say, when I had some of the current wits of the day about me? But here, though a poor devil, I am among still poorer devils than myself; men who look up to me as a man of letters, and a belle-esprit, and all my jokes pass as sterling gold from the mint."

"You surely do yourself injustice, sir," said I; "I have certainly heard more good things from you this evening, than from any of those beaux-esprits by whom you appear to have been so daunted."

"Ah, sir! but they have luck on their sides; they are in the fashion—there's nothing like being in fashion. A man that has once got his character up for a wit is always sure of a laugh, say what he may. He may utter as much nonsense as he pleases, and all will pass current. No one stops to question the coin of a rich man; but a poor devil cannot pass off either a joke or a guinea, without its being examined on both sides. Wit and coin are always doubted with a threadbare coat.

"For my part," continued he, giving his hat a twitch a little more on one side—"for my part, I hate your fine dinners; there's nothing, sir, like the freedom of a chophouse. I'd rather, any time, have my steak and tankard among my own set, than drink claret and eat venison with your cursed civil, elegant company, who never laugh at a good joke from a poor devil for fear of its being vulgar. A good joke grows in a wet soil; it flourishes in low places, but withers on your d—d high, dry grounds. I once kept high company, sir, until I nearly ruined myself; I grew so dull, and vapid, and genteel. Nothing saved me but being arrested by my landlady, and thrown into prison; where a course of catch-clubs, eightpenny ale, and poor-devil company, manured my mind, and brought it back to itself again."

As it was now growing late, we parted for the evening, though

I felt anxious to know more of this practical philosopher. I was glad, therefore, when Buckthorne proposed to have another meeting, to talk over old school-times, and inquired his schoolmate's address. The latter seemed at first a little shy of naming his lodgings; but suddenly, assuming an air of hardihood—"Green-arbor Court, sir," exclaimed he—"Number——in Green-arbor Court. You must know the place. Classic ground, sir, classic ground! It was there Goldsmith wrote his 'Vicar of Wakefield'—I always like to live in literary haunts."

I was amused with this whimsical apology for shabby quarters. On our way homeward, Buckthorne assured me that this Dribble had been the prime wit and great wag of the school in their boyish days, and one of those unlucky urchins denominated bright geniuses. As he perceived me curious respecting his old schoolmate, he promised to take me with him in his proposed visit to Green-arbor Court.

A few mornings afterward he called upon me, and we set forth on our expedition. He led me through a variety of singular alleys, and courts, and blind passages; for he appeared to be perfectly versed in all the intricate geography of the metropolis. At length we came out upon Fleet Market, and traversing it, turned up a narrow street to the bottom of a long steep flight of stone steps, called Break-neck Stairs. These, he told me, led up to Green-arbor Court, and that down them poor Goldsmith might many a time have risked his neck. When we entered the court, I could not but smile to think in what out-of-the-way corners genius produces her bantlings! And the muses, those capricious dames, who, forsooth, so often refuse to visit palaces, and deny a single smile to votaries in splendid studies, and gilded drawing-rooms—what holes and burrows will they frequent to lavish their favors on some ragged disciple!

This Green-arbor Court I found to be a small square, surrounded by tall and miserable houses, the very intestines of which seemed turned inside out, to judge from the old garments and frippery fluttering from every window. It appeared to be a region of washerwomen, and lines were stretched about the little square, on which clothes were dangling to dry.

Just as we entered the square, a scuffle took place between two viragoes about a disputed right to a wash-tub, and immediately the whole community was in a hubbub. Heads in mob-caps popped out of every window, and such a clamor of tongues ensued, that I was fain to stop my ears. Every amazon took part with one or other of the disputants, and brandished her arms, dripping with soap-suds, and fired away from her window as from the embrazure of a fortress; while the swarms of children nestled and cradled in every procreant chamber of this hive, waking with the noise, set up their shrill pipes to swell the general concert.

Poor Goldsmith! what a time he must have had of it, with his quiet disposition and nervous habits, penned up in this den of noise and vulgarity! How strange, that, while every sight and sound was sufficient to embitter the heart, and fill it with misanthropy, his pen should be dropping the honey of Hybla! Yet it is more than probable that he drew many of his inimitable pictures of low life from the scenes which surrounded him in this abode. The circumstance of Mrs. Tibbs being obliged to wash her husband's two shirts in a neighbor's house, who refused to lend her wash-tub, may have been no sport of fancy, but a fact passing under his own eye. His landlady may have sat for the picture, and Beau Tibbs's scanty wardrobe have been a *fac-simile* of his own.

It was with some difficulty that we found our way to Dribble's lodgings. They were up two pair of stairs, in a room that looked upon the court; and when we entered, he was seated on the edge of his bed, writing at a broken table. He received us, however, with a free, open, poor-devil air, that was irresistible. It is true he did at first appear slightly confused; buttoned up his waistcoat a little higher, and tucked in a stray frill of linen. But he recollected himself in an instant; gave a half swagger, half leer, as he stepped forth to receive us; drew a three-legged stool for Mr. Buckthorne; pointed me to a lumbering old damask chair, that looked like a dethroned monarch in exile; and bade us welcome to his garret.

We soon got engaged in conversation. Buckthorne and he had much to say about early school-scenes; and as nothing opens a man's heart more than recollections of the kind, we soon drew from him a brief outline of his literary career.

The Poor-Devil Author

I BEGAN life unluckily by being the wag and bright fellow at school; and I had the further misfortune of becoming the great genius of my native village. My father was a country attorney, and intended I should succeed him in business; but I had too much genius to study, and he was too fond of my genius to force it into the traces; so I fell into bad company, and took to bad habits. Do not mistake me. I mean that I fell into the company of village-literati, and village-blues, and took to writing village-poetry.

It was quite the fashion in the village to be literary. There was a little knot of choice spirits of us, who assembled frequently together, formed ourselves into a Literary, Scientific, and Philosophical Society, and fancied ourselves the most learned Philos in existence. Every one had a great character assigned him, suggested by some casual habit or affectation. One heavy fellow drank an enormous quantity of tea, rolled in his armchair, talked sententiously, pronounced dogmatically, and was considered a second Dr. Johnson; another, who happened to be a curate, uttered coarse jokes, wrote doggerel rhymes, and was the Swift of our association. Thus we had also our Popes, and Goldsmiths, and Addisons; and a blue-stocking lady, whose drawing-room we frequented, who corresponded about nothing with all the world, and wrote letters with the stiffness and formality of a printed book, was cried up as another Mrs. Montagu. I was, by common consent, the juvenile prodigy, the poetical youth, the great genius, the pride and hope of the village, through whom it was to become one day as celebrated as Stratford-on-Avon.

My father died, and left me his blessing and his business. His blessing brought no money into my pocket; and as to his business, it soon deserted me; for I was busy writing poetry, and could not attend to law, and my clients, though they had great respect for my talents, had no faith in a poetical attorney.

I lost my business, therefore, spent my money, and finished my poem. It was the Pleasures of Melancholy, and was cried up to the skies by the whole circle. The Pleasures of Imagination, the Pleasures of Hope, and the Pleasures of Memory, though each had placed its author in the first rank of poets, were blank prose in comparison. Our Mrs. Montagu would cry over it from beginning to end. It was pronounced by all the members of the Literary, Scientific, and Philosophical Society the greatest poem of the age, and all anticipated the noise it would make in the great world. There was not a doubt but the London booksellers would be mad after it; and the only fear of my friends was, that I would make a sacrifice by selling it too cheap. Every time they talked the matter over, they increased the price. They reckoned up the great sums given for the poems of certain popular writers, and determined that mine was worth more than all put together, and ought to be paid for accordingly. For my part, I was modest in my expectations, and determined that I would be satisfied with a thousand guineas. So I put my poem in my pocket, and set off for London.

My journey was joyous. My heart was light as my purse, and my head full of anticipations of fame and fortune. With what swelling pride did I cast my eyes upon old London from the heights of Highgate! I was like a general, looking down upon a place he expects to conquer. The great metropolis lay stretched before me, buried under a home-made cloud of murky smoke, that wrapped it from the brightness of a sunny day, and formed for it a kind of artificial bad weather. At the outskirts of the city, away to the west, the smoke gradually decreased until all was clear and sunny, and the view stretched uninterrupted to the blue line of the Kentish hills.

My eye turned fondly to where the mighty cupola of St. Paul's swelled dimly through this misty chaos, and I pictured to myself the solemn realm of learning that lies about its base. How soon should the Pleasures of Melancholy throw this world of booksellers and printers into a bustle of business and delight! How soon should I hear my name repeated by printers' devils throughout Paternoster Row, and Angel Court, and Ave Maria Lane, until Amen Corner should echo back the sound!

Arrived in town, I repaired at once to the most fashionable publisher. Every new author patronizes him of course. In fact, it had been determined in the village circle that he should be the fortunate man. I cannot tell you how vain-gloriously I walked the streets. My head was in the clouds. I felt the airs of heaven playing about it, and fancied it already encircled by a halo of literary glory. As I passed by the windows of bookshops, I anticipated the time when my work would be shining among the hot-pressed wonders of the day; and my face, scratched on copper, or cut on wood, figuring in fellowship with those of Scott, and Byron, and Moore.

When I applied at the publisher's house, there was something in the loftiness of my air, and the dinginess of my dress, that struck the clerks with reverence. They doubtless took me for some person of consequence; probably a digger of Greek roots, or a penetrator of pyramids. A proud man in a dirty shirt is always an imposing character in the world of letters; one must feel intellectually secure before he can venture to dress shabbily; none but a great genius, or a great scholar, dares to be dirty; so I was ushered at once to the sanctum sanctorum of this high-priest of Minerva.

The publishing of books is a very different affair nowadays from what it was in the time of Bernard Lintot. I found the publisher a fashionably dressed man, in an elegant drawing-room, furnished with sofas, and portraits of celebrated authors, and cases of splendidly bound books. He was writing letters at an elegant table. This was transacting business in style. The place seemed suited to the magnificent publications that issued from it. I rejoiced at the choice I had made of a publisher, for I always like to encourage men of taste and spirit.

I stepped up to the table with the lofty poetical port I had been accustomed to maintain in our village circle; though I threw in it something of a patronizing air, such as one feels when about to make a man's fortune. The publisher paused with his pen in hand, and seemed waiting in mute suspense to know what was to be announced by so singular an apparition.

I put him at his ease in a moment, for I felt that I had but to come, see, and conquer. I made known my name, and the name of my poem; produced my precious roll of blotted manuscript; laid it on the table with an emphasis; and told him at once, to save time, and come directly to the point, the price was one thousand guineas.

I had given him no time to speak, nor did he seem so inclined. He continued looking at me for a moment with an air of whimsical perplexity; scanned me from head to foot; looked down at the manuscript, then up again at me, then pointed to a chair; and whistling softly to himself, went on writing his letter.

I sat for some time waiting his reply, supposing he was making up his mind; but he only paused occasionally to take a fresh dip of ink, to stroke his chin, or the tip of his nose, and then resumed his writing. It was evident his mind was intently occupied upon some other subject; but I had no idea that any other subject could be attended to, and my poem lie unnoticed on the table. I had supposed that everything would make way for the "Pleasures of Melancholy."

My gorge at length rose within me. I took up my manuscript, thrust it into my pocket, and walked out of the room; making some noise as I went out, to let my departure be heard. The publisher, however, was too much buried in minor concerns to notice it. I was suffered to walk down-stairs without being called back. I sallied forth into the street, but no clerk was sent after me; nor did the publisher call after me from the drawing-room window. I have been told since, that he considered me either a madman or a fool. I leave you to judge how much he was in the wrong in his opinion.

When I turned the corner, my crest fell. I cooled down in my pride and my expectations, and reduced my terms with the next bookseller to whom I applied. I had no better success; nor with a third, nor with a fourth. I then desired the booksellers to make an offer themselves; but the deuce an offer would they make. They told me poetry was a mere drug; everybody wrote poetry; the market was overstocked with it. And then they said, the title of my poem was not taking; that pleasures of all kinds were worn threadbare, nothing but horrors did nowadays, and even those were almost worn out. Tales of Pirates, Robbers, and bloody Turks, might answer tolerably well; but then they must come from some established, well-known name, or the public would not look at them.

At last I offered to leave my poem with a bookseller to read it, and judge for himself. "Why, really, my dear Mr.——a—a—I forget your name," said he, casting his eye at my rusty coat and shabby gaiters, "really, sir, we are so pressed with business just now, and have so many manuscripts on hand to read, that we have not time to look at any new productions; but if you can call again in a week or two, or say the middle of next month, we may be able to look over your writings, and give you an answer. Don't forget, the month after next; good morning, sir; happy to see you any time you are passing this way." So saying, he bowed me out in the civilest way imaginable. In short, sir, instead of an eager competition to secure my poem, I could not even get it read! In the meantime I was harassed by letters from my friends, wanting to know when the work was to appear; who was to be my publisher; and above all things, warning me not to let it go too cheap.

There was but one alternative left. I determined to publish the poem myself; and to have my triumph over the booksellers when it should become the fashion of the day. I accordingly published the "Pleasures of Melancholy"—and ruined myself. Excepting the copies sent to the reviews, and to my friends in the country, not one, I believe, ever left the bookseller's warehouse. The printer's bill drained my purse; and the only notice that was taken of my work was contained in the advertisements paid for by myself.

I could have borne all this, and have attributed it, as usual, to the mismanagement of the publisher, or the want of taste in the public; and could have made the usual appeal to posterity; but my village friends would not let me rest in quiet. They were picturing me to themselves feasting with the great, communing with the literary, and in the high career of fortune and renown. Every little while, some one would call on me with a letter of introduction from the village circle, recommending him to my attentions, and requesting that I would make him known in society; with a hint, that an introduction to a celebrated literary nobleman would be extremely agreeable. I determined, therefore, to change my lodgings, drop my correspondence, and disappear altogether from the view of my village admirers. Besides, I was anxious to make one more poetic attempt. I was by no means disheartened by the failure of my first. My poem was evidently too didactic. The public was wise enough. It no longer read for instruction. "They want horrors, do they?" said I: "I'faith! then they shall have enough of them." So I looked out for some quiet, retired place, where I might be out of the reach of my friends, and have leisure to cook up some delectable dish of poetical "hell-broth."

I had some difficulty in finding a place to my mind, when chance threw me in the way of Canonbury Castle. It is an ancient brick tower, hard by "merry Islington"; the remains of a hunting-seat of Queen Elizabeth, where she took the pleasure of the country when the neighborhood was all woodland. What gave it particular interest in my eyes was the circumstance that it had been the residence of a poet.

It was here Goldsmith resided when he wrote his "Deserted Village." I was shown the very apartment. It was a relic of the original style of the castle, with panelled wainscots and Gothic windows. I was pleased with its air of antiquity, and with its having been the residence of poor Goldy.

"Goldsmith was a pretty poet," said I to myself, "a very pretty poet, though rather of the old school. He did not think and feel so strongly as is the fashion nowadays; but had he lived in these times of hot hearts and hot heads, he would no doubt have written quite differently."

In a few days I was quietly established in my new quarters; my books all arranged; my writing-desk placed by a window looking out into the fields; and I felt as snug as Robinson Crusoe, when he had finished his bower. For several days I enjoyed all the novelty of the change and the charms which grace new lodgings, before one has found out their defects. I rambled about the fields where I fancied Goldsmith had rambled. I explored merry Islington; ate my solitary dinner at the Black Bull, which, according to tradition, was a country-seat of Sir Walter Raleigh; and would sit and sip my wine, and muse on old times, in a quaint old room, where many a council had been held.

All this did very well for a few days. I was stimulated by novelty; inspired by the associations awakened in my mind by these curious haunts; and began to think I felt the spirit of composition stirring within me. But Sunday came, and with it the whole city world, swarming about Canonbury Castle. I could not open my window but I was stunned with shouts and noises from the cricket-ground; the late quiet road beneath my window was alive with the tread of feet and clack of tongues; and, to complete my misery, I found that my quiet retreat was absolutely a "show-house," the tower and its contents being shown to strangers at sixpence a head.

There was a perpetual tramping up-stairs of citizens and their families, to look about the country from the top of the tower, and to take a peep at the city through the telescope, to try if they could discern their own chimneys. And then, in the midst of a vein of thought, or a moment of inspiration, I was interrupted, and all my ideas put to flight, by my intolerable landlady's tapping at the door, and asking me if I would "just please to let a lady and gentleman come in, to take a look at Mr. Goldsmith's room." If you know anything of what an author's study is, and what an author is himself, you must know that there was no standing this. I put positive interdict on my room's being exhibited; but then it was shown when I was absent, and my papers put in confusion; and, on returning home one day, I absolutely found a cursed tradesman and his daughters gaping over my manuscripts, and my landlady in a panic at my appearance. I tried to make out a little longer, by taking the key in my pocket; but it would not do. I overheard mine hostess one day telling some of her customers on the stairs, that the room was occupied by an author, who was always in a tantrum if interrupted; and I immediately perceived, by a slight noise at the door, that they were peeping at me through the key-hole. By the head of Apollo, but this was quite too much! With all my eagerness for fame, and my ambition of the stare of the million, I had no idea of being exhibited by retail, at sixpence a head, and that through a key-hole. So I bid adieu to Canonbury Castle, merry Islington, and the haunts of poor Goldsmith, without having advanced a single line in my labors.

My next quarters were at a small, whitewashed cottage, which stands not far from Hampstead, just on the brow of a hill; looking over Chalk Farm and Camden Town, remarkable for the rival houses of Mother Red Cap and Mother Black Cap; and so across Crackskull Common to the distant city.

The cottage was in nowise remarkable in itself; but I regarded it with reverence, for it had been the asylum of a persecuted author. Hither poor Steele had retreated, and laid perdu, when persecuted by creditors and bailiffs—those immemorial plagues of authors and free-spirited gentlemen; and here he had written many numbers of the "Spectator." It was hence, too, that he had dispatched those little notes to his lady, so full of affection and whimsicality, in which the fond husband, the careless gentleman, and the shifting spendthrift, were so oddly blended. I thought, as I first eyed the window of his apartment, that I could sit within it and write volumes.

No such thing! It was haymaking season, and, as ill luck would have it, immediately opposite the cottage was a little alehouse, with the sign of the Load of Hay. Whether it was there in Steele's time, I cannot say; but it set all attempts at conception or inspiration at defiance. It was the resort of all the Irish haymakers who mow the broad fields in the neighborhood; and of drovers and teamsters who travel that road. Here they would gather in the endless summer twilight, or by the light of the harvest moon, and sit around a table at the door; and tipple, and laugh, and quarrel, and fight, and sing drowsy songs, and dawdle away the hours, until the deep solemn notes of St. Paul's clock would warn the varlets home.

In the daytime I was less able to write. It was broad summer. The haymakers were at work in the fields, and the perfume of the new-mown hay brought with it the recollection of my native fields. So instead of remaining in my room to write, I went wandering about Primrose Hill, and Hampstead Heights, and Shepherd's Fields, and all those Arcadian scenes so celebrated by London bards. I cannot tell you how many delicious hours I have passed, lying on the cocks of the new-mown hay, on the pleasant slopes of some of those hills, inhaling the fragrance of the fields, while the summer-fly buzzed about me, or the grasshopper leaped into my bosom; and how I have gazed with half-shut eye upon the smoky mass of London, and listened to the distant sound of its population, and pitied the poor sons of earth, toiling in its bowels, like Gnomes in the "dark goldmines."

People may say what they please about cockney pastorals, but, after all, there is a vast deal of rural beauty about the western vicinity of London; and any one that has looked down upon the valley of the West End, with its soft bosom of green pasturage lying open to the south, and dotted with cattle; the steeple of Hampstead rising among rich groves on the brow of the hill;

and the learned height of Harrow in the distance; will confess that never has he seen a more absolutely rural landscape in the vicinity of a great metropolis.

Still, however, I found myself not a whit the better off for my frequent change of lodgings; and I began to discover, that in literature, as in trade, the old proverb holds good, "a rolling stone gathers no moss."

The tranquil beauty of the country played the very vengeance with me. I could not mount my fancy into the termagant vein. I could not conceive, amidst the smiling landscape, a scene of blood and murder; and the smug citizens in breeches and gaiters put all ideas of heroes and bandits out of my brain. I could think of nothing but dulcet subjects, "the Pleasures of Spring"—"the Pleasures of Solitude"—"the Pleasures of Tranquillity"—"the Pleasures of Sentiment"—nothing but pleasures; and I had the painful experience of "the Pleasures of Melancholy" too strongly in my recollection to be beguiled by them.

Chance at length befriended me. I had frequently, in my ramblings, loitered about Hampstead Hill, which is a kind of Parnassus of the metropolis. At such times I occasionally took my dinner at Jack Straw's Castle. It is a country inn so named; the very spot where that notorious rebel and his followers held their council of war. It is a favorite resort of citizens when rurally inclined, as it commands fine fresh air, and a good view of the city. I sat one day in the public room of this inn, ruminating over a beefsteak and a pint of porter, when my imagination kindled up with ancient and heroic images. I had long wanted a theme and a hero; both suddenly broke upon my mind. I determined to write a poem on the history of Jack Straw. I was so full of the subject, that I was fearful of being anticipated. I wondered that none of the poets of the day in their search after ruffian heroes, had never thought of Jack Straw. I went to work pell-mell, blotted several sheets of paper with choice floating thoughts, and battles, and descriptions, to be ready at a moment's warning. In a few days' time I sketched out the skeleton of my poem, and nothing was wanting but to give it flesh and blood. I used to take my manuscript and stroll about Caen Wood, and read aloud; and would dine at the Castle, by way of keeping up the vein of thought.

I was there one day, at rather a late hour, in the public room.

There was no other company but one man, who sat enjoying his pint of porter at the window, and noticing the passers-by. He was dressed in a green shooting-coat. His countenance was strongly marked: he had a hooked nose; a romantic eye, excepting that it had something of a squint; and altogether, as I thought, a poetical style of head. I was quite taken with the man, for you must know I am a little of a physiognomist; I set him down at once for either a poet or a philosopher.

As I like to make new acquaintances, considering every man a volume of human nature, I soon fell into conversation with the stranger, who, I was pleased to find, was by no means difficult of access. After I had dined, I joined him at the window, and we became so sociable that I proposed a bottle of wine together, to which he most cheerfully assented.

I was too full of my poem to keep long quiet on the subject, and began to talk about the origin of the tavern, and the history of Jack Straw. I found my new acquaintance to be perfectly at home on the topic, and to jump exactly with my humor in every respect. I became elevated by the wine and the conversation. In the fulness of an author's feelings, I told him of my projected poem, and repeated some passages, and he was in raptures. He was evidently of a strong poetical turn.

"Sir," said he, filling my glass at the same time, "our poets don't look at home. I don't see why we need go out of old England for robbers and rebels to write about. I like your Jack Straw, sir—he's a home-made hero. I like him, sir—I like him exceedingly. He's English to the backbone—damme—Give me honest old England after all! Them's my sentiments, sir."

"I honor your sentiment," cried I, zealously; "it is exactly my own. An English ruffian is as good a ruffian for poetry as any in Italy, or Germany, or the Archipelago; but it is hard to make our poets think so."

"More shame for them!" replied the man in green. "What a plague would they have? What have we to do with their Archipelagos of Italy and Germany? Haven't we heaths and commons and highways on our own little island—ay, and stout fellows to pad the hoof over them too? Stick to home, I say—them's my sentiments.—Come, sir, my service to you—I agree with you perfectly."

"Poets, in old times, had right notions on this subject," continued I; "witness the fine old ballads about Robin Hood, Allan a'Dale, and other stanch blades of yore."

"Right, sir, right," interrupted he; "Robin Hood! he was the lad to cry stand! to a man, and never to flinch."

"Ah, sir," said I, "they had famous bands of robbers in the good old times; those were glorious poetical days. The merry crew of Sherwood Forest, who led such a roving picturesque life, 'under the greenwood tree.' I have often wished to visit their haunts, and tread the scenes of the exploits of Friar Tuck, and Clymm of the Clough, and Sir William of Cloudeslie."

"Nay, sir," said the gentleman in green, "we have had several very pretty gangs since that day. Those gallant dogs that kept about the great heaths in the neighborhood of London, about Bagshot, and Hounslow, and Blackheath, for instance. Come, sir, my service to you. You don't drink."

"I suppose," cried I, emptying my glass, "I suppose you have heard of the famous Turpin, who was born in this very village of Hampstead, and who used to lurk with his gang in Epping Forest about a hundred years since?"

"Have I?" cried he, "to be sure I have! A hearty old blade that. Sound as pitch. Old Turpentine! as we used to call him. A famous fine fellow, sir."

"Well, sir," continued I, "I have visited Waltham Abbey and Chingford Church merely from the stories I heard when a boy of his exploits there, and I have searched Epping Forest for the cavern where he used to conceal himself. You must know," added I, "that I am a sort of amateur of highwaymen. They were dashing daring fellows: the best apologies that we had for the knights-errant of yore. Ah, sir! the country has been sinking gradually into tameness and commonplace. We are losing the old English spirit. The bold knights of the Post have all dwindled down into lurking footpads, and sneaking pickpockets; there's no such thing as a dashing, gentleman-like robbery committed nowadays on the King's highway: a man may roll from one end of England to the other in a drowsy coach, or jingling post-chaise, without any other adventure than that of being occasionally overturned, sleeping in damp sheets, or having an ill-cooked dinner. We hear no more of public coaches being stopped and robbed by a well-mounted gang of resolute fellows, with pistols in their hands, and crapes over their faces. What a pretty poetical incident was it, for example, in domestic life, for a family-carriage, on its way to a country-seat, to be attacked about dark; the old gentleman eased of his purse and watch, the ladies of their necklaces and ear-rings, by a politely-spoken highwayman on a blood-mare, who afterwards leaped the hedge and galloped across the country, to the admiration of Miss Caroline, the daughter, who would write a long and romantic account of the adventure to her friend, Miss Juliana, in town. Ah, sir! we meet with nothing of such incidents nowadays."

"That, sir," said my companion, taking advantage of a pause, when I stopped to recover breath, and to take a glass of wine which he had just poured out, "that, sir, craving your pardon, is not owing to any want of old English pluck. It is the effect of this cursed system of banking. People do not travel with bags of gold as they did formerly. They have post-notes, and drafts on bankers. To rob a coach is like catching a crow, where you have nothing but carrion flesh and feathers for your pains. But a coach in old times, sir, was as rich as a Spanish galleon. It turned out the yellow boys bravely. And a private carriage was a cool hundred or two at least."

I cannot express how much I was delighted with the sallies of my new acquaintance. He told me that he often frequented the Castle, and would be glad to know more of me; and I proposed myself many a pleasant afternoon with him, when I should read him my poem as it proceeded, and benefit by his remarks; for it was evident he had the true poetical feeling.

"Come, sir," said he, pushing the bottle: "Damme, I like you! you're a man after my own heart. I'm cursed slow in making new acquaintances. One must be on the reserve, you know. But when I meet with a man of your kidney, damme, my heart jumps at once to him. Them's my sentiments, sir. Come, sir, here's Jack Straw's health! I presume one can drink it nowadays without treason!"

"With all my heart," said I, gayly, "and Dick Turpin's into the bargain!"

"Ah, sir," said the man in green, "those are the kind of men for poetry. The Newgate Calendar, sir! the Newgate Calendar is your only reading! There's the place to look for bold deeds and dashing fellows."

We were so much pleased with each other that we sat until a late hour. I insisted on paying the bill, for both my purse and my heart were full, and I agreed that he should pay the score at our next meeting. As the coaches had all gone that run between Hampstead and London, we had to return on foot. He was so delighted with the idea of my poem, that he could talk of nothing else. He made me repeat such passages as I could remember; and though I did it in a very mangled manner, having a wretched memory, yet he was in raptures.

Every now and then he would break out with some scrap which he would misquote most terribly, would rub his hands and exclaim, "By Jupiter, that's fine, that's noble! Damme, sir, if I can conceive how you hit upon such ideas!"

I must confess I did not always relish his misquotations, which sometimes made absolute nonsense of the passages; but what author stands upon trifles when he is praised?

Never had I spent a more delightful evening. I did not perceive how the time flew. I could not bear to separate, but continued walking on, arm in arm, with him, past my lodgings, through Camden Town, and across Crackskull Common, talking the whole way about my poem.

When we were half-way across the common, he interrupted me in the midst of a quotation, by telling me that this had been a famous place for footpads, and was still occasionally infested by them; and that a man had recently been shot there in attempting to defend himself. "The more fool he!" cried I; "a man is an idiot to risk life, or even limb, to save a paltry purse of money. It's quite a different case from that of a duel, where one's honor is concerned. For my part," added I, "I should never think of making resistance against one of those desperadoes."

"Say you so?" cried my friend in green, turning suddenly upon me, and putting a pistol to my breast; "why, then, have at you, my lad!—come—disburse! empty! unsack!"

In a word, I found that the muse had played me another of her tricks, and had betrayed me into the hands of a footpad. There was no time to parley; he made me turn my pockets inside out; and hearing the sound of distant footsteps, he made one fell swoop upon purse, watch, and all; gave me a thwack on my unlucky pate that laid me sprawling on the ground, and scampered away with his booty.

I saw no more of my friend in green until a year or two afterwards; when I caught sight of his poetical countenance among a crew of scapegraces heavily ironed, who were on the way for transportation. He recognized me at once, tipped me an impudent wink, and asked me how I came on with the history of Jack Straw's Castle.

The catastrophe at Crackskull Common put an end to my summer's campaign. I was cured of my poetical enthusiasm for rebels, robbers, and highwaymen. I was put out of conceit of my subject, and, what was worse, I was lightened of my purse, in which was almost every farthing I had in the world. So I abandoned Sir Richard Steele's cottage in despair, and crept into less celebrated, though no less poetical and airy lodgings in a garret in town.

I now determined to cultivate the society of the literary, and to enroll myself in the fraternity of authorship. It is by the constant collision of mind, thought I, that authors strike out the sparks of genius, and kindle up with glorious conceptions. Poetry is evidently a contagious complaint. I will keep company with poets; who knows but I may catch it as others have done?

I found no difficulty in making a circle of literary acquaintances, not having the sin of success lying at my door: indeed the failure of my poem was a kind of recommendation to their favor. It is true my new friends were not of the most brilliant names in literature; but then if you would take their words for it, they were like the prophets of old, men of whom the world was not worthy; and who were to live in future ages, when the ephemeral favorites of the day should be forgotten.

I soon discovered, however, that the more I mingled in literary society, the less I felt capable of writing; that poetry was not so catching as I imagined; and that in familiar life there was often nothing less poetical than a poet. Besides, I wanted the *esprit du corps* to turn these literary fellowships to any account. I could not bring myself to enlist in any particular sect. I saw something to like in them all, but found that would never do, for that the tacit condition on which a man enters into one of these sects is, that he abuses all the rest.

I perceived that there were little knots of authors who lived with, and for, and by one another. They considered themselves the salt of the earth. They fostered and kept up a conventional vein of thinking and talking, and joking on all subjects; and they cried each other up to the skies. Each sect had its particular creed; and set up certain authors as divinities, and fell down and worshipped them; and considered every one who did not worship them, or who worshipped any other, as a heretic, and an infidel.

In quoting the writers of the day, I generally found them extolling names of which I had scarcely heard, and talking slightingly of others who were the favorites of the public. If I mentioned any recent work from the pen of a first-rate author, they had not read it; they had not time to read all that was spawned from the press; he wrote too much to write well;—and then they would break out into raptures about some Mr. Timson, or Tomson, or Jackson, whose works were neglected at the present day, but who was to be the wonder and delight of posterity! Alas! what heavy debts is this neglectful world daily accumulating on the shoulders of poor posterity!

But, above all, it was edifying to hear with what contempt they would talk of the great. Ye gods! how immeasurably the great are despised by the small fry of literature! It is true, an exception was now and then made of some nobleman, with whom, perhaps, they had casually shaken hands at an election, or hob or nobbed at a public dinner, and was pronounced a "devilish good fellow," and "no humbug"; but, in general, it was enough for a man to have a title, to be the object of their sovereign disdain: you have no idea how poetically and philosophically they would talk of nobility.

For my part, this affected me but little; for though I had no bitterness against the great, and did not think the worse of a man for having innocently been born to a title, yet I did not feel myself at present called upon to resent the indignities poured upon them by the little. But the hostility to the great writers of the day went sore against the grain with me. I could not enter into such feuds, nor participate in such animosities. I had not become author sufficiently to hate other authors. I could still find pleasure in the novelties of the press, and could find it in my heart to praise a contemporary, even though he were successful. Indeed I was miscellaneous in my taste, and could not confine it to any age or growth of writers. I could turn with delight from the glowing pages of Byron to the cool and polished raillery of Pope; and after wandering among the sacred groves of "Paradise Lost," I could give myself up to voluptuous abandonment in the enchanted bowers of "Lalla Rookh."

"I would have my authors," said I, "as various as my wines, and, in relishing the strong and the racy, would never decry the sparkling and exhilarating. Port and Sherry are excellent standbys, and so is Madeira; but Claret and Burgundy may be drunk now and then without disparagement to one's palate, and Champagne is a beverage by no means to be despised."

Such was the tirade I uttered one day when a little flushed with ale at a literary club. I uttered it, too, with something of a flourish, for I thought my simile a clever one. Unluckily, my auditors were men who drank beer and hated Pope; so my figure about wines went for nothing, and my critical toleration was looked upon as downright heterodoxy. In a word, I soon became like a freethinker in religion, an outlaw from every sect, and fair game for all. Such are the melancholy consequences of not hating in literature.

I see you are growing weary, so I will be brief with the residue of my literary career. I will not detain you with a detail of my various attempts to get astride of Pegasus; of the poems I have written which were never printed, the plays I have presented which were never performed, and the tracts I have published which were never purchased. It seemed as if booksellers, managers, and the very public, had entered into a conspiracy to starve me. Still I could not prevail upon myself to give up the trial, nor abandon those dreams of renown in which I had indulged. How should I be able to look the literary circle of my native village in the face, if I were so completely to falsify their predictions? For some time longer, therefore, I continued to write for fame, and was, of course, the most miserable dog in existence, besides being in continual risk of starvation. I accumulated loads of literary treasure on my shelves—loads which were to be treasures to posterity; but, alas! they put not a penny into my purse. What was all this wealth to my present necessities? I could not patch my elbows with an ode; nor satisfy my hunger with blank verse. "Shall a man fill his belly with the east wind?" says the proverb. He may as well do so as with poetry.

I have many a time strolled sorrowfully along, with a sad heart and an empty stomach, about five o'clock, and looked wistfully down the areas in the west end of the town, and seen through the kitchen-windows the fires gleaming, and the joints of meat turning on the spits and dripping with gravy, and the cook-maids beating up puddings, or trussing turkeys, and felt for the moment that if I could but have the run of one of those kitchens, Apollo and the Muses might have the hungry heights of Parnassus for me. Oh, sir! talk of meditations among the tombs—they are nothing so melancholy as the meditations of a poor devil without penny in pouch, along a line of kitchen-windows towards dinner-time.

At length, when almost reduced to famine and despair, the idea all at once entered my head, that perhaps I was not so clever a fellow as the village and myself had supposed. It was the salvation of me. The moment the idea popped into my brain it brought conviction and comfort with it. I awoke as from a dream: I gave up immortal fame to those who could live on air; took to writing for mere bread; and have ever since had a very tolerable life of it. There is no man of letters so much at his ease, sir, as he who has no character to gain or lose. I had to train myself to it a little, and to clip my wings short at first, or they would have carried me up into poetry in spite of myself. So I determined to begin by the opposite extreme, and abandoning the higher regions of the craft, I came plump down to the lowest, and turned creeper.

"Creeper! and pray what is that?" said I.

"Oh, sir, I see you are ignorant of the language of the craft; a creeper is one who furnishes the newspapers with paragraphs at so much a line; and who goes about in quest of misfortunes; attends the Bow Street Office; the Courts of Justice, and every other den of mischief and iniquity. We are paid at the rate of a penny a line, and as we can sell the same paragraph to almost every paper, we sometimes pick up a very decent day's work. Now and then the Muse is unkind, or the day uncommonly quiet, and then we rather starve; and sometimes the unconscionable editors will clip our paragraphs when they are a little too rhetorical, and snip off twopence or threepence at a go. I have many a time had my pot of porter snipped off my dinner in this way, and have had to dine with dry lips. However, I cannot complain. I rose gradually in the lower ranks of the craft, and am now, I think, in the most comfortable region of literature."

"And pray," said I, "what may you be at present?"

"At present," said he, "I am a regular job-writer, and turn my hand to anything. I work up the writings of others at so much a sheet, turn off translations; write second-rate articles to fill up reviews and magazines; compile travels and voyages, and furnish theatrical criticisms for the newspapers. All this authorship, you perceive, is anonymous; it gives me no reputation, except among the trade; where I am considered an author of all work, and am always sure of employ. That's the only reputation I want. I sleep soundly, without dread of duns or critics, and leave immortal fame to those that choose to fret and fight about it. Take my word for it, the only happy author in this world is he who is below the care of reputation."

IV. From *The Alhambra*

Palace of the Alhambra

TO the traveller imbued with a feeling for the historical and poetical, so inseparably intertwined in the annals of romantic Spain, the Alhambra is as much an object of devotion as is the Caaba to all true Moslems. How many legends and traditions, true and fabulous—how many songs and ballads, Arabian and Spanish, of love and war and chivalry, are associated with this Oriental pile! It was the royal abode of the Moorish kings, where, surrounded with the splendors and refinements of Asiatic luxury, they held dominion over what they vaunted as a terrestrial paradise, and made their last stand for empire in Spain. The royal palace forms but a part of a fortress, the walls of which, studded with towers, stretch irregularly round the whole crest of a hill, a spur of the Sierra Nevada or Snowy Mountains, and overlook the city; externally it is a rude congregation of towers and battlements, with no regularity of plan nor grace of architecture, and giving little promise of the grace and beauty which prevail within.

In the time of the Moors the fortress was capable of containing within its outward precincts an army of forty thousand men, and served occasionally as a stronghold of the sovereigns against their rebellious subjects. After the kingdom had passed into the hands of the Christians, the Alhambra continued to be a royal demesne, and was occasionally inhabited by the Castilian monarchs. The emperor Charles V. commenced a sumptuous palace within its walls, but was deterred from completing it by repeated shocks of earthquakes. The last royal residents were Philip V. and his beautiful queen, Elizabetta of Parma, early in the eighteenth century. Great preparations were made for their reception. The palace and gardens were placed in a state of repair, and a new suite of apartments erected, and decorated by artists brought from Italy. The sojourn of the sovereigns was transient, and after their departure the palace once more became desolate. Still the place was maintained with some military state. The governor held it immediately from the crown, its jurisdiction extended down into the suburbs of the city, and was independent of the captain-general of Granada. A considerable garrison was kept up; the governor had his apartments in the front of the old Moorish palace, and never descended into Granada without some military parade. The fortress, in fact, was a little town of itself, having several streets of houses within its walls, together with a Franciscan convent and a parochial church.

The desertion of the court, however, was a fatal blow to the Alhambra. Its beautiful halls became desolate, and some of them fell to ruin; the gardens were destroyed, and the fountains ceased to play. By degrees the dwellings became filled with a loose and lawless population: contrabandistas, who availed themselves of its independent jurisdiction to carry on a wide and daring course of smuggling, and thieves and rogues of all sorts, who made this their place of refuge whence they might depredate upon Granada and its vicinity. The strong arm of government at length interfered; the whole community was thoroughly sifted; none were suffered to remain but such as were of honest character, and had legitimate right to a residence; the greater part of the houses were demolished and a mere hamlet left, with the parochial church and the Franciscan convent. During the recent troubles in Spain, when Granada was in the hands of the French, the Alhambra was garrisoned by their troops, and the palace was occasionally inhabited by the French commander. With that enlightened taste which has ever distinguished the French nation in their conquests, this monument of Moorish elegance and grandeur was rescued from the absolute ruin and desolation that were overwhelming it. The roofs were repaired, the saloons and galleries protected from the weather, the gardens cultivated, the watercourses restored, the fountains once more made to throw up their sparkling showers; and Spain may thank her invaders for having preserved to her the most beautiful and interesting of her historical monuments.

On the departure of the French they blew up several towers of the outer wall, and left the fortifications scarcely tenable. Since that time the military importance of the post is at an end. The garrison is a handful of invalid soldiers, whose principal duty is to guard some of the outer towers, which serve occasionally as a prison of state; and the governor, abandoning the lofty hill of the Alhambra, resides in the centre of Granada, for the more convenient dispatch of his official duties. I cannot conclude this brief notice of the state of the fortress without bearing testimony to the honorable exertions of its present commander, Don Francisco de Serna, who is tasking all the limited resources at his command to put the palace in a state of repair, and by his judicious precautions has for some time arrested its too certain decay. Had his predecessors discharged the duties of their station with equal fidelity, the Alhambra might yet have remained in almost its pristine beauty: were government to second him with means equal to his zeal, this relic of it might still be preserved for many generations to adorn the land, and attract the curious and enlightened of every clime.

Our first object of course, on the morning after our arrival, was a visit to this time-honored edifice; it has been so often, however, and so minutely described by travellers, that I shall not undertake to give a comprehensive and elaborate account of it, but merely occasional sketches of parts, with the incidents and associations connected with them.

Leaving our posada, and traversing the renowned square of the Vivarrambla, once the scene of Moorish jousts and tournaments, now a crowded market-place, we proceeded along the Zacatin, the main street of what, in the time of the Moors, was the Great Bazaar, and where small shops and narrow alleys still retain the Oriental character. Crossing an open place in front of the palace of the captain-general, we ascended a confined and winding street, the name of which reminded us of the chivalric days of Granada. It is called the Calle, or street of the Gomeres, from a Moorish family famous in chronicle and song. This street led up to the Puerta de las Granadas, a massive gateway of Grecian architecture, built by Charles V., forming the entrance to the domains of the Alhambra.

At the gate were two or three ragged superannuated soldiers, dozing on a stone bench, the successors of the Zegris and the Abencerrages; while a tall, meagre varlet, whose rusty-brown cloak was evidently intended to conceal the ragged state of his nether garments, was lounging in the sunshine and gossiping with an ancient sentinel on duty. He joined us as we entered the gate, and offered his services to show us the fortress.

I have a traveller's dislike to officious ciceroni, and did not altogether like the garb of the applicant.

"You are well acquainted with the place, I presume?"

"Ninguno mas; pues señor, soy hijo de la Alhambra."—(Nobody better; in fact, sir, I am a son of the Alhambra!)

The common Spaniards have certainly a most poetical way of expressing themselves. "A son of the Alhambra!" the appellation caught me at once; the very tattered garb of my new acquaintance assumed a dignity in my eyes. It was emblematic of the fortunes of the place, and befitted the progeny of a ruin.

I put some further questions to him, and found that his title was legitimate. His family had lived in the fortress from generation to generation ever since the time of the Conquest. His name was Mateo Ximenes. "Then, perhaps," said I, "you may be a descendant from the great Cardinal Ximenes?"—"Dios Sabe! God knows, Señor! It may be so. We are the oldest family in the Alhambra—*Christianos Viejos*, old Christians, without any taint of Moor or Jew. I know we belong to some great family or other, but I forget whom. My father knows all about it: he has the coat of arms hanging up in his cottage, up in the fortress." There is not any Spaniard, however poor, but has some claim to high pedigree. The first title of this ragged worthy, however, had completely captivated me; so I gladly accepted the services of the "son of the Alhambra."

We now found ourselves in a deep narrow ravine, filled with beautiful groves, with a steep avenue, and various footpaths winding through it, bordered with stone seats, and ornamented with fountains. To our left we beheld the towers of the Alhambra beetling above us; to our right, on the opposite side of the ravine, we were equally dominated by rival towers on a rocky eminence. These, we were told, were the Torres Vermejos, or vermilion towers, so called from their ruddy hue. No one knows their origin. They are of a date much anterior to the Alhambra: some suppose them to have been built by the Romans; others, by some wandering colony of Phœnicians. Ascending the steep and shady avenue, we arrived at the foot of a huge square Moorish tower, forming a kind of barbican, through which passed the main entrance to the fortress. Within the barbican was another group of veteran invalids, one mounting guard at the portal, while the rest, wrapped in their tattered cloaks, slept on the stone benches. This portal is called the Gate of Justice, from the tribunal held within its porch during the Moslem domination, for the immediate trial of petty causes: a custom common to the Oriental nations, and occasionally alluded to in the Sacred Scriptures. "Judges and officers shalt thou make thee *in all thy gates*, and they shall judge the people with just judgment."

The great vestibule, or porch of the gate, is formed by an immense Arabian arch, of the horseshoe form, which springs to half the height of the tower. On the keystone of this arch is engraven a gigantic hand. Within the vestibule, on the keystone of the portal, is sculptured, in like manner, a gigantic key. Those who pretend to some knowledge of Mohammedan symbols, affirm that the hand is the emblem of doctrine; the five fingers designating the five principal commandments of the creed of Islam, fasting, pilgrimage, alms-giving, ablution, and war against infidels. The key, say they, is the emblem of the faith or of power; the key of Daoud, or David, transmitted to the prophet. "And the key of the house of David will I lay upon his shoulder; so he shall open and none shall shut, and he shall shut and none shall open." (Isaiah xxii. 22.) The key we are told was emblazoned on the standard of the Moslems in opposition to the Christian emblem of the cross, when they subdued Spain or Andalusia. It betokened the conquering power invested in the prophet. "He that hath the key of David, he that openeth and no man shutteth; and shutteth and no man openeth." (Rev. iii. 7.)

A different explanation of these emblems, however, was given by the legitimate son of the Alhambra, and one more in unison with the notions of the common people, who attach something of mystery and magic to everything Moorish, and have all kinds of superstitions connected with this old Moslem fortress. According to Mateo, it was a tradition handed down from the oldest inhabitants, and which he had from his father and grandfather, that the hand and key were magical devices on which the fate of the Alhambra depended. The Moorish king who built it was a great magician, or, as some believed, had sold himself to the devil, and had laid the whole fortress under a magic spell. By this means it had remained standing for several years, in defiance of storms and earthquakes, while almost all other buildings of the Moors had fallen to ruin and disappeared. This spell, the tradition went on to say, would last until the hand on the outer arch should reach down and grasp the key, when the whole pile would tumble to pieces, and all the treasures buried beneath it by the Moors would be revealed.

Notwithstanding this ominous prediction, we ventured to pass through the spell-bound gateway, feeling some little assurance against magic art in the protection of the Virgin, a statue of whom we observed above the portal.

After passing through the barbican, we ascended a narrow lane, winding between walls, and came on an open esplanade within the fortress, called the Plaza de los Algibes, or Place of the Cisterns, from great reservoirs which undermine it, cut in the living rock by the Moors to receive the water brought by conduits from the Darro, for the supply of the fortress. Here, also, is a well of immense depth, furnishing the purest and coldest of water—another monument of the delicate taste of the Moors, who were indefatigable in their exertions to obtain that element in its crystal purity.

In front of this esplanade is the splendid pile commenced by Charles V., and intended, it is said, to eclipse the residence of the Moorish kings. Much of the Oriental edifice intended for the winter season was demolished to make way for this massive pile. The grand entrance was blocked up; so that the present entrance to the Moorish palace is through a simple and almost humble portal in a corner. With all the massive grandeur and architectural merit of the palace of Charles V., we regarded it as an arrogant intruder, and passing by it with a feeling almost of scorn, rang at the Moslem portal.

While waiting for admittance, our self-imposed cicerone, Mateo Ximenes, informed us that the royal palace was intrusted to the care of a worthy old maiden dame called Doña Antonia-Molina, but who, according to Spanish custom, went by the more neighborly appellation of Tia Antonia (Aunt Antonia), who maintained the Moorish halls and gardens in order and showed them to strangers. While we were talking, the door was opened by a plump little black-eyed Andalusian damsel, whom Mateo addressed as Dolores, but who from her bright looks and cheerful disposition evidently merited a merrier name. Mateo informed me in a whisper that she was the niece of Tia Antonia, and I found she was the good fairy who was to conduct us through the enchanted palace. Under her guidance we crossed the threshold, and were at once transported, as if by magic wand, into other times and an oriental realm, and were treading the scenes of Arabian story. Nothing could be in greater contrast than the unpromising exterior of the pile with the scene now before us. We found ourselves in a vast patio or court, one hundred and fifty feet in length, and upwards of eighty feet in breadth, paved with white marble, and decorated at each end with light Moorish peristyles, one of which supported an elegant gallery of fretted architecture. Along the mouldings of the cornices and on various parts of the walls were escutcheons and ciphers, and cufic and Arabic characters in high relief, repeating the pious mottoes of the Moslem monarchs, the builders of the Alhambra, or extolling their grandeur and munificence. Along the centre of the court extended an immense basin or tank (estanque), a hundred and twenty-four feet in length, twenty-seven in breadth, and five in depth, receiving its water from two marble vases. Hence it is called the Court of the Alberca (from al Beerkah, the Arabic for a pond or tank). Great numbers of gold-fish were to be seen gleaming through the waters of the basin, and it was bordered by hedges of roses.

Passing from the court of the Alberca under a Moorish archway, we entered the renowned court of Lions. No part of the edifice gives a more complete idea of its original beauty than this, for none has suffered so little from the ravages of time. In the centre stands the fountain famous in song and story. The alabaster basins still shed their diamond drops; the twelve lions which support them, and give the court its name, still cast forth crystal streams as in the days of Boabdil. The lions, however, are unworthy of their fame, being of miserable sculpture, the work probably of some Christian captive. The court is laid out in flower-beds, instead of its ancient and appropriate pavement of tiles or marble; the alteration, an instance of bad taste, was made by the French when in possession of Granada. Round the four sides of the court are light Arabian arcades of open filigree work, supported by slender pillars of white marble, which it is supposed were originally gilded. The architecture, like that in most parts of the interior of the palace, is characterized by elegance rather than grandeur, bespeaking a delicate and graceful taste, and a disposition to indolent enjoyment. When one looks upon the fairy traces of the peristyles, and the apparently fragile fret-work of the walls, it is difficult to believe that so much has survived the wear and tear of centuries, the shocks of earthquakes, the violence of war, and the quiet, though no less baneful, pilferings of the tasteful traveller: it is almost sufficient to excuse the popular tradition, that the whole is protected by a magic charm.

On one side of the court a rich portal opens into the Hall of the Abencerrages: so called from the gallant cavaliers of that illustrious line who were here perfidiously massacred. There are some who doubt the whole story, but our humble cicerone Mateo pointed out the very wicket of the portal through which they were introduced one by one into the court of Lions, and the white marble fountain in the centre of the hall beside which they were beheaded. He showed us also certain broad ruddy stains on the pavement, traces of their blood, which, according to popular belief, can never be effaced.

Finding we listened to him apparently with easy faith, he added, that there was often heard at night, in the court of Lions, a low confused sound, resembling the murmuring of a multitude, and now and then a faint tinkling, like the distant clank of chains. These sounds were made by the spirits of the murdered Abencerrages; who nightly haunt the scene of their suffering and invoke the vengeance of Heaven on their destroyer.

The sounds in question had no doubt been produced, as I had afterwards an opportunity of ascertaining, by the bubbling currents and tinkling falls of water conducted under the pavement through pipes and channels to supply the fountains; but I was too considerate to intimate such an idea to the humble chronicler of the Alhambra.

Encouraged by my easy credulity, Mateo gave me the following as an undoubted fact, which he had from his grandfather:—

There was once an invalid soldier, who had charge of the Alhambra to show it to strangers; as he was one evening, about twilight, passing through the court of Lions, he heard footsteps on the Hall of the Abencerrages; supposing some strangers to be lingering there, he advanced to attend upon them, when to his astonishment he beheld four Moors richly dressed, with gilded cuirasses and cimeters, and poniards glittering with precious stones. They were walking to and fro, with solemn pace; but paused and beckoned to him. The old soldier, however, took to flight, and could never afterwards be prevailed upon to enter the Alhambra. Thus it is that men sometimes turn their backs upon fortune; for it is the firm opinion of Mateo, that the Moors intended to reveal the place where their treasures lay buried. A successor to the invalid soldier was more knowing; he came to the Alhambra poor; but at the end of a year went off to Malaga, bought houses, set up a carriage, and still lives there, one of the richest as well as oldest men of the place; all which, Mateo sagely surmised, was in consequence of his finding out the golden secret of these phantom Moors.

I now perceived I had made an invaluable acquaintance in this son of the Alhambra, one who knew all the apocryphal history of the place, and firmly believed in it, and whose memory was stuffed with a kind of knowledge for which I have a lurking fancy, but which is too apt to be considered rubbish by less indulgent philosophers. I determined to cultivate the acquaintance of this learned Theban.

Immediately opposite the hall of the Abencerrages, a portal, richly adorned, leads into a hall of less tragical associations. It is light and lofty, exquisitely graceful in its architecture, paved with white marble, and bears the suggestive name of the Hall of the Two Sisters. Some destroy the romance of the name by attributing it to two enormous slabs of alabaster which lie side by side, and form a great part of the pavement: an opinion strongly supported by Mateo Ximenes. Others are disposed to give the name a more poetical significance, as the vague memorial of Moorish beauties who once graced this hall, which was evidently a part of the royal harem. This opinion I was happy to find entertained by our little bright-eyed guide, Dolores, who pointed to a balcony over an inner porch, which gallery, she had been told, belonged to the women's apartment. "You see, señor," said she, "it is all grated and latticed, like the gallery in a convent chapel where the nuns hear mass; for the Moorish kings," added she, indignantly, "shut up their wives just like nuns."

The latticed "jalousies," in fact, still remain, whence the dark-eyed beauties of the harem might gaze unseen upon the zambras and other dances and entertainments of the hall below.

On each side of this hall are recesses or alcoves for ottomans and couches, on which the voluptuous lords of the Alhambra indulged in that dreamy repose so dear to the Orientalists. A cupola or lantern admits a tempered light from above and a free circulation of air; while on one side is heard the refreshing sound of waters from the fountain of the lions, and on the other side the soft plash from the basin in the garden of Lindaraxa.

It is impossible to contemplate this scene, so perfectly Oriental, without feeling the early associations of Arabian romance, and almost expecting to see the white arm of some mysterious princess beckoning from the gallery, or some dark eye sparkling through the lattice. The abode of beauty is here as if it had been inhabited but yesterday; but where are the two sisters, where the Zoraydas and Lindaraxas!

An abundant supply of water, brought from the mountains by old Moorish aqueducts, circulates throughout the palace, supplying its baths and fish-pools, sparkling in jets within its halls or murmuring in channels along the marble pavements. When it has paid its tribute to the royal pile, and visited its gardens and parterres, it flows down the long avenue leading to the city, tinkling in rills, gushing in fountains, and maintaining a perpetual verdure in those groves that embower and beautify the whole hill of the Alhambra.

Those only who have sojourned in the ardent climates of the South can appreciate the delights of an abode combining the breezy coolness of the mountain with the freshness and verdure of the valley. While the city below pants with the noontide heat, and the parched Vega trembles to the eye, the delicate airs from the Sierra Nevada play through these lofty halls, bringing with them the sweetness of the surrounding gardens. Everything invites to that indolent repose, the bliss of southern climes; and while the half-shut eye looks out from shaded balconies upon the glittering landscape, the ear is lulled by the rustling of groves and the murmur of running streams. . . .

Inhabitants of the Alhambra

I HAVE often observed that the more proudly a mansion has been tenanted in the day of its prosperity, the humbler are its inhabitants in the day of its decline, and that the palace of a king commonly ends in being the nestling-place of the beggar.

The Alhambra is in a rapid state of similar transition. Whenever a tower falls to decay, it is seized upon by some tatterdemalion family, who become joint-tenants, with the bats and owls, of its gilded halls; and hang their rags, those standards of poverty, out of its windows and loopholes.

I have amused myself with remarking some of the motley characters that have thus usurped the ancient abode of royalty, and who seem as if placed here to give a farcical termination to the drama of human pride. One of these even bears the mockery of a regal title. It is a little old woman named Maria Antonia Sabonea, but who goes by the appellation of la Reyna Coquina, or the Cockle-queen. She is small enough to be a fairy; and a fairy she may be for aught I can find out, for no one seems to know her origin. Her habitation is in a kind of closet under the outer staircase of the palace, and she sits in the cool stone corridor, plying her needle and singing from morning till night, with a ready joke for every one that passes; for though one of the poorest, she is one of the merriest little women breathing. Her great merit is a gift for story-telling, having, I verily believe, as many stories at her command as the inexhaustible Scheherezade of the Thousand and One Nights. Some of these I have heard her relate in the evening tertulias of Dame Antonia, at which she is occasionally a humble attendant.

That there must be some fairy gift about this mysterious little old woman, would appear from her extraordinary luck, since, notwithstanding her being very little, very ugly, and very poor, she has had, according to her own account, five husbands and a half, reckoning as a half one a young dragoon, who died during courtship. A rival personage to this little fairy queen is a portly old fellow with a bottle-nose, who goes about in a rusty garb, with a cocked hat of oil-skin and a red cockade. He is one of the legitimate sons of the Alhambra, and has lived here all his life, filling various offices, such as deputy alguazil, sexton of the parochial church, and marker of a fives-court, established at the foot of one of the towers. He is as poor as a rat, but as proud as he is ragged, boasting of his descent from the illustrious house of Aguilar, from which sprang Gonzalvo of Cordova, the grand captain. Nay, he actually bears the name of Alonzo de Aguilar, so renowned in the history of the Conquest; though the graceless wags of the fortress have given him the title of *el padre santo*, or the holy father, the usual appellation of the Pope, which I had thought too sacred in the eyes of true Catholics to be thus ludicrously applied. It is a whimsical caprice of fortune to present, in the grotesque person of this tatterdemalion, a namesake and descendant of the proud Alonzo de Aguilar, the mirror of Andalusian chivalry, leading an almost mendicant existence about this once haughty fortress, which his ancestor aided to reduce; yet such might have been the lot of the descendants of Agamemnon and Achilles, had they lingered about the ruins of Troy!

Of this motley community, I find the family of my gossiping squire, Mateo Ximenes, to form, from their numbers at least, a very important part. His boast of being a son of the Alhambra is not unfounded. His family has inhabited the fortress ever since the time of the Conquest, handing down an hereditary poverty from father to son; not one of them having ever been known to be worth a maravedi. His father, by trade a ribbon-weaver, and who succeeded the historical tailor as the head of the family, is now near seventy years of age, and lives in a hovel of reeds and plaster, built by his own hands, just above the iron gate. The furniture consists of a crazy bed, a table, and two or three chairs; a wooden chest, containing, besides his scanty clothing, the "archives of the family." These are nothing more nor less than the papers of various lawsuits sustained by different generations; by which it would seem that, with all their apparent carelessness and good-humor, they are a litigious brood. Most of the suits have been brought against gossiping neighbors for questioning the purity of their blood, and denying their being *Christianos viejos*, *i. e.* old Christians, without Jewish or Moorish taint. In fact, I doubt whether this jealousy about their blood has not kept them so poor in purse: spending all their earnings on escribanos and alguazils. The pride of the hovel is an escutcheon suspended against the wall, in which are emblazoned quarterings of the arms of the Marquis of Caiesedo, and of various other noble houses, with which this poverty-stricken brood claim affinity.

As to Mateo himself, who is now about thirty-five years of age, he has done his utmost to perpetuate his line and continue the poverty of the family, having a wife and a numerous progeny, who inhabit an almost dismantled hovel in the hamlet. How they manage to subsist, he only who sees into all mysteries can tell; the subsistence of a Spanish family of the kind is always a riddle to me; yet they do subsist, and what is more, appear to enjoy their existence. The wife takes her holiday stroll on the Paseo of Granada, with a child in her arms and half a dozen at her heels; and the eldest daughter, now verging into womanhood, dresses her hair with flowers, and dances gayly to the castanets.

There are two classes of people to whom life seems one long holiday—the very rich and the very poor; one, because they need do nothing; the other, because they have nothing to do; but there are none who understand the art of doing nothing and living upon nothing, better than the poor classes of Spain. Climate does one half, and temperament the rest. Give a Spaniard the shade in summer and the sun in winter, a little bread, garlic, oil, and garbances, an old brown cloak and a guitar, and let the world roll on as it pleases. Talk of poverty! with him it has no disgrace. It sits upon him with a grandiose style, like his ragged cloak. He is a hidalgo, even when in rags.

The "sons of the Alhambra" are an eminent illustration of this practical philosophy. As the Moors imagined that the celestial paradise hung over this favored spot, so I am inclined at times to fancy that a gleam of the golden age still lingers about this ragged community. They possess nothing, they do nothing, they care for nothing. Yet, though apparently idle all the week, they are as observant of all holy days and saints' days as the most laborious artisan. They attend all fêtes and dancings in Granada and its vicinity, light bonfires on the hills on St. John's eve, and dance away the moonlight nights on the harvest-home of a small field within the precincts of the fortress, which yield a few bushels of wheat.

Before concluding these remarks, I must mention one of the

amusements of the place, which has particularly struck me. I had repeatedly observed a long lean fellow perched on the top of one of the towers, manœuvring two or three fishing-rods, as though he were angling for the stars. I was for some time perplexed by the evolutions of this aërial fisherman, and my perplexity increased on observing others employed in like manner on different parts of the battlements and bastions; it was not until I consulted Mateo Ximenes that I solved the mystery.

It seems that the pure and airy situation of this fortress has rendered it, like the castle of Macbeth, a prolific breeding-place for swallows and martlets, who sport about its towers in myriads, with the holiday glee of urchins just let loose from school. To entrap these birds in their giddy circlings, with hooks baited with flies, is one of the favorite amusements of the ragged "sons of the Alhambra," who, with the good-for-nothing ingenuity of arrant idlers, have thus invented the art of angling in the sky.

The Hall of Ambassadors

IN one of my visits to the old Moorish chamber where the good Tia Antonia cooks her dinner and receives her company, I observed a mysterious door in one corner, leading apparently into the ancient part of the edifice. My curiosity being aroused, I opened it, and found myself in a narrow, blind corridor, groping along which I came to the head of a dark winding staircase, leading down an angle of the tower of Comares. Down this staircase I descended darkling, guiding myself by the wall until I came to a small door at the bottom, throwing which open, I was suddenly dazzled by emerging into the brilliant antechamber of the Hall of Ambassadors; with the fountain of the court of the Alberca sparkling before me. The antechamber is separated from the court by an elegant gallery, supported by slender columns with spandrels of open work in the Morisco style. At each end of the antechamber are alcoves, and its ceiling is richly stuccoed and painted. Passing through a magnificent portal, I found myself in the far-famed Hall of Ambassadors, the audience chamber of the Moslem monarchs. It is said to be thirty-seven feet square, and sixty feet high; occupies the whole interior of the Tower of Comares; and still bears the traces of past magnificence. The walls are beautifully stuccoed and decorated with Morisco fancifulness; the lofty ceiling was originally of the same favorite material, with the usual frostwork and pensile ornaments or stalactites; which, with the embellishments of vivid coloring and gilding, must have been gorgeous in the extreme. Unfortunately it gave way during an earthquake, and brought down with it an immense arch which traversed the hall. It was replaced by the present vault or dome of larch or cedar, with intersecting ribs, the whole curiously wrought and richly colored; still Oriental in its character, reminding one of "those ceilings of cedar and vermilion that we read of in the Prophets and the Arabian Nights." *

From the great height of the vault above the windows, the upper part of the hall is almost lost in obscurity; yet there is a

* Urquhart's *Pillars of Hercules.*

magnificence as well as solemnity in the gloom, as through it we have gleams of rich gilding and the brilliant tints of the Moorish pencil.

The royal throne was placed opposite the entrance in a recess, which still bears an inscription intimating that Yusef I. (the monarch who completed the Alhambra) made this the throne of his empire. Everything in this noble hall seems to have been calculated to surround the throne with impressive dignity and splendor; there was none of the elegant voluptuousness which reigns in other parts of the palace. The tower is of massive strength, domineering over the whole edifice and overhanging the steep hillside. On three sides of the Hall of Ambassadors are windows cut through the immense thickness of the walls and commanding extensive prospects. The balcony of the central window especially looks down upon the verdant valley of the Darro, with its walks, its groves, and gardens. To the left it enjoys a distant prospect of the Vega; while directly in front rises the rival height of the Albaycin, with its medley of streets, and terraces, and gardens, and once crowned by a fortress that vied in power with the Alhambra. "Ill fated the man who lost all this!" exclaimed Charles V., as he looked forth from this window upon the enchanting scenery it commands.

The balcony of the window where this royal exclamation was made has of late become one of my favorite resorts. I have just been seated there, enjoying the close of a long brilliant day. The sun, as he sank behind the purple mountains of Alhama, sent a stream of effulgence up the valley of the Darro, that spread a melancholy pomp over the ruddy towers of the Alhambra; while the Vega, covered with a slight sultry vapor that caught the setting ray, seemed spread out in the distance like a golden sea. Not a breath of air disturbed the stillness of the hour, and though the faint sound of music and merriment now and then rose from the gardens of the Darro, it but rendered more impressive the monumental silence of the pile which overshadowed me. It was one of those hours and scenes in which memory asserts an almost magical power: and, like the evening sun beaming on these mouldering towers, sends back her retrospective rays to light up the glories of the past.

As I sat watching the effect of the declining daylight upon

this Moorish pile, I was led into a consideration of the light, elegant, and voluptuous character prevalent throughout its internal architecture, and to contrast it with the grand but gloomy solemnity of the Gothic edifices reared by the Spanish conquerors. The very architecture thus bespeaks the opposite and irreconcilable natures of the two warlike people who so long battled here for the mastery of the Peninsula. By degrees I fell into a course of musing upon the singular fortunes of the Arabian or Morisco-Spaniards, whose whole existence is as a tale that is told, and certainly forms one of the most anomalous yet splendid episodes in history. Potent and durable as was their dominion, we scarcely know how to call them. They were a nation without a legitimate country or name. A remote wave of the great Arabian inundation, cast upon the shores of Europe, they seem to have all the impetus of the first rush of the torrent. Their career of conquest, from the rock of Gibraltar to the cliffs of the Pyrenees, was as rapid and brilliant as the Moslem victories of Syria and Egypt. Nay, had they not been checked on the plains of Tours, all France, all Europe, might have been overrun with the same facility as the empires of the East, and the Crescent at this day have glittered on the fanes of Paris and London.

Repelled within the limits of the Pyrenees, the mixed hordes of Asia and Africa, that formed this great irruption, gave up the Moslem principle of conquest, and sought to establish in Spain a peaceful and permanent dominion. As conquerors, their heroism was only equalled by their moderation; and in both, for a time, they excelled the nations with whom they contended. Severed from their native homes, they loved the land given them as they supposed by Allah, and strove to embellish it with everything that could administer to the happiness of man. Laying the foundations of their power in a system of wise and equitable laws, diligently cultivating the arts and sciences, and promoting agriculture, manufactures, and commerce, they gradually formed an empire unrivalled for its prosperity by any of the empires of Christendom; and diligently drawing round them the graces and refinements which marked the Arabian empire in the East, at the time of its greatest civilization, they diffused the light of Oriental knowledge through the western regions of benighted Europe.

The cities of Arabian Spain became the resort of Christian artisans, to instruct themselves in the useful arts. The universities of Toledo, Cordova, Seville, and Granada were sought by the pale student from other lands to acquaint himself with the sciences of the Arabs and the treasured lore of antiquity; the lovers of the gay science resorted to Cordova and Granada, to imbibe the poetry and music of the East; and the steel-clad warriors of the North hastened thither to accomplish themselves in the graceful exercises and courteous usages of chivalry.

If the Moslem monuments in Spain, if the Mosque of Cordova, the Alcazar of Seville, and the Alhambra of Granada, still bear inscriptions fondly boasting of the power and permanency of their dominion, can the boast be derided as arrogant and vain? Generation after generation, century after century, passed away, and still they maintained possession of the land. A period elapsed longer than that which has passed since England was subjugated by the Norman Conqueror, and the descendants of Musa and Taric might as little anticipate being driven into exile across the same straits, traversed by their triumphant ancestors, as the descendants of Rollo and William, and their veteran peers, may dream of being driven back to the shores of Normandy.

With all this, however, the Moslem empire in Spain was but a brilliant exotic, that took no permanent root in the soil it embellished. Severed from all their neighbors in the West by impassable barriers of faith and manners, and separated by seas and deserts from their kindred of the East, the Morisco-Spaniards were an isolated people. Their whole existence was a prolonged, though gallant and chivalric struggle for a foothold in a usurped land.

They were the outposts and frontiers of Islamism. The Peninsula was the great battle-ground where the Gothic conquerors of the North and the Moslem conquerors of the East met and strove for mastery; and the fiery courage of the Arab was at length subdued by the obstinate and persevering valor of the Goth.

Never was the annihilation of a people more complete than that of the Morisco-Spaniards. Where are they? Ask the shores of Barbary and its desert places. The exiled remnant of their once powerful empire disappeared among the barbarians of

Africa, and ceased to be a nation. They have not even left a distinct name behind them, though for nearly eight centuries they were a distinct people. The home of their adoption, and of their occupation for ages, refuses to acknowledge them, except as invaders and usurpers. A few broken monuments are all that remain to bear witness to their power and dominion, as solitary rocks, left far in the interior, bear testimony to the extent of some vast inundation. Such is the Alhambra—a Moslem pile in the midst of a Christian land; an Oriental palace amidst the Gothic edifices of the West; an elegant memento of a brave, intelligent, and graceful people, who conquered, ruled, flourished, and passed away.

The Mysterious Chambers

AS I was rambling one day about the Moorish halls, my attention was, for the first time, attracted to a door in a remote gallery, communicating apparently with some part of the Alhambra which I had not yet explored. I attempted to open it, but it was locked. I knocked, but no one answered, and the sound seemed to reverberate through empty chambers. Here then was a mystery. Here was the haunted wing of the castle. How was I to get at the dark secrets here shut up from the public eye? Should I come privately at night with lamp and sword, according to the prying custom of heroes of romance; or should I endeavor to draw the secret from Pépe the stuttering gardener; or the ingenuous Dolores, or the loquacious Mateo? Or should I go frankly and openly to Dame Antonia the chatelaine, and ask her all about it? I chose the latter course, as being the simplest though the least romantic; and found, somewhat to my disappointment, that there was no mystery in the case. I was welcome to explore the apartment, and there was the key.

Thus provided, I returned forthwith to the door. It opened, as I had surmised, to a range of vacant chambers; but they were quite different from the rest of the palace. The architecture, though rich and antiquated, was European. There was nothing Moorish about it. The first two rooms were lofty; the ceilings, broken in many places, were of cedar, deeply panelled and skilfully carved with fruits and flowers, intermingled with grotesque masks or faces.

The walls had evidently in ancient times been hung with damask; but now were naked, and scrawled over by that class of aspiring travellers who defile noble monuments with their worthless names. The windows, dismantled and open to wind and weather, looked out into a charming little secluded garden, where an alabaster fountain sparkled among roses and myrtles, and was surrounded by orange and citron trees, some of which flung their branches into the chambers. Beyond these rooms were two saloons, longer but less lofty, looking also into the garden. In the compartments of the panelled ceilings were baskets of fruit and garlands of flowers, painted by no mean hand, and in tolerable preservation. The walls also had been painted in fresco in the Italian style, but the paintings were nearly obliterated; the windows were in the same shattered state with those of the other chambers. This fanciful suite of rooms terminated in an open gallery with balustrades, running at right angles along another side of the garden. The whole apartment, so delicate and elegant in its decorations, so choice and sequestered in its situation along this retired little garden, and so different in architecture from the neighboring halls, awakened an interest in its history. I found on inquiry that it was an apartment fitted up by Italian artists in the early part of the last century, at the time when Philip V. and his second wife, the beautiful Elizabetta of Farnese, daughter of the Duke of Parma, were expected at the Alhambra. It was destined for the queen and the ladies of her train. One of the loftiest chambers had been her sleeping-room. A narrow staircase, now walled up, led up to a delightful belvidere, originally a mirador of the Moorish sultanas, communicating with the harem; but which was fitted up as a boudoir for the fair Elizabetta, and still retains the name of *el tocador de la Reyna*, or the queen's toilette.

One window of the royal sleeping-room commanded a prospect of the Generalife and its embowered terraces; another looked out into the little secluded garden I have mentioned, which was decidedly Moorish in its character, and also had its history. It was in fact the garden of Lindaraxa, so often mentioned in descriptions of the Alhambra, but who this Lindaraxa was I had never heard explained. A little research gave me the few particulars known about her. She was a Moorish beauty who flourished in the court of Muhamed the Left-Handed, and was the daughter of his loyal adherent, the alcayde of Malaga, who sheltered him in his city when driven from the throne. On regaining his crown, the alcayde was rewarded for his fidelity. His daughter had her apartment in the Alhambra, and was given by the king in marriage to Nasar, a young Cetimerien prince descended from Aben Hud the Just. Their espousals were doubtless celebrated in the royal palace, and their honeymoon may have passed among these very bowers.*

* Una de las cosas en que tienen precisa intervencion los Reyes Moros as en el matrimonio de sus grandes: de aqui nace que todos los señores llegadas

Four centuries had elapsed since the fair Lindaraxa passed away, yet how much of the fragile beauty of the scenes she inhabited remained! The garden still bloomed in which she delighted; the fountain still presented the crystal mirror in which her charms may once have been reflected; the alabaster, it is true, had lost its whiteness; the basin beneath, overrun with weeds, had become the lurking-place of the lizard, but there was something in the very decay that enhanced the interest of the scene, speaking as it did of that mutability, the irrevocable lot of man and all his works.

The desolation too of these chambers, once the abode of the proud and elegant Elizabetta, had a more touching charm for me than if I had beheld them in their pristine splendor, glittering with the pageantry of a court.

When I returned to my quarters, in the governor's apartment, everything seemed tame and commonplace after the poetic region I had left. The thought suggested itself: Why could I not change my quarters to these vacant chambers? that would indeed be living in the Alhambra, surrounded by its gardens and fountains, as in the time of the Moorish sovereigns. I proposed the change to Dame Antonia and her family, and it occasioned vast surprise. They could not conceive any rational inducement for the choice of an apartment so forlorn, remote, and solitary. Dolores exclaimed at its frightful loneliness; nothing but bats and owls flitting about—and then a fox and wildcat kept in the vaults of the neighboring baths, and roamed about at night. The good Tia had more reasonable objections. The neighborhood was infested by vagrants; gipsies swarmed in the caverns of the adjacent hills; the palace was ruinous and easy to be entered in many places; the rumor of a stranger quartered alone in one of the remote and ruined apartments, out of the hearing of the rest of the inhabitants, might tempt unwelcome visitors in the night, especially as foreigners were always supposed to be well stocked with money. I was not to be diverted from my humor, however,

à la persona real si casan en palacio, y siempre huvo su quarto destinado para esta ceremonia.

One of the things in which the Moorish kings interfered was in the marriage of their nobles: hence it came that all the señors attached to the royal person were married in the palace; and there was always a chamber destined for the ceremony.—*Paseos por Granada,* Paseo XXI.

and my will was law with these good people. So, calling in the assistance of a carpenter, and the ever officious Mateo Ximenes, the doors and windows were soon placed in a state of tolerable security, and the sleeping-room of the stately Elizabetta prepared for my reception. Mateo kindly volunteered as a body-guard to sleep in my ante-chamber; but I did not think it worth while to put his valor to the proof.

With all the hardihood I had assumed and all the precautions I had taken, I must confess the first night passed in these quarters was inexpressibly dreary. I do not think it was so much the apprehension of dangers from without that affected me, as the character of the place itself, with all its strange associations: the deeds of violence committed there; the tragical ends of many of those who had once reigned there in splendor. As I passed beneath the fated halls of the tower of Comares on the way to my chamber, I called to mind a quotation, that used to thrill me in the days of boyhood:

> "Fate sits on these dark battlements and frowns;
> And, as the portal opens to receive me,
> A voice in sullen echoes through the courts
> Tells of a nameless deed!"

The whole family escorted me to my chamber, and took leave of me as of one engaged on a perilous enterprise; and when I heard their retreating steps die away along the waste ante-chambers and echoing galleries; and turned the key of my door, I was reminded of those hobgoblin stories, where the hero is left to accomplish the adventure of an enchanted house.

Even the thoughts of the fair Elizabetta and the beauties of her court, who had once graced these chambers, now, by a perversion of fancy, added to the gloom. Here was the scene of their transient gayety and loveliness; here were the very traces of their elegance and enjoyment; but what and where were they? Dust and ashes! tenants of the tomb! phantoms of the memory!

A vague and indescribable awe was creeping over me. I would fain have ascribed it to the thoughts of robbers awakened by the evening's conversation, but I felt it was something more unreal and absurd. The long-buried superstitions of the nursery were reviving, and asserting their power over my imagination.

Everything began to be affected by the working of my mind. The whispering of the wind among the citron-trees beneath my window had something sinister. I cast my eyes into the garden of Lindaraxa; the groves presented a gulf of shadows; the thickets, indistinct and ghastly shapes. I was glad to close the window, but my chamber itself became infected. There was a slight rustling noise overhead; a bat suddenly emerged from a broken panel of the ceiling, flitting about the room and athwart my solitary lamp; and as the fateful bird almost flouted my face with his noiseless wing, the grotesque faces carved in high relief in the cedar ceiling, whence he had emerged, seemed to mope and mow at me.

Rousing myself, and half smiling at this temporary weakness, I resolved to brave it out in the true spirit of the hero of the enchanted house; so, taking lamp in hand, I sallied forth to make a tour of the palace. Notwithstanding every mental exertion the task was a severe one. I had to traverse waste halls and mysterious galleries, where the rays of the lamp extended but a short distance around me. I walked, as it were, in a mere halo of light, walled in by impenetrable darkness. The vaulted corridors were as caverns; the ceilings of the halls were lost in gloom. I recalled all that had been said of the danger from interlopers in these remote and ruined apartments. Might not some vagrant foe be lurking before or behind me, in the outer darkness? My own shadow, cast upon the wall, began to disturb me. The echoes of my own footsteps along the corridors made me pause and look round. I was traversing scenes fraught with dismal recollections. One dark passage led down to the mosque where Yusef, the Moorish monarch, the finisher of the Alhambra, had been basely murdered. In another place I trod the gallery where another monarch had been struck down by the poniard of a relative whom he had thwarted in his love.

A low murmuring sound, as of stifled voices and clanking chains, now reached me. It seemed to come from the Hall of the Abencerrages. I knew it to be the rush of water through subterranean channels, but it sounded strangely in the night, and reminded me of the dismal stories to which it had given rise.

Soon, however, my ear was assailed by sounds too fearfully real to be the work of fancy. As I was crossing the Hall of Ambassadors, low moans and broken ejaculations rose, as it were, from beneath my feet. I paused and listened. They then appeared to be outside of the tower—then again within. Then broke forth howlings as of an animal—then stifled shrieks and inarticulate ravings. Heard in that dead hour and singular place, the effect was thrilling. I had no desire for further perambulation; but returned to my chamber with infinitely more alacrity than I had sallied forth, and drew my breath more freely when once more within its walls and the door bolted behind me. When I awoke in the morning, with the sun shining in at my window and lighting up every part of the building with his cheerful and truth-telling beams, I could scarcely recall the shadows and fancies conjured up by the gloom of the preceding night; or believe that the scenes around me, so naked and apparent, could have been clothed with such imaginary horrors.

Still, the dismal howlings and ejaculations I had heard were not ideal; they were soon accounted for, however, by my handmaid Dolores: being the ravings of a poor maniac, a brother of her aunt, who was subject to violent paroxysms, during which he was confined in a vaulted room beneath the Hall of Ambassadors.

In the course of a few evenings a thorough change took place in the scene and its associations. The moon, which when I took possession of my new apartments was invisible, gradually gained each evening upon the darkness of the night, and at length rolled in full splendor above the towers, pouring a flood of tempered light into every court and hall. The garden beneath my window, before wrapped in gloom, was gently lighted up; the orange and citron trees were tipped with silver; the fountain sparkled in the moonbeams, and even the blush of the rose was faintly visible.

I now felt the poetic merit of the Arabic inscription on the walls—"How beauteous is this garden; where the flowers of the earth vie with the stars of heaven. What can compare with the vase of yon alabaster fountain filled with crystal water? nothing but the moon in her fulness, shining in the midst of an unclouded sky!"

On such heavenly nights I would sit for hours at my window inhaling the sweetness of the garden, and musing on the checkered fortunes of those whose history was dimly shadowed out in the elegant memorials around. Sometimes, when all was quiet, and the clock from the distant cathedral of Granada struck the midnight hour, I have sallied out on another tour and wandered over the whole building; but how different from my first tour! No longer dark and mysterious; no longer peopled with shadowy foes; no longer recalling scenes of violence and murder; all was open, spacious, beautiful; everything called up pleasing and romantic fancies; Lindaraxa once more walked in her garden; the gay chivalry of Moslem Granada once more glittered about the Court of Lions! Who can do justice to a moonlight night in such a climate and such a place? The temperature of a summer midnight in Andalusia is perfectly ethereal. We seem lifted up into a purer atmosphere; we feel a serenity of soul, a buoyancy of spirits, an elasticity of frame, which render mere existence happiness. But when moonlight is added to all this, the effect is like enchantment. Under its plastic sway the Alhambra seems to regain its pristine glories. Every rent and chasm of time; every mouldering tint and weather-stain is gone; the marble resumes its original whiteness; the long colonnades brighten in the moonbeams; the halls are illuminated with a softened radiance—we tread the enchanted palace of an Arabian tale!

What a delight, at such a time, to ascend to the little airy pavilion of the queen's toilet (el tocador de la reyna), which, like a bird-cage, overhangs the valley of the Darro, and gaze from its light arcades upon the moonlight prospect! To the right, the swelling mountains of the Sierra Nevada, robbed of their ruggedness and softened into a fairy land, with their snowy summits gleaming like silver clouds against the deep blue sky. And then to lean over the parapet of the Tocador and gaze down upon Granada and the Albaycin spread out like a map below; all buried in deep repose; the white palaces and convents sleeping in the moonshine, and beyond all these the vapory Vega fading away like a dreamland in the distance.

Sometimes the faint click of castanets rise from the Alameda, where some gay Andalusians are dancing away the summer night. Sometimes the dubious tones of a guitar and the notes of an amorous voice, tell perchance the whereabout of some moonstruck lover serenading his lady's window.

Such is a faint picture of the moonlight nights I have passed loitering about the courts and halls and balconies of this most suggestive pile; "feeding my fancy with sugared suppositions," and enjoying that mixture of reverie and sensation which steal away existence in a southern climate; so that it has been almost morning before I have retired to bed, and been lulled to sleep by the falling waters of the fountain of Lindaraxa.

The Court of Lions

THE peculiar charm of this old dreamy palace is its power of calling up vague reveries and picturings of the past, and thus clothing naked realities with the illusions of the memory and the imagination. As I delight to walk in these "vain shadows," I am prone to seek those parts of the Alhambra which are most favorable to this phantasmagoria of the mind; and none are more so than the Court of Lions, and its surrounding halls. Here the hand of time has fallen the lightest, and the traces of Moorish elegance and splendor exist in almost their original brilliancy. Earthquakes have shaken the foundations of this pile, and rent its rudest towers; yet see! not one of those slender columns has been displaced, not an arch of that light and fragile colonnade given way, and all the fairy fretwork of these domes, apparently as unsubstantial as the crystal fabrics of a morning's frost, exist after the lapse of centuries, almost as fresh as if from the hand of the Moslem artist. I write in the midst of these mementos of the past, in the fresh hour of early morning, in the fated Hall of the Abencerrages. The blood-stained fountain, the legendary monument of their massacre, is before me; the lofty jet almost casts its dew upon my paper. How difficult to reconcile the ancient tale of violence and blood with the gentle and peaceful scene around! Everything here appears calculated to inspire kind and happy feelings, for everything is delicate and beautiful. The very light falls tenderly from above, through the lantern of a dome tinted and wrought as if by fairy hands. Through the ample and fretted arch of the portal I behold the Court of Lions, with brillant sunshine gleaming along its colonnades and sparkling in its fountains. The lively swallow dives into the court, and, rising with a surge, darts away twittering over the roofs; the busy bee toils humming among the flower-beds; and painted butterflies hover from plant to plant, and flutter up and sport with each other in the sunny air. It needs but a slight exertion of the fancy to picture some pensive beauty of the harem, loitering in these secluded haunts of Oriental luxury.

He, however, who would behold this scene under an aspect

more in unison with its fortunes, let him come when the shadows of evening temper the brightness of the court, and throw a gloom into the surrounding halls. Then nothing can be more serenely melancholy, or more in harmony with the tale of departed grandeur.

At such times I am apt to seek the Hall of Justice, whose deep shadowy arcades extend across the upper end of the court. Here was performed, in presence of Ferdinand and Isabella and their triumphant court, the pompous ceremonial of high mass, on taking possession of the Alhambra. The very cross is still to be seen upon the wall, where the altar was erected, and where officiated the Grand Cardinal of Spain, and others of the highest religious dignitaries of the land. I picture to myself the scene when this place was filled with the conquering host, that mixture of mitred prelate and shaven monk, and steel-clad knight and silken courtier; when crosses and crosiers and religious standards were mingled with proud armorial ensigns and the banners of the haughty chiefs of Spain, and flaunted in triumph through these Moslem halls. I picture to myself Columbus, the future discoverer of a world, taking his modest stand in a remote corner, the humble and neglected spectator of the pageant. I see in imagination the Catholic sovereigns prostrating themselves before the altar, and pouring forth thanks for their victory; while the vaults resound with sacred minstrelsy, and the deep-toned Te Deum.

The transient illusion is over—the pageant melts from the fancy—monarch, priest, and warrior return into oblivion with the poor Moslems over whom they exulted. The hall of their triumph is waste and desolate. The bat flits about its twilight vault, and the owl hoots from the neighboring tower of Comares.

Entering the Court of the Lions a few evenings since, I was almost startled at beholding a turbaned Moor quietly seated near the fountain. For a moment one of the fictions of the place seemed realized: an enchanted Moor had broken the spell of centuries, and become visible. He proved, however, to be a mere ordinary mortal: a native of Tetuan in Barbary, who had a shop in the Zacatin of Granada, where he sold rhubarb, trinkets, and perfumes. As he spoke Spanish fluently, I was enabled to hold conversation with him, and found him shrewd and intelligent.

He told me that he came up the hill occasionally in the summer, to pass a part of the day in the Alhambra, which reminded him of the old palaces in Barbary, being built and adorned in similar style, though with more magnificence.

As we walked about the palace, he pointed out several of the Arabic inscriptions, as possessing much poetic beauty.

"Ah, señor," said he, "when the Moors held Granada, they were a gayer people than they are nowadays. They thought only of love, music, and poetry. They made stanzas upon every occasion, and set them all to music. He who could make the best verses, and she who had the most tuneful voice, might be sure of favor and preferment. In those days, if any one asked for bread, the reply was, make me a couplet; and the poorest beggar, if he begged in rhyme, would often be rewarded with a piece of gold."

"And is the popular feeling for poetry," said I, "entirely lost among you?"

"By no means, señor; the people of Barbary, even those of the lower classes, still make couplets, and good ones too, as in old times; but talent is not rewarded as it was then; the rich prefer the jingle of their gold to the sound of poetry or music."

As he was talking, his eye caught one of the inscriptions which foretold perpetuity to the power and glory of the Moslem monarchs, the masters of this pile. He shook his head, and shrugged his shoulders, as he interpreted it. "Such might have been the case," said he; "the Moslems might still have been reigning in the Alhambra, had not Boabdil been a traitor, and given up his capital to the Christians. The Spanish monarchs would never have been able to conquer it by open force."

I endeavored to vindicate the memory of the unlucky Boabdil from this aspersion, and to show that the dissensions which led to the downfall of the Moorish throne originated in the cruelty of his tiger-hearted father; but the Moor would admit of no palliation.

"Muley Abul Hassan," said he, "might have been cruel; but he was brave, vigilant, and patriotic. Had he been properly seconded, Granada would still have been ours; but his son Boabdil thwarted his plans, crippled his power, sowed treason in his palace, and dissension in his camp. May the curse of God light upon him for his treachery!" With these words the Moor left the Alhambra.

The indignation of my turbaned companion agrees with an anecdote related by a friend, who, in the course of a tour in Barbary, had an interview with the Pacha of Tetuan. The Moorish governor was particular in his inquiries about Spain, and especially concerning the favored region of Andalusia, the delights of Granada, and the remains of its royal palace. The replies awakened all those fond recollections, so deeply cherished by the Moors, of the power and splendor of their ancient empire in Spain. Turning to his Moslem attendants, the Pacha stroked his beard, and broke forth in passionate lamentations, that such a sceptre should have fallen from the sway of true believers. He consoled himself, however, with the persuasion, that the power and prosperity of the Spanish nation were on the decline; that a time would come when the Moors would conquer their rightful domains; and that the day was perhaps not far distant when Mohammedan worship would again be offered up in the mosque of Cordova, and a Mohammedan prince sit on his throne in the Alhambra.

Such is the general aspiration and belief among the Moors of Barbary; who consider Spain, or Andaluz, as it was anciently called, their rightful heritage, of which they have been despoiled by treachery and violence. These ideas are fostered and perpetuated by the descendants of the exiled Moors of Granada, scattered among the cities of Barbary. Several of these reside in Tetuan, preserving their ancient names, such as Paez and Medina, and refraining from intermarriage with any families who cannot claim the same high origin. Their vaunted lineage is regarded with a degree of popular deference rarely shown in Mohammedan communities to any hereditary distinction, excepting in the royal line.

These families, it is said, continue to sigh after the terrestrial paradise of their ancestors, and to put up prayers in their mosques on Fridays, imploring Allah to hasten the time when Granada shall be restored to the faithful: an event to which they look forward as fondly and confidently as did the Christian crusaders to the recovery of the Holy Sepulchre. Nay, it is added, that some of them retain the ancient maps and deeds of the estates and gardens of their ancestors at Granada, and even the keys of the houses; holding them as evidences of their hereditary claims, to be produced at the anticipated day of restoration.

My conversation with the Moors set me to musing on the fate of Boabdil. Never was surname more applicable than that bestowed upon him by his subjects of el Zogoybi, or the Unlucky. His misfortunes began almost in his cradle, and ceased not even with his death. If ever he cherished the desire of leaving an honorable name on the historic page, how cruelly has he been defrauded of his hopes! Who is there that has turned the least attention to the romantic history of the Moorish domination in Spain, without kindling with indignation at the alleged atrocities of Boabdil? Who has not been touched with the woes of his lovely and gentle queen, subjected by him to a trial of life and death, on a false charge of infidelity? Who has not been shocked by his alleged murder of his sister and her two children, in a transport of passion? Who has not felt his blood boil at the inhuman massacre of the gallant Abencerrages, thirty-six of whom, it is affirmed, he ordered to be beheaded in the Court of Lions? All these charges have been reiterated in various forms; they have passed into ballads, dramas, and romances, until they have taken too thorough possession of the public mind to be eradicated. There is not a foreigner of education that visits the Alhambra, but asks for the fountain where the Abencerrages were beheaded; and gazes with horror at the grated gallery where the queen is said to have been confined; not a peasant of the Vega or the Sierra, but sings the story in rude couplets, to the accompaniment of his guitar, while his hearers learn to execrate the very name of Boabdil.

Never, however, was name more foully and unjustly slandered. I have examined all the authentic chronicles and letters written by Spanish authors, contemporary with Boabdil; some of whom were in the confidence of the Catholic sovereigns, and actually present in the camp throughout the war. I have examined all the Arabian authorities I could get access to, through the medium of translation, and have found nothing to justify these dark and hateful accusations. The most of these tales may be traced to a work commonly called "The Civil Wars of Granada," containing a pretended history of the feuds of the Zegries and Abencerrages, during the last struggle of the Moorish empire. The work appeared originally in Spanish, and professed to be translated from the Arabic by one Gines Perez de Hita, an inhabitant of Murcia. It has since passed into various languages, and Florian has taken from it much of the fable of his Gonsalvo of Cordova: it has thus, in a great measure, usurped the authority of real history, and is currently believed by the people, and especially the peasantry of Granada. The whole of it, however, is a mass of fiction, mingled with a few disfigured truths, which give it an air of veracity. It bears internal evidence of its falsity; the manners and customs of the Moors being extravagantly misrepresented in it, and scenes depicted totally incompatible with their habits and their faith, and which never could have been recorded by a Mohammedan writer.

I confess there seems to me something almost criminal in the wilful perversions of this work: great latitude is undoubtedly to be allowed to romantic fiction, but there are limits which it must not pass; and the names of the distinguished dead, which belong to history, are no more to be calumniated than those of the illustrious living. One would have thought, too, that the unfortunate Boabdil had suffered enough for his justifiable hostility to the Spaniards, by being stripped of his kingdom, without having his name thus wantonly traduced, and rendered a byword and a theme of infamy in his native land, and in the very mansion of his fathers!

Local Traditions

THE common people of Spain have an Oriental passion for story-telling, and are fond of the marvellous. They will gather round the doors of their cottages in summer evenings, or in the great cavernous chimney-corners of the ventas in the winter, and listen with insatiable delight to miraculous legends of saints, perilous adventures of travellers, and daring exploits of robbers and contrabandistas. The wild and solitary character of the country, the imperfect diffusion of knowledge, the scarceness of general topics of conversation, and the romantic adventurous life that every one leads in a land where travelling is yet in its primitive state, all contribute to cherish this love of oral narration, and to produce a strong infusion of the extravagant and incredible. There is no theme, however, more prevalent and popular than that of treasures buried by the Moors; it pervades the whole country. In traversing the wild sierras, the scenes of ancient foray and exploit, you cannot see a Moorish atalaya, or watch-tower, perched among the cliffs, or beetling above its rock-built village, but your muleteer, on being closely questioned, will suspend the smoking of his cigarillo to tell some tale of Moslem gold buried beneath its foundations; nor is there a ruined alcazar in a city but has its golden tradition, handed down from generation to generation among the poor people of the neighborhood.

These, like most popular fictions, have sprung from some scanty groundwork of fact. During the wars between Moor and Christian, which distracted this country for centuries, towns and castles were liable frequently and suddenly to change owners, and the inhabitants, during sieges and assaults, were fain to bury their money and jewels in the earth, or hide them in vaults and wells, as is often done at the present day in the despotic and belligerent countries of the East. At the time of the expulsion of the Moors also, many of them concealed their most precious effects, hoping that their exile would be but temporary, and that they would be enabled to return and retrieve their treasures at some future day. It is certain that from time to time hoards of gold and silver coin have been accidentally digged up, after a lapse of centuries, from among the ruins of Moorish fortresses and habitations; and it requires but a few facts of the kind to give birth to a thousand fictions.

The stories thus originating have generally something of an Oriental tinge, and are marked with that mixture of the Arabic and the Gothic which seems to me to characterize everything in Spain, and especially in its southern provinces. The hidden wealth is always laid under magic spell, and secured by charm and talisman. Sometimes it is guarded by uncouth monsters or fiery dragons, sometimes by enchanted Moors, who sit by it in armor, with drawn swords, but motionless as statues, maintaining a sleepless watch for ages.

The Alhambra of course, from the peculiar circumstances of its history, is a strong-hold for popular fictions of the kind; and various relics, digged up from time to time, have contributed to strengthen them. At one time an earthen vessel was found containing Moorish coins and the skeleton of a cock, which, according to the opinion of certain shrewd inspectors, must have been buried alive. At another time a vessel was dug up containing a great scarabæus or beetle of baked clay, covered with Arabic inscriptions, which was pronounced a prodigious amulet of occult virtues. In this way the wits of the ragged brood who inhabit the Alhambra have been set wool-gathering, until there is not a hall, nor tower, nor vault, of the old fortress, that has not been made the scene of some marvellous tradition. Having, I trust, in the preceding papers made the reader in some degree familiar with the localities of the Alhambra, I shall now launch out more largely into the wonderful legends connected with it, and which I have diligently wrought into shape and form, from various legendary scraps and hints picked up in the course of my perambulations—in the same manner that an antiquary works out a regular historical document from a few scattered letters of an almost defaced inscription.

If anything in these legends should shock the faith of the over-scrupulous reader, he must remember the nature of the place, and make due allowances. He must not expect here the same laws of probability that govern commonplace scenes and every-day life; he must remember that he treads the halls of an enchanted palace, and that all is "haunted ground."

Legend of the Arabian Astrologer

IN old times, many hundred years ago, there was a Moorish king named Aben Habuz, who reigned over the kingdom of Granada. He was a retired conqueror, that is to say, one who, having in his more youthful days led a life of constant foray and depredation, now that he was grown feeble and superannuated, "languished for repose," and desired nothing more than to live at peace with all the world, to husband his laurels, and to enjoy in quiet the possessions he had wrested from his neighbors.

It so happened, however, that this most reasonable and pacific old monarch had young rivals to deal with; princes full of his early passion for fame and fighting, and who were disposed to call him to account for the scores he had run up with their fathers. Certain distant districts of his own territories, also, which during the days of his vigor he had treated with a high hand, were prone, now that he languished for repose, to rise in rebellion and threaten to invest him in his capital. Thus he had foes on every side; and as Granada is surrounded by wild and craggy mountains, which hide the approach of an enemy, the unfortunate Aben Habuz was kept in a constant state of vigilance and alarm, not knowing in what quarter hostilities might break out.

It was in vain that he built watch-towers on the mountains, and stationed guards at every pass with orders to make fires by night and smoke by day, on the approach of an enemy. His alert foes, baffling every precaution, would break out of some unthought-of defile, ravage his lands beneath his very nose, and then make off with prisoners and booty to the mountains. Was ever peaceable and retired conqueror in a more uncomfortable predicament?

While Aben Habuz was harassed by these perplexities and molestations, an ancient Arabian physician arrived at his court. His gray beard descended to his girdle, and he had every mark of extreme age, yet he had travelled almost the whole way from Egypt on foot, with no other aid than a staff, marked with hieroglyphics. His fame had preceded him. His name was Ibrahim Ebn Abu Ayub; he was said to have lived ever since the days of Mahomet, and to be son of Abu Ayub; the last of the companions of the Prophet. He had, when a child, followed the conquering army of Amru into Egypt, where he had remained many years studying the dark sciences, and particularly magic, among the Egyptian priests.

It was, moreover, said that he had found out the secret of prolonging life, by means of which he had arrived to the great age of upwards of two centuries, though, as he did not discover the secret until well stricken in years, he could only perpetuate his gray hairs and wrinkles.

This wonderful old man was honorably entertained by the king; who, like most superannuated monarchs, began to take physicians into great favor. He would have assigned him an apartment in his palace, but the astrologer preferred a cave in the side of the hill which rises above the city of Granada, being the same on which the Alhambra has since been built. He caused the cave to be enlarged so as to form a spacious and lofty hall, with a circular hole at the top, through which, as through a well, he could see the heavens and behold the stars even at mid-day. The walls of this hall were covered with Egyptian hieroglyphics with cabalistic symbols, and with the figures of the stars in their signs. This hall he furnished with many implements, fabricated under his directions by cunning artificers of Granada, but the occult properties of which were known only to himself.

In a little while the sage Ibrahim became the bosom counsellor of the king, who applied to him for advice in every emergency. Aben Habuz was once inveighing against the injustice of his neighbors, and bewailing the restless vigilance he had to observe to guard himself against their invasions; when he had finished, the astrologer remained silent for a moment, and then replied, "Know, O king, that, when I was in Egypt, I beheld a great marvel devised by a pagan priestess of old. On a mountain, above the city of Borsa, and overlooking the great valley of the Nile, was a figure of a ram, and above it a figure of a cock, both of molten brass, and turning upon a pivot. Whenever the country was threatened with invasion, the ram would turn in the direction of the enemy, and the cock would crow; upon this the inhabitants of the city knew of the danger, and of the quarter from which it was approaching, and could take timely means to guard against it."

"God is great!" exclaimed the pacific Aben Habuz, "what a treasure would be such a ram to keep an eye upon these mountains around me; and then such a cock, to crow in time of danger! Allah Akbar! how securely I might sleep in my palace with such sentinels on the top!"

The astrologer waited until the ecstasies of the king had subsided, and then proceeded.

"After the victorious Amru (may he rest in peace!) had finished his conquest of Egypt, I remained among the priests of the land, studying the rites and ceremonies of their idolatrous faith, and seeking to make myself master of the hidden knowledge for which they are renowned. I was one day seated on the banks of the Nile, conversing with an ancient priest, when he pointed to the mighty pyramids which rose like mountains out of the neighboring desert. 'All that we can teach thee,' said he, 'is nothing to the knowledge locked up in those mighty piles In the centre of the central pyramid is a sepulchral chamber, in which is enclosed the mummy of the high-priest who aided in rearing that stupendous pile; and with him is buried a wondrous book of knowledge, containing all the secrets of magic and art. This book was given to Adam after his fall, and was handed down from generation to generation to King Solomon the Wise, and by its aid he built the Temple of Jerusalem. How it came into the possession of the builder of the pyramids is known to Him alone who knows all things.'

"When I heard these words of the Egyptian priest, my heart burned to get possession of that book. I could command the services of many of the soldiers of our conquering army, and of a number of the native Egyptians: with these I set to work, and pierced the solid mass of the pyramid, until, after great toil, I came upon one of its interior and hidden passages. Following this up, and threading a fearful labyrinth, I penetrated into the very heart of the pyramids, even to the sepulchral chamber, where the mummy of the high-priest had lain for ages. I broke through the outer cases of the mummy, unfolded its many wrappers and bandages, and at length found the precious volume on its bosom. I seized it with a trembling hand, and groped my way out of the pyramid, leaving the mummy in its dark and silent sepulchre, there to await the final day of resurrection and judgment."

"Son of Abu Ayub," exclaimed Aben Habuz, "thou hast been a great traveller, and seen marvellous things; but of what avail to me is the secret of the pyramid, and the volume of knowledge of the wise Solomon?"

"This it is, O king! By the study of that book I am instructed in all magic arts, and can command the assistance of genii to accomplish my plans. The mystery of the Talisman of Borsa is therefore familiar to me, and such a talisman can I make, nay, one of greater virtues."

"O wise son of Abu Ayub," cried Aben Habuz, "better were such a talisman than all the watch-towers on the hills, and sentinels upon the borders. Give me such a safeguard, and the riches of my treasury are at thy command."

The astrologer immediately set to work to gratify the wishes of the monarch. He caused a great tower to be erected upon the top of the royal palace, which stood on the brow of the hill of the Albaycin. The tower was built of stones brought from Egypt, and taken, it is said, from one of the pyramids. In the upper part of the tower was a circular hall, with windows looking towards every point of the compass, and before each window was a table, on which was arranged, as on a chess-board, a mimic army of horse and foot, with the effigy of the potentate that ruled in that direction, all carved of wood. To each of these tables there was a small lance, no bigger than a bodkin, on which were engraved certain Chaldaic characters. This hall was kept constantly closed, by a gate of brass, with a great lock of steel, the key of which was in possession of the king.

On the top of the tower was a bronze figure of a Moorish horseman, fixed on a pivot, with a shield on one arm, and his lance elevated perpendicularly. The face of this horseman was towards the city, as if keeping guard over it; but if any foe were at hand, the figure would turn in that direction, and would level the lance as if for action.

When this talisman was finished, Aben Habuz was all impatient to try its virtues, and longed as ardently for an invasion as he had ever sighed after repose. His desire was soon gratified. Tidings were brought, early one morning, by the sentinel appointed to watch the tower, that the face of the bronze horseman was turned towards the mountains of Elvira, and that his lance pointed directly against the Pass of Lope.

"Let the drums and trumpets sound to arms, and all Granada be put on the alert," said Aben Habuz.

"O king," said the astrologer, "let not your city be disquieted, nor your warriors called to arms; we need no aid of force to deliver you from your enemies. Dismiss your attendants, and let us proceed alone to the secret hall of the tower."

The ancient Aben Habuz mounted the staircase of the tower, leaning on the arm of the still more ancient Ibrahim Ebn Abu Ayub. They unlocked the brazen door and entered. The window that looked towards the Pass of Lope was open. "In this direction," said the astrologer, "lies the danger; approach, O king, and behold the mystery of the table."

King Aben Habuz approached the seeming chess-board, on which were arranged the small wooden effigies, when, to his surprise, he perceived that they were all in motion. The horses pranced and curveted, the warriors brandished their weapons, and there was a faint sound of drums and trumpets, and the clang of arms, and neighing of steeds; but all no louder, nor more distinct, than the hum of the bee, or the summer-fly, in the drowsy ear of him who lies at noontide in the shade.

"Behold, O king," said the astrologer, "a proof that thy enemies are even now in the field. They must be advancing through yonder mountains, by the Pass of Lope. Would you produce a panic and confusion amongst them, and cause them to retreat without loss of life, strike these effigies with the butend of this magic lance; would you cause bloody feud and carnage, strike with the point."

A livid streak passed across the countenance of Aben Habuz; he seized the lance with trembling eagerness; his gray beard wagged with exultation as he tottered toward the table: "Son of Abu Ayub," exclaimed he, in chuckling tone, "I think we will have a little blood!"

So saying, he thrust the magic lance into some of the pigmy effigies, and belabored others with the but-end, upon which the former fell as dead upon the board, and the rest turning upon each other, began, pell-mell, a chance-medley fight.

It was with difficulty the astrologer could stay the hand of the most pacific of monarchs, and prevent him from absolutely exterminating his foes; at length he prevailed upon him to leave the tower, and to send out scouts to the mountains by the Pass of Lope.

They returned with the intelligence that a Christain army had advanced through the heart of the Sierra, almost within sight of Granada, where a dissension had broken out among them; they had turned their weapons against each other, and after much slaughter had retreated over the border.

Aben Habuz was transported with joy on thus proving the efficacy of the talisman. "At length," said he, "I shall lead a life of tranquillity, and have all my enemies in my power. O wise son of Abu Ayub, what can I bestow on thee in reward for such a blessing?"

"The wants of an old man and a philosopher, O king, are few and simple; grant me but the means of fitting up my cave as a suitable hermitage, and I am content."

"How noble is the moderation of the truly wise!" exclaimed Aben Habuz, secretly pleased at the cheapness of the recompense. He summoned his treasurer, and bade him dispense whatever sums might be required by Ibrahim to complete and furnish his hermitage.

The astrologer now gave orders to have various chambers hewn out of the solid rock, so as to form ranges of apartments connected with his astrological hall; these he caused to be furnished with luxurious ottomans and divans, and the walls to be hung with the richest silks of Damascus. "I am an old man," said he, "and can no longer rest my bones on stone couches, and these damp walls require covering."

He had baths too constructed, and provided with all kinds of perfumes and aromatic oils. "For a bath," said he, "is necessary to counteract the rigidity of age, and to restore freshness and suppleness to the frame withered by study."

He caused the apartments to be hung with innumerable silver and crystal lamps, which he filled with a fragrant oil prepared according to a receipt discovered by him in the tombs of

Egypt. This oil was perpetual in its nature, and diffused a soft radiance like the tempered light of day. "The light of the sun," said he, "is too garish and violent for the eyes of an old man, and the light of the lamp is more congenial to the studies of a philosopher."

The treasurer of King Aben Habuz groaned at the sums daily demanded to fit up this hermitage, and he carried his complaints to the king. The royal word, however, had been given; Aben Habuz shrugged his shoulders: "We must have patience," said he; "this old man has taken his idea of a philosophic retreat from the interior of the pyramids, and of the vast ruins of Egypt; but all things have an end, and so will the furnishing of his cavern."

The king was in the right; the hermitage was at length complete, and formed a sumptuous subterranean palace. The astrologer expressed himself perfectly content, and, shutting himself up, remained for three whole days buried in study. At the end of that time he appeared again before the treasurer. "One thing more is necessary," said he, "one trifling solace for the intervals of mental labor."

"O wise Ibrahim, I am bound to furnish everything necessary for thy solitude; what more dost thou require?"

"I would fain have a few dancing-women."

"Dancing-women!" echoed the treasurer, with surprise.

"Dancing-women," replied the sage, gravely; "and let them be young and fair to look upon; for the sight of youth and beauty is refreshing. A few will suffice, for I am a philosopher of simple habits and easily satisfied."

While the philosophic Ibrahim Ebn Abu Ayub passed his time thus sagely in his hermitage, the pacific Aben Habuz carried on furious campaigns in effigy in his tower. It was a glorious thing for an old man, like himself, of quiet habits, to have war made easy, and to be enabled to amuse himself in his chamber by brushing away whole armies like so many swarms of flies.

For a time he rioted in the indulgence of his humors, and even taunted and insulted his neighbors, to induce them to make incursions; but by degrees they grew wary from repeated disasters, until no one ventured to invade his territories. For many months the bronze horseman remained on the peace establishment, with his lance elevated in the air; and the worthy old monarch began to repine at the want of his accustomed sport, and to grow peevish at his monotonous tranquillity.

At length, one day, the talismanic horseman veered suddenly round, and lowering his lance, made a dead point towards the mountains of Guadix. Aben Habuz hastened to his tower, but the magic table in that direction remained quiet: not a single warrior was in motion. Perplexed at the circumstance, he sent forth a troop of horse to scour the mountains and reconnoitre. They returned after three days' absence.

"We have searched every mountain pass," said they, "but not a helm nor spear was stirring. All that we have found in the course of our foray, was a Christian damsel of surpassing beauty, sleeping at noontide beside a fountain, whom we have brought away captive."

"A damsel of surpassing beauty!" exclaimed Aben Habuz, his eyes gleaming with animation; "let her be conducted into my presence."

The beautiful damsel was accordingly conducted into his presence. She was arrayed with all the luxury of ornament that had prevailed among the Gothic Spaniards at the time of the Arabian conquest. Pearls of dazzling whiteness were entwined with her raven tresses; and jewels sparkled on her forehead, rivalling the lustre of her eyes. Around her neck was a golden chain, to which was suspended a silver lyre, which hung by her side.

The flashes of her dark refulgent eye were like sparks of fire on the withered yet combustible, heart of Aben Habuz; the swimming voluptuousness of her gait made his senses reel. "Fairest of women," cried he, with rapture, "who and what art thou?"

"The daughter of one of the Gothic princes, who but lately ruled over this land. The armies of my father have been destroyed, as if by magic, among these mountains; he has been driven into exile, and his daughter is a captive."

"Beware, O king!" whispered Ibrahim Ebn Abu Ayub, "this may be one of those northern sorceresses of whom we have heard, who assume the most seductive forms to beguile the unwary. Methinks I read witchcraft in her eye, and sorcery in every movement. Doubtless this is the enemy pointed out by the talisman."

"Son of Abu Ayub," replied the king, "thou art a wise man, I grant, a conjurer for aught I know; but thou art little versed in the ways of woman. In that knowledge will I yield to no man; no, not to the wise Solomon himself, notwithstanding the number of his wives and concubines. As to this damsel, I see no harm in her; she is fair to look upon, and finds favor in my eyes."

"Hearken, O king!" replied the astrologer. "I have given thee many victories by means of my talisman, but have never shared any of the spoil. Give me then this stray captive, to solace me in my solitude with her silver lyre. If she be indeed a sorceress, I have counter spells that set her charms at defiance."

"What! more women!" cried Aben Habuz. "Hast thou not already dancing-women enough to solace thee?"

"Dancing-women have I, it is true, but no singing-women. I would fain have a little minstrelsy to refresh my mind when weary with the toils of study."

"A truce with thy hermit cravings," said the king, impatiently. "This damsel have I marked for my own. I see much comfort in her: even such comfort as David, the father of Solomon the Wise, found in the society of Abishag the Shunamite."

Further solicitations and remonstrances of the astrologer only provoked a more peremptory reply from the monarch, and they parted in high displeasure. The sage shut himself up in his hermitage to brood over his disappointment; ere he departed, however, he gave the king one more warning to beware of his dangerous captive. But where is the old man in love that will listen to counsel? Aben Habuz resigned himself to the full sway of his passion. His only study was how to render himself amiable in the eyes of the Gothic beauty. He had not youth to recommend him, it is true, but then he had riches; and when a lover is old, he is generally generous. The Zacatin of Granada was ransacked for the most precious merchandise of the East; silks, jewels, precious gems, exquisite perfumes, all that Asia and Africa yielded of rich and rare, were lavished upon the princess. All kinds of spectacles and festivities were devised for her entertainment; minstrelsy, dancing, tournaments, bull-fights; Granada for a time was a scene of perpetual pageant. The Gothic princess regarded all this splendor with the air of one accustomed to magnificence. She received everything as a homage due to her rank, or rather to her beauty; for beauty is more lofty in its exactions even than rank. Nay, she seemed to take a secret pleasure in exciting the monarch to expenses that made his treasury shrink, and then treating his extravagant generosity as a mere matter of course. With all his assiduity and munificence, also, the venerable lover could not flatter himself that he had made any impression on her heart. She never frowned on him, it is true, but then she never smiled. Whenever he began to plead his passion, she struck her silver lyre. There was a mystic charm in the sound. In an instant the monarch began to nod; a drowsiness stole over him, and he gradually sank into a sleep, from which he awoke wonderfully refreshed, but perfectly cooled for the time of his passion. This was very baffling to his suit; but then these slumbers were accompanied by agreeable dreams, which completely enthralled the senses of the drowsy lover; so he continued to dream on, while all Granada scoffed at his infatuation, and groaned at the treasures lavished for a song.

At length a danger burst on the head of Aben Habuz, against which his talisman yielded him no warning. An insurrection broke out in his very capital; his palace was surrounded by an armed rabble, who menaced his life and the life of his Christian paramour. A spark of his ancient warlike spirit was awakened in the breast of the monarch. At the head of a handful of his guards he sallied forth, put the rebels to flight, and crushed the insurrection in the bud.

When quiet was again restored, he sought the astrologer, who still remained shut up in his hermitage, chewing the bitter cud of resentment.

Aben Habuz approached him with a conciliatory tone. "O wise son of Abu Ayub," said he, "well didst thou predict dangers to me from this captive beauty: tell me then, thou who art so quick at foreseeing peril, what I should do to avert it."

"Put from thee the infidel damsel who is the cause."

"Sooner would I part with my kingdom," cried Aben Habuz.

"Thou art in danger of losing both," replied the astrologer.

"Be not harsh and angry, O most profound of philosophers; consider the double distress of a monarch and a lover, and devise some means of protecting me from the evils by which I am menaced. I care not for grandeur, I care not for power, I languish only for repose; would that I had some quiet retreat where I might take refuge from the world, and all its cares, and pomps, and troubles, and devote the remainder of my days to tranquillity and love.

The astrologer regarded him from under his bushy eyebrows. "And what wouldst thou give, if I could provide thee such a retreat?"

"Thou shouldst name thy own reward; and whatever it might be, if within the scope of my power, as my soul liveth, it should be thine."

"Thou hast heard, O king, of the garden of Irem, one of the prodigies of Arabia the happy."

"I have heard of that garden; it is recorded in the Koran, even in the chapter entitled 'The Dawn of Day.' I have, moreover, heard marvellous things related of it by pilgrims who had been to Mecca; but I considered them wild fables, such as travellers are wont to tell who have visited remote countries."

"Discredit not, O king, the tales of travellers," rejoined the astrologer, gravely, "for they contain precious rarities of knowledge brought from the ends of the earth. As to the palace and garden of Irem, what is generally told of them is true; I have seen them with mine own eyes;—listen to my adventure, for it has a bearing upon the object of your request.

"In my younger days, when a mere Arab of the desert, I tended my father's camels. In traversing the desert of Aden, one of them strayed from the rest, and was lost. I searched after it for several days, but in vain, until, wearied and faint, I laid myself down at noon-tide, and slept under a palm-tree by the side of a scanty well. When I awoke I found myself at the gate of a city. I entered, and beheld noble streets, and squares, and market-places; but all were silent and without an inhabitant. I wandered on until I came to a sumptuous palace, with a garden adorned with fountains and fish-ponds, and groves and flowers, and orchards laden with delicious fruit; but still no one was to be seen. Upon which, appalled at this loneliness, I hastened to depart; and, after issuing forth at the gate of the city, I turned to look upon the place, but it was no longer to be seen: nothing but the silent desert extended before my eyes.

"In the neighborhood I met with an aged dervise, learned

in the traditions and secrets of the land, and related to him what had befallen me. 'This,' said he, 'is the far-famed garden of Irem, one of the wonders of the desert. It only appears at times to some wanderer like thyself, gladdening him with the sight of towers and palaces and garden-walls overhung with richly-laden fruit-trees and then vanishes, leaving nothing but a lonely desert. And this is the story of it. In old times, when this country was inhabited by the Addites, King Sheddad, the son of Ad, the great grand-son of Noah, founded here a splendid city. When it was finished, and he saw its grandeur, his heart was puffed up with pride and arrogance, and he determined to build a royal palace, with gardens which should rival all related in the Koran of the celestial paradise. But the curse of heaven fell upon him for his persumption. He and his subjects were swept from the earth, and his splendid city, and palace, and gardens, were laid under a perpetual spell, which hides them from human sight, excepting that they are seen at intervals, by way of keeping his sin in perpetual remembrance.'

"This story, O king, and the wonders I had seen, ever dwelt in my mind; and in after-years, when I had been in Egypt, and was possessed of the book of knowledge of Solomon the Wise, I determined to return and revisit the garden of Irem. I did so, and found it revealed to my instructed sight. I took possession of the palace of Sheddad, and passed several days in his mock paradise. The genii who watch over the place were obedient to my magic power, and revealed to me the spells by which the whole garden had been, as it were, conjured into existence, and by which it was rendered invisible. Such a palace and garden, O king, can I make for thee, even here, on the mountain above thy city. Do I not know all the secret spells? and am I not in possession of the book of knowledge of Solomon the Wise?"

"O wise son of Abu Ayub!" exclaimed Aben Habuz, trembling with eagerness, "thou art a traveller indeed, and hast seen and learned marvellous things! Contrive me such a paradise, and ask any reward, even to the half of my kingdom."

"Alas!" replied the other, "thou knowest I am an old man, and a philosopher, and easily satisfied; all the reward I ask is the first beast of burden, with its load, which shall enter the magic portal of the palace."

The monarch gladly agreed to so moderate a stipulation, and the astrologer began his work. On the summit of the hill, immediately above his subterranean hermitage, he caused a great gateway or barbican to be erected, opening through the centre of a strong tower.

There was an outer vestibule or porch, with a lofty arch, and within it a portal secured by massive gates. On the keystone of the portal the astrologer, with his own hand, wrought the figure of a huge key; and on the keystone of the outer arch of the vestibule, which was loftier than that of the portal, he carved a gigantic hand. These were potent talismans, over which he repeated many sentences in an unknown tongue.

When this gateway was finished, he shut himself up for two days in his astrological hall, engaged in secret incantations; on the third he ascended the hill, and passed the whole day on its summit. At a late hour of the night he came down, and presented himself before Aben Habuz. "At length, O king," said he, "my labor is accomplished. On the summit of the hill stands one of the most delectable palaces that ever the head of man devised, or the heart of man desired. It contains sumptuous halls and galleries, delicious gardens, cool fountains, and fragrant baths; in a word, the whole mountain is converted into a paradise. Like the garden of Irem, it is protected by a mighty charm, which hides it from the view and search of mortals, excepting such as possess the secret of its talismans."

"Enough!" cried Aben Habuz, joyfully, "to-morrow morning with the first light we will ascend and take possession." The happy monarch slept but little that night. Scarcely had the rays of the sun begun to play about the snowy summit of the Sierra Nevada, when he mounted his steed, and, accompanied only by a few chosen attendants, ascended a steep and narrow road leading up the hill. Beside him, on a white palfrey, rode the Gothic princess, her whole dress sparkling with jewels, while round her neck was suspended her silver lyre. The astrologer walked on the other side of the king, assisting his steps with his hieroglyphic staff, for he never mounted steed of any kind.

Aben Habuz looked to see the towers of the palace brightening above him, and the embowered terraces of its gardens stretching along the heights; but as yet nothing of the kind was to be descried. "That is the mystery and safeguard of the place," said the astrologer," nothing can be discerned until you have passed the spell-bound gateway, and been put in possession of the place."

As they approached the gateway, the astrologer paused, and pointed out to the king the mystic hand and key carved upon the portal of the arch. "These," said he, "are the talismans which guard the entrance to this paradise. Until yonder hand shall reach down and seize that key, neither mortal power nor magic artifice can prevail against the lord of this mountain."

While Aben Habuz was gazing, with open mouth and silent wonder, at these mystic talismans, the palfrey of the princess proceeded, and bore her in at the portal, to the very centre of the barbican.

"Behold," cried the astrologer, "my promised reward; the first animal with its burden which should enter the magic gateway."

Aben Habuz smiled at what he considered a pleasantry of the ancient man; but when he found him to be in earnest, his gray beard trembled with indignation.

"Son of Abu Ayub," said he, sternly, "what equivocation is this? Thou knowest the meaning of my promise: the first beast of burden, with its load, that should enter this portal. Take the strongest mule in my stables, load it with the most precious things of my treasury, and it is thine; but dare not raise thy thoughts to her who is the delight of my heart."

"What need I of wealth?" cried the astrologer, scornfully; "have I not the book of knowledge of Solomon the Wise, and through it the command of the secret treasures of the earth? The princess is mine by right; thy royal word is pledged; I claim her as my own."

The princess looked down haughtily from her palfrey, and a light smile of scorn curled her rosy lip at this dispute between two gray-beards for the possession of youth and beauty. The wrath of the monarch got the better of his discretion. "Base son of the desert," cried he, "thou mayst be master of many arts, but know me for thy master, and presume not to juggle with thy king."

"My master! my king!" echoed the astrologer—"the monarch

of a mole-hill to claim sway over him who possesses the talismans of Solomon! Farewell, Aben Habuz; reign over thy petty kingdom, and revel in thy paradise of fools; for me, I will laugh at thee in my philosophic retirement."

So saying, he seized the bridle of the palfrey, smote the earth with his staff, and sank with the Gothic princess through the centre of the barbican. The earth closed over them, and no trace remained of the opening by which they had descended.

Aben Habuz was struck dumb for a time with astonishment. Recovering himself, he ordered a thousand workmen to dig, with pickaxe and spade, into the ground where the astrologer had disappeared. They digged and digged, but in vain; the flinty bosom of the hill resisted their implements; or if they did penetrate a little way, the earth filled in again as fast as they threw it out. Aben Habuz sought the mouth of the cavern at the foot of the hill, leading to the subterranean palace of the astrologer; but it was nowhere to be found. Where once had been an entrance, was now a solid surface of primeval rock. With the disappearance of Ibrahim Ebn Abu Ayub ceased the benefit of his talismans. The bronze horseman remained fixed, with his face turned toward the hill, and his spear pointed to the spot where the astrologer had descended, as if there still lurked the deadliest foe of Aben Habuz.

From time to time the sound of music, and the tones of a female voice, could be faintly heard from the bosom of the hill; and a peasant one day brought word to the king, that in the preceding night he had found a fissure in the rock, by which he had crept in, until he looked down into a subterranean hall, in which sat the astrologer, on a magnificent divan, slumbering and nodding to the silver lyre of the princess, which seemed to hold a magic sway over his senses.

Aben Habuz sought the fissure in the rock, but it was again closed. He renewed the attempt to unearth his rival, but all in vain. The spell of the hand and key was too potent to be counteracted by human power. As to the summit of the mountain, the site of the promised palace and garden, it remained a naked waste; either the boasted elysium was hidden from sight by enchantment, or was a mere fable of the astrologer. The world charitably supposed the latter, and some used to call the place

"The King's Folly"; while others named it "The Fool's Paradise."

To add to the chagrin of Aben Habuz, the neighbors whom he had defied and taunted, and cut up at his leisure while master of the talismanic horseman, finding him no longer protected by magic spell, made inroads into his territories from all sides, and the remainder of the life of the most pacific ot monarchs was a tissue of turmoils.

At length Aben Habuz died, and was buried. Ages have since rolled away. The Alhambra has been built on the eventful mountain, and in some measure realizes the fabled delights of the garden of Irem. The spell-bound gateway still exists entire, protected no doubt by the mystic hand and key, and now forms the Gate of Justice, the grand entrance to the fortress. Under that gateway, it is said, the old astrologer remains in his subterranean hall, nodding on his divan, lulled by the silver lyre of the princess.

The old invalid sentinels who mount guard at the gate hear the strains occasionally in the summer nights; and, yielding to their soporific power, doze quietly at their posts. Nay, so drowsy an influence prevades the place, that even those who watch by day may generally be seen nodding on the stone benches of the barbican, or sleeping under the neighboring trees; so that in fact it is the drowsiest military post in all Christendom. All this, say the ancient legends, will endure from age to age. The princess will remain captive to the astrologer; and the astrologer, bound up in magic slumber by the princess, until the last day, unless the mystic hand shall grasp the fated key, and dispel the whole charm of this enchanted mountain.

Legend of the Moor's Legacy

JUST within the fortress of the Alhambra, in front of the royal palace, is a broad open esplanade, called the Place or Square of the Cisterns (la Plaza de los Algibes), so called from being undermined by reservoirs of water, hidden from sight, and which have existed from the time of the Moors. At one corner of this esplanade is a Moorish well, cut through the living rock to a great depth, the water of which is cold as ice and clear as crystal. The wells made by the Moors are always in repute, for it is well known what pains they took to penetrate to the purest and sweetest springs and fountains. The one of which we now speak is famous throughout Granada, insomuch that water-carriers, some bearing great water-jars on their shoulders, others driving asses before them laden with earthen vessels, are ascending and descending the steep woody avenues of the Alhambra, from early dawn until a late hour of the night.

Fountains and wells, ever since the scriptural days, have been noted gossiping-places in hot climates; and at the well in question there is a kind of perpetual club kept up during the livelong day, by the invalids, old women, and other curious do-nothing folk of the fortress, who sit here on the stone benches, under an awning spread over the well to shelter the toll-gatherer from the sun, and dawdle over the gossip of the fortress, and question every water-carrier that arrives about the news of the city, and make long comments on everything they hear and see. Not an hour of the day but loitering housewives and idle maid-servants may be seen, lingering, with pitcher on head or in hand, to hear the last of the endless tattle of these worthies.

Among the water-carriers who once resorted to this well, there was a sturdy, strong-backed, bandy-legged little fellow, named Pedro Gil, but called Peregil for shortness. Being a water-carrier, he was a Gallego, or native of Gallicia, of course. Nature seems to have formed races of men, as she has of animals, for different kinds of drudgery. In France the shoeblacks are all Savoyards, the porters of hotels all Swiss, and in the days of hoops and hair-powder in England, no man could give the regular swing to a sedan-chair but a bog-trotting Irishman. So in Spain, the carriers of water and bearers of burdens are all sturdy little natives of Gallicia. No man says, "Get me a porter," but, "Call a Gallego."

To return from this digression, Peregil the Gallego had begun business with merely a great earthen jar which he carried upon his shoulder; by degrees he rose in the world, and was enabled to purchase an assistant of a correspondent class of animals, being a stout shaggy-haired donkey. On each side of this his long-eared aide-de-camp, in a kind of pannier, were slung his water-jars, covered with fig-leaves to protect them from the sun. There was not a more industrious water-carrier in all Granada, nor one more merry withal. The streets rang with his cheerful voice as he trudged after his donkey, singing forth the usual summer note that resounds through the Spanish towns: "*Quien quiere agua—agua mas fria que la nieve?*"—"Who wants water—water colder than snow? Who wants water from the well of the Alhambra, cold as ice and clear as crystal?" When he served a customer with a sparkling glass, it was always with a pleasant word that caused a smile; and if, perchance, it was a comely dame or dimpling damsel, it was always with a sly leer and a compliment to her beauty that was irresistible. Thus Peregil the Gallego was noted throughout all Granada for being one of the civilest, pleasantest, and happiest of mortals. Yet it is not he who sings loudest and jokes most that has the lightest heart. Under all this air of merriment, honest Peregil had his cares and troubles. He had a large family of ragged children to support, who were hungry and clamorous as a nest of young swallows, and beset him with their outcries for food whenever he came home of an evening. He had a helpmate, too, who was anything but a help to him. She had been a village beauty before marriage, noted for her skill at dancing the bolero and rattling the castanets; and she still retained her early propensities, spending the hard earnings of honest Peregil in frippery, and laying the very donkey under requisition for junketing parties into the country on Sundays and saints' days, and those innumerable holidays, which are rather more numerous in Spain than the days of the week. With all this she was a little of a slattern, something more of a lie-abed, and, above all, a gossip of the first water; neglecting house, household, and everything else, to loiter slipshod in the houses of her gossip neighbors.

He, however, who tempers the wind to the shorn lamb, accommodates the yoke of matrimony to the submissive neck. Peregil bore all the heavy dispensations of wife and children with as meek a spirit as his donkey bore the water-jars; and, however he might shake his ears in private, never ventured to question the household virtues of his slattern spouse.

He loved his children, too, even as an owl loves its owlets, seeing in them his own image multiplied and perpetuated; for they were a sturdy, long-backed, bandy-legged little brood. The great pleasure of honest Peregil was, whenever he could afford himself a scanty holiday, and had a handful of maravedis to spare, to take the whole litter forth with him, some in his arms, some tugging at his skirts, and some trudging at his heels, and to treat them to a gambol among the orchards of the Vega, while his wife was dancing with her holiday friends in the Angosturas of the Darro.

It was a late hour one summer night, and most of the water-carriers had desisted from their toils. The day had been uncommonly sultry; the night was one of those delicious moonlights which tempt the inhabitants of southern climes to indemnify themselves for the heat and inaction of the day, by lingering in the open air, and enjoying its tempered sweetness until after midnight. Customers for water were therefore still abroad. Peregil, like a considerate, painstaking father, thought of his hungry children. "One more journey to the well," said he to himself, "to earn a Sunday's puchero for the little ones." So saying, he trudged manfully up the steep avenue of the Alhambra, singing as he went, and now and then bestowing a hearty thwack with a cudgel on the flanks of his donkey, either by way of cadence to the song, or refreshment to the animal; for dry blows serve in lieu of provender in Spain for all beasts of burden.

When arrived at the well, he found it deserted by every one except a solitary stranger in Moorish garb, seated on a stone bench in the moonlight. Peregil paused at first and regarded him with surprise, not unmixed with awe, but the Moor feebly beckoned him to approach. "I am faint and ill," said he; "aid me to return to the city, and I will pay thee double what thou couldst gain by thy jars of water."

The honest heart of the little water-carrier was touched with compassion at the appeal of the stranger. "God forbid," said he, "that I should ask fee or reward for doing a common act of humanity." He accordingly helped the Moor on his donkey, and set off slowly for Granada, the poor Moslem being so weak that it was necessary to hold him on the animal to keep him from falling to the earth.

When they entered the city, the water-carrier demanded whither he should conduct him. "Alas!" said the Moor, faintly, "I have neither home nor habitation; I am a stranger in the land. Suffer me to lay my head this night beneath thy roof, and thou shalt be amply repaid."

Honest Peregil thus saw himself unexpectedly saddled with an infidel guest, but he was too humane to refuse a night's shelter to a fellow-being in so forlorn a plight; so he conducted the Moor to his dwelling. The children, who had sallied forth open-mouthed as usual on hearing the tramp of the donkey, ran back with affright when they beheld the turbaned stranger, and hid themselves behind their mother. The latter stepped forth intrepidly, like a ruffling hen before her brood when a vagrant dog approaches.

"What infidel companion," cried she, "is this you have brought home at this late hour, to draw upon us the eyes of the inquisition?"

"Be quiet, wife," replied the Gallego; "here is a poor sick stranger, without friend or home; wouldst thou turn him forth to perish in the streets?"

The wife would still have remonstrated, for although she lived in a hovel, she was a furious stickler for the credit of her house; the little water-carrier, however, for once was stiffnecked, and refused to bend beneath the yoke. He assisted the poor Moslem to alight, and spread a mat and a sheep-skin for him, on the ground, in the coolest part of the house; being the only kind of bed that his poverty afforded.

In a little while the Moor was seized with violent convulsions, which defied all the ministering skill of the simple water-carrier.

The eye of the poor patient acknowledged his kindness. During an interval of his fits he called him to his side, and addressing him in a low voice, "My end," said he, "I fear is at hand. If I die, I bequeath you this box as a reward for your charity:" so saying, he opened his albornoz, or cloak, and showed a small box of sandal-wood, strapped round his body. "God grant, my friend," replied the worthy little Gallego, "that you may live many years to enjoy your treasure, whatever it may be." The Moor shook his head; he laid his hand upon the box, and would have said something more concerning it, but his convulsions returned with increasing violence, and in a little while he expired.

The water-carrier's wife was now as one distracted. "This comes," said she, "of your foolish good-nature, always running into scrapes to oblige others. What will become of us when this corpse is found in our house? We shall be sent to prison as murderers; and if we escape with our lives, shall be ruined by notaries and alguazils."

Poor Peregil was in equal tribulation, and almost repented himself of having done a good deed. At length a thought struck him. "It is not yet day," said he; "I can convey the dead body out of the city, and bury it in the sands on the banks of the Xenil. No one saw the Moor enter our dwelling, and no one will know anything of his death."

So said, so done. The wife aided him; they rolled the body of the unfortunate Moslem in the mat on which he had expired, laid it across the ass, and Peregil set out with it for the banks of the river.

As ill luck would have it, there lived opposite to the water-carrier a barber named Pedrillo Pedrugo, one of the most prying, tattling, and mischief-making of his gossip tribe. He was a weasel-faced, spider-legged varlet, supple and insinuating; the famous barber of Seville could not surpass him for his universal knowledge of the affairs of others, and he had no more power of retention than a sieve. It was said that he slept but with one eye at a time, and kept one ear uncovered, so that even in his sleep he might see and hear all that was going on. Certain it is, he was a sort of scandalous chronicle for the quidnuncs of Granada, and had more customers than all the rest of his fraternity.

This meddlesome barber heard Peregil arrive at an unusual

hour at night, and the exclamations of his wife and children. His head was instantly popped out of a little window which served him as a look-out, and he saw his neighbor assist a man in Moorish garb into his dwelling. This was so strange an occurrence, that Pedrillo Pedrugo slept not a wink that night. Every five minutes he was at his loophole, watching the lights that gleamed through the chinks of his neighbor's door, and before daylight he beheld Peregil sally forth with his donkey unusually laden.

The inquisitive barber was in a fidget; he slipped on his clothes, and, stealing forth silently, followed the water-carrier at a distance, until he saw him dig a hole in the sandy bank of the Xenil, and bury something that had the appearance of a dead body.

The barber hied him home, and fidgeted about his shop, setting everything upside down, until sunrise. He then took a basin under his arm, and sallied forth to the house of his daily customer the alcalde.

The alcalde was just risen. Pedrillo Pedrugo seated him in a chair, threw a napkin round his neck, put a basin of hot water under his chin, and began to mollify his beard with his fingers.

"Strange doings!" said Pedrugo, who played barber and newsmonger at the same time—"strange doings! Robbery, and murder, and burial all in one night!"

"Hey!—how!—what is that you say?" cried the alcalde.

"I say," replied the barber, rubbing a piece of soap over the nose and mouth of the dignitary, for a Spanish barber disdains to employ a brush—"I say that Peregil the Gallego has robbed and murdered a Moorish Mussulman, and buried him, this blessed night. *Maldita sea la noche*—Accursed be the night for the same!"

"But how do you know all this?" demanded the alcalde.

"Be patient, Señor, and you shall hear all about it," replied Pedrillo, taking him by the nose and sliding a razor over his cheek. He then recounted all that he had seen, going through both operations at the same time, shaving his beard, washing his chin, and wiping him dry with a dirty napkin, while he was robbing, murdering, and burying the Moslem.

Now it so happened that this alcalde was one of the most

overbearing, and at the same time most griping and corrupt curmudgeons in all Granada. It could not be denied, however, that he set a high value upon justice, for he sold it at its weight in gold. He presumed the case in point to be one of murder and robbery; doubtless there must be a rich spoil; how was it to be secured into the legitimate hands of the law? for as to merely entrapping the delinquent—that would be feeding the gallows; but entrapping the booty—that would be enriching the judge, and such, according to his creed, was the great end of justice. So thinking, he summoned to his presence his trustiest alguazil—a gaunt, hungry-looking varlet, clad, according to the custom of his order, in the ancient Spanish garb, a broad black beaver turned up at its sides; a quaint ruff; a small black cloak dangling from his shoulders; rusty black under-clothes that set off his spare wiry frame, while in his hand he bore a slender white wand, the dreaded insignia of his office. Such was the legal bloodhound of the ancient Spanish breed, that he put upon the traces of the unlucky water-carrier, and such was his speed and certainty, that he was upon the haunches of poor Peregil before he had returned to his dwelling, and brought both him and his donkey before the dispenser of justice.

The alcalde bent upon him one of the most terrific frowns. "Hark ye, culprit!" roared he, in a voice that made the knees of the little Gallego smite together—"hark ye, culprit! there is no need of denying thy guilt, everything is known to me. A gallows is the proper reward for the crime thou hast committed, but I am merciful, and readily listen to reason. The man that has been murdered in thy house was a Moor, an infidel, the enemy of our faith. It was doubtless in a fit of religious zeal that thou hast slain him. I will be indulgent, therefore; render up the property of which thou hast robbed him, and we will hush the matter up."

The poor water-carrier called upon all the saints to witness his innocence; alas! not one of them appeared; and if they had, the alcalde would have disbelieved the whole calendar. The water-carrier related the whole story of the dying Moor with the straightforward simplicity of truth, but it was all in vain. "Wilt thou persist in saying," demanded the judge, "that this Moslem had neither gold nor jewels, which were the object of thy cupidity?"

"As I hope to be saved, your worship," replied the water-carrier, "he had nothing but a small box of sandal-wood, which he bequeathed to me in reward for my services."

"A box of sandal-wood! a box of sandal-wood!" exclaimed the alcalde, his eyes sparkling at the idea of precious jewels. "And where is this box? where have you concealed it?"

"An' it please your grace," replied the water-carrier, "it is in one of the panniers of my mule, and heartily at the service of your worship."

He had hardly spoken the words, when the keen alguazil darted off, and reappeared in an instant with the mysterious box of sandal-wood. The alcalde opened it with an eager and trembling hand; all pressed forward to gaze upon the treasure it was expected to contain; when, to their disappointment, nothing appeared within, but a parchment scroll, covered with Arabic characters, and an end of a waxen taper.

When there is nothing to be gained by the conviction of a prisoner, justice, even in Spain, is apt to be impartial. The alcalde, having recovered from his disappointment, and found that there was really no booty in the case, now listened dispassionately to the explanation of the water-carrier, which was corroborated by the testimony of his wife. Being convinced, therefore, of his innocence, he discharged him from arrest; nay more, he permitted him to carry off the Moor's legacy, the box of sandal-wood and its contents, as the well-merited reward of his humanity; but he retained his donkey in payment of costs and charges.

Behold the unfortunate little Gallego reduced once more to the necessity of being his own water-carrier, and trudging up to the well of the Alhambra, a great earthen jar upon his shoulder.

As he toiled up the hill in the heat of a summer noon, his usual good-humor forsook him. "Dog of an alcalde!" would he cry, "to rob a poor man of the means of his subsistence, of the best friend he had in the world!" And then at the remembrance of the beloved companion of his labors, all the kindness of his nature would break forth. "Ah, donkey of my heart!" would he exclaim, resting his burden on a stone, and wiping the sweat from his brow—"ah, donkey of my heart! I warrant me thou thinkest of thy old master! I warrant me thou missest the water-jars—poor beast."

To add to his afflictions, his wife received him, on his return home, with whimperings and repinings; she had clearly the vantage-ground of him, having warned him not to commit the egregious act of hospitality which had brought on him all these misfortunes; and, like a knowing woman, she took every occasion to throw her superior sagacity in his teeth. If her children lacked food, or needed a new garment, she could answer with a sneer, "Go to your father—he is heir to king Chico of the Alhambra: ask him to help you out of the Moor's strong box."

Was ever poor mortal so soundly punished for having done a good action? The unlucky Peregil was grieved in flesh and spirit, but still he bore meekly with the railings of his spouse. At length, one evening, when, after a hot day's toil, she taunted him in the usual manner, he lost all patience. He did not venture to retort upon her, but his eye rested upon the box of sandal-wood, which lay on a shelf with lid half open, as if laughing in mockery at his vexation. Seizing it up, he dashed it with indignation to the floor. "Unlucky was the day that I ever set eyes on thee," he cried, "or sheltered thy master beneath my roof!"

As the box struck the floor, the lid flew wide open, and the parchment scroll rolled forth.

Peregil sat regarding the scroll for some time in moody silence. At length rallying his ideas, "Who knows," thought he, "but this writing may be of some importance, as the Moor seems to have guarded it with such care?" Picking it up therefore, he put it in his bosom, and the next morning, as he was crying water through the streets, he stopped at the shop of a Moor, a native of Tangiers, who sold trinkets and perfumery in the Zacatin, and asked him to explain the contents.

The Moor read the scroll attentively, then stroked his beard and smiled. "This manuscript," said he, "is a form of incantation for the recovery of hidden treasure that is under the power of enchantment. It is said to have such virtue that the strongest bolts and bars, nay the adamantine rock itself, will yield before it!"

"Bah!" cried the little Gallego, "what is all that to me? I am no enchanter, and know nothing of buried treasure." So saying, he shouldered his water-jar, left the scroll in the hands of the Moor, and trudged forward on his daily rounds.

That evening, however, as he rested himself about twilight at the well of the Alhambra, he found a number of gossips assembled at the place, and their conversation, as is not unusual at that shadowy hour, turned upon old tales and traditions of a supernatural nature. Being all poor as rats, they dwelt with peculiar fondness upon the popular theme of enchanted riches left by the Moors in various parts of the Alhambra. Above all, they concurred in the belief that there were great treasures buried deep in the earth under the tower of the seven floors.

These stories made an unusual impression on the mind of the honest Peregil, and they sank deeper and deeper into his thoughts as he returned alone down the darkling avenues. "If, after all, there should be treasure hid beneath that tower; and if the scroll I left with the Moor should enable me to get at it!" In the sudden ecstasy of the thought he had wellnigh let fall his water-jar.

That night he tumbled and tossed, and could scarcely get a wink of sleep for the thoughts that were bewildering his brain. Bright and early he repaired to the shop of the Moor, and told him all that was passing in his mind. "You can read Arabic," said he; "suppose we go together to the tower, and try the effect of the charm; if it fails, we are no worse off than before; but if it succeeds, we will share equally all the treasure we may discover."

"Hold," replied the Moslem; "this writing is not sufficient of itself; it must be read at midnight, by the light of a taper singularly compounded and prepared, the ingredients of which are not within my reach. Without such a taper the scroll is of no avail."

"Say no more!" cried the little Gallego; "I have such a taper at hand, and will bring it here in a moment." So saying, he hastened home, and soon returned with the end of yellow wax taper that he had found in the box of sandal-wood.

The Moor felt it and smelt to it. "Here are rare and costly perfumes," said he, "combined with this yellow wax. This is the kind of taper specified in the scroll. While this burns, the strongest walls and most secret caverns will remain open. Woe to him, however, who lingers within until it be extinguished. He will remain enchanted with the treasure."

It was now agreed between them to try the charm that very

night. At a late hour, therefore, when nothing was stirring but bats and owls, they ascended the woody hill of the Alhambra, and approached that awful tower, shrouded by trees and rendered formidable by so many traditionary tales. By the light of a lantern they groped their way through bushes, and over fallen stones, to the door of a vault beneath the tower. With fear and trembling they descended a flight of steps cut into the rock. It led to an empty chamber, damp and drear, from which another flight of steps led to a deeper vault. In this way they descended four several flights, leading into as many vaults, one below the other, but the floor of the fourth was solid; and though, according to tradition, there remained three vaults still below, it was said to be impossible to penetrate further, the residue being shut up by strong enchantment. The air of this vault was damp and chilly, and had an earthy smell, and the light scarce cast forth any rays. They paused here for a time, in breathless suspense, until they faintly heard the clock of the watch-tower strike midnight; upon this they lit the waxen taper, which diffused an odor of myrrh and frankincense and storax.

The Moor began to read in a hurried voice. He had scarce finished when there was a noise as of subterraneous thunder. The earth shook, and the floor, yawning open, disclosed a flight of steps. Trembling with awe, they descended, and by the light of the lantern found themselves in another vault covered with Arabic inscriptions. In the centre stood a great chest, secured with seven bands of steel, at each end of which sat an enchanted Moor in armor, but motionless as a statue, being controlled by the power of the incantation. Before the chest were several jars filled with gold and silver and precious stones. In the largest of these they thrust their arms up to the elbow, and at every dip hauled forth handfuls of broad yellow pieces of Moorish gold, or bracelets and ornaments of the same precious metal, while occasionally a necklace of Oriental pearl would stick to their fingers. Still they trembled and breathed short while cramming their pockets with the spoils; and cast many a fearful glance at the two enchanted Moors, who sat grim and motionless, glaring upon them with unwinking eyes. At length, struck with a sudden panic at some fancied noise, they both rushed up the staircase, tumbled over one another into the upper apartment, overturned and extinguished the waxen taper, and the pavement again closed with a thundering sound.

Filled with dismay, they did not pause until they had groped their way out of the tower, and beheld the stars shining through the trees. Then seating themselves upon the grass, they divided the spoil, determining to content themselves for the present with this mere skimming of the jars, but to return on some future night and drain them to the bottom. To make sure of each other's good faith, also, they divided the talismans between them, one retaining the scroll and the other the taper; this done, they set off with light hearts and well-lined pockets for Granada.

As they wended their way down the hill, the shrewd Moor whispered a word of counsel in the ear of the simple little water-carrier.

"Friend Peregil," said he, "all this affair must be kept a profound secret until we have secured the treasure, and conveyed it out of harm's way. If a whisper of it gets to the ear of the alcalde, we are undone!"

"Certainly," replied the Gallego, "nothing can be more true."

"Friend Peregil," said the Moor, "you are a discreet man, and I make no doubt can keep a secret; but you have a wife."

"She shall not know a word of it," replied the little water-carrier, sturdily.

"Enough," said the Moor, "I depend upon thy discretion and thy promise."

Never was promise more positive and sincere; but, alas! what man can keep a secret from his wife? Certainly not such a one as Peregil the water-carrier, who was one of the most loving and tractable of husbands. On his return home, he found his wife moping in a corner. "Mighty well," cried she as he entered, "you've come at last, after rambling about until this hour of the night. I wonder you have not brought home another Moor as a house-mate." Then bursting into tears, she began to wring her hands and smite her breast. "Unhappy woman that I am!" exclaimed she, "what will become of me? My house stripped and plundered by lawyers and alguazils; my husband a do-no-good, that no longer brings home bread to his family, but goes rambling about day and night, with infidel Moors! O my children!

my children! what will become of us? We shall all have to beg in the streets!"

Honest Peregil was so moved by the distress of his spouse, that he could not help whimpering also. His heart was as full as his pocket, and not to be restrained. Thrusting his hand into the latter he hauled forth three or four broad gold pieces, and slipped them into her bosom. The poor woman stared with astonishment, and could not understand the meaning of this golden shower. Before she could recover her surprise, the little Gallego drew forth a chain of gold and dangled it before her, capering with exultation, his mouth distended from ear to ear.

"Holy Virgin protect us!" exclaimed the wife. "What hast thou been doing, Peregil? surely thou hast not been committing murder and robbery!"

The idea scarce entered the brain of the poor woman, than it became a certainty with her. She saw a prison and a gallows in the distance, and a little bandy-legged Gallego hanging pendent from it; and, overcome by the horrors conjured up by imagination, fell into violent hysterics.

What could the poor man do? He had no other means of pacifying his wife, and dispelling the phantoms of her fancy, than by relating the whole story of his good fortune. This, however, he did not do until he had exacted from her the most solemn promise to keep it a profound secret from every living being.

To describe her joy would be impossible. She flung her arms round the neck of her husband, and almost strangled him with her caresses. "Now, wife," exclaimed the little man with honest exultation, "what say you now to the Moor's legacy? Henceforth never abuse me for helping a fellow-creature in distress."

The honest Gallego retired to his sheep-skin mat, and slept as soundly as if on a bed of down. Not so his wife; she emptied the whole contents of his pockets upon the mat, and sat counting gold pieces of Arabic coin, trying on necklaces and earrings, and fancying the figure she should one day make when permitted to enjoy her riches.

On the following morning the honest Gallego took a broad golden coin, and repaired with it to a jeweller's shop in the Zacatin to offer it for sale, pretending to have found it among the ruins of the Alhambra. The jeweller saw that it had an Arabic inscription, and was of the purest gold; he offered, however, but a third of its value, with which the water-carrier was perfectly content. Peregil now bought new clothes for his little flock, and all kinds of toys, together with ample provisions for a hearty meal, and returning to his dwelling, set all his children dancing around him, while he capered in the midst, the happiest of fathers.

The wife of the water-carrier kept her promise of secrecy with surprising strictness. For a whole day and a half she went about with a look of mystery and a heart swelling almost to bursting, yet she held her peace, though surrounded by her gossips. It is true, she could not help giving herself a few airs, apologized for her ragged dress, and talked of ordering a new basquina all trimmed with gold lace and bugles, and a new lace mantilla. She threw out hints of her husband's intention of leaving off his trade of water-carrying, as it did not altogether agree with his health. In fact she thought they should all retire to the country for the summer, that the children might have the benefit of the mountain air, for there was no living in the city in this sultry season.

The neighbors stared at each other, and thought the poor woman had lost her wits; and her airs and graces and elegant pretensions were the theme of universal scoffing and merriment among her friends, the moment her back was turned.

If she restrained herself abroad, however, she indemnified herself at home, and putting a string of rich Oriental pearls round her neck, Moorish bracelets on her arms, and an aigrette of diamonds on her head, sailed backwards and forwards in her slattern rags about the room, now and then stopping to admire herself in a broken mirror. Nay, in the impulse of her simple vanity, she could not resist, on one occasion, showing herself at the window to enjoy the effect of her finery on the passers-by.

As the fates would have it, Pedrillo Pedrugo, the meddlesome barber, was at this moment sitting idly in his shop on the opposite side of the street, when his ever-watchful eye caught the sparkle of a diamond. In an instant he was at his loophole reconnoitring the slattern spouse of the water-carrier, decorated with the splendor of an eastern bride. No sooner had he taken an accurate inventory of her ornaments, than he posted off with all speed to the alcalde. In a little while the hungry alguazil was again on the scent, and before the day was over the unfortunate Peregil was once more dragged into the presence of the judge.

"How is this, villain!" cried the alcalde, in a furious voice. "You told me that the infidel who died in your house left nothing behind but an empty coffer, and now I hear of your wife flaunting in her rags decked out with pearls and diamonds. Wretch that thou art! prepare to render up the spoils of thy miserable victim, and to swing on the gallows that is already tired of waiting for thee."

The terrified water-carrier fell on his knees, and made a full relation of the marvellous manner in which he had gained his wealth. The alcalde, the alguazil, and the inquisitive barber listened with greedy ears to this Arabian tale of enchanted treasure. The alguazil was dispatched to bring the Moor who had assisted in the incantation. The Moslem entered half frightened out of his wits at finding himself in the hands of the harpies of the law. When he beheld the water-carrier standing with sheepish looks and downcast countenance, he comprehended the whole matter. "Miserable animal," said he, as he passed near him, "did I not warn thee against babbling to thy wife?"

The story of the Moor coincided exactly with that of his colleague; but the alcalde affected to be slow of belief, and threw out menaces of imprisonment and rigorous investigation.

"Softly, good Señor Alcalde," said the Mussulman, who by this time had recovered his usual shrewdness and self-possession. "Let us not mar fortune's favors in the scramble for them. Nobody knows anything of this matter but ourselves; let us keep the secret. There is wealth enough in the cave to enrich us all. Promise a fair division, and all shall be produced; refuse, and the cave shall remain forever closed."

The alcalde consulted apart with alguazil. The latter was an old fox in his profession. "Promise anything," said he, "until you get possession of the treasure. You may then seize upon the whole, and if he and his accomplice dare to murmur, threaten them with the fagot and the stake as infidels and sorcerers."

The alcalde relished the advice. Smoothing his brow and turning to the Moor, "This is a strange story," said he, "and may be true, but I must have ocular proof of it. This very night you must repeat the incantation in my presence. If there be really such treasure, we will share it amicably between us, and say nothing further of the matter; if ye have deceived me, expect no mercy at my hands. In the meantime you must remain in custody."

The Moor and the water-carrier cheerfully agreed to these conditions, satisfied that the event would prove the truth of their words.

Towards midnight the alcalde sallied forth secretly, attended by the alguazil and the meddlesome barber, all strongly armed. They conducted the Moor and the water-carrier as prisoners, and were provided with the stout donkey of the latter to bear off the expected treasure. They arrived at the tower without being observed, and tying the donkey to a fig-tree, descended into the fourth vault of the tower.

The scroll was produced, the yellow waxen taper lighted, and the Moor read the form of incantation. The earth trembled as before, and the pavement opened with a thundering sound, disclosing the narrow flight of steps. The alcalde, the alguazil, and the barber were struck aghast, and could not summon courage to descend. The Moor and the water-carrier entered the lower vault, and found the two Moors seated as before, silent and motionless. They removed two of the great jars, filled with golden coin and precious stones. The water-carrier bore them up one by one upon his shoulders, but though a strong-backed little man, and accustomed to carry burdens, he staggered beneath their weight, and found, when slung on each side of his donkey, they were as much as the animal could bear.

"Let us be content for the present," said the Moor; "here is as much treasure as we can carry off without being perceived, and enough to make us all wealthy to our heart's desire."

"Is there more treasure remaining behind?" demanded the alcalde.

"The greatest prize of all," said the Moor, "a huge coffer bound with bands of steel, and filled with pearls and precious stones."

"Let us have up the coffer by all means," cried the grasping alcalde.

"I will descend for no more," said the Moor, doggedly;

"enough is enough for a reasonable man—more is superfluous."

"And I," said the water-carrier, "will bring up no further burden to break the back of my poor donkey."

Finding commands, threats, and entreaties equally vain, the alcalde turned to his two adherents. "Aid me," said he, "to bring up the coffer, and its contents shall be divided between us." So saying, he descended the steps, followed with trembling reluctance by the alguazil and the barber.

No sooner did the Moor behold them fairly earthed than he extinguished the yellow taper; the pavement closed with its usual crash, and the three worthies remained buried in its womb.

He then hastened up the different flight of steps, nor stopped until in the open air. The little water-carrier followed him as fast as his short legs would permit.

"What hast thou done?" cried Peregil, as soon as he could recover breath. "The alcalde and the other two are shut up in the vault."

"It is the will of Allah!" said the Moor, devoutly.

"And will you not release them?" demanded the Gallego.

"Allah forbid!" replied the Moor, smoothing his beard. "It is written in the book of fate that they shall remain enchanted until some future adventurer arrive to break the charm. The will of God be done!" so saying, he hurled the end of the waxen taper far among the gloomy thickets of the glen.

There was now no remedy; so the Moor and the water-carrier proceeded with the richly laden donkey toward the city, nor could honest Peregil refrain from hugging and kissing his long-eared fellow-laborer, thus restored to him from the clutches of the law; and, in fact, it is doubtful which gave the simple-hearted little man most joy at the moment, the gaining of the treasure, or the recovery of the donkey.

The two partners in good luck divided their spoil amicably and fairly, except that the Moor, who had a little taste for trinketry, made out to get into his heap the most of the pearls and precious stones and other baubles, but then he always gave the water-carrier in lieu magnificent jewels of massy gold, of five times the size, with which the latter was heartily content. They took care not to linger within reach of accidents, but made off to enjoy their wealth undisturbed in other countries. The Moor returned to Africa, to his native city of Tangiers, and the Gallego, with his wife, his children, and his donkey, made the best of his way to Portugal. Here, under the admonition and tuition of his wife, he became a personage of some consequence, for she made the worthy little man array his long body and short legs in doublet and hose, with a feather in his hat and a sword by his side, and laying aside his familiar appellation of Peregil, assume the more sonorous title of Don Pedro Gil: his progeny grew up a thriving and merry-hearted, though short and bandy-legged generation, while Señora Gil, befringed, belaced, and betasselled from her head to her heels, with glittering rings on every finger, became a model of slattern fashion and finery.

As to the alcalde and his adjuncts, they remained shut up under the great tower of the seven floors, and there they remain spellbound at the present day. Whenever there shall be a lack in Spain of pimping barbers, sharking alguazils, and corrupt alcaldes, they may be sought after; but if they have to wait until such time for their deliverance, there is danger of their enchantment enduring until doomsday.

V. From Wolfert's *Roost and Other Papers*

Wolfert's Roost

CHRONICLE I

ABOUT five-and-twenty miles from the ancient and renowned city of Manhattan, formerly called New Amsterdam, and vulgarly called New York, on the eastern bank of that expansion of the Hudson known among Dutch mariners of yore as the Tappan Zee, being in fact the great Mediterranean Sea of the New Netherlands, stands a little, old-fashioned stone mansion, all made up of gable ends, and as full or angles and corners as an old cocked hat. It is said, in fact, to have been modelled after the cocked hat of Peter the Headstrong, as the Escurial was modelled after the gridiron of the blessed St. Lawrence. Though but of small dimensions, yet, like many small people, it is of mighty spirit, and values itself greatly on its antiquity, being one of the oldest edifices, for its size, in the whole country. It claims to be an ancient seat of empire—I may rather say an empire in itself—and like all empires, great and small, has had its grand historical epochs. In speaking of this doughty and valorous little pile, I shall call it by its usual appellation of "The Roost"; though that is a name given to it in modern days, since it became the abode of the white man.

Its origin, in truth, dates far back in that remote region commonly called the fabulous age, in which vulgar fact becomes mystified and tinted up with delectable fiction. The eastern shore of the Tappan Sea was inhabited in those days by an unsophisticated race, existing in all the simplicity of nature; that is to say, they lived by hunting and fishing, and recreated themselves occasionally with a little tomahawking and scalping. Each stream that flows down from the hills into the Hudson had its petty sachem, who ruled over a hand's-breath of forest on either side, and had his seat of government at its mouth. The chieftain who ruled at the Roost was not merely a great warrior, but a medicine-man, or prophet, or conjurer, for they all mean the same thing in Indian parlance. Of his fighting propensities evidences still remain, in various arrow-heads of flint, and stone battle-axes, occasionally digged up about the Roost; of his wizard powers we have a token in a spring which wells up at the foot of the bank, on the very margin of the river, which, it is said, was gifted by him with rejuvenating powers, something like the renowned Fountain of Youth in the Floridas, so anxiously but vainly sought after by the veteran Ponce de Leon. This story, however, is stoutly contradicted by an old Dutch matter-of-fact tradition, which declares that the spring in question was smuggled over from Holland in a churn, by Femmetie Van Blarcom, wife of Goosen Garret Van Blarcom, one of the first settlers, and that she took it up by night, unknown to her husband, from beside their farmhouse near Rotterdam; being sure she should find no water equal to it in the new country—and she was right.

The wizard sachem had a great passion for discussing territorial questions, and settling boundary lines; in other words, he had the spirit of annexation. This kept him in continual feud with the neighboring sachems, each of whom stood up stoutly for his hand-breadth of territory; so that there is not a petty stream nor rugged hill in the neighborhood that has not been the subject of long talks and hard battles. The sachem, however, as has been observed, was a medicine-man as well as warrior, and vindicated his claims by arts as well as arms; so that, by dint of a little hard fighting here, and hocus-pocus (or diplomacy) there, he managed to extend his boundary line from field to field, and stream to stream, until it brought him into collision with the powerful sachem of Sing-Sing.* Many were the sharp conflicts between these rival chieftains for the sovereignty of a winding valley, a favorite hunting-ground watered by a beautiful stream called the Pocantico. Many were the ambuscades, surprisals, and deadly onslaughts that took place among its fastnesses, of which it grieves me much that I cannot pursue the details, for the gratification of those gentle but bloody-minded readers, of both sexes, who delight in the romance of the tomahawk and scalping-knife. Suffice it to say, that the wizard chieftain was at length victorious, though his victory is attributed, in Indian tradition, to a

* A corruption of the old Indian name, O-sin-sing. Some have rendered it, O-sin-song, or, O-sing-song, in token of its being a great market-town, where anything may be had for a mere song. Its present melodious alteration to Sing-sing is said to have been made in compliment to a Yankee singing-master, who taught the inhabitants the art of singing through their nose.

great medicine, or charm, by which he laid the sachem of Sing Sing and his warriors asleep among the rocks and recesses of the valley, where they remain asleep to the present day, with their bows and war-clubs beside them. This was the origin of that potent and drowsy spell, which still prevails over the valley of the Pocantico, and which has gained it the well-merited appellation of Sleepy Hollow. Often, in secluded and quiet parts of that valley, where the stream is overhung by dark woods and rocks, the ploughman, on some calm and sunny day, as he shouts to his oxen, is surprised at hearing faint shouts from the hill-sides in reply; being, it is said, the spell-bound warriors, who half start from their rocky couches and grasp their weapons, but sink to sleep again.

The conquest of the Pocantico was the last triumph of the wizard sachem. Notwithstanding all his medicines and charms, he fell in battle, in attempting to extend his boundary line to the east, so as to take in the little wild valley of the Sprain; and his grave is still shown, near the banks of that pastoral stream. He left, however, a great empire to his successors, extending along the Tappan Sea, from Yonkers quite to Sleepy Hollow, and known in old records and maps by the Indian name of Wicquaes-Keck.

The wizard sachem was succeeded by a line of chiefs of whom nothing remarkable remains on record. One of them was the very individual on whom master Hendrick Hudson and his mate Robert Juet made that sage experiment gravely recorded by the latter in the narrative of the discovery.

"Our master and his mate determined to try some of the cheefe men of the country, whether they had any treacherie in them. So they took them down into the cabin, and gave them so much wine and aqua vitæ, that they were all very merrie; one of them had his wife with him, which sate so modestly as any of our country-women who would do in a strange place. In the end, one of them was drunke; and that was strange to them, for they could not tell how to take it." *

How far master Hendrick Hudson and his worthy mate carried their experiment with the sachem's wife, is not recorded; neither does the curious Robert Juet make any mention of the

* See Juet's Journal, Purchas' Pilgrams.

after consequences of this grand moral test; tradition, however, affirms that the sachem, on landing, gave his modest spouse a hearty rib-roasting, according to the connubial discipline of the aboriginals; it farther affirms that he remained a hard drinker to the day of his death, trading away all his lands, acre by acre, for aqua vitæ; by which means the Roost and all its domains, from Yonkers to Sleepy Hollow, came, in the regular course of trade, and by right of purchase, into the possession of the Dutchmen.

The worthy government of the New Netherlands was not suffered to enjoy this grand acquisition unmolested. In the year 1654, the losel Yankees of Connecticut, those swapping, bargaining, squatting enemies of the Manhattoes, made a daring inroad into this neighborhood, and founded a colony called Westchester, or, as the ancient Dutch records term it, Vest Dorp, in the right of one Thomas Pell, who pretended to have purchased the whole surrounding country of the Indians, and stood ready to argue their claims before any tribunal of Christendom.

This happened during the chivalrous reign of Peter Stuyvesant, and roused the ire of that gunpowder old hero. Without waiting to discuss claims and titles, he pounced at once upon the nest of nefarious squatters, carried off twenty-five of them in chains to the Manhattoes; nor did he stay his hand, nor give rest to his wooden leg, until he had driven the rest of the Yankees back into Connecticut, or obliged them to acknowledge allegiance to their High Mightinesses. In revenge, however, they introduced the plague of witchcraft into the province. This doleful malady broke out at Vest Dorp, and would have spread throughout the country had not the Dutch farmers nailed horse-shoes to the doors of their houses and barns, sure protections against witchcraft, many of which remain to the present day.

The seat of empire of the wizard sachem now came into the possession of Wolfert Acker, one of the privy councillors of Peter Stuyvesant. He was a worthy, but ill-starred man, whose aim through life had been to live in peace and quiet. For this he had emigrated from Holland, driven abroad by family feuds and wrangling neighbors. He had warred for quiet through the fidgety reign of William the Testy, and the fighting reign of Peter the Headstrong, sharing in every brawl and rib-roasting, in his eagerness to keep the peace and promote public tranquillity. It was his doom, in fact, to meet a head-wind at every turn, and be kept in a constant fume and fret by the perverseness of mankind. Had he served on a modern jury, he would have been sure to have eleven unreasonable men opposed to him.

At the time when the province of the New Netherlands was wrested from the domination of their High Mightinesses by the combined forces of Old and New England, Wolfert retired in high dudgeon to this fastness in the wilderness, with the bitter determination to bury himself from the world, and live here for the rest of his days in peace and quiet. In token of that fixed purpose, he inscribed over his door (his teeth clinched at the time) his favorite Dutch motto, "Lust in Rust" (pleasure in quiet). The mansion was thence called Wolfert's Rust (Wolfert's Rest), but by the uneducated, who did not understand Dutch, Wolfert's Roost; probably from its quaint cockloft look, and from its having a weathercock perched on every gable.

Wolfert's luck followed him into retirement. He had shut himself up from the world, but he had brought with him a wife, and it soon passed into a proverb throughout the neighborhood that the cock of the Roost was the most henpecked bird in the country. His house too was reputed to be harassed by Yankee witchcraft. When the weather was quiet everywhere else, the wind, it was said, would howl and whistle about the gables; witches and warlocks would whirl about upon the weathercocks, and scream down the chimneys; nay, it was even hinted that Wolfert's wife was in league with the enemy, and used to ride on a broomstick to a witches' sabbath in Sleepy Hollow. This, however, was all mere scandal, founded perhaps on her occasionally flourishing a broomstick in the course of a curtain lecture, or raising a storm within doors, as termagant wives are apt to do, and against which sorcery horse-shoes are of no avail.

Wolfert Acker died and was buried, but found no quiet even in the grave; for if popular gossip be true, his ghost has occasionally been seen walking by moonlight among the old gray moss-grown trees of his apple orchard.

CHRONICLE II

The next period at which we find this venerable and eventful pile rising into importance, was during the dark and troublous time of the revolutionary war. It was the keep or stronghold of Jacob Van Tassel, a valiant Dutchman of the old stock of Van Tassels, who abound in Westchester County. The name, as originally written, was Van Texel, being derived from the Texel in Holland, which gave birth to that heroic line.

The Roost stood in the very heart of what at that time was called the debatable ground, lying between the British and American lines. The British held possession of the city and island of New York; while the Americans drew up towards the Highlands, holding their headquarters at Peekskill. The intervening country from Croton River to Spiting Devil Creek was the debatable ground in question, liable to be harried by friend and foe, like the Scottish borders of yore.

It is a rugged region, full of fastnesses. A line of rocky hills extends through it like a backbone sending out ribs on either side; but these rude hills are for the most part richly wooded, and enclose little fresh pastoral valleys watered by the Neperan, the Pocantico,* and other beautiful streams, along which the Indians built their wigwams in the olden time.

In the fastnesses of these hills, and along these valleys, existed, in the time of which I am treating, and indeed exist to the present day, a race of hard-headed, hard-handed, stout-hearted yeomen, descendants of the primitive Nederlanders. Men obstinately attached to the soil, and neither to be fought nor bought out of their paternal acres. Most of them were strong Whigs throughout the war; some, however, were Tories, or adherents to

* The Neperan, vulgarly called the Saw-Mill River, winds for many miles through a lovely valley, shrouded by groves, and dotted by Dutch farm-houses, and empties itself into the Hudson at the ancient Dorp of Yonkers. The Pocantico, rising among woody hills, winds in many a wizard maze through the sequestered haunts of Sleepy Hollow. We owe it to the indefatigable researches of Mr. Knickerbocker, that those beautiful streams are rescued from modern commonplace, and reinvested with their ancient Indian names. The correctness of the venerable historian may be ascertained by reference to the records of the original Indian grants to the Herr Frederick Philipsen, preserved in the county clerk's office at White Plains.

the old kingly rule, who considered the revolution a mere rebellion, soon to be put down by his majesty's forces. A number of these took refuge within the British lines, joined the military bands of refugees, and became pioneers or leaders to foraging parties sent out from New York to scour the country and sweep off supplies for the British army.

In a little while the debatable ground became infested by roving bands, claiming from either side, and all pretending to redress wrongs and punish political offences; but all prone in the exercise of their high functions—to sack hen-roosts, drive off cattle, and lay farm-houses under contribution; such was the origin of two great orders of border chivalry, the Skinners and the Cow Boys, famous in revolutionary story: the former fought, or rather marauded, under the American, the latter, under the British banner. In the zeal of service, both were apt to make blunders, and confound the property of friend and foe. Neither of them in the heat and hurry of a foray had time to ascertain the politics of a horse or cow, which they were driving off into captivity; nor, when they wrung the neck of a rooster, did they trouble their heads whether he crowed for Congress or King George.

To check these enormities, a confederacy was formed among the yeomanry who had suffered from these maraudings. It was composed for the most part of farmers' sons, bold, hard-riding lads, well armed, and well mounted, and undertook to clear the country round of Skinner and Cow Boy, and all other border vermin; as the Holy Brotherhood in old times cleared Spain of the banditti which infested her highways.

Wolfert's Roost was one of the rallying places of this confederacy, and Jacob Van Tassel one of its members. He was eminently fitted for the service; stout of frame, bold of heart, and like his predecessor, the warrior sachem of yore, delighting in daring enterprises. He had an Indian's sagacity in discovering when the enemy was on the maraud, and in hearing the distant tramp of cattle. It seemed as if he had a scout on every hill, and an ear as quick as that of Fine Ear in the fairy tale.

The foraging parties of tories and refugees had now to be secret and sudden in their forays into Westchester County; to make a hasty maraud among the farms, sweep the cattle into a drove, and hurry down to the lines along the river road, or the valley of the Neperan. Before they were half-way down, Jacob Van Tassel, with the holy brotherhood of Tarrytown, Petticoat Lane, and Sleepy Hollow, would be clattering at their heels. And now there would be a general scamper for King's Bridge, the pass over Spiting Devil Creek, into the British lines. Sometimes the moss-tropers would be overtaken, and eased of part of their booty. Sometimes the whole cavalgada would urge its headlong course across the bridge with thundering tramp and dusty whirlwind. At such times their pursuers would rein up their steeds, survey that perilous pass with wary eye, and, wheeling about, indemnify themselves by foraging the refugee region of Morrisania.

While the debatable land was liable to be thus harried, the great Tappan Sea, along which it extends, was likewise domineered over by the foe. British ships of war were anchored here and there in the wide expanses of the river, mere floating castles to hold it in subjection. Stout galleys armed with eighteen pounders, and navigated with sails and oars, cruised about like hawks, while row-boats made descents upon the land, and foraged the country along shore.

It was a sore grievance to the yeomanry along the Tappan Sea to behold that little Mediterranean ploughed by hostile prows, and the noble river of which they were so proud reduced to a state of thraldom. Councils of war were held by captains of market-boats and other river-craft, to devise ways and means of dislodging the enemy. Here and there on a point of land extending into the Tappan Sea, a mud work would be thrown up, and an old field-piece mounted, with which a knot of rustic artillerymen would fire away for a long summer's day at some frigate dozing at anchor far out of reach; and reliques of such works may still be seen overgrown with weeds and brambles, with peradventure the half-buried fragment of a cannon which may have burst.

Jacob Van Tassel was a prominent man in these belligerent operations; but he was prone, moreover, to carry on a petty warfare of his own for his individual recreation and refreshment. On a row of hooks above the fireplace of the Roost, reposed his great piece of ordnance—a duck, or rather goose-gun, of unparalleled longitude, with which it was said he could kill a wild-goose half way across the Tappan Sea. Indeed, there are as many wonders told of this renowned gun, as of the enchanted weapons of classic story. When the belligerent feeling was strong upon Jacob, he would take down his gun, sally forth alone, and prowl along shore, dodging behind rocks and trees, watching for hours together any ship or galley at anchor or becalmed, as a valorous mouser will watch a rat-hole. So sure as a boat approached the shore, bang went the great goose-gun, sending on board a shower of slugs and buckshot; and away scuttled Jacob Van Tassel through some woody ravine. As the Roost stood in a lonely situation, and might be attacked, he guarded against surprise by making loop-holes in the stone walls, through which to fire upon an assailant. His wife was stout-hearted as himself, and could load as fast as he could fire; and his sister, Nochie Van Wurmer, a redoubtable widow, was a match, as he said, for the stoutest man in the country. Thus garrisoned, his little castle was fitted to stand a siege, and Jacob was the man to defend it to the last charge of powder.

In the process of time the Roost became one of the secret stations, or lurking-places, of the Water Guard. This was an aquatic corps in the pay of government, organized to range the waters of the Hudson, and keep watch upon the movements of the enemy. It was composed of nautical men of the river, and hardy youngsters of the adjacent country, expert at pulling an oar or handling a musket. They were provided with whale-boats, long and sharp, shaped like canoes, and formed to lie lightly on the water, and be rowed with great rapidity. In these they would lurk out of sight by day, in nooks and bays, and behind points of land, keeping a sharp look-out upon the British ships, and giving intelligence to head-quarters of any extraordinary movement. At night they rowed about in pairs, pulling quietly along with muffled oars, under shadow of the land, or gliding like spectres about frigates and guard-ships to cut off any boat that might be sent to shore. In this way they were a source of constant uneasiness and alarm to the enemy.

The Roost, as has been observed, was one of their lurking-places; having a cove in front where their whale-boats could be drawn up out of sight, and Jacob Van Tassel being a vigilant ally, ready to take a part in any "scout or scrummage" by land or water. At this little warrior nest the hard-riding lads from the hills would hold consultations with the chivalry of the river and here were concerted divers of those daring enterprises which resounded from Spiting Devil Creek even unto Anthony's Nose. Here was concocted the midnight invasion of New York Island, and the conflagration of Delancy's Tory mansion, which makes such a blaze in revolutionary history. Nay, more, if the traditions of the Roost may be credited, here was meditated, by Jacob Van Tassel and his compeers, a nocturnal foray into New York itself, to surprise and carry off the British commanders, Howe and Clinton, and put a triumphant close to the war.

There is no knowing whether this notable scheme might not have been carried into effect, had not one of Jacob Van Tassel's egregious exploits along shore with his goose-gun, with which he thought himself a match for anything, brought vengeance on his house.

It so happened, that in the course of one of his solitary prowls he descried a British transport aground; the stern swung toward shore within point-blank shot. The temptation was too great to be resisted. Bang! went the great goose-gun, from the covert of the trees, shivering the cabin-windows and driving all hands forward. Bang! bang! the shots were repeated. The reports brought other of Jacob's fellow bush-fighters to the spot. Before the transport could bring a gun to bear, or land a boat to take revenge, she was soundly peppered, and the coast evacuated.

This was the last of Jacob's triumphs. He fared like some heroic spider that has unwittingly ensnared a hornet to the utter ruin of his web. It was not long after the above exploit that he fell into the hands of the enemy in the course of one of his forays, and was carried away prisoner to New York. The Roost itself, as a pestilent rebel nest, was marked out for signal punishment. The cock of the Roost being captive, there was none to garrison it but his stout-hearted spouse, his redoubtable sister, Nochie Van Wurmer, and Dinah, a strapping Negro wench. An armed vessel came to anchor in front; a boat full of men pulled to shore. The garrison flew to arms; that is to say, to mops, broomsticks, shovels, tongs, and all kinds of domestic weapons—for unluckily the great piece of ordnance, the goose-gun, was absent with its owner. Above all, a vigorous defence was made with that most potent of female weapons, the tongue. Never did invaded hen-roost make a more vociferous outcry. It was all in vain.

The house was sacked and plundered, fire was set to each corner, and in a few moments its blaze shed a baleful light far over the Tappan Sea. The invaders then pounced upon the blooming Laney Van Tassel, the beauty of the Roost, and endeavored to bear her off to the boat. But here was the real tug of war. The mother, the aunt, and the strapping Negro wench, all flew to the rescue. The struggle continued down to the very water's edge, when a voice from the armed vessel at anchor ordered the spoilers to desist; they relinquished their prize, jumped into their boats, and pulled off, and the heroine of the Roost escaped with a mere rumpling of her feathers.

As to the stout Jacob himself, he was detained a prisoner in New York for the greater part of the war; in the meantime the Roost remained a melancholy ruin, its stone walls and brick chimneys alone standing, the resorts of bats and owls. Superstitious notions prevailed about it. None of the country people would venture alone at night down the rambling lane which led to it, overhung with trees, and crossed here and there by a wild wandering brook. The story went that one of the victims of Jacob Van Tassel's great goose-gun had been buried there in unconsecrated ground.

Even the Tappan Sea in front was said to be haunted. Often in the still twilight of a summer evening, when the sea would be as glass, and the opposite hills would throw their purple shadows half across it, a low sound would be heard as of the steady, vigorous pull of oars, though not a boat was to be descried. Some might have supposed that a boat was rowed along unseen under the deep shadows of the opposite shores; but the ancient traditionists of the neighborhood knew better. Some said it was one of the whale-boats of the old Water Guard, sunk by the British ships during the war, but now permitted to haunt its old cruising-grounds; but the prevalent opinion connected it with the awful fate of Rambout Van Dam of graceless memory. He was a roistering Dutchman of Spiting Devil, who in times long past had navigated his boat alone one Saturday the whole length of the Tappan Sea, to attend a quilting frolic at Kakiat, on the western shore. Here he had danced and drunk until midnight, when he entered his boat to return home. He was warned that he was on the verge of Sunday morning; but he pulled off nevertheless, swearing he would not land until he reached Spiting Devil, if it took him a month of Sundays. He was never seen afterwards; but may be heard plying his oars, as above mentioned—being the Flying Dutchman of the Tappan Sea, doomed to ply between Kakiat and Spiting Devil until the day of judgment.

CHRONICLE III

THE revolutionary war was over. The debatable ground had once more become a quiet agricultural region; the border chivalry had turned their swords into ploughshares, and their spears into pruning-hooks, and hung up their guns, only to be taken down occasionally in a campaign against wild pigeons on the hills, or wild ducks upon the Hudson. Jacob Van Tassel, whilome carried captive to New York, a flagitious rebel, had come forth from captivity a "hero of seventy-six." In a little while he sought the scenes of his former triumphs and mishaps, rebuilt the Roost, restored his goose-gun to the hooks over the fireplace, and reared once more on high the glittering weathercocks.

Years and years passed over the time-honored little mansion. The honeysuckle and the sweet-brier crept up its walls; the wren and the Phœbe-bird built under the eaves; it gradually became almost hidden among trees, through which it looked forth, as with half-shut eyes, upon the Tappan Sea. The Indian spring, famous in the days of the wizard sachem, still welled up at the bottom of the green bank; and the wild brook, wild as ever, came babbling down the ravine, and threw itself into the little cove where of yore the Water Guard harbored their whale-boats.

Such was the state of the Roost many years since, at the time when Diedrich Knickerbocker came into this neighborhood, in the course of his researches among the Dutch families for materials for his immortal history. The exterior of the eventful little pile seemed to him full of promise. The crow-step gables were of the primitive architecture of the province. The weathercocks which surmounted them had crowed in the glorious days of the New Netherlands. The one above the porch had actually glittered of yore on the great Vander Heyden palace at Albany.

The interior of the mansion fulfilled its external promise. Here were records of old times; documents of the Dutch dynasty, rescued from the profane hands of the English by Wolfert Acker, when he retreated from New Amsterdam. Here he had treasured them up like buried gold, and here they had been miraculously preserved by St. Nicholas, at the time of the conflagration of the Roost.

Here then did old Diedrich Knickerbocker take up his abode for a time, and set to work with antiquarian zeal to decipher these precious documents, which, like the lost books of Livy, had baffled the research of former historians; and it is the facts drawn from these sources which give his work the preference, in point of accuracy, over every other history.

It was during his sojourn in this eventful neighborhood that the historian is supposed to have picked up many of those legends, which have since been given by him to the world, or found among his papers. Such was the legend connected with the old Dutch Church of Sleepy Hollow. The Church itself was a monument of by-gone days. It had been built in the early times of the province. A tablet over the portal bore the names of its founders —Frederick Filipson, a mighty man of yore, patroon of Yonkers, and his wife Katrina Van Courtland, of the Van Courtlands of Croton; a powerful family connection—with one foot resting on Spiting Devil Creek, and the other on the Croton River.

Two weathercocks, with the initials of these illustrious personages, graced each end of the Church, one perched over the belfry, the other over the chancel. As usual with ecclesiastical weathercocks, each pointed a different way; and there was a perpetual contradiction between them on all points of windy doctrine; emblematic, alas, of the Christian propensity to schism and controversy.

In the burying-ground adjacent to the Church, reposed the earliest fathers of a wide rural neighborhood. Here families were garnered together, side by side, in long platoons, in this last gathering place of kindred. With pious hand would Diedrich Knickerbocker turn down the weeds and brambles which had overgrown the tombstones, to decipher inscriptions in Dutch and English, of the names and virtues of succeeding generations of

Van Tassels, Van Warts, and other historical worthies, with their portraitures faithfully carved, all bearing the family likeness to cherubs.

The congregation in those days was of a truly rural character. City fashions had not as yet stolen up to Sleepy Hollow. Dutch sun-bonnets and honest homespun still prevailed. Everything was in primitive style, even to the bucket of water and tin cup near the door in summer, to assuage the thirst caused by the heat of the weather or the drought of the sermon.

The pulpit, with its wide-spreading sounding-board, and the communion-table, curiously carved, had each come from Holland in the olden time, before the arts had sufficiently advanced in the colony for such achievements. Around these on Sundays would be gathered the elders of the church, gray-headed men, who led the psalmody, and in whom it would be difficult to recognize the hard-riding lads of yore, who scoured the debatable land in the time of the revolution.

The drowsy influence of Sleepy Hollow was apt to breathe into this sacred edifice; and now and then an elder might be seen with his handkerchief over his face to keep off the flies, and apparently listening to the dominie; but really sunk into a summer slumber, lulled by the sultry notes of the locust from the neighboring trees.

And now a word or two about Sleepy Hollow, which many have rashly deemed a fanciful creation, like the Lubberland of mariners. It was probably the mystic and dreamy sound of the name which first tempted the historian of the Manhattoes into its spellbound mazes. As he entered, all nature seemed for the moment to awake from its slumbers and break forth in gratulations. The quail whistled a welcome from the cornfield; the loquacious cat-bird flew from bush to bush with restless wing proclaiming his approach, or perked inquisitively into his face as if to get a knowledge of his physiognomy. The woodpecker tapped a tattoo on the hollow apple-tree, and then peered round the trunk, as if asking how he relished the salutation; while the squirrel scampered along the fence, whisking his tail over his head by way of a huzza.

Here reigned the golden mean extolled by the poets, in which no gold was to be found and very little silver. The inhabitants of the Hollow were of the primitive stock, and had intermarried and bred in and in, from the earliest time of the province, never swarming far from the parent hive, but dividing and subdividing their paternal acres as they swarmed.

Here were small farms, each having its little portion of meadow and cornfield; its orchard of gnarled and sprawling apple-trees; its garden, in which the rose, the marigold, and hollyhock, grew sociably with the cabbage, the pea, and the pumpkin; each had its low-eaved mansion redundant with white-headed children; with an old hat nailed against the wall for the housekeeping wren; the coop on the grass-plot, where the motherly hen clucked round with her vagrant brood: each had its stone well, with a moss-covered bucket suspended to the long balancing-pole, according to antediluvian hydraulics; while within doors resounded the eternal hum of the spinning-wheel.

Many were the great historical facts which the worthy Diedrich collected in these lowly mansions, and patiently would he sit by the old Dutch housewives with a child on his knee, or a purring grimalkin on his lap, listening to endless ghost stories spun forth to the humming accompaniment of the wheel.

The delighted historian pursued his explorations far into the foldings of the hills where the Pocantico winds its wizard stream among the mazes of its old Indian haunts; sometimes running darkly in pieces of woodland beneath balancing sprays of beech and chestnut; sometimes sparkling between grassy borders in fresh, green intervales; here and there receiving the tributes of silver rills which came whimpering down the hill-sides from their parent springs.

In a remote part of the Hollow, where the Pocantico forced its way down rugged rocks, stood Carl's mill, the haunted house of the neighborhood. It was indeed a goblin-looking pile: shattered and time-worn, dismal with clanking wheels and rushing streams, and all kinds of uncouth noises. A horse-shoe nailed to the door to keep off witches, seemed to have lost its power; for as Diedrich approached, an old Negro thrust his head all dabbled with flour out of a hole above the water-wheel, and grinned and rolled his eyes, and appeared to be the very hobgoblin of the place. Yet this proved to be the great historic genius of the Hollow, abounding in that valuable information never to be acquired from books. Diedrich Knickerbocker soon discovered his merit. They had long talks together seated on a broken millstone, heedless of the water and the clatter of the mill; and to his conference with that African sage many attribute the surprising, though true story, of Ichabod Crane and the Headless Horseman of Sleepy Hollow. We refrain, however, from giving farther researches of the historian of the Manhattoes during his sojourn at the Roost, but may return to them in future pages.

Reader! the Roost still exists. Time, which changes all things, is slow in its operations on a Dutchman's dwelling. The stout Jacob Van Tassel, it is true, sleeps with his fathers; and his great goose-gun with him: yet his stronghold still bears the impress of its Dutch origin. Odd rumors have gathered about it, as they are apt to do about old mansions, like moss and weather-stains. The shade of Wolfert Acker still walks his unquiet rounds at night in the orchard; and a white figure has now and then been seen seated at a window and gazing at the moon, from a room in which a young lady is said to have died of love and green apples.

Mementos of the sojourn of Diedrich Knickerbocker are still cherished at the Roost. His elbow-chair and antique writing-desk maintain their place in the room he occupied, and his old cocked-hat still hangs on a peg against the wall.

"A Time of Unexampled Prosperity"

IN the course of a voyage from England, I once fell in with a convoy of merchant ships, bound for the West Indies. The weather was uncommonly bland; and the ships vied with each other in spreading sail to catch a light, favoring breeze, until their hulls were almost hidden beneath a cloud of canvas. The breeze went down with the sun, and his last yellow rays shone upon a thousand sails, idly flapping against the masts.

I exulted in the beauty of the scene, and augured a prosperous voyage; but the veteran master of the ship shook his head, and pronounced this halcyon calm a "weather-breeder." And so it proved. A storm burst forth in the night; the sea roared and raged; and when the day broke I beheld the late gallant convoy scattered in every direction; some dismasted, others scudding under bare poles, and many firing signals of distress.

I have since been occasionally reminded of this scene, by those calm, sunny seasons in the commercial world, which are known by the name of "times of unexampled prosperity." They are the sure weather-breeders of traffic. Every now and then the world is visited by one of these delusive seasons, when "the credit system," as it is called, expands to full luxuriance; everybody trusts everybody; a bad debt is a thing unheard of; the broad way to certain and sudden wealth lies plain and open; and men are tempted to dash forward boldly, from the facility of borrowing.

Promissory notes, interchanged between scheming individuals, are liberally discounted at the banks, which become so many mints to coin words into cash; and as the supply of words is inexhaustible, it may readily be supposed what a vast amount of promissory capital is soon in circulation. Every one now talks in thousands; nothing is heard but gigantic operations in trade; great purchases and sales of real property, and immense sums made at every transfer. All, to be sure, as yet exists in promise; but the believer in promises calculates the aggregate as solid capital, and falls back in amazement at the amount of public wealth, the "unexampled state of public prosperity!"

Now is the time for speculative and dreaming or designing men. They relate their dreams and projects to the ignorant and credulous, dazzle them with golden visions, and set them maddening after shadows. The example of one stimulates another; speculation rises on speculation; bubble rises on bubble; every one helps with his breath to swell the windy superstructure, and admires and wonders at the magnitude of the inflation he has contributed to produce.

Speculation is the romance of trade, and casts contempt upon all its sober realities. It renders the stock-jobber a magician, and the exchange a region of enchantment. It elevates the merchant into a kind of knight-errant, or rather a commercial Quixote. The slow but sure gains of snug percentage become despicable in his eyes: no "operation" is thought worthy of attention that does not double or treble the investment. No business is worth following, that does not promise an immediate fortune. As he sits musing over his ledger, with pen behind his ear, he is like La Mancha's hero in his study, dreaming over his books of chivalry. His dusty counting house fades before his eyes, or changes into a Spanish mine; he gropes after diamonds, or dives after pearls. The subterranean garden of Aladdin is nothing to the realms of wealth that break upon his imagination.

Could this delusion always last, the life of a merchant would indeed be a golden dream; but it is as short as it is brilliant. Let but a doubt enter, and the "season of unexampled prosperity" is at an end. The coinage of words is suddenly curtailed; the promissory capital begins to vanish into smoke; a panic succeeds, and the whole superstructure, built upon credit, and reared by speculation, crumbles to the ground, leaving scarce a wreck behind:

"It is such stuff as dreams are made of."

When a man of business, therefore, hears on every side rumors of fortunes suddenly acquired; when he finds banks liberal, and brokers busy; when he sees adventurers flush of paper capital, and full of scheme and enterprise; when he perceives a greater disposition to buy than to sell; when trade overflows its accustomed channels, and deluges the country; when he hears of new regions of commercial adventure; of distant marts and distant mines, swallowing merchandise and disgorging gold; when he finds joint stock companies of all kinds forming; railroads, canals, and locomotive engines, springing up on every side; when idlers suddenly become men of business, and dash into the game of commerce as they would into the hazards of the faro-table; when he beholds the streets glittering with new equipages, palaces conjured up by the magic of speculation, tradesmen flushed with sudden success, and vying with each other in ostentatious expense; in a word, when he hears the whole community joining in the theme of "unexampled prosperity," let him look upon the whole as a "weather-breeder," and prepare for the impending storm.

The foregoing remarks are intended merely as a prelude to a narrative I am about to lay before the public, of one of the most memorable instances of the infatuation of gain to be found in the whole history of commerce. I allude to the famous Mississippi bubble. It is a matter that has passed into a proverb, and become a phrase in every one's mouth, yet of which not one merchant in ten has probably a distinct idea. I have therefore thought that an authentic account of it would be interesting and salutary, at the present moment, when we are suffering under the effects of a severe access of the credit system, and just recovering from one of its ruinous delusions.

The Great Mississippi Bubble

BEFORE entering into the story of this famous chimera, it is proper to give a few particulars concerning the individual who engendered it. JOHN LAW was born in Edinburgh, in 1671. His father, William Law, was a rich goldsmith, and left his son an estate of considerable value, called Lauriston, situated about four miles from Edinburgh. Goldsmiths, in those days, acted occasionally as bankers, and his father's operations, under this character, may have originally turned the thoughts of the youth to the science of calculation, in which he became an adept; so that at an early age he excelled in playing at all games of combination.

In 1694, he appeared in London, where a handsome person and an easy and insinuating address gained him currency in the first circles, and the nickname of "Beau Law." The same personal advantages gave him success in the world of gallantry, until he became involved in a quarrel with Beau Wilson, his rival in fashion, whom he killed in a duel, and then fled to France to avoid prosecution.

He returned to Edinburgh in 1700, and remained there several years; during which time he first broached his great credit system, offering to supply the deficiency of coin by the establishment of a bank, which, according to his views, might emit a paper currency equivalent to the whole landed estate of the kingdom.

His scheme excited great astonishment in Edinburgh; but, though the government was not sufficiently advanced in financial knowledge to detect the fallacies upon which it was founded, Scottish caution and suspicion served in place of wisdom, and the project was rejected. Law met with no better success with the English parliament; and the fatal affair of the death of Wilson still hanging over him, for which he had never been able to procure a pardon, he again went to France.

The financial affairs of France were at this time in a deplorable condition. The wars, the pomp, and profusion of Louis XIV., and his religious persecutions of whole classes of the most industrious of his subjects, had exhausted his treasury, and overwhelmed the nation with debt. The old monarch clung to his selfish magnificence, and could not be induced to diminish his enormous expenditure; and his minister of finance was driven to his wits' end to devise all kinds of disastrous expedients to keep up the royal state, and to extricate the nation from its embarrassments.

In this state of things Law ventured to bring forward his financial project. It was founded on the plan of the Bank of England, which had already been in successful operation several years. He met with immediate patronage and a congenial spirit in the Duke of Orleans, who had married a natural daughter of the king. The duke had been astonished at the facility with which England had supported the burden of a public debt, created by the wars of Anne and William, and which exceeded in amount that under which France was groaning. The whole matter was soon explained by Law to his satisfaction. The latter maintained that England had stopped at the mere threshold of an art capable of creating unlimited sources of national wealth. The duke was dazzled with his splendid views and specious reasonings, and thought he clearly comprehended his system. Demarets, the Comptroller-General of Finance, was not so easily deceived. He pronounced the plan of Law more pernicious than any of the disastrous expedients that the government had yet been driven to. The old king also, Louis XIV., detested all innovations, especially those which came from a rival nation: the project of a bank, therefore, was utterly rejected.

Law remained for a while in Paris, leading a gay and affluent existence, owing to his handsome person, easy manners, flexible temper, and a faro-bank which he had set up. His agreeable career was interrupted by a message from D'Argenson, Lieutenant-General of Police, ordering him to quit Paris, alleging that he was "*rather too skilful at the game which he had introduced!*"

For several succeeding years he shifted his residence from state to state of Italy and Germany, offering his scheme of finance to every court that he visited, but without success. The Duke of Savoy, Victor Amadeas, afterward King of Sardinia, was much struck with his project; but after considering it for a time, replied, "*I am not sufficiently powerful to ruin myself.*"

The shifting, adventurous life of Law, and the equivocal means by which he appeared to live, playing high, and always with great success, threw a cloud of suspicion over him wherever he went, and caused him to be expelled by the magistracy from the semi-commercial, semi-aristocratical cities of Venice and Genoa.

The events of 1715 brought Law back again to Paris. Louis XIV. was dead. Louis XV. was a mere child, and during his minority the Duke of Orleans held the reins of government as Regent. Law had at length found his man.

The Duke of Orleans has been differently represented by different contemporaries. He appears to have had excellent natural qualities, perverted by a bad education. He was of the middle size, easy and graceful, with an agreeable countenance, and open, affable demeanor. His mind was quick and sagacious, rather than profound; and his quickness of intellect and excellence of memory supplied the lack of studious application. His wit was prompt and pungent; he expressed himself with vivacity and precision; his imagination was vivid, his temperament sanguine and joyous, his courage daring. His mother, the Duchess of Orleans, expressed his character in a *jeu d'esprit*. "The fairies," said she, "were invited to be present at his birth, and each one conferring a talent on my son, he possesses them all. Unfortunately, we had forgotten to invite an old fairy, who, arriving after all the others, exclaimed, 'He shall have all the talents, excepting that to make good use of them.' "

Under proper tuition, the duke might have risen to real greatness; but in his early years he was put under the tutelage of the Abbé Dubois, one of the subtlest and basest spirits that ever intrigued its way into eminent place and power. The Abbé was of low origin and despicable exterior, totally destitute of morals, and perfidious in the extreme; but with a supple, insinuating address, and an accommodating spirit, tolerant of all kinds of profligacy in others. Conscious of his own inherent baseness, he sought to secure an influence over his pupil by corrupting his principles and fostering his vices; he debased him, to keep himself from being despised. Unfortunately he succeeded. To the early precepts of this infamous pander have been attributed those excesses that disgraced the manhood of the Regent, and gave a licentious character to his whole course of government. His love of pleasure, quickened and indulged by those who should have restrained it, led him into all kinds of sensual indulgence. He had been taught to think lightly of the most serious duties and sacred ties, to turn virtue into a jest, and consider religion mere hypocrisy. He was a gay misanthrope, that had a sovereign but sportive contempt for mankind; believed that his most devoted servant would be his enemy if interest prompted, and maintained that an honest man was he who had the art to conceal that he was the contrary.

He surrounded himself with a set of dissolute men like himself, who, let loose from the restraint under which they had been held during the latter hypocritical days of Louis XIV., now gave way to every kind of debauchery. With these men the Regent used to shut himself up, after the hours of business, and excluding all graver persons and graver concerns, celebrate the most drunken and disgusting orgies, where obscenity and blasphemy formed the seasoning of conversation. For the profligate companions of these revels he invented the appellation of his *roués*, the literal meaning of which is, men broken on the wheel; intended, no doubt, to express their broken-down characters and dislocated fortunes; although a contemporary asserts that it designated the punishment that most of them merited. Madame de Labran, who was present at one of the Regent's suppers, was disgusted by the conduct and conversation of the host and his guests, and observed at table, that God, after he had created man, took the refuse clay that was left and made of it the souls of lackeys and princes.

Such was the man that now ruled the destinies of France. Law found him full of perplexities from the disastrous state of the finances. He had already tampered with the coinage, calling in the coin of the nation, restamping it, and issuing it at a nominal increase of one fifth, thus defrauding the nation out of twenty per cent. of its capital. He was not likely, therefore, to be scrupulous about any means likely to relieve him from financial difficulties; he had even been led to listen to the cruel alternative of a national bankruptcy.

Under these circumstances Law confidently brought forward his scheme of a bank that was to pay off the national debt, increase the revenue, and at the same time diminish the taxes. The following is stated as the theory by which he recommended his system to the Regent. The credit enjoyed by a banker or a merchant, he observed, increases his capital tenfold; that is to say, he who has a capital of one hundred thousand livres, may, if he possess sufficient credit, extend his operations to a million, and reap profits to that amount. In like manner, a state that can collect into a bank all the current coin of the kingdom, would be as powerful as if its capital were increased tenfold. The specie must be drawn into the bank, not by way of loan, or by taxations, but in the way of deposit. This might be effected in different modes, either by inspiring confidence, or by exerting authority. One mode, he observed, had already been in use. Each time that a state makes a recoinage, it becomes momentarily the depository of all the money called in belonging to the subjects of that state. His bank was to effect the same purpose; that is to say, to receive in deposit all the coin of the kingdom, but to give in exchange its bills, which, being of an invariable value, bearing an interest, and being payable on demand, would not only supply the place of coin, but prove a better and more profitable currency.

The Regent caught with avidity at the scheme. It suited his bold, reckless spirit and his grasping extravagance. Not that he was altogether the dupe of Law's specious projects; still he was apt, like many other men unskilled in the arcana of finance, to mistake the multiplication of money for the multiplication of wealth, not understanding that it was a mere agent or instrument in the interchange of traffic, to represent the value of the various productions of industry; and that an increased circulation of coin or bank-bills, in the shape of currency, only adds a proportionably increased and fictitious value to such productions. Law enlisted the vanity of the Regent in his cause. He persuaded him that he saw more clearly than others into sublime theories of finance, which were quite above the ordinary apprehension. He used to declare that, excepting the Regent and the Duke of Savoy, no one had thoroughly comprehended his system.

It is certain that it met with strong opposition from the Regent's ministers, the Duke de Noailles and the Chancellor d'Anguesseau, and it was no less strenuously opposed by the parliament of Paris. Law, however, had a potent though secret coadjutor in the Abbé Dubois, now rising, during the regency, into great political power, and who retained a baneful influence over the mind of the Regent. This wily priest, as avaricious as he was ambitious, drew large sums from Law as subsidies, and aided him greatly in many of his most pernicious operations. He aided him, in the present instance, to fortify the mind of the Regent against all the remonstrances of his ministers and the parliament.

Accordingly, on the 2d of May, 1716, letters patent were granted to Law to establish a bank of deposit, discount, and circulation, under the firm of "Law and Company," to continue for twenty years. The capital was fixed at six millions of livres, divided into shares of five hundred livres each, which were to be sold for twenty-five per cent. of the Regent's debased coin, and seventy-five per cent. of the public securities, which were then at a great reduction from their nominal value, and which then amounted to nineteen hundred millions. The ostensible object of the bank, as set forth in the patent, was to encourage the commerce and manufactures of France. The louis-d'ors and crowns of the bank were always to retain the same standard of value, and its bills to be payable in them on demand.

At the outset, while the bank was limited in its operations, and while its paper really represented the specie in its vaults, it seemed to realize all that had been promised from it. It rapidly acquired public confidence and an extended circulation, and produced an activity in commerce unknown under the baneful government of Louis XIV. As the bills of the bank bore an interest, and as it was stipulated they would be of invariable value, and as hints had been artfully circulated that the coin would experience successive diminution, everybody hastened to the bank to exchange gold and silver for paper. So great became the throng of depositors, and so intense their eagerness, that there was quite a press and struggle at the back door, and a ludicrous panic was awakened, as if there was danger of their not being admitted. An anecdote of the time relates that one of the clerks, with an ominous smile, called out to the struggling multitude, "Have a little patience, my friends; we mean to take all your money;" an assertion disastrously verified in the sequel.

Thus by the simple establishment of a bank, Law and the Regent obtained pledges of confidence for the consummation of farther and more complicated schemes, as yet hidden from the public. In a little while the bank shares rose enormously, and the amount of its notes in circulation exceeded one hundred and ten millions of livres. A subtle stroke of policy had rendered it popular with the aristocracy. Louis XIV. had, several years previously, imposed an income tax of a tenth, giving his royal word that it should cease in 1717. This tax had been exceedingly irksome to the privileged orders; and, in the present disastrous times, they had dreaded an augmentation of it. In consequence of the successful operation of Law's scheme, however, the tax was abolished, and now nothing was to be heard among the nobility and clergy but praises of the Regent and the bank.

Hitherto all had gone well, and all might have continued to go well, had not the paper system been farther expanded. But Law had yet the grandest part of his scheme to develop. He had to open his ideal world of speculation, his El Dorado of unbounded wealth. The English had brought the vast imaginary commerce of the South Seas in aid of their banking operations. Law sought to bring, as an immense auxiliary of his bank, the whole trade of the Mississippi. Under this name was included not merely the river so called, but the vast region known as Louisiana, extending from north latitude 29° up to Canada in north latitude 40°. This country had been granted by Louis XIV. to the Sieur Crozat, but he had been induced to resign his patent. In conformity to the plea of Mr. Law, letters patent were granted in August, in 1717, for the creation of a commercial company, which was to have the colonizing of this country, and the monopoly of its trade and resources, and of the beaver or fur trade with Canada. It was called the Western, but became better known as the Mississippi Company. The capital was fixed at one hundred millions of livres, divided into shares, bearing an interest of four per cent., which was subscribed for in the public securities. As the bank was to coöperate with the company, the Regent ordered that its bills should be received the same as coin, in all payments of the public revenue. Law was appointed chief director of this company, which was an exact copy of the Earl of Oxford's South Sea Company, set on foot in 1711, and which distracted all England with the frenzy of speculation. In like manner with the delusive picturings given in that memorable scheme of the sources of rich trade to be opened in the South Sea countries, Law held forth magnificent prospects of the fortunes to be made in colonizing Louisiana, which was represented as a veritable land of promise, capable of yielding every variety of the most precious produce. Reports, too, were artfully circulated, with great mystery, as if to the "chosen few," of mines of gold and silver recently discovered in Louisiana, and which would insure instant wealth to the early purchasers. These confidential whispers, of course, soon became public; and were confirmed by travellers fresh from the Mississippi, and doubtless bribed, who had seen the mines in question, and declared them superior in richness to those of Mexico and Peru. Nay more, ocular proof was furnished to public credulity, in ingots of gold, conveyed to the mint, as if just brought from the mines of Louisiana.

Extraordinary measures were adopted to force a colonization. An edict was issued to collect and transport settlers to the Mississippi. The police lent its aid. The streets and prisons of Paris, and of the provincial cities, were swept of mendicants and vagabonds of all kinds, who were conveyed to Havre de Grace. About six thousand were crowded into ships, where no precautions had been taken for their health or accommodation. Instruments of all kinds proper for the working of mines were ostentatiously paraded in public, and put on board the vessels; and the whole set sail for this fabled El Dorado, which was to prove the grave of the greater part of its wretched colonists.

D'Anguesseau, the chancellor, a man of probity and integrity, still lifted his voice against the paper system of Law, and his project of colonization, and was eloquent and prophetic in picturing the evils they were calculated to produce; the private distress and public degradation; the corruption of morals and manners; the triumph of knaves and schemers; the ruin of fortunes, and the downfall of families. He was incited more and more to this opposition by the Duke de Noailles, the Minister of Finance, who was jealous of the growing ascendency of Law over the mind of the Regent, but was less honest than the chancellor in his opposition. The Regent was excessively annoyed by the difficulties they conjured up in the way of his darling schemes of finance, and the countenance they gave to the opposition of parliament; which body, disgusted more and more with the abuses of the regency, and the system of Law, had gone so far as to carry its remonstrances to the very foot of the throne.

He determined to relieve himself from these two ministers, who, either through honesty or policy, interfered with all his plans. Accordingly, on the 28th of January, 1718, he dismissed the chancellor from office, and exiled him to his estate in the country; and shortly afterward removed the Duke de Noailles from the administration of the finance.

The opposition of parliament to the Regent and his measures was carried on with increasing violence. That body aspired to an equal authority with the Regent in the administration of affairs, and pretended, by its decree, to suspend an edict of the regency ordering a new coinage, and altering the value of the currency. But its chief hostility was levelled against Law, a foreigner and a heretic, and one who was considered by a majority of the members in the light of a malefactor. In fact, so far was this hostility carried, that secret measures were taken to investigate his malversations, and to collect evidence against him; and it was resolved in parliament that, should the testimony collected justify their suspicions, they would have him seized and brought before them; would give him a brief trial, and, if convicted, would hang him in the court-yard of the palace, and throw open the gates after the execution, that the public might behold his corpse!

Law received intimation of the danger hanging over him, and was in terrible trepidation. He took refuge in the Palais Royal, the residence of the Regent, and implored his protection. The Regent himself was embarrassed by the sturdy opposition of parliament, which contemplated nothing less than a decree reversing most of his public measures, especially those of finance. His indecision kept Law for a time in an agony of terror and suspense. Finally, by assembling a board of justice, and bringing to his aid the absolute authority of the king, he triumphed over parliament, and relieved Law from his dread of being hanged.

The system now went on with flowing sail. The Western,

or Mississippi Company, being identified with the bank, rapidly increased in power and privileges. One monopoly after another was granted to it—the trade of the Indian Seas, the slave-trade with Senegal and Guinea, the farming of tobacco, the national coinage, etc. Each new privilege was made a pretext for issuing more bills, and caused an immense advance in the price of stock. At length, on the 4th of December, 1718, the Regent gave the establishment the imposing title of the Royal Bank, and proclaimed that he had effected the purchase of all the shares, the proceeds of which he had added to its capital. This measure seemed to shock the public feeling more than any other connected with the system, and roused the indignation of parliament. The French nation had been so accustomed to attach an idea of everything noble, lofty, and magnificent, to the royal name and person, especially during the stately and sumptuous reign of Louis XIV., that they could not at first tolerate the idea of royalty being in any degree mingled with matters of traffic and finance, and the king being, in a manner, a banker. It was one of the downward steps, however, by which royalty lost its illusive splendor in France and became gradually cheapened in the public mind.

Arbitrary measures now began to be taken to force the bills of the bank into artificial currency. On the 27th of December appeared an order in council, forbidding, under severe penalties, the payment of any sum above six hundred livres in gold or silver. This decree rendered bank-bills necessary in all transactions of purchase and sale, and called for a new emission. The prohibition was occasionally evaded or opposed; confiscations were the consequence; informers were rewarded, and spies and traitors began to spring up in all the domestic walks of life.

The worst effect of this illusive system was the mania for gain, or rather for gambling in stocks, that now seized upon the whole nation. Under the exciting effects of lying reports, and the forcing effects of government decrees, the shares of the company went on rising in value, until they reached thirteen hundred per cent. Nothing was now spoken of but the price of shares, and the immense fortunes suddenly made by lucky speculators. Those whom Law had deluded used every means to delude others. The most extravagant dreams were indulged concerning the wealth to flow in upon the company from its colonies, its trade, and its various monopolies. It is true nothing as yet had been realized, nor could in some time be realized, from these distant sources, even if productive; but the imaginations of speculators are ever in the advance, and their conjectures are immediately converted into facts. Lying reports now flew from mouth to mouth, of sure avenues to fortune suddenly thrown open. The more extravagant the fable, the more readily was it believed. To doubt, was to awaken anger or incur ridicule. In a time of public infatuation it requires no small exercise of courage to doubt a popular fallacy.

Paris now became the centre of attraction for the adventurous and the avaricious, who flocked to it not merely from the provinces, but from neighboring countries. A stock exchange was established in a house in the Rue Quincampoix, and became immediately the gathering-place of stock-jobbers. The exchange opened at seven o'clock with the beat of drum and sound of bell, and closed at night with the same signals. Guards were stationed at each end of the street, to maintain order and exclude carriages and horses. The whole street swarmed throughout the day like a beehive. Bargains of all kinds were seized upon with avidity. Shares of stock passed from hand to hand, mounting in value, one knew not why. Fortunes were made in a moment, as if by magic; and every lucky bargain prompted those around to a more desperate throw of the dice. The fever went on, increasing in intensity as the day declined; and when the drum beat and the bell rang at night, to close the exchange, there were exclamations of impatience and despair, as if the wheel of fortune had suddenly been stopped, when about to make its luckiest revolution.

To ingulf all classes in this ruinous vortex, Law now split the shares of fifty millions of stock each into one hundred shares; thus, as in the splitting of lottery tickets, accommodating the venture to the humblest purse. Society was thus stirred up to its very dregs, and adventurers of the lowest order hurried to the stock market. All honest, industrious pursuits and modest gains were now despised. Wealth was to be obtained instantly, without labor and without stint. The upper classes were as base in their venality as the lower. The highest and most powerful nobles, abandoning all generous pursuits and lofty aims, engaged in the vile scuffle for gain. They were even baser than the lower classes; for some of them, who were members of the council of the regency, abused their station and their influence, and promoted measures by which shares rose while in their hands, and they made immense profits.

The Duke de Bourbon, the Prince of Conti, the Dukes de la Force and D'Antin, were among the foremost of these illustrious stock-jobbers. They were nicknamed the Mississippi Lords, and they smiled at the sneering title. In fact, the usual distinctions of society had lost their consequence, under the reign of this new passion. Rank, talent, military fame, no longer inspired deference. All respect for others, all self-respect, were forgotten in the mercenary struggle of the stock-market. Even prelates and ecclesiastical corporations, forgetting their true objects of devotion, mingled among the votaries of Mammon. They were not behind those who wielded the civil power in fabricating ordinances suited to their avaricious purposes. Theological decisions forthwith appeared, in which the anathema launched by the Church against usury was conveniently construed as not extending to the traffic in bank shares!

The Abbé Dubois entered into the mysteries of stock-jobbing with all the zeal of an apostle, and enriched himself by the spoils of the credulous; and he continually drew large sums from Law, as considerations for his political influence. Faithless to his country, in the course of his gambling speculations he transferred to England a great amount of specie, which had been paid into the royal treasury; thus contributing to the subsequent dearth of the precious metals.

The female sex participated in this sordid frenzy. Princesses of the blood, and ladies of the highest nobility, were among the most rapacious of stock-jobbers. The Regent seemed to have the riches of Crœsus at his command, and lavished money by hundreds of thousands upon his female relatives and favorites, as well as upon his *roués*, the dissolute companions of his debauches. "My son," writes the Regent's mother, in her correspondence, "gave me shares to the amount of two millions, which I distributed among my household. The king also took several millions for his own household. All the royal family have had them; all the children and grandchildren of France, and the princes of the blood."

Luxury and extravagance kept pace with this sudden inflation of fancied wealth. The hereditary palaces of nobles were pulled down, and rebuilt on a scale of augmented splendor. Entertainments were given, of incredible cost and magnificence. Never before had been such display in houses, furniture, equipages, and amusements. This was particularly the case among persons of the lower ranks, who had suddenly become possessed of millions Ludicrous anecdotes are related of some of these upstarts. One, who had just launched a splendid carriage, when about to use it for the first time, instead of getting in at the door, mounted, through habitude, to his accustomed place behind. Some ladies of quality, seeing a well-dressed woman covered with diamonds, but whom nobody knew, alight from a very handsome carriage, inquired who she was, of the footman. He replied, with a sneer, "It is a lady who has recently tumbled from a garret into this carriage." Mr. Law's domestics were said to become in like manner suddenly enriched by the crumbs that fell from his table. His coachman, having made a fortune, retired from his service. Mr. Law requested him to procure a coachman in his place. He appeared the next day with two, whom he pronounced equally good, and told Mr. Law, "Take which of them you choose, and I will take the other!"

Nor were these *novi homini* treated with the distance and disdain they would formerly have experienced from the haughty aristocracy of France. The pride of the old noblesse had been stifled by the stronger instinct of avarice. They rather sought the intimacy and confidence of these lucky upstarts; and it has been observed that a nobleman would gladly take his seat at the table of the fortunate lackey of yesterday, in hopes of learning from him the secret of growing rich!

Law now went about with a countenance radiant with success, and apparently dispensing wealth on every side. "He is admirably skilled in all that relates to finance," writes the Duchess of Orleans, the Regent's mother, "and has put the affairs of the state in such good order, that all the king's debts have been paid. He is so much run after, that he has no repose night or day. A duchess even kissed his hand publicly. If a duchess can do this, what will other ladies do?"

Wherever he went his path, we are told, was beset by a sordid throng, who waited to see him pass, and sought to obtain the favor of a word, a nod, or smile, as if a mere glance from him would bestow fortune. When at home his house was absolutely besieged by furious candidates for fortune. "They forced the doors," says the Duke de St. Simon; "they scaled his windows from the garden; they made their way into his cabinet down the chimney!"

The same venal court was paid by all classes to his family. The highest ladies of the court vied with each other in meannesses, to purchase the lucrative friendship of Mrs. Law and her daughter. They waited upon them with as much assiduity and adulation as if they had been princesses of the blood. The Regent one day expressed a desire that some duchess should accompany his daughter to Genoa. "My Lord," said some one present, "if you would have a choice from among the duchesses, you need but send to Mrs. Law's; you will find them all assembled there."

The wealth of Law rapidly increased with the expansion of the bubble. In the course of a few months he purchased fourteen titled estates, paying for them in paper; and the public hailed these sudden and vast acquisitions of landed property, as so many proofs of the soundness of his system. In one instance he met with a shrewd bargainer, who had not the general faith in his paper money. The President de Novion insisted on being paid for an estate in hard coin. Law accordingly brought the amount, four hundred thousand livres, in specie, saying, with a sarcastic smile, that he preferred paying in money, as its weight rendered it a mere incumbrance. As it happened, the President could give no clear title to the land, and the money had to be refunded. He paid it back *in paper*, which Law dared not refuse, lest he should depreciate it in the market!

The course of illusory credit went on triumphantly for eighteen months. Law had nearly fulfilled one of his promises, for the greater part of the public debt had been paid off; but how paid? In bank shares, which had been trumped up several hundred per cent. above their value, and which were to vanish like smoke in the hands of the holders.

One of the most striking attributes of Law, was the imperturbable assurance and self-possession with which he replied to every objection, and found a solution for every problem. He had the dexterity of a juggler in evading difficulties; and what was peculiar, made figures themselves, which are the very elements of exact demonstration, the means to dazzle and bewilder.

Toward the latter end of 1719 the Mississippi scheme had reached its highest point of glory. Half a million of strangers had crowded into Paris, in quest of fortune. The hotels and lodging-houses were overflowing; lodgings were procured with excessive difficulty; granaries were turned into bedrooms; provisions had risen enormously in price; splendid houses were multiplying on every side; the streets were crowded with carriages; above a thousand new equipages had been launched.

On the eleventh of December Law obtained another prohibitory decree, for the purpose of sweeping all the remaining specie in circulation into the bank. By this it was forbidden to make any payments in silver above ten livres, or in gold above three hundred.

The repeated decrees of this nature, the object of which was to depreciate the value of gold and increase the illusive credit of paper, began to awaken doubts of a system which required such bolstering. Capitalists gradually awoke from their bewilderment. Sound and able financiers consulted together, and agreed to make common cause against this continual expansion of a paper system. The shares of the bank and of the company began to decline in value. Wary men took the alarm, and began to *realize*, a word now first brought into use, to express the conversion of *ideal* property into something *real*.

The Prince of Conti, one of the most prominent and grasping of the Mississippi lords, was the first to give a blow to the credit of the bank. There was a mixture of ingratitude in his conduct that characterized the venal baseness of the times. He had received, from time to time, enormous sums from Law, as the price of his influence and patronage. His avarice had increased with every acquisition, until Law was compelled to refuse one of his exactions. In revenge, the prince immediately sent such an amount of paper to the bank to be cashed, that it required four wagons to bring away the silver, and he had the meanness to loll out of the window of his hotel, and jest and exult, as it was trundled into his porte-cochère.

This was the signal for other drains of like nature. The English and Dutch merchants, who had purchased a great amount of bank paper at low prices, cashed them at the bank, and carried the money out of the country. Other strangers did the like, thus draining the kingdom of its specie, and leaving paper in its place.

The Regent, perceiving these symptoms of decay in the system, sought to restore it to public confidence by conferring marks of confidence upon its author. He accordingly resolved to make Law Comptroller-General of the Finances of France. There was a material obstacle in the way. Law was a Protestant, and the Regent, unscrupulous as he was himself, did not dare publicly to outrage the severe edicts which Louis XIV., in his bigot days, had fulminated against all heretics. Law soon let him know that there would be no difficulty on that head. He was ready at any moment to abjure his religion in the way of business. For decency's sake, however, it was judged proper he should previously be convinced and converted. A ghostly instructor was soon found ready to accomplish his conversion in the shortest possible time. This was the Abbé Tencin, a profligate creature of the profligate Dubois, and like him working his way to ecclesiastical promotion and temporal wealth by the basest means.

Under the instructions of the Abbé Tencin, Law soon mastered the mysteries and dogmas of the Catholic doctrine; and, after a brief course of ghostly training, declared himself thoroughly convinced and converted. To avoid the sneers and jests of the Parisian public, the ceremony of abjuration took place at Melun. Law made a pious present of one hundred thousand livres to the Church of St. Roque, and the Abbé Tencin was rewarded for his edifying labors by sundry shares and bank-bills, which he shrewdly took care to convert into cash, having as little faith in the system as in the piety of his new convert. A more grave and moral community might have been outraged by this scandalous farce; but the Parisians laughed at it with their usual levity, and contented themselves with making it the subject of a number of songs and epigrams.

Law being now orthodox in his faith, took out letters of

naturalization, and having thus surmounted the intervening obstacles, was elevated by the Regent to the post of Comptroller-General. So accustomed had the community become to all juggles and transmutations in this hero of finance, that no one seemed shocked or astonished at his sudden elevation. On the contrary, being now considered perfectly established in place and power, he became more than ever the object of venal adoration. Men of rank and dignity thronged his antechamber, waiting patiently their turn for an audience; and titled dames demeaned themselves to take the front seats of the carriages of his wife and daughter, as if they had been riding with princesses of the blood royal. Law's head grew giddy with his elevation, and he began to aspire after aristocratical distinction. There was to be a court ball, at which several of the young noblemen were to dance in a ballet with the youthful king. Law requested that his son might be admitted into the ballet, and the Regent consented. The young scions of nobility, however, were indignant, and scouted the "intruding upstart." Their more worldly parents, fearful of displeasing the modern Midas, reprimanded them in vain. The striplings had not yet imbibed the passion for gain, and still held to their high blood. The son of the banker received slights and annoyances on all sides, and the public applauded them for their spirit. A fit of illness came opportunely to relieve the youth from an honor which would have cost him a world of vexations and affronts.

In February, 1720, shortly after Law's instalment in office, a decree came out uniting the bank to the India Company, by which last name the whole establishment was now known. The decree stated, that, as the bank was royal, the king was bound to make good the value of its bills; that he committed to the company the government of the bank for fifty years, and sold to it fifty millions of stock belonging to him, for nine hundred millions, a simple advance of eighteen hundred per cent. The decree farther declared, in the king's name, that he would never draw on the bank until the value of his drafts had first been lodged in it by his receivers-general.

The bank, it was said, had by this time issued notes to the amount of one thousand millions, being more paper than all the banks of Europe were able to circulate. To aid its credit, the receivers of the revenue were directed to take bank-notes of the sub-receivers. All payments, also, of one hundred livres and upward, were ordered to be made in bank-notes. These compulsory measures for a short time gave a false credit to the bank, which proceeded to discount merchants' notes, to lend money on jewels, plate, and other valables, as well as on mortgages.

Still farther to force on the system, an edict next appeared, forbidding any individual, or any corporate body, civil or religious, to hold in possession more than five hundred livres in current coin; that is to say, about seven louis-d'ors; the value of the louis-d'or in paper being, at the time, seventy-two livres. All the gold and silver they might have, above this pittance, was to be brought to the royal bank, and exchanged either for shares or bills.

As confiscation was the penalty of disobedience to this decree, and informers were assured a share of the forfeitures, a bounty was in a manner held out to domestic spies and traitors, and the most odious scrutiny was awakened into the pecuniary affairs of families and individuals. The very confidence between friends and relatives was impaired, and all the domestic ties and virtues of society were threatened, until a general sentiment of indignation broke forth, that compelled the Regent to rescind the odious decree. Lord Stairs, the British ambassador, speaking of the system of espionage encouraged by this edict, observed that it was impossible to doubt that Law was a thorough Catholic, since he had thus established the *inquisition*, after having already proved *transubstantiation* by changing specie into paper.

Equal abuses had taken place under the colonizing project. In his thousand expedients to amass capital, Law had sold parcels of land in Mississippi, at the rate of three thousand livres for a league square. Many capitalists had purchased estates large enough to constitute almost a principality; the only evil was, Law had sold a property which he could not deliver. The agents of police, who aided in recruiting the ranks of the colonists, had been guilty of scandalous impositions. Under pretence of taking up mendicants and vagabonds, they had scoured the streets at night, seizing upon honest mechanics or their sons, and hurrying them to their crimping-houses for the sole purpose of extorting money from them as a ransom. The populace was roused to indignation by these abuses. The officers of police were mobbed in the exercise of their odious functions, and several of them were killed, which put an end to this flagrant abuse of power.

In March, a most extraordinary decree of the council fixed the price of shares of the India Company at nine thousand livres each. All ecclesiastical communities and hospitals were now prohibited from investing money at interest in anything but India stock. With all these props and stays, the system continued to totter. How could it be otherwise, under a despotic government that could alter the value of property at every moment? The very compulsory measures that were adopted to establish the credit of the bank hastened its fall, plainly showing there was a want of solid security. Law caused pamphlets to be published, setting forth, in eloquent language, the vast profits that must accrue to holders of the stock, and the impossibility of the king's ever doing it any harm. On the very back of these assertions came forth an edict of the king, dated the 22d of May, wherein, under pretence of having reduced the value of his coin, it was declared necessary to reduce the value of his bank-notes one half, and of the India shares from nine thousand to five thousand livres!

This decree came like a clap of thunder upon shareholders. They found one half of the pretended value of the paper in their hands annihilated in an instant; and what certainty had they with respect to the other half? The rich considered themselves ruined; those in humbler circumstances looked forward to abject beggary.

The parliament seized the occasion to stand forth as the protector of the public, and refused to register the decree. It gained the credit of compelling the Regent to retrace his step, though it is more probable he yielded to the universal burst of public astonishment and reprobation. On the 27th of May the edict was revoked, and bank-bills were restored to their previous value. But the fatal blow had been struck; the delusion was at an end. Government itself had lost all public confidence equally with the bank it had engendered, and which its own arbitrary acts had brought into discredit. "All Paris," says the Regent's mother, in her letters, "has been mourning at the cursed decree which Law has persuaded my son to make. I have received anonymous letters stating that I have nothing to fear on my own account, but that my son shall be pursued with fire and sword."

The Regent now endeavored to avert the odium of his ruinous schemes from himself. He affected to have suddenly lost confidence in Law, and on the 29th of May discharged him from his employ as Comptroller-General, and stationed a Swiss guard of sixteen men in his house. He even refused to see him, when, on the following day, he applied at the portal of the Palais Royal for admission; but having played off this farce before the public, he admitted him secretly the same night, by a private door, and continued as before to coöperate with him in his financial schemes.

On the first of June, the Regent issued a decree permitting persons to have as much money as they pleased in their possession. Few, however, were in a state to benefit by this permission. There was a run upon the bank, but a royal ordinance immediately suspended payment until farther orders. To relieve the public mind, a city stock was created of twenty-five millions, bearing an interest of two and a half per cent., for which bank-notes were taken in exchange. The bank-notes thus withdrawn from circulation were publicly burnt before the Hôtel de Ville. The public, however, had lost confidence in everything and everybody, and suspected fraud and collusion in those who pretended to burn the bills.

A general confusion now took place in the financial world. Families who had lived in opulence found themselves suddenly reduced to indigence. Schemers who had been revelling in the delusion of princely fortunes found their estates vanishing into thin air. Those who had any property remaining sought to secure it against reverses. Cautious persons found there was no safety for property in a country where the coin was continually shifting in value, and where a despotism was exercised over public securities, and even over the private purses of individuals. They began to send their effects into other countries; when lo! on the 20th of June, a royal edict commanded them to bring back their effects, under penalty of forfeiting twice their value, and forbade them, under like penalty, from investing their money in foreign stocks. This was soon followed by another decree, forbidding any one to retain precious stones in his possession, or to sell them to foreigners; all must be deposited in the bank in exchange for depreciating paper!

Execrations were now poured out, on all sides, against Law, and menaces of vengeance. What a contrast, in a short time, to the venal incense once offered up to him! "This person," writes the Regent's mother, "who was formerly worshipped as a god, is now not sure of his life. It is astonishing how greatly terrified he is. He is as a dead man; he is pale as a sheet, and it is said he can never get over it. My son is not dismayed, though he is threatened on all sides, and is very much amused with Law's terrors."

About the middle of July, the last grand attempt was made by Law and the Regent to keep up the system and provide for the immense emission of paper. A decree was fabricated, giving the India Company the entire monopoly of commerce, on condition that it would, in the course of a year, reimburse six hundred millions of livres of its bills, at the rate of fifty millions per month.

On the 17th this decree was sent to parliament to be registered. It at once raised a storm of opposition in that assembly, and a vehement discussion took place. While that was going on, a disastrous scene was passing out of doors.

The calamitous effects of the system had reached the humblest concerns of human life. Provisions had risen to an enormous price; paper money was refused at all the shops; the people had not wherewithal to buy bread. It had been found absolutely indispensable to relax a little from the suspension of specie payments, and to allow small sums to be scantily exchanged for paper. The doors of the bank and the neighboring street were immediately thronged with a famishing multitude seeking cash for bank-notes of ten livres. So great was the press and struggle, that several persons were stifled and crushed to death. The mob carried three of the bodies to the court-yard of the Palais Royal. Some cried for the Regent to come forth, and behold the effect of his system; others demanded the death of Law, the impostor, who had brought this misery and ruin upon the nation.

The moment was critical: the popular fury was rising to a tempest, when Le Blanc, the Secretary of State, stepped forth.

He had previously sent for the military, and now only sought to gain time. Singling out six or seven stout fellows, who seemed to be the ringleaders of the mob, "My good fellows," said he, calmly, "carry away these bodies, and place them in some church, and then come back quickly to me for your pay." They immediately obeyed; a kind of funeral procession was formed; the arrival of troops dispersed those who lingered behind; and Paris was probably saved from an insurrection.

About ten o'clock in the morning, all being quiet, Law ventured to go in his carriage to the Palais Royal. He was saluted with cries and curses as he passed along the streets; and he reached the Palais Royal in a terrible fright. The Regent amused himself with his fears, but retained him with him, and sent off his carriage, which was assailed by the mob, pelted with stones, and the glasses shivered. The news of this outrage was communicated to parliament in the midst of a furious discussion of the decree for the commercial monopoly. The first president, who had been absent for a short time, reëntered, and communicated the tidings in a whimsical couplet:

"Messieurs, Messieurs! bonne nouvelle!
Le carrosse de Law est reduit en carrelle!"

"Gentlemen, Gentlemen! good news!
The carriage of Law is shivered to atoms!"

The members sprang up with joy. "And Law!" exclaimed they, "has he been torn to pieces?" The president was ignorant of the result of the tumult; whereupon the debate was cut short, the decree rejected, and the house adjourned, the members hurrying to learn the particulars. Such was the levity with which public affairs were treated at that dissolute and disastrous period.

On the following day there was an ordinance from the king, prohibiting all popular assemblages; and troops were stationed at various points, and in all public places. The regiment of guards was ordered to hold itself in readiness, and the musketeers to be at their hotels, with their horses ready saddled. A number of small offices were opened, where people might cash small notes, though with great delay and difficulty. An edict was also issued, declaring that whoever should refuse to take bank-notes in the course of trade, should forfeit double the amount!

The continued and vehement opposition of parliament to the whole delusive system of finance had been a constant source of annoyance to the Regent; but this obstinate rejection of his last grand expedient of a commercial monopoly was not to be tolerated. He determined to punish that intractable body. The Abbé Dubois and Law suggested a simple mode; it was to suppress the parliament altogether, being, as they observed, so far from useful, that it was a constant impediment to the march of public affairs. The Regent was half inclined to listen to their advice; but upon calmer consideration, and the advice of friends, he adopted a more moderate course. On the 20th of July, early in the morning, all the doors of the parliament-house were taken possession of by the troops. Others were sent to surround the house of the first president, and others to the houses of the various members; who were all at first in great alarm, until an order from the king was put into their hands, to render themselves at Pontoise, in the course of two days, to which place the parliament was thus suddenly and arbitrarily transferred.

This despotic act, says Voltaire, would at any other time have caused an insurrection; but one half of the Parisians were occupied by their ruin, and the other half by their fancied riches, which were soon to vanish. The president and members of parliament acquiesced in the mandate without a murmur; they even went as if on a party of pleasure, and made every preparation to lead a joyous life in their exile. The musketeers, who held possession of the vacated parliament-house, a gay corps of fashionable young fellows, amused themselves with making songs and pasquinades, at the expense of the exiled legislators; and at length, to pass away time, formed themselves into a mock parliament; elected their presidents, kings, ministers, and advocates; took their seats in due form; arraigned a cat at their bar, in place of the Sieur Law, and, after giving it a "fair trial," condemned it to be hanged. In this manner, public affairs and public institutions were lightly turned to jest.

As to the exiled parliament, it lived gayly and luxuriously at Pontoise, at the public expense; for the Regent had furnished funds, as usual, with a lavish hand. The first president had the mansion of the Duke de Bouillon put at his disposal, all ready furnished, with a vast and delightful garden on the borders of a river. There he kept open house to all the members of parliament. Several tables were spread every day, all furnished luxuriously and splendidly; the most exquisite wines and liquors, the choicest fruits and refreshments of all kinds, abounded. A number of small chariots for one and two horses were always at hand, for such ladies and old gentlemen as wished to take an airing after dinner, and card and billiard tables for such as chose to amuse themselves in that way until supper. The sister and the daughter of the first president did the honors of his house, and he himself presided there with an air of great ease, hospitality, and magnificence. It became a party of pleasure to drive from Paris to Pontoise, which was six leagues distant, and partake of the amusements and festivities of the place. Business was openly slighted; nothing was thought of but amusement. The Regent and his government were laughed at, and made the subjects of continual pleasantries; while the enormous expenses incurred by this idle and lavish course of life more than doubled the liberal sums provided. This was the way in which the parliament resented their exile.

During all this time the system was getting more and more involved. The stock exchange had some time previously been removed to the Place Vendôme; but the tumult and noise becoming intolerable to the residents of that polite quarter, and especially to the chancellor, whose hotel was there, the Prince and Princess Carignan, both deep gamblers in Mississippi stock, offered the extensive garden of their Hôtel de Soissons as a rallying-place for the worshippers of Mammon. The offer was accepted. A number of barracks were immediately erected in the garden, as offices for the stock-brokers, and an order was obtained from the Regent, under pretext of police regulations, that no bargain should be valid, unless concluded in these barracks. The rent of them immediately mounted to a hundred livres a month for each, and the whole yielded these noble proprietors an ignoble revenue of half a million of livres.

The mania for gain, however, was now at an end. A universal panic succeeded. "*Sauve qui peut!*" was the watchword. Every one was anxious to exchange falling paper for something of intrinsic and permanent value. Since money was not to be had, jewels, precious stones, plate, porcelain, trinkets of gold and silver, all commanded any price, in paper. Land was bought at fifty years' purchase, and he esteemed himself happy who could get it even at this price. Monopolies now became the rage among the noble holders of paper. The Duke de la Force bought up nearly all the tallow, grease, and soap; others, the coffee and spices; others, hay and oats. Foreign exchanges were almost impracticable. The debts of Dutch and English merchants were paid in this fictitious money, all the coin of the realm having disappeared. All the relations of debtor and creditor were confounded. With one thousand crowns one might pay a debt of eighteen thousand livres.

The Regent's mother, who once exulted in the affluence of bank paper, now wrote in a very different tone. "I have often wished," said she, in her letters, "that these bank-notes were in the depths of the infernal regions. They have given my son more trouble than relief. Nobody in France has a penny. . . . My son was once popular; but since the arrival of this cursed Law he is hated more and more. Not a week passes without my receiving letters filled with frightful threats, and speaking of him as a tyrant. I have just received one, threatening him with poison. When I showed it to him, he did nothing but laugh."

In the meantime, Law was dismayed by the increasing troubles, and terrified at the tempest he had raised. He was not a man of real courage; and, fearing for his personal safety, from popular tumult, or the despair of ruined individuals, he again took refuge in the palace of the Regent. The latter, as usual, amused himself with his terrors, and turned every new disaster into a jest; but he, too, began to think of his own security.

In pursuing the schemes of Law, he had, no doubt, calculated to carry through his term of government with ease and splendor, and to enrich himself, his connections, and his favorites: and had hoped that the catastrophe of the system would not take place until after the expiration of the regency.

He now saw his mistake—that it was impossible much longer to prevent an explosion; and he determined at once to get Law out of the way, and then to charge him with the whole tissue of delusions of this paper alchemy. He accordingly took occasion of the recall of parliament in December, 1720, to suggest to Law the policy of his avoiding an encounter with that hostile and exasperated body. Law needed no urging to the measure. His only desire was to escape from Paris and its tempestuous populace. Two days before the return of parliament he took his sudden and secret departure. He travelled in a chaise bearing the arms of the Regent, and was escorted by a kind of safeguard of servants, in the duke's livery. His first place of refuge was an estate of the Regent's about six leagues from Paris, from whence he pushed forward to Bruxelles.

As soon as Law was fairly out of the way, the Duke of Orleans summoned a council of the regency, and informed them that they were assembled to deliberate on the state of the finances and the affairs of the India Company. Accordingly La Houssaye, Comptroller-General, rendered a perfectly clear statement, by which it appeared that there were bank-bills in circulation to the amount of two milliards seven hundred millions of livres, without any evidence that this enormous sum had been emitted in virtue of any ordinance from the general assembly of the India Company, which alone had the right to authorize such emissions.

The council was astonished at this disclosure, and looked to the Regent for explanation. Pushed to the extreme, the Regent avowed that Law had emitted bills to the amount of twelve hundred millions beyond what had been fixed by ordinances, and in contradiction to express prohibitions; that, the thing being done, he, the Regent, had legalized or rather covered the transaction, by decrees ordering such emissions, which decrees he had *antedated.*

A stormy scene ensued between the Regent and the Duke de Bourbon, little to the credit of either, both having been deeply implicated in the cabalistic operations of the system. In fact, the several members of the council had been among the most venal "beneficiaries" of the scheme, and had interests at stake which they were anxious to secure. From all the circumstances of the case, I am inclined to think that others were more to blame than Law for the disastrous effects of his financial projects. His bank, had it been confined to its original limits, and left to the control of its own internal regulations, might have gone on prosperously, and been of great benefit to the nation. It was an institution fitted for a free country; but, unfortunately, it was subject to the control of a despotic government, that could, at its pleasure, alter the value of the specie within its vaults, and compel the most extravagant expansions of its paper circulation. The vital principle of a bank is security in the regularity of its operations, and the immediate convertibility of its paper into coin; and what confidence could be reposed in an institution, or its paper promises, when the sovereign could at any moment centuple those promises in the market, and seize upon all the money in the bank? The compulsory measures used, likewise, to force bank-notes into currency, against the judgment of the public, was fatal to the system; for credit must be free and uncontrolled as the common air. The Regent was the evil spirit of the system, that forced Law on to an expansion of his paper currency far beyond what he had ever dreamed of. He it was that in a manner compelled the unlucky projector to devise all kinds of collateral companies and monopolies, by which to raise funds to meet the constantly and enormously increasing emissions of shares and notes. Law was but like a poor conjurer in the hands of a potent spirit that he has evoked, and that obliges him to go on, desperately and ruinously, with his conjurations. He only thought at the outset to raise the wind, but the Regent compelled him to raise the whirlwind.

The investigation of the affairs of the company by the council resulted in nothing beneficial to the public. The princes and nobles who had enriched themselves by all kinds of juggles and extortions escaped unpunished, and retained the greater part of their spoils. Many of the "suddenly rich," who had risen from obscurity to a giddy height of imaginary prosperity, and had indulged in all kinds of vulgar and ridiculous excesses, awoke as out of a dream, in their original poverty, now made more galling and humiliating by their transient elevation.

The weight of the evil, however, fell on more valuable classes of society—honest tradesmen and artisans, who had been seduced away from the slow accumulations of industry, to the specious chances of speculation. Thousands of meritorious families, also, once opulent, had been reduced to indigence by a too great confidence in government. There was a general derangement in the finances, that long exerted a baneful influence over the national prosperity; but the most disastrous effects of the system were upon the morals and manners of the nation. The faith of engagements, the sanctity of promises in affairs of business, were at an end. Every expedient to grasp present profit, or to evade present difficulty, was tolerated. While such deplorable laxity of principle was generated in the busy classes, the chivalry of France had soiled their pennons; and honor and glory, so long the idols of the Gallic nobility, had been tumbled to the earth, and trampled in the dirt of the stock-market.

As to Law, the originator of the system, he appears eventually to have profited but little by his schemes. "He was a quack," says Voltaire, "to whom the state was given to be cured, but who poisoned it with his drugs, and who poisoned himself." The effects which he left behind in France were sold at a low price, and the proceeds dissipated. His landed estates were confiscated. He carried away with him barely enough to maintain himself, his wife, and daughter, with decency. The chief relic of his immense fortune was a great diamond, which he was often obliged to pawn. He was in England in 1721, and was presented to George the First. He returned, shortly afterward, to the Continent, shifting about from place to place, and died in Venice, in 1729. His wife and daughter, accustomed to live with the prodigality of princesses, could not conform to their altered fortunes, but dissipated the scanty means left to them, and sank into abject poverty. "I saw his wife," says Voltaire, "at Bruxelles, as much humiliated as she had been haughty and triumphant at Paris." An elder brother of Law remained in France, and was protected by the Duchess of Bourbon. His descendants acquitted themselves honorably, in various public employments; and one of them was the Marquis Lauriston, sometimes Lieutenant-General and Peer of France.

A History of New York

FROM THE BEGINNING OF THE WORLD TO THE END OF THE DUTCH DYNASTY

Containing, among many surprising and curious matters, the unutterable ponderings of Walter the Doubter, the disastrous projects of William the Testy, and the chivalric achievements of Peter the Headstrong—the three Dutch Governors of New Amsterdam; being the only authentic history of the times that ever hath been or ever will be published

by Diedrich Knickerbocker

De waarheid die in duister lag,
De komt mit klaarheid aan den dag.

Contents

BOOK III

IN WHICH IS RECORDED THE GOLDEN REIGN OF WOUTER VAN TWILLER

BOOK IV

CONTAINING THE CHRONICLES OF THE REIGN OF WILLIAM THE TESTY

BOOK V

CONTAINING THE FIRST PART OF THE REIGN OF PETER STUYVESANT, AND HIS TROUBLES WITH THE AMPHICTYONIC COUNCIL

BOOK VI

CONTAINING THE SECOND PART OF THE REIGN OF PETER THE HEADSTRONG, AND HIS GALLANT ACHIEVEMENTS ON THE DELAWARE

BOOK VII

CONTAINING THE THIRD PART OF THE REIGN OF PETER THE HEADSTRONG HIS TROUBLES WITH THE BRITISH NATION, AND THE DECLINE AND FALL OF THE DUTCH DYNASTY

Notices

WHICH APPEARED IN THE NEWSPAPERS PREVIOUS TO THE PUBLICATION OF THIS WORK

* * *

From the Evening Post of October 26, 1809

DISTRESSING

Left his lodgings, some time since, and has not since been heard of, a small elderly gentleman, dressed in an old black coat and cocked hat, by the name of *Knickerbocker.* As there are some reasons for believing he is not entirely in his right mind, and as great anxiety is entertained about him, any information concerning him left either at the Columbian Hotel, Mulberry Street, or at the office of this paper, will be thankfully received.

P. S. Printers of newspapers would be aiding the cause of humanity in giving an insertion to the above.

* * *

From the same, November 6, 1809

To the Editor of the Evening Post:

SIR,—Having read in your paper of the 26th October last, a paragraph respecting an old gentleman by the name of *Knickerbocker,* who was missing from his lodgings; if it would be any relief to his friends, or furnish them with any clue to discover where he is, you may inform them that a person answering the description given, was seen by the passengers of the Albany stage, early in the morning, about four or five weeks since, resting himself by the side of the road, a little above King's Bridge. He had in his hand a small bundle, tied in a red bandana handkerchief; he appeared to be travelling northward, and was very much fatigued and exhausted.

A TRAVELLER.

* * *

From the same, November 16, 1809

To the Editor of the Evening Post:

SIR,—You have been good enough to publish in your paper a paragraph about Mr. *Diedrich Knickerbocker,* who was missing so strangely sometime since. Nothing satisfactory has been heard of the old gentleman since; but *a very curious kind of a written book* has been found in his room, in his own handwriting. Now I wish you to notice him, if he is still alive, that if he does not return and pay off his bill for boarding and lodging, I shall have to dispose of his book to satisfy me for the same.

I am, sir, your humble servant,

SETH HANDASIDE,

Landlord of the Independent Columbian Hotel, Mulberry Street.

* * *

From the same, November 28, 1809

LITERARY NOTICE

INSKEEP & BRADFORD have in press, and will shortly publish,

A HISTORY OF NEW YORK,

In two volumes, duodecimo. Price Three Dollars.

Containing an account of its discovery and settlement, with its internal policies, manners, customs, wars, &c., &c., under the Dutch government, furnishing many curious and interesting particulars never before published, and which are gathered from various manuscript and other authenticated sources, the whole being interspersed with philosophical speculations and moral precepts.

This work was found in the chamber of Mr. Diedrich Knickerbocker, the old gentleman whose sudden and mysterious disappearance has been noticed. It is published in order to discharge certain debts he has left behind.

* * *

From the American Citizen, December 6, 1809

Is this day published

By INSKEEP & BRADFORD, No. 128 Broadway,

A HISTORY OF NEW YORK,

&c., &c.

(*Containing same as above.*)

The Author's Apology

THE following work, in which, at the outset, nothing more was contemplated than a temporary *jeu d'esprit*, was commenced in company with my brother, the late Peter Irving, Esq. Our idea was, to parody a small handbook which had recently appeared, entitled "A Picture of New York." Like that, our work was to begin with an historical sketch; to be followed by notices of the customs, manners, and institutions of the city; written in a serio-comic vein, and treating local errors, follies, and abuses with good-humored satire.

To burlesque the pedantic lore displayed in certain American works, our historical sketch was to commence with the creation of the world; and we laid all kinds of works under contribution for trite citations, relevant, or irrelevant, to give it the proper air of learned research. Before this crude mass of mock erudition could be digested into form, my brother departed for Europe, and I was left to prosecute the enterprise alone.

I now altered the plan of the work. Discarding all idea of a parody on the "Picture of New York," I determined that what had been originally intended as an introductory sketch, should comprise the whole work, and form a comic history of the city. I accordingly moulded the mass of citations and disquisitions into introductory chapters, forming the first book; but it soon became evident to me, that, like Robinson Crusoe with his boat, I had begun on too large a scale, and that, to launch my history successfully, I must reduce its proportions. I accordingly resolved to confine it to the period of the Dutch domination, which, in its rise, progress, and decline, presented that unity of subject required by classic rule. It was a period, also, at that time almost a *terra incognita* in history. In fact, I was surprised to find how few of my fellow-citizens were aware that New York had ever been called New Amsterdam, or had heard of the names of its early Dutch governors, or cared a straw about their ancient Dutch progenitors.

This, then, broke upon me as the poetic age of our city; poetic from its very obscurity; and open, like the early and obscure days of ancient Rome, to all the embellishments of heroic fiction. I hailed my native city, as fortunate above all other American cities, in having an antiquity thus extending back into the regions of doubt and fable; neither did I conceive I was committing any grievous historical sin in helping out the few facts I could collect in this remote and forgotten region with figments of my own brain, or in giving characteristic attributes to the few names connected with it which I might dig up from oblivion.

In this, doubtless, I reasoned like a young and inexperienced writer, besotted with his own fancies; and my presumptuous trespasses into this sacred, though neglected region of history have met with deserved rebuke from men of soberer minds. It is too late, however, to recall the shaft thus rashly launched. To any one whose sense of fitness it may wound, I can only say with Hamlet—

> Let my disclaiming from a purposed evil
> Free me so far in your most generous thoughts,
> That I have shot my arrow o'er the house,
> And hurt my brother.

I will say this in further apology for my work: that, if it has taken an unwarrantable liberty with our early provincial history, it has at least turned attention to that history and provoked research. It is only since this work appeared that the forgotten archives of the province have been rummaged, and the facts and personages of the olden time rescued from the dust of oblivion, and elevated into whatever importance they may virtually possess.

The main object of my work, in fact, had a bearing wide from the sober aim of history; but one which, I trust, will meet with some indulgence from poetic minds. It was to embody the traditions of our city in an amusing form; to illustrate its local humors, customs, and peculiarities; to clothe home scenes and places and familiar names with those imaginative and whimsical associations so seldom met with in our new country, but which live like charms and spells about the cities of the old world, binding the heart of the native inhabitant to his home.

In this I have reason to believe I have in some measure succeeded. Before the appearance of my work the popular traditions of our city were unrecorded; the peculiar and racy customs and usages derived from our Dutch progenitors were unnoticed or regarded with indifference, or adverted to with a sneer. Now they form a convivial currency, and are brought forward on all occasions; they link our whole community together in good humor and good fellowship; they are the rallying points of home feeling, the seasoning of our civic festivities, the staple of local tales and local pleasantries, and are so harped upon by our writers of popular fiction, that I find myself almost crowded off the legendary ground which I was the first to explore, by the host who have followed in my footsteps.

I dwell on this head, because, at the first appearance of my work, its aim and drift were misapprehended by some of the descendants of the Dutch worthies; and because I understand that now and then one may still be found to regard it with a captious eye. The far greater part, however, I have reason to flatter myself, receive my good-humored picturings in the same temper in which they were executed; and when I find, after a lapse of nearly forty years, this hap-hazard production of my youth still cherished among them—when I find its very name become a "household word" and used to give the home stamp to everything recommended for popular acceptation, such as Knickerbocker societies, Knickerbocker insurance companies, Knickerbocker steamboats, Knickerbocker omnibuses, Knickerbocker bread, and Knicerbocker ice—and when I find New Yorkers of Dutch descent priding themselves upon being "genuine Knickerbockers"—I please myself with the persuasion that I have struck the right chord; that my dealings with the good old Dutch times, and the customs and usages derived from them, are in harmony with the feelings and humors of my townsmen; that I have opened a vein of pleasant associations and quaint characteristics peculiar to my native place, and which its inhabitants will not willingly suffer to pass away; and that, though other histories of New York may appear of higher claims to learned acceptation, and may take their dignified and appropriate rank in the family library, Knickerbocker's history will still be received with good-humored indulgence, and be thumbed and chuckled over by the family fireside. W. I.

SUNNYSIDE, 1848.

Account of the Author

IT was some time, if I recollect right, in the early part of the autumn of 1808, that a stranger applied for lodgings at the Independent Columbian Hotel in Mulberry Street, of which I am landlord. He was a small, brisk-looking old gentleman, dressed in a rusty black coat, a pair of olive velvet breeches, and a small cocked hat. He had a few gray hairs plaited and clubbed behind, and his beard seemed to be of some eight-and-forty hours' growth. The only piece of finery which he bore about him was a bright pair of square silver shoe-buckles; and all his baggage was contained in a pair of saddle-bags, which he carried under his arm. His whole appearance was something out of the common run; and my wife, who is a very shrewd body, at once set him down for some eminent country schoolmaster.

As the Independent Columbian Hotel is a very small house, I was a little puzzled at first where to put him; but my wife, who seemed taken with his looks, would needs put him in her best chamber, which is genteelly set off with the profiles of the whole family, done in black, by those two great painters, Jarvis and Wood; and commands a very pleasant view of the new grounds on the Collect, together with the rear of the Poor-House and Bridewell, and a full front of the Hospital; so that it is the cheerfullest room in the whole house.

During the whole time that he stayed with us, we found him a very worthy good sort of an old gentleman, though a little queer in his ways. He would keep in his room for days together, and if any of the children cried, or made a noise about his door, he would bounce out in a great passion, with his hands full of papers, and say something about "deranging his ideas"; which made my wife believe sometimes that he was not altogether *compos*. Indeed, there was more than one reason to make her think so, for his room was always covered with scraps of paper and old mouldy books, laying about at sixes and sevens, which he would never let anybody touch; for he said he had laid them all away in their proper places, so that he might know where to find them; though for that matter, he was half his time worrying about the house in search of some book or writing which he had carefully put out of the way. I shall never forget what a pother he once made, because my wife cleaned out his room when his back was turned, and put everything to rights; for he swore he would never be able to get his papers in order again in a twelvemonth. Upon this, my wife ventured to ask him what he did with so many books and papers; and he told her that he was "seeking for immortality"; which made her think more than ever that the poor old gentleman's head was a little cracked.

He was a very inquisitive body, and when not in his room, was continually poking about town, hearing all the news, and prying into everything that was going on: this was particularly the case about election time, when he did nothing but bustle about from poll to poll, attending all ward meetings, and committee rooms; though I could never find that he took part with either side of the question. On the contrary, he would come home and rail at both parties with great wrath—and plainly proved one day, to the satisfaction of my wife and three old ladies who were drinking tea with her, that the two parties were like two rogues, each tugging at a skirt of the nation; and that in the end they would tear the very coat off its back, and expose its nakedness. Indeed, he was an oracle among the neighbors, who would collect around him to hear him talk of an afternoon, as he smoked his pipe on the bench before the door; and I really believe he would have brought over the whole neighborhood to his own side of the question, if they could ever have found out what it was.

He was very much given to argue, or, as he called it, *philosophize*, about the most trifling matter; and to do him justice, I never knew anybody that was a match for him, except it was a grave-looking old gentleman who called now and then to see him, and often posed him in an argument. But this is nothing surprising, as I have since found out this stranger is the city librarian; who, of course, must be a man of great learning: and I have my doubts if he had not some hand in the following history.

As our lodger had been a long time with us, and we had never received any pay, my wife began to be somewhat uneasy, and curious to find out who and what he was. She accordingly made bold to put the question to his friend, the librarian, who replied in his dry way that he was one of the *literati*, which she supposed to mean some new party in politics. I scorn to push a lodger for his pay; so I let day after day pass on without dunning the old gentleman for a farthing: but my wife, who always takes these matters on herself, and is, as I said, a shrewd kind of a woman, at last got out of patience, and hinted that she thought it high time "some people should have a sight of some people's money." To which the old gentleman replied, in a mighty touchy manner, that she need not make herself uneasy, for that he had a treasure there (pointing to his saddle-bags) worth her whole house put together. This was the only answer we could ever get from him; and as my wife, by some of those odd ways in which women find out everything, learnt that he was of very great connections, being related to the Knickerbockers of Scaghtikoke, and cousin-german to the congressman of that name, she did not like to treat him uncivilly. What is more, she even offered, merely by way of making things easy, to let him live scot-free, if he would teach the children their letters; and to try her best and get her neighbors to send their children also: but the old gentleman took it in such dudgeon, and seemed so affronted at being taken for a schoolmaster, that she never dared to speak on the subject again.

About two months ago, he went out of a morning, with a bundle in his hand, and has never been heard of since. All kinds of inquiries were made after him, but in vain. I wrote to his relations at Scaghtikoke, but they sent for answer, that he had not been there since the year before last, when he had a great dispute with the congressman about politics, and left the place in a huff, and they had neither heard nor seen anything of him from that time to this. I must own I felt very much worried about the poor old gentleman, for I thought something bad must have happened to him, that he should be missing so long, and never return to pay his bill. I therefore advertised him in the newspapers, and though my melancholy advertisement was published by several humane printers, yet I have never been able to learn anything satisfactory about him.

My wife now said it was high time to take care of ourselves, and see if he had left anything behind in his room, that would pay us for his board and lodging. We found nothing, however, but some old books and musty writings, and his saddle-bags; which, being opened in the presence of the librarian, contained only a few articles of worn-out clothes, and a large bundle of blotted paper. On looking over this, the librarian told us he had no doubt it was the treasure which the old gentleman had spoken about; as it proved to be a most excellent and faithful HISTORY OF NEW YORK, which he advised us by all means to publish, assuring us that it would be so eagerly bought up by a discerning public, that he had no doubt it would be enough to pay our arrears ten times over. Upon this we got a very learned schoolmaster, who teaches our children, to prepare it for the press, which he accordingly has done; and has, moreover, added to it a number of valuable notes of his own.

This, therefore, is a true statement of my reasons for having this work printed, without waiting for the consent of the author; and I here declare, that, if he ever returns (though I much fear some unhappy accident has befallen him) I stand ready to account with him like a true and honest man. Which is all at present,

From the public's humble servant,

SETH HANDASIDE.

Independent Columbian Hotel, New York.

The foregoing account of the author was prefixed to the first edition of this work. Shortly after its publication, a letter was received from him, by Mr. Handaside, dated at a small Dutch village on the banks of the Hudson, whither he had travelled for the purpose of inspecting certain ancient records. As this was one of those few and happy villages into which newspapers never find their way, it is not a matter of surprise that Mr. Knickerbocker should never have seen the numerous advertisements that were made concerning him, and that he should learn of the publication of his history by mere accident.

He expressed much concern at its premature appearance, as thereby he was prevented from making several important corrections and alterations, as well as from profiting by many curious hints which he had collected during his travels along the shores of the Tappan Sea, and his sojourn at Haverstraw and Esopus.

Finding that there was no longer any immediate necessity for his return to New York, he extended his journey up to the residence of his relations at Scaghtikoke. On his way thither he stopped for some days at Albany, for which city he is known to have entertained a great partiality. He found it, however, considerably altered, and was much concerned at the inroads and improvements which the Yankees were making, and the consequent decline of the good old Dutch manners. Indeed, he was informed that these intruders were making sad innovations in all parts of the State; where they had given great trouble and vexation to the regular Dutch settlers by the introduction of turnpike-gates, and country schoolhouses. It is said, also, that Mr. Knickerbocker shook his head sorrowfully at noticing the gradual decay of the great Vander Heyden palace; but was highly indignant at finding that the ancient Dutch church, which stood in the middle of the street, had been pulled down since his last visit.

The fame of Mr. Knickerbocker's history having reached even to Albany, he received much flattering attention from its worthy burghers, some of whom, however, pointed out two or three very great errors he had fallen into, particularly that of suspending a lump of sugar over the Albany tea-tables, which, they assured him, had been discontinued for some years past. Several families, moreover, were somewhat piqued that their ancestors had not been mentioned in his work, and showed great jealousy of their neighbors who had thus been distinguished; while the latter, it must be confessed, plumed themselves vastly thereupon; considering these recordings in the light of letters-patent of nobility, establishing their claims to ancestry—which, in this republican country, is a matter of no little solicitude and vainglory.

It is also said, that he enjoyed high favor and countenance from the governor, who once asked him to dinner, and was seen two or three times to shake hands with him, when they met in the streets; which certainly was going great lengths, considering that they differed in politics. Indeed, certain of the governor's confidential friends, to whom he could venture to speak his mind freely on such matters, have assured us, that he privately entertained a considerable good will for our author—nay, he even once went so far as to declare, and that openly too, and at his own table, just after dinner, that "Knickerbocker was a very well-meaning sort of an old gentleman, and no fool." From all which many have been led to suppose that, had our author been of different politics, and written for the newspapers instead of wasting his talents on histories, he might have risen to some post of honor and profit—peradventure, to be a notary-public, or even a justice in the ten-pound court.

Besides the honors and civilities already mentioned, he was much caressed by the *literati* of Albany; particularly by Mr. John Cook, who entertained him very hospitably at his circulating library and reading-room, where they used to drink Spa water, and talk about the ancients. He found Mr. Cook a man after his own heart—of great literary research, and a curious collector of books. At parting, the latter, in testimony of friendship, made him a present of the two oldest works in his collection; which were the earliest edition of the Heidelberg Catechism, and Adrian Vander Donck's famous account of the New Netherlands: by the last of which, Mr. Knickerbocker profited greatly in his second edition.

Having passed some time very agreeably at Albany, our author proceeded to Scaghtikoke, where, it is but justice to say, he was received with open arms, and treated with wonderful loving-kindness. He was much looked up to by the family, being the first historian of the name; and was considered almost as great a man as his cousin the congressman—with whom, by the by, he became perfectly reconciled, and contracted a strong friendship.

In spite, however, of the kindness of his relations and their great attention to his comforts, the old gentleman soon became restless and discontented. His history being published, he had no longer any business to occupy his thoughts, or any scheme to excite his hopes and anticipations. This, to a busy mind like his, was a truly deplorable situation; and, had he not been a man of inflexible morals and regular habits, there would have been great danger of his taking to politics, or drinking—both which pernicious vices we daily see men driven to by mere spleen and idleness.

It is true, he sometimes employed himself in preparing a second edition of his history, wherein he endeavored to correct and improve many passages with which he was dissatisfied, and to rectify some mistakes that had crept into it; for he was particularly anxious that his work should be noted for its authenticity; which, indeed, is the very life and soul of history. But the glow of composition had departed—he had to leave many places untouched, which he would fain have altered; and even where he did make alterations, he seemed always in doubt whether they were for the better or the worse.

After a residence of some time at Scaghtikoke, he began to feel a strong desire to return to New York, which he ever regarded with the warmest affection; not merely because it was his native city, but because he really considered it the very best city in the whole world. On his return, he entered into the full enjoyment of the advantages of a literary reputation. He was continually importuned to write advertisements, petitions, handbills, and productions of similar import; and, although he never meddled with the public papers, yet had he the credit of writing innumerable essays, and smart things, that appeared on all subjects, and all sides of the question; in all which he was clearly detected "by his style."

He contracted, moreover, a considerable debt at the post-office, in consequence of the numerous letters he received from authors and printers soliciting his subscription, and he was applied to by every charitable society for yearly donations, which he gave very cheerfully, considering these applications as so many compliments. He was once invited to a great corporation dinner; and was even twice summoned to attend as a juryman at the court of quarter sessions. Indeed, so renowned did he become, that he could no longer pry about, as formerly, in all holes and corners of the city, according to the bent of his humor, unnoticed and uninterrupted; but several times when he has been sauntering the streets, on his usual rambles of observation, equipped with his cane and cocked hat, the little boys at play have been known to cry, "There goes Diedrich!"—at which the old gentleman seemed not a little pleased, looking upon these salutations in the light of the praise of posterity.

In a word, if we take into consideration all these various honors and distinctions, together with an exuberant eulogium passed on him in the Port Folio (with which, we are told, the old gentleman was so much overpowered, that he was sick for two or three days) it must be confessed, that few authors have ever lived to receive such illustrious rewards, or have so completely enjoyed in advance their own immortality.

After his return from Scaghtikoke, Mr. Knickerbocker took up his residence at a little rural retreat, which the Stuyvesants had granted him on the family domain, in gratitude for his honorable mention of their ancestor. It was pleasantly situated on the borders of one of the salt marshes beyond Corlear's Hook; subject, indeed, to be occasionally overflowed, and much infested, in the summer time, with mosquitoes; but otherwise very agreeable, producing abundant crops of salt grass and bulrushes.

Here, we are sorry to say, the good old gentleman fell dangerously ill of a fever, occasioned by the neighboring marshes. When he found his end approaching, he disposed of his worldly affairs, leaving the bulk of his fortune to the New York Historical Society; his Heidelberg Catechism, and Vander Donck's work to the city library; and his saddle-bags to Mr. Handaside. He forgave all his enemies—that is to say, all who bore any enmity towards him; for as to himself, he declared he died in good will with all the world. And, after dictating several kind messages to his relations at Scaghtikoke, as well as to certain of our most substantial Dutch citizens, he expired in the arms of his friend the librarian.

His remains were interred, according to his own request, in St. Mark's churchyard, close by the bones of his favorite hero, Peter Stuyvesant; and it is rumored, that the Historical Society have it in mind to erect a wooden monument to his memory in the Bowling Green.

To the Public

"TO rescue from oblivion the memory of former incidents, and to render a just tribute of renown to the many great and wonderful transactions of our Dutch progenitors, Diedrich Knickerbocker, native of the city of New York, produces this historical essay." * Like the great Father of History, whose words I have just quoted, I treat of times long past, over which the twilight of uncertainty had already thrown its shadows, and the night of forgetfulness was about to descend forever. With a great solici-

* Beloe's Herodotus.

tude had I long beheld the early history of this venerable and ancient city gradually slipping from our grasp, trembling on the lips of narrative old age, and day by day dropping piecemeal into the tomb. In a little while, thought I, and those reverend Dutch burghers, who serve as the tottering monuments of good old times, will be gathered to their fathers; their children, engrossed by the empty pleasures or insignificant transactions of the present age, will neglect to treasure up the recollections of the past, and posterity will search in vain for memorials of the days of the Patriarchs. The origin of our city will be buried in eternal oblivion, and even the names and achievements of Wouter Van Twiller, William Kieft, and Peter Stuyvesant, be enveloped in doubt and fiction, like those of Romulus and Remus, of Charlemagne, King Arthur, Rinaldo, and Godfrey of Bologne.

Determined, therefore, to avert if possible this threatened misfortune, I industriously set myself to work, to gather together all the fragments of our infant history which still existed, and like my reverend prototype, Herodotus, where no written records could be found, I have endeavored to continue the chain of history by well-authenticated traditions.

In this arduous undertaking, which has been the whole business of a long and solitary life, it is incredible the number of learned authors I have consulted; and all but to little purpose. Strange as it may seem, though such multitudes of excellent works have been written about this country, there are none extant which give any full and satisfactory account of the early history of New York, or of its three first Dutch governors. I have, however, gained much valuable and curious matter, from an elaborate manuscript written in exceeding pure and classic Low Dutch, excepting a few errors in orthography, which was found in the archives of the Stuyvesant family. Many legends, letters, and other documents have I likewise gleaned, in my researches among the family chests and lumber-garrets of our respectable Dutch citizens; and I have gathered a host of well-authenticated traditions from divers excellent old ladies of my acquaintance, who requested that their names might not be mentioned. Nor must I neglect to acknowledge how greatly I have been assisted by that admirable and praiseworthy institution, the NEW YORK HISTORICAL SOCIETY, to which I here publicly return my sincere acknowledgments.

In the conduct of this inestimable work I have adopted no individual model; but, on the contrary, have simply contented myself with combining and concentrating the excellences of the most approved ancient historians. Like Xenophon, I have maintained the utmost impartiality, and the strictest adherence to truth throughout my history. I have enriched it after the manner of Sallust, with various characters of ancient worthies, drawn at full length, and faithfully colored. I have seasoned it with profound political speculations like Thucydides, sweetened it with the graces of sentiment like Tacitus, and infused into the whole the dignity, the grandeur, and magnificence of Livy.

I am aware that I shall incur the censure of numerous very learned and judicious critics, for indulging too frequently in the bold excursive manner of my favorite Herodotus. And to be candid, I have found it impossible always to resist the allurements of those pleasing episodes which, like flowery banks and fragrant bowers, beset the dusty road of the historian, and entice him to turn aside, and refresh himself from his wayfaring. But I trust it will be found that I have always resumed my staff, and addressed myself to my weary journey with renovated spirits, so that both my readers and myself have been benefited by the relaxation.

Indeed, though it has been my constant wish and uniform endeavor to rival Polybius himself, in observing the requisite unity of history, yet the loose and unconnected manner in which many of the facts herein recorded have come to hand, rendered such an attempt extremely difficult. This difficulty was likewise increased by one of the grand objects contemplated in my work, which was to trace the rise of sundry customs and institutions in this best of cities, and to compare them, when in the germ of infancy, with what they are in the present old age of knowledge and improvement.

But the chief merit on which I value myself, and found my hopes for future regard, is that faithful veracity with which I have compiled this invaluable little work; carefully winnowing away the chaff of hypothesis, and discarding the tares of fable, which are too apt to spring up and choke the seeds of truth and wholesome knowledge. Had I been anxious to captivavte the superficial throng, who skim like swallows over the surface of literature; or had I been anxious to commend my writings to the pampered palates of literary epicures, I might have availed myself of the obscurity that overshadows the infant years of our city, to introduce a thousand pleasing fictions. But I have scrupulously discarded many a pithy tale and marvellous adventure, whereby the drowsy ear of summer indolence might be enthralled; jealously maintaining that fidelity, gravity, and dignity, which should ever distinguish the historian. "For a writer of this class," observes an elegant critic, "must sustain the character of a wise man, writing for the instruction of posterity; one who has studied to inform himself well, who has pondered his subject with care, and addresses himself to our judgment, rather than to our imagination."

Thrice happy, therefore, is this our renowned city in having incidents worthy of swelling the theme of history; and doubly thrice happy is it in having such an historian as myself to relate them. For after all, gentle reader, cities *of themselves*, and, in fact, empires *of themselves*, are nothing without an historian. It is the patient narrator who records their prosperity as they rise—who blazons forth the splendor of their noon-tide meridian—who props their feeble memorials as they totter to decay—who gathers together their scattered fragments as they rot—and who piously, at length, collects their ashes into the mausoleum of his work and rears a monument that will transmit their renown to all succeeding ages.

What has been the fate of many fair cities of antiquity, whose nameless ruins encumber the plains of Europe and Asia, and awaken the fruitless inquiry of the traveller? They have sunk into dust and silence—they have perished from remembrance for want of an historian! The philanthropist may weep over their desolation—the poet may wander among their mouldering arches and broken columns, and indulge the visionary flights of his fancy—but, alas! alas! the modern historian, whose pen, like my own, is doomed to confine itself to dull matter-of-fact, seeks in vain among their oblivious remains for some memorial that may tell the instructive tale of their glory and their ruin.

"Wars, conflagrations, deluges," says Aristotle, "destroy nations, and with them all their monuments, their discoveries, and their vanities. The torch of science has more than once been extinguished and rekindled—a few indivivduals, who have escaped by accident, reunite the thread of generations."

The same sad misfortune which has happened to so many ancient cities will happen again, and from the same sad cause, to nine tenths of those which now flourish on the face of the globe. With most of them the time for recording their early history is gone by; their origin, their foundation, together with the eventful period of their youth, are forever buried in the rubbish of years; and the same would have been the case with this fair portion of the earth, if I had not snatched it from obscurity in the very nick of time, at the moment that those matters herein recorded were about entering into the wide-spread, insatiable maw of oblivion—if I had not dragged them out, as it were, by the very locks, just as the monster's adamantine fangs were closing upon them forever! And here have I, as before observed, carefully collected, collated, and arranged them, scrip and scrap, "*punt en punt, gat en gat,*" and commenced in this little work a history, to serve as a foundation on which other historians may hereafter raise a noble superstructure, swelling in process of time, until *Knickerbocker's New York* may be equally voluminous with *Gibbon's Rome*, or *Hume and Smollett's England!*

And now indulge me for a moment, while I lay down my pen, skip to some little eminence at the distance of two or three hundred years ahead; and, casting back a bird's-eye glance over the waste of years that is to roll between, discover myself—little I—at this moment the progenitor, prototype, and precursor of them all, posted at the head of this host of literary worthies, with my book under my arm, and New York on my back, pressing forward, like a gallant commander, to honor and immortality.

Such are the vainglorious imaginings that will now and then enter into the brain of the author—that irradiate, as with celestial light, his solitary chamber, cheering his weary spirits, and animating him to persevere in his labors. And I have freely given utterance to these rhapsodies whenever they have occurred; not, I trust, from an unusual spirit of egotism, but merely that the reader may for once have an idea how an author thinks and feels while he is writing—a kind of knowledge very rare and curious, and much to be desired.

Book I

CONTAINING DIVERS INGENIOUS THEORIES AND PHILOSOPHIC SPECULATIONS, CONCERNING THE CREATION AND POPULATION OF THE WORLD, AS CONNECTED WITH THE HISTORY OF NEW YORK

CHAPTER I

Description of the World

ACCORDING to the best authorities, the world in which we dwell is a huge, opaque, reflecting, inanimate mass, floating in the vast ethereal ocean of infinite space. It has the form of an orange, being an oblate spheroid, curiously flattened at opposite parts, for the insertion of two imaginary poles, which are supposed to penetrate and unite at the centre, thus forming an axis on which the mighty orange turns with a regular diurnal revolution.

The transitions of light and darkness, whence proceed the alternations of day and night, are produced by this diurnal revolution successively presenting the different parts of the earth to the rays of the sun. The latter is, according to the best, that is to say, the latest accounts, a luminous or fiery body, of a prodigious magnitude, from which this world is driven by a centrifugal or repelling power, and to which it is drawn by a centripetal or attractive force; otherwise called the attraction of gravitation; the combination, or rather the counteraction of these two opposing impulses producing a circular and annual revolution. Hence result the different seasons of the year, viz.: spring, summer, autumn, and winter.

This I believe to be the most approved modern theory on the subject—though there be many philosophers who have entertained very different opinions; some, too, of them entitled to much deference from their great antiquity and illustrious char acter. Thus it was advanced by some of the ancient sages, that the earth was an extended plain, supported by vast pillars; and by others, that it rested on the head of a snake, or the back of a huge tortoise; but as they did not provide a resting-place for either the pillars or the tortoise, the whole theory fell to the ground, for want of proper foundation.

The Brahmins assert, that the heavens rest upon the earth, and the sun and moon swim therein like fishes in the water, moving from east to west by day, and gliding along the edge of the horizon to their original stations during night; * while, according to the Pauranicas of India, it is a vast plain, encircled by seven oceans of milk, nectar, and other delicious liquids; that it is studded with seven mountains, and ornamented in the centre by a mountainous rock of burnished gold; and that a great dragon occasionally swallows up the moon, which accounts for the phenomena of lunar eclipses.†

Beside these, and many other equally sage opinions, we have the profound conjectures of ABOUL-HASSAN-ALY, son of Al Khan, son of Aly, son of Abderrahman, son of Abdallah, son of Masoud-el-Hadheli who is commonly called MASOUDI, and surnamed Cothbiddin, but who takes the humble title of Laheb-ar-rasoul, which means the companion of the ambassador of God. He has written a universal history, entitled "Mouroudge-ed-dharab, or the Golden Meadows, and the Mines of Precious Stones." ‡ In this valuable work he has related the history of the world from the creation down to the moment of writing; which was under the Khaliphat of Mothi Billah, in the month Dgioumadi-el-aoual of the 336th year of the Hegira or flight of the Prophet. He informs us that the earth is a huge bird, Mecca and Medina constituting the head, Persia and India the right wing, the land of Gog the left wing, and Africa the tail. He informs us, moreover, that an earth has existed before the present (which he considers as a mere chicken of 7000 years), that it has undergone divers deluges, and that, according to the opinion of some well-informed Brahmins of his acquaintance, it will be renovated every seventy thousandth hazarouam; each hazarouam consisting of 12,000 years.

* Faria y Souza. Mick. lus. note b. 7.
† Sir W. Jones, Diss. Antiq. Ind. Zod.
‡ MSS. Bibliot. Roi Fr.

These are a few of the many contradictory opinions of philosophers concerning the earth, and we find that the learned have had equal perplexity as to the nature of the sun. Some of the ancient philosophers have affirmed that it is a vast wheel of brilliant fire; * others, that it is merely a mirror or sphere of transparent crystal; † and a third class, at the head of whom stands Anaxagoras, maintained that it was nothing but a huge ignited mass of iron or stone—indeed, he declared the heavens to be merely a vault of stone—and that the stars were stones whirled upward from the earth, and set on fire by the velocity of its revolutions.‡ But I give little attention to the doctrines of this philosopher, the people of Athens having fully refuted them, by banishing him from their city: a concise mode of answering unwelcome doctrines, much resorted to in former days. Another sect of philosophers do declare, that certain fiery particles exhale constantly from the earth, which, concentrating in a single point of the firmament by day, constitute the sun, but being scattered and rambling about in the dark at night, collect in various points, and form stars. These are regularly burnt out and extinguished, not unlike to the lamps in our streets, and require a fresh supply of exhalations for the next occasion.§

It is even recorded, that at certain remote and obscure periods, in consequence of a great scarcity of fuel, the sun has been completely burnt out, and sometimes not rekindled for a month at a time. A most melancholy circumstance, the very idea of which gave vast concern to Heraclitus, that worthy weeping philosopher of antiquity. In addition to these various speculations, it was the opinion of Herschel, that the sun is a magnificent, habitable abode; the light it furnishes arising from certain empyreal, luminous or phosphoric clouds, swimming in its transparent atmosphere.‖

But we will not enter farther at present into the nature of

* Plutarch de placitis Philosoph. lib. ii. cap. 20.

† Achill. Tat. isag. cap. 19. Ap. Petav. t. iii. p. 81. Stob. Eclog. Phys. lib. i. p. 56. Plut. de Plac. Phi.

‡ Diogenes Laertius in Anaxag. l. ii. sec. 8. Plat. Apol. t. i. p. 26. Plut. de Plac. Philo. Xenoph. Mem. l. iv. p. 815.

§ Aristot. Meteor. l. ii. c. 2. Idem. Probl. sec. 15, Stob. Ecl. Phys. l. i. p. 55. Bruck. Hist. Phil. t. i. p. 1154, &c.

‖ Philos. Trans. 1795, p. 72. Idem. 1801, p. 265. Nich. Philos. Journ. I. p. 13.

the sun, that being an inquiry not immediately necessary to the development of this history; neither will we embroil ourselves in any more of the endless disputes of philosophers touching the form of this globe, but content ourselves with the theory advanced in the beginning of this chapter, and will proceed to illustrate, by experiment, the complexity of motion therein ascribed to this our rotatory planet.

Professor Von Poddingcoft (or Puddinghead, as the name may be rendered into English) was long celebrated in the university of Leyden, for profound gravity of deportment, and a talent at going to sleep in the midst of examinations, to the infinite relief of his hopeful students, who thereby worked their way through college with great ease and little study. In the course of one of his lectures, the learned professor, seizing a bucket of water, swung it around his head at arm's length. The impulse with which he threw the vessel from him, being a centrifugal force, the retention of his arm operating as a centripetal power, and the bucket, which was a substitute for the earth, describing a circular orbit round about the globular head and ruby visage of Professor Von Poddingcoft, which formed no bad representation of the sun. All of these particulars were duly explained to the class of gaping students around him. He apprised them, moreover, that the same principle of gravitation, which retained the water in the bucket, restrains the ocean from flying from the earth in its rapid revolutions; and he further informed them that should the motion of the earth be suddenly checked, it would incontinently fall into the sun, through the centripetal force of gravitation—a most ruinous event to this planet, and one which would also obscure, though it most probably would not extinguish, the solar luminary. An unlucky stripling, one of those vagrant geniuses, who seem sent into the world merely to annoy worthy men of the puddinghead order, desirous of ascertaining the correctness of the experiment, suddenly arrested the arm of the professor, just at the moment that the bucket was in its zenith, which immediately descended with astonishing precision upon the philosophic head of the instructor of youth. A hollow sound, and a red-hot hiss, attended the contact; but the theory was in the amplest manner illustrated, for the unfortunate bucket perished in the conflict; but the blazing countenance of Professor Von Poddingcoft emerged from amidst the waters, glowing fiercer than ever with unutterable indignation, whereby the students were marvellously edified, and departed considerably wiser than before.

It is a mortifying circumstance, which greatly perplexes many a painstaking philosopher, that nature often refuses to second his most profound and elaborate efforts; so that after having invented one of the most ingenious and natural theories imaginable, she will have the perverseness to act directly in the teeth of his system, and flatly contradict his most favorite positions. This is a manifest and unmerited grievance, since it throws the censure of the vulgar and unlearned entirely upon the philosopher; whereas the fault is not to be ascribed to his theory, which is unquestionably correct, but to the waywardness of dame nature, who, with the proverbial fickleness of her sex, is continually indulging in coquetries and caprices, and seems really to take pleasure in violating all philosophic rules, and jilting the most learned and indefatigable of her adorers. Thus it happened with respect to the foregoing satisfactory explanation of the motion of our planet; it appears that the centrifugal force has long since ceased to operate, while its antagonist remains in undiminished potency; the world, therefore, according to the theory as it originally stood, ought in strict propriety to tumble into the sun; philosophers were convinced that it would do so, and awaited in anxious impatience the fulfilment of their prognostics. But the untoward planet pertinaciously continued her course, notwithstanding that she had reason, philosophy, and a whole university of learned professors opposed to her conduct. The philosophers took this in very ill part, and it is thought they would never have pardoned the slight and affront which they conceived put upon them by the world, had not a good-natured professor kindly officiated as a mediator between the parties, and effected a reconciliation.

Finding the world would not accommodate itself to the theory, he wisely determined to accommodate the theory to the world; he therefore informed his brother philosophers, that the circular motion of the earth round the sun was no sooner engendered by the conflicting impulses above described, than it became a regular revolution, independent of the causes which gave it origin. His learned brethren readily joined in the opinion, being heartily glad of any explanation that would decently extricate them from their embarrassment; and ever since that memorable era the world has been left to take her own course, and to revolve around the sun in such orbit as she thinks proper.

CHAPTER II

Cosmogony, or Creation of the World; with a Multitude of Excellent Theories, by Which the Creation of a World Is Shown to Be No Such Difficult Matter as Common Folk Would Imagine

HAVING thus briefly introduced my reader to the world, and given him some idea of its form and situation, he will naturally be curious to know from whence it came, and how it was created. And, indeed, the clearing up of these points is absolutely essential to my history, inasmuch as if this world had not been formed, it is more than probable that this renowned island, on which is situated the city of New York, would never have had an existence. The regular course of my history, therefore, requires that I should proceed to notice the cosmogony or formation of this our globe.

And now I give my readers fair warning that I am about to plunge, for a chapter or two, into as complete a labyrinth as ever historian was perplexed withal; therefore, I advise them to take fast hold of my skirts, and keep close at my heels, venturing neither to the right hand nor to the left, lest they get bemired in a slough of unintelligible learning, or have their brains knocked out by some of those hard Greek names which will be flying about in all directions. But should any of them be too indolent or chicken-hearted to accompany me in this perilous undertaking, they had better take a short cut round, and wait for me at the beginning of some smoother chapter.

Of the creation of the world, we have a thousand contradictory accounts; and though a very satisfactory one is furnished us by divine revelation, yet every philosopher feels himself in honor bound to furnish us with a better. As an impartial historian I consider it my duty to notice their several theories, by which mankind have been so exceedingly edified and instructed.

Thus it was the opinion of certain ancient sages, that the earth and the whole system of the universe was the Deity himself; * a doctrine most strenuously maintained by Zenophanes and the whole tribe of Eleatics, as also by Strabo and the sect of peripatetic philosophers. Pythagoras likewise inculcated the famous numerical system of the monad, dyad, and triad, and by means of his sacred quaternary elucidated the formation of the world, the arcana of nature, and the principles both of music and morals.† Other sages adhered to the mathematical system of squares and triangles; the cube, the pyramid, and the sphere; the tetrahedron, the octahedron, the icosahedron, and the dodecahedron.‡ While others advocated the great elementary theory which refers the construction of our globe and all that it contains to the combinations of four material elements: air, earth, fire, and water, with the assistance of a fifth, an immaterial and vivifying principle.

Nor must I omit to mention the great atomic system taught by old Moschus, before the siege of Troy; revived by Democritus of laughing memory; improved by Epicurus, that king of good fellows, and modernized by the fanciful Descartes. But I decline inquiring whether the atoms, of which the earth is said to be composed, are eternal or recent; whether they are animate or inanimate; whether, agreeably to the opinion of the atheists, they were fortuitously aggregated, or, as the theists maintain, were arranged by a supreme intelligence.§ Whether, in fact, the earth be an insenate clod, or whether it be animated by a soul;‖ which opinion was strenuously maintained by a host of philosophers, at the head of whom stands the great Plato, that temperate sage, who threw the cold water of philosophy on the form of sexual intercourse, and inculcated the doctrine of Platonic love—an exquisitely refined intercourse, but much better adapted to the ideal inhabitants of his imaginary island of Atlantis than to the sturdy race, composed of rebellious flesh and

* Aristot. ap. Cic. lib. i. cap. 3.

† Aristot. Metaph. lib. i. c. 5. Idem. de Cœlo. l. iii. c. 1. Rousseau Mem. sur Musique ancien. p. 39. Plutarch de Plac. Philos. lib. i. cap. 3.

‡ Tim. Locr. ap. Plato. t. iii. p. 90.

§ Aristot. Nat. Auscult. l. ii. cap. 6. Aristoph. Metaph. lib. i. cap. 3. Cic. de Nat. Deor. lib. i. cap. 10. Justin Mart. prat. ad gent. p. 20.

‖ Mosheim in Cudw. lib. i. cap. 4. Tim. de anim. mund. sp. Plat. lib iii. Mem. de l'Acad. des Belles-Lettr. t. xxxii. p. 19, et al.

blood, which populates the little matter-of-fact island we inhabit.

Beside these systems, we have, moreover, the poetical theogony of old Hesiod, who generated the whole universe in the regular mode of procreation, and the plausible opinion of others, that the earth was hatched from the great egg of night, which floated in chaos, and was cracked by the horns of the celestial bull. To illustrate this last doctrine, Burnet, in his theory of the earth,* has favored us with an accurate drawing and description, both of the form and texture of this mundane egg; which is found to bear a marvellous resemblance to that of a goose. Such of my readers as take a proper interest in the origin of this our planet, will be pleased to learn that the most profound sages of antiquity among the Egyptians, Chaldeans, Persians, Greeks, and Latins, have alternately assisted at the hatching of this strange bird, and that their cacklings have been caught, and continued in different tones and inflections, from philosopher to philosopher, unto the present day.

But while briefly noticing long-celebrated systems of ancient sages, let me not pass over with neglect those of other philosophers; which, though less universal and renowned, have equal claims to attention, and equal chance for correctness. Thus, it is recorded by the Brahmins, in the pages of their inspired Shastah, that the angel Bistnoo transforming himself into a great boar, plunged into the watery abyss, and brought up the earth on his tusks. Then issued from him a mighty tortoise, and a mighty snake; and Bistnoo placed the the snake erect upon the back of the tortoise, and he placed the earth upon the head of the snake.†

The Negro philosophers of Congo affirm that the world was made by the hands of angels, excepting their own country, which the Supreme Being constructed himself, that it might be supremely excellent. And he took great pains with the inhabitants, and made them very black, and beautiful; and when he had finished the first man, he was well pleased with him, and smoothed him over the face, and hence his nose, and the nose of all his descendants, became flat.

* Book i. ch. 5.
† Holwell. Gent. Philosophy.

The Mohawk philosophers tell us that a pregnant woman fell down from heaven, and that a tortoise took her upon its back, because every place was covered with water; and that the woman, sitting upon the tortoise, paddled with her hands in the water, and raked up the earth, whence it finally happened that the earth became higher than the water.*

But I forbear to quote a number more of these ancient and outlandish philosophers, whose deplorable ignorance, in despite of all their erudition, compelled them to write in languages which but few of my readers can understand; and I shall proceed briefly to notice a few more intelligible and fashionable theories of their modern successors.

And, first, I shall mention the great Buffon, who conjectures that this globe was originally a globe of liquid fire, scintillated from the body of the sun, by the percussion of a comet, as a spark is generated by the collision of flint and steel. That at first it was surrounded by gross vapors, which, cooling and condensing in process of time, constituted, according to their densities, earth, water, and air; which gradually arranged themselves, according to their respective gravities, round the burning or vitrified mass that formed their centre.

Hutton, on the contrary, supposes that the waters at first were universally paramount; and he terrifies himself with the idea that the earth must be eventually washed away by the force of rain, rivers, and mountain torrents, until it is confounded with the ocean, or, in other words absolutely dissolves into itself. Sublime idea! far surpassing that of the tender-hearted damsel of antiquity, who wept herself into a fountain; or the good dame of Narbonne in France, who, for a volubility of tongue unusual in her sex, was doomed to peel five hundred thousand and thirty-nine ropes of onions, and actually run out at her eyes before half the hideous task was accomplished.

Whiston, the same ingenious philosopher who rivalled Ditton in his researches after the longitude (for which the mischief-loving Swift discharged on their heads a most savory stanza) has distinguished himself by a very admirable theory respecting the earth. He conjectures that it was originally a *chaotic comet*, which being selected for the abode of man, was

* Johannes Megapolensis, Jun. Account of Maquaas or Mohawk Indians.

removed from its eccentric orbit, and whirled round the sun in its present regular motion; by which change of direction, order succeeded to confusion in the arrangement of its component parts. The philosopher adds, that the deluge was produced by an uncourteous salute from the watery tail of another comet; doubtless through sheer envy of its improved condition; thus furnishing a melancholy proof that jealousy may prevail, even among the heavenly bodies, and discord interrupt that celestial harmony of the spheres, so melodiously sung by the poets.

But I pass over a variety of excellent theories, among which are those of Burnet, and Woodward, and Whitehurst; regretting extremely that my time will not suffer me to give them the notice they deserve—and shall conclude with that of the renowned Dr. Darwin. This learned Theban, who is as much distinguished for rhyme as reason, and for good-natured credulity as serious research, and who has recommended himself wonderfully to the good graces of the ladies, by letting them into all the gallantries, amours, debaucheries, and other topics of scandal of the court of Flora, has fallen upon a theory worthy of his combustible imagination. According to his opinion, the huge mass of chaos took a sudden occasion to explode, like a barrel of gunpowder, and in that act exploded the sun—which in its flight, by a similar convulsion, exploded the earth, which in like guise exploded the moon—and thus by a concatenation of explosions, the whole solar system was produced, and set most systematically in motion! *

By the great variety of theories here alluded to, every one of which, if thoroughly examined, will be found surprisingly consistent in all its parts, my unlearned readers will perhaps be led to conclude, that the creation of a world is not so difficult a task as they at first imagined. I have shown at least a score of ingenious methods in which a world could be constructed; and I have no doubt, that, had any of the philosophers above quoted the use of a good manageable comet, and the philosophical warehouse *chaos* at his command, he would engage to manufacture a planet as good, or, if you would take his word for it, better than this we inhabit.

And here I cannot help noticing the kindness of Providence,

* Darw. Bot. Garden, Part I. Cant. i. l. 105.

in creating comets for the great relief of bewildered philosophers. By their assistance more sudden evolutions and transitions are effected in the system of nature than are wrought in a pantomimic exhibition by the wonder-working sword of Harlequin. Should one of our modern sages, in his theoretical flights among the stars, ever find himself lost in the clouds, and in danger of tumbling into the abyss of nonsense and absurdity, he has but to seize a comet by the beard, mount astride of his tail, and away he gallops in triumph, like an enchanter on his hyppogriff, or a Connecticut witch on her broomstick, "to sweep the cobwebs out of the sky."

It is an old and vulgar saying about a "beggar on horseback," which I would not for the world have applied to these reverend philosophers; but I must confess that some of them, when they are mounted on one of those fiery steeds, are as wild in their curvetings as was Phaeton of yore, when he aspired to manage the chariot of Phœbus. One drives his comet at full speed against the sun, and knocks the world out of him with the mighty concussion; another, more moderate, makes his comet a kind of beast of burden, carrying the sun a regular supply of food and fagots; a third, of more combustible disposition, threatens to throw his comet, like a bomb-shell, into the world, and blow it up like a powder-magazine; while a fourth, with no great delicacy to this planet and its inhabitants, insinuates that some day or other his comet—my modest pen blushes while I write it—shall absolutely turn tail upon our world, and deluge it with water! Surely, as I have already observed, comets were bountifully provided by Providence for the benefit of philosophers, to assist them in manufacturing theories.

And now, having adduced several of the most prominent theories that occur to my recollection, I leave my judicious readers at full liberty to choose among them. They are all serious speculations of learned men—all differ essentially from each other—and all have the same title to belief. It has ever been the task of one race of philosophers to demolish the works of their predecessors, and elevate more splendid fantasies in their stead, which in their turn are demolished and replaced by the air-castles of a succeeding generation. Thus it would seem that knowledge and genius, of which we make such great parade, consist but in detecting the errors and absurdities of those who have gone before, and devising new errors and absurdities, to be detected by those who are to come after us. Theories are the mighty soap-bubbles with which the grown-up children of science amuse themselves—while the honest vulgar stand gazing in stupid admiration, and dignify these learned vagaries with the name of wisdom! Surely, Socrates was right in his opinion, that philosophers are but a soberer sort of madmen, busying themselves in things totally incomprehensible, or which, if they could be comprehended, would be found not worthy the trouble of discovery.

For my own part, until the learned have come to an agreement among themselves, I shall content myself with the account handed down to us by Moses; in which I do but follow the example of our ingenious neighbors of Connecticut; who at their first settlement proclaimed, that the colony should be governed by the laws of God—until they had time to make better.

One thing, however, appears certain—from the unanimous authority of the before-quoted philosophers, supported by the evidence of our own senses (which, though very apt to deceive us, may be cautiously admitted as additional testimony)—it appears, I say, and I make the assertion deliberately, without fear of contradiction, that this globe really *was created,* and that it is composed of *land and water.* It farther appears that it is curiously divided and parcelled out into continents and islands, among which I boldly declare the renowned Island of New York will be found by any one who seeks for it in its proper place.

CHAPTER III

How That Famous Navigator, Noah, Was Shamefully Nicknamed, and How He Committed an Unpardonable Oversight in Not Having Four Sons; with the Great Trouble of Philosophers Caused Thereby, and the Discovery of America

NOAH, who is the first seafaring man we read of, begat three sons: Shem, Ham, and Japhet. Authors, it is true, are not wanting, who affirm that the patriarch had a number of other children. Thus, Berosus makes him father of the gigantic Titans; Methodius gives him a son called Jonithus, or Jonicus; and others have mentioned a son, named Thuiscon, from whom descended the Teutons or Teutonic, or in other words, the Dutch nation.

I regret exceedingly that the nature of my plan will not permit me to gratify the laudable curiosity of my readers, by investigating minutely the history of the great Noah. Indeed, such an undertaking would be attended with more trouble than many people would imagine, for the good old patriarch seems to have been a great traveller in his day, and to have passed under a different name in every country that he visited. The Chaldeans, for instance, give us his story, merely altering his name into Xisuthrus—a trivial alteration, which, to an historian, skilled in etymologies, will appear wholly unimportant. It appears, likewise, that he had exchanged his tarpaulin and quadrant among the Chaldeans for the gorgeous insignia of royalty, and appears as a monarch in their annals. The Egyptians celebrate him under the name of Osiris; the Indians as Menu; the Greek and Roman writers confound him with Ogyges, and the Theban with Deucalion and Saturn. But the Chinese, who deservedly rank among the most extensive and authentic historians, inasmuch as they have known the world much longer than any one else, declare that Noah was no other than Fohi; and what gives this assertion some air of credibility is, that it is a fact, admitted by the most enlightened *literati*, that Noah travelled into China, at the time of the building of the tower of Babel (probably to improve himself in the study of languages), and the learned Dr. Shackford gives us the additional information, that the ark rested on a mountain on the frontiers of China.

From this mass of rational conjectures and sage hypotheses, many satisfactory deductions might be drawn; but I shall content myself with the simple fact stated in the Bible, viz.: that Noah begat three sons, Shem, Ham, and Japhet. It is astonishing on what remote and obscure contingencies the great affairs of this world depend, and how events the most distant, and to the common observer unconnected, are inevitably consequent the one to the other. It remains to the philosopher to discover these mysterious affinities, and it is the proudest triumph of his skill, to detect and drag forth some latent chain of causation which at first sight appears a paradox to the inexperienced observer. Thus many of my readers will doubtless wonder what connection the family of Noah can possibly have with this history—and many will stare when informed, that the whole history of this quarter of the world has taken its character and course from the simple circumstance of the patriarch's having but three sons. But to explain:

Noah, we are told by sundry very credible historians, becoming sole surviving heir and proprietor of the earth, in fee-simple, after the deluge, like a good father, portioned out his estate among his children. To Shem he gave Asia; to Ham, Africa; and to Japhet, Europe. Now it is a thousand times to be lamented that he had but three sons, for had there been a fourth, he would doubtless have inherited America; which, of course, would have been dragged forth from its obscurity on the occasion; and thus many a hard-working historian and philosopher would have been spared a prodigious mass of weary conjecture respecting the first discovery and population of this country. Noah, however, having provided for his three sons, looked in all probability upon our country as a mere wild unsettled land, and said nothing about it; and to this unpardonable taciturnity of the patriarch may we ascribe the misfortune that America did not come into the world as early as the other quarters of the globe.

It is true, some writers have vindicated him from this misconduct towards posterity, and asserted that he really did discover America. Thus it was the opinion of Mark Lescarbot, a French writer, possessed of that ponderosity of thought, and profoundness of reflection, so peculiar to his nation, that the immediate descendants of Noah peopled this quarter of the globe, and that the old patriarch himself, who still retained a passion for the seafaring life, superintended the transmigration. The pious and enlightened father, Charlevoix, a French Jesuit, remarkable for his aversion to the marvellous, common to all great travellers, is conclusively of the same opinion; nay, he goes still farther, and decides upon the manner in which the discovery was effected, which was by sea, and under the immediate direction of the great Noah. "I have already observed," exclaims the good father, in a tone of becoming indignation, "that it is an arbitrary supposition that the grandchildren of Noah were not able to penetrate into the new world, or that they never thought of it. In effect, I can see no reason that can justify such a notion. Who can seriously believe that Noah and his immediate descendants knew less than we do, and that the builder and pilot of the greatest ship that ever was—a ship which was formed to traverse an unbounded ocean, and had so many shoals and quicksands to guard against—should be ignorant of, or should not have communicated to his descendants the art of sailing on the ocean?" Therefore, they did sail on the ocean; therefore, they sailed to America; therefore, America was discovered by Noah!

Now all this exquisite chain of reasoning, which is so strikingly characteristic of the good father, being addressed to the faith, rather than the understanding, is flatly opposed by Hans de Laet, who declares it a real and most ridiculous paradox to suppose that Noah ever entertained the thought of discovering America; and as Hans is a Dutch writer, I am inclined to believe he must have been much better acquainted with the worthy crew of the ark than his competitors, and of course possessed of more accurate sources of information. It is astonishing how intimate historians do daily become with the patriarchs and other great men of antiquity. As intimacy improves with time, and as the learned are particularly inquisitive and familiar in their acquaintance with the ancients, I should not be surprised if some future writers should gravely give us a picture of men and manners as they existed before the flood, far more copious and accurate than the Bible; and that, in the course of another century, the log-book of the good Noah should be as current among historians as the voyages of Captain Cook, or the renowned history of Robinson Crusoe.

I shall not occupy my time by discussing the huge mass of additional suppositions, conjectures, and probabilities respecting the first discovery of this country, with which unhappy historians overload themselves, in their endeavors to satisfy the doubts of an incredulous world. It is painful to see these laborious wights panting, and toiling, and sweating, under an enormous burden, at the very outset of their works, which, on being opened, turns out to be nothing but a mighty bundle of straw. As, however, by unwearied assiduity, they seem to have established the fact, to the satisfaction of all the world, that this country *has been discovered*. I shall avail myself of their useful labors to be extremely brief upon this point.

I shall not, therefore, stop to inquire, whether America was first discovered by a wandering vessel of that celebrated Phœnician fleet, which, according to Herodotus, circumnavigated Africa; or by that Carthaginian expedition, which Pliny, the naturalist, informs us, discovered the Canary Islands; or whether it was settled by a temporary colony from Tyre, as hinted by Aristotle and Seneca. I shall neither inquire whether it was first discovered by the Chinese, as Vossius with great shrewdness advances; nor by the Norwegians in 1002, under Biorn; nor by Behem, the German navigator, as Mr. Otto has endeavored to prove to the *savans* of the learned city of Philadelphia.

Nor shall I investigate the more modern claims of the Welsh, founded on the voyage of Prince Madoc in the eleventh century, who having never returned, it has since been wisely concluded that he must have gone to America, and that for a plain reason—if he did not go there, where else could he have gone?—a question which most socratically shuts out all farther dispute.

Laying aside, therefore, all the conjectures above mentioned, with a multitude of others, equally satisfactory, I shall take for granted the vulgar opinion, that America was discovered on the 12th of October, 1492, by Christoval Colon, a Genoese, who has been clumsily nicknamed Columbus, but for what reason I cannot discern. Of the voyages and adventures of this Colon, I shall say nothing, seeing that they are already sufficiently known. Nor shall I undertake to prove that this country should have been called Colonia, after his name, that being notoriously self-evident.

Having thus happily got my readers on this side of the Atlantic, I picture them to myself all impatience to enter upon the enjoyment of the land of promise, and in full expectation that I will immediately deliver it into their possession. But if

I do may I ever forfeit the reputation of a regular-bred historian! No—no—most curious and thrice learned readers (for thrice learned ye are if ye have read all that has gone before, and nine times learned shall ye be if ye read that which comes after), we have yet a world of work before us. Think you the first discoverers of this fair quarter of the globe had nothing to do but go on shore and find a country ready laid out and cultivated like a garden, wherein they might revel at their ease? No such thing: they had forests to cut down, underwood to grub up, marshes to drain, and savages to exterminate.

In like manner, I have sundry doubts to clear away, questions to resolve, and paradoxes to explain, before I permit you to range at random; but these difficulties once overcome, we shall be enabled to jog on right merrily through the rest of our history. Thus my work shall, in a manner, echo the nature of the subject, in the same manner as the sound of poetry has been found by certain shrewd critics to echo the sense—this being an improvement in history which I claim the merit of having invented.

CHAPTER IV

Showing the Great Difficulty Philosophers Have Had in Peopling America; and How the Aborigines Came to Be Begotten by Accident —to the Great Relief and Satisfaction of the Author

THE next inquiry at which we arrive in the regular course of our history is to ascertain, if possible, how this country was originally peopled—a point fruitful of incredible embarrassments; for unless we prove that the Aborigines did absolutely come from somewhere, it will be immediately asserted, in this age of skepticism, that they did not come at all; and if they did not come at all, then was this country never populated—a conclusion perfectly agreeable to the rules of logic, but wholly irreconcilable to every feeling of humanity, inasmuch as it must syllogistically prove fatal to the innumerable Aborigines of this populous region.

To avert so dire a sophism, and to rescue from logical annihilation so many millions of fellow-creatures, how many wings of geese have been plundered! what oceans of ink have been benevolently drained! and how many capacious heads of learned historians have been addled, and forever confounded! I pause with reverential awe, when I contemplate the ponderous tomes, in different languages, with which they have endeavored to solve this question, so important to the happiness of society, but so involved in clouds of impenetrable obscurity.

Historian after historian has engaged in the endless circle of hypothetical argument, and after leading us a weary chase through octavos, quartos, and folios, has let us out at the end of his work just as wise as we were at the beginning. It was doubtless some philosophical wild-goose chase of the kind that made the old poet Macrobius rail in such a passion at curiosity, which he anathematizes most heartily as "an irksome agonizing care, a superstitious industry about unprofitable things, an itching humor to see what is not to be seen, and to be doing what signifies nothing when it is done." But to proceed.

Of the claims of the children of Noah to the original population of this country I shall say nothing, as they have already been touched upon in my last chapter. The claimants next in celebrity are the descendants of Abraham. Thus, Christoval Colon (vulgarly called Columbus) when he first discovered the gold mines of Hispaniola, immediately concluded, with a shrewdness that would have done honor to a philosopher, that he had found the ancient Ophir, from whence Solomon procured the gold for embellishing the temple at Jerusalem; nay, Colon even imagined that he saw the remains of furnaces of veritable Hebraic construction, employed in refining the precious ore.

So golden a conjecture, tinctured with such fascinating extravagance, was too tempting not to be immediately snapped at by the gudgeons of learning; and, accordingly, there were divers profound writers ready to swear to its correctness, and to bring in their usual load of authorities, and wise surmises, wherewithal to prop it up. Vetablus and Robertus Stephens declared nothing could be more clear; Arius Montanus, without the least hesitation, asserts that Mexico was the true Ophir, and the Jews the early settlers of the country; while Possevin,

Becan, and several other sagacious writers, lug in a *supposed* prophecy of the fourth book of Esdras, which being inserted in the mighty hypothesis, like the key-stone of an arch, gives it, in their opinion, perpetual durability.

Scarce, however, have they completed their goodly superstructure, than in trudges a phalanx of opposite authors, with Hans de Laet, the great Dutchman, at their head, and at one blow tumbles the whole fabric about their ears. Hans, in fact, contradicts outright all the Israelitish claims to the first settlement of this country, attributing all those equivocal symptoms, and traces of Christianity and Judaism, which have been said to be found in divers provinces of the new world, to the *Devil*, who has always affected to counterfeit the worship of the true Deity. "A remark," says the knowing old Padre d'Acosta, "made by all good authors who have spoken of the religion of nations newly discovered, and founded besides on the authority of the *fathers of the church*." Some writers again, among whom it is with much regret I am compelled to mention Lopez de Gomara, and Juan de Leri, insinuate that the Canaanites, being driven from the land of promise by the Jews, were seized with such a panic that they fled without looking behind them, until stopping to take breath, they found themselves safe in America. As they brought neither their national language, manners, nor features with them, it is supposed they left them behind in the hurry of their flight; I cannot give my faith to this opinion.

I pass over the supposition of the learned Grotius—who being both an ambassador and a Dutchman to boot, is entitled to great respect—that North America was peopled by a strolling company of Norwegians, and that Peru was founded by a colony from China—Manco, or Mango Capac, the first Incas, being himself a Chinese. Nor shall I more than barely mention, that father Kircher ascribes the settlement of America to the Egyptians, Rudbeck to the Scandinavians, Charron to the Gauls, Juffredus Petri to a skating party from Friesland, Milius to the Celtæ, Marinocus the Sicilian to the Romans, Le Compte to the Phœnicians, Postel to the Moors, Martyn d'Angleria to the Abyssinians, together with the sage surmise of De Laet, that England, Ireland, and the Orcades may contend for that honor.

Nor will I bestow any more attention or credit to the idea

that America is the fairy region of Zipangri, described by that dreaming traveller, Marco Polo, the Venetian; or that it comprises the visionary island of Atlantis, described by Plato. Neither will I stop to investigate the heathenish assertion of Paracelsus, that each hemisphere of the globe was originally furnished with an Adam and Eve; or the more flattering opinion of Dr. Romayne, supported by many nameless authorities, that Adam was of the Indian race; or the startling conjecture of Buffon, Helvetius, and Darwin, so highly honorable to mankind, that the whole human species is accidentally descended from a remarkable family of monkeys!

This last conjecture, I must own, came upon me very suddenly and very ungraciously. I have often beheld the clown in a pantomime, while gazing in stupid wonder at the extravagant gambols of a harlequin, all at once electrified by a sudden stroke of the wooden sword across his shoulders. Little did I think, at such times, that it would ever fall to my lot to be treated with equal discourtesy, and that, while I was quietly beholding these grave philosophers, emulating the eccentric transformations of the hero of pantomime, they would on a sudden turn upon me and my readers, and with one hypothetical flourish metamorphose us into beasts! I determined from that moment not to burn my fingers with any more of their theories, but content myself with detailing the different methods by which they transported the descendants of these ancient and respectable monkeys to this great field of theoretical warfare.

This was done either by migrations by land or transmigrations by water. Thus Padre Joseph d'Acosta enumerates three passages by land; first, by the north of Europe; secondly, by the north of Asia; and thirdly, by regions southward of the Straits of Magellan. The learned Grotius marches his Norwegians by a pleasant route across frozen rivers and arms of the sea, through Iceland, Greenland, Estotiland, and Naremberga; and various writers, among whom are Angleria, De Hornn, and Buffon, anxious for the accommodation of these travellers, have fastened the two continents together by a strong chain of deductions—by which means they could pass over dry-shod. But should even this fail, Pinkerton, that industrious old gentleman, who compiles books, and manufactures Geographies, has constructed a natural bridge of ice, from continent to continent, at the distance of four or five miles from Behring's Straits—for which he is entitled to the grateful thanks of all the wandering Aborigines who ever did or ever will pass over it.

It is an evil much to be lamented, that none of the worthy writers above quoted could ever commence his work without immediately declaring hostilities against every writer who had treated of the same subject. In this particular, authors may be compared to a certain sagacious bird, which in building its nest is sure to pull to pieces the nests of all the birds in its neighborhood. This unhappy propensity tends grievously to impede the progress of sound knowledge. Theories are at best but brittle productions, and when once committed to the stream, they should take care that, like the notable pots which were fellow-voyagers, they do not crack each other.

My chief surprise is, that among the many writers I have noticed, no one has attempted to prove that this country was peopled from the moon—or that the first inhabitants floated hither on islands of ice, as white bears cruise about the northern oceans—or that they were conveyed hither by balloons, as modern aëronauts pass from Dover to Calais—or by witchcraft, as Simon Magus posted among the stars—or after the manner of the renowned Scythian Abaris, who, like the New England witches on full-blooded broomsticks, made most unheard-of journeys on the back of a golden arrow, given him by the Hyperborean Apollo.

But there is still one mode left by which this country could have been peopled, which I have reserved for the last, because I consider it worth all the rest: it is—*by accident!* Speaking of the islands of Solomon, New Guinea, and New Holland, the profound father Charlevoix observes, "in fine, all these countries are peopled, and *it is possible* some have been so *by accident.* Now if it could have happened in that manner, why might it not have been at the *same time,* and by the *same means* with *the other* parts of the globe?" This ingenious mode of deducing certain conclusions from possible premises is an improvement in syllogistic skill, and proves the good father superior even to Archimedes, for he can turn the world without anything to rest his lever upon. It is only surpassed by the dexterity with which the sturdy old Jesuit, in another place, cuts the gordian knot: "Nothing," says he, "is more easy. The inhabitants of both hemispheres are certainly the descendants of the same father. The common father of mankind received an express order from Heaven to people the world, and accordingly *it has been peopled*. To bring this about, it was necessary to overcome all difficulties in the way, *and they have also been overcome!*" Pious logician! How does he put all the herd of laborious theorists to the blush, by explaining, in five words, what it has cost them volumes to prove they knew nothing about!

From all the authorities here quoted, and a variety of others which I have consulted, but which are omitted through fear of fatiguing the unlearned reader, I can only draw the following conclusions, which luckily, however, are sufficient for my purpose. First, that this part of the world has actually *been peopled*, (Q. E. D.) to support which we have living proofs in the numerous tribes of Indians that inhabit it. Secondly, that it has been peopled in five hundred different ways, as proved by a cloud of authors who, from the positiveness of their assertions, seem to have been eye-witnesses to the fact. Thirdly, that the people of this country had a *variety of fathers*, which, as it may not be thought much to their credit by the common run of readers, the less we say on the subject the better. The question, therefore, I trust, is forever at rest.

CHAPTER V

In Which the Author Puts a Mighty Question to the Rout, by the Assistance of the Man in the Moon—Which Not Only Delivers Thousands of People from Great Embarrassment, but Likewise Concludes This Introductory Book

THE writer of a history may, in some respects, be likened unto an adventurous knight, who, having undertaken a perilous enterprise by way of establishing his fame, feels bound, in honor and chivalry, to turn back for no difficulty nor hardship, and never to shrink or quail, whatever enemy he may encounter.

Under this impression, I resolutely draw my pen, and fall to, with might and main, at those doughty questions and subtle paradoxes, which, like fiery dragons and bloody giants, beset the entrance to my history, and would fain repulse me from the very threshold. And at this moment a gigantic question has started up, which I must needs take by the beard and utterly subdue, before I can advance another step in my historic undertaking; but I trust this will be the last adversary I shall have to contend with, and that in the next book I shall be enabled to conduct my readers in triumph into the body of my work.

The question which has thus suddenly arisen is, What right had the first discoverers of America to land and take possession of a country, without first gaining the consent of its inhabitants, or yielding them an adequate compensation for their territory?—a question which has withstood many fierce assaults, and has given much distress of mind to multitudes of kind-hearted folk. And indeed, until it be totally vanquished, and put to rest, the worthy people of America can by no means enjoy the soil they inhabit, with clear right and title, and quiet, unsullied consciences.

The first source of right, by which property is acquired in a country, is DISCOVERY. For as all mankind have an equal right to anything which has never before been appropriated, so any nation that discovers an uninhabited country, and takes possession thereof, is considered as enjoying full property, and absolute, unquestionable empire therein.*

This proposition being admitted, it follows clearly, that the Europeans who first visited America were the real discoverers of the same; nothing being necessary to the establishment of this fact, but simply to prove that it was totally uninhabited by men. This would at first appear to be a point of some difficulty, for it is well known that this quarter of the world abounded with certain animals, that walked erect on two feet, had something of a human countenance, uttered certain unintelligible sounds, very much like language; in short, had a marvellous resemblance to human beings. But the zealous and enlightened fathers, who accompanied the discoverers, for the purpose of promoting the kingdom of heaven by establishing

* Grotius. Puffendorff, b. v. c. 4. Vattel, b. i. c. 18, &c.

fat monasteries and bishoprics on earth, soon cleared up this point, greatly to the satisfaction of his holiness the pope, and of all Christian voyagers and discoverers.

They plainly proved, and as there were no Indian writers arose on the other side, the fact was considered as fully admitted and established, that the two-legged race of animals before mentioned were mere cannibals, detestable monsters, and many of them giants—which last description of vagrants have, since the time of Gog, Magog, and Goliath, been considered as outlaws, and have received no quarter in either history, chivalry, or song. Indeed, even the philosophic Bacon declared the Americans to be people proscribed by the laws of nature, inasmuch as they had a barbarous custom of sacrificing men, and feeding upon man's flesh.

Nor are these all the proofs of their utter barbarism; among many other writers of discernment, Ulloa tells us "their imbecility is so visible, that one can hardly form an idea of them different from what one has of the brutes. Nothing disturbs the tranquillity of their souls, equally insensible to disasters and to prosperity. Though half naked, they are as contented as a monarch in his most splendid array. Fear makes no impression on them, and respect as little." All this is furthermore supported by the authority of M. Bouguer. "It is not easy," says he, "to describe the degree of their indifference for wealth and all its advantages. One does not well know what motives to propose to them when one would persuade them to any service. It is vain to offer them money; they answer they are not hungry." And Vanegas confirms the whole, assuring us that "ambition they have none, and are more desirous of being thought strong than valiant. The objects of ambition with us—honor, fame, reputation, riches, posts, and distinctions—are unknown among them. So that this powerful spring of action, the cause of so much *seeming* good and *real* evil in the world, has no power over them. In a word, these unhappy mortals may be compared to children in whom the development of reason is not completed."

Now all these peculiarities, although in the most unenlightened states of Greece they would have entitled their possessors to immortal honor, as having reduced to practice those rigid and abstemious maxims, the mere talking about which acquired certain old Greeks the reputation of sages and philosophers—yet, were they clearly proved in the present instance to betoken a most abject and brutified nature, totally beneath the human character. But the benevolent fathers, who had undertaken to turn these unhappy savages into dumb beasts, by dint of argument, advanced still stronger proofs; for, as certain divines of the sixteenth century, and among the rest Lullus, affirm—the Americans go naked, and have no beards! "They have nothing," says Lullus, "of the reasonable animal, except the mask." And even that mask was allowed to avail them but little, for it was soon found that they were of a hideous copper complexion: and being of a copper complexion, it was all the same as if they were Negroes: and Negroes are black—"and black," said the pious fathers, devoutly crossing themselves, "is the color of the Devil!" Therefore, so far from being able to own property, they had no right even to personal freedom; for liberty is too radiant a deity to inhabit such gloomy temples. All which circumstances plainly convinced the righteous followers of Cortes and Pizarro, that these miscreants had no title to the soil that they infested—that they were a perverse, illiterate, dumb, beardless, black-seed—mere wild beasts of the forests, and like them should either be subdued or exterminated.

From the foregoing arguments, therefore, and a variety of others equally conclusive, which I forbear to enumerate, it is clearly evident that this fair quarter of the globe, when first visited by Europeans, was a howling wilderness, inhabited by nothing but wild beasts; and that the transatlantic visitors acquired an incontrovertible property therein by the *right of discovery*.

This right being fully established, we now come to the next, which is the right acquired by *cultivation*. "The cultivation of the soil," we are told, "is an obligation imposed by nature on mankind. The whole world is appointed for the nourishment of its inhabitants; but it would be incapable of doing it, was it uncultivated. Every nation is then obliged by the law of nature to cultivate the ground that has fallen to its share. Those people, like the ancient Germans and modern Tartars, who, having fertile countries, disdain to cultivate the earth, and choose to live by rapine, are wanting to themselves, and *deserve to be exterminated as savage and pernicious beasts*." *

Now it is notorious that the savages knew nothing of agriculture, when first discovered by the Europeans, but lived a most vagabond, disorderly, unrighteous life—rambling from place to place, and prodigally rioting upon the spontaneous luxuries of nature, without tasking her generosity to yield them anything more; whereas it has been most unquestionably shown, that Heaven intended the earth should be ploughed and sown, and manured, and laid out into cities, and towns, and farms, and country-seats, and pleasure-grounds, and public gardens; all which the Indians knew nothing about: therefore, they did not improve the talents Providence had bestowed on them: therefore, they were careless stewards: therefore, they had no right to the soil: therefore, they deserved to be exterminated.

It is true, the savages might plead that they drew all the benefits from the land which their simple wants required—they found plenty of game to hunt, which, together with the roots and uncultivated fruits of the earth, furnished a sufficient variety for their frugal repasts—and that, as Heaven merely designed the earth to form the abode, and satisfy the wants of man, so long as those purposes were answered, the will of Heaven was accomplished. But this only proves how undeserving they were of the blessings around them: they were so much the more savages, for not having more wants; for knowledge is in some degree an increase of desires; and it is this superiority both in the number and magnitude of his desires, that distinguishes the man from the beast. Therefore the Indians, in not having more wants, were very unreasonable animals; and it was but just that they should make way for the Europeans, who had a thousand wants to their one, and, therefore, would turn the earth to more account, and by cultivating it, more truly fulfil the will of Heaven. Besides—Grotius, and Lauterbach, and Puffendorff, and Titius, and many wise men beside, who have considered the matter properly, have determined that the property of a country cannot be acquired by hunting, cutting wood, or drawing water in it—nothing but precise demarcation of limits, and the intention of cultivation, can establish the possession.

* Vattel, b. i. ch. 17.

Now, as the savages (probably from never having read the authors above quoted) had never complied with any of these necessary forms, it plainly follows that they had no right to the soil, but that it was completely at the disposal of the first comers, who had more knowledge, more wants, and more elegant, that is to say artificial desires than themselves.

In entering upon a newly discovered, uncultivated country, therefore, the new comers were but aking possession of what, according to the aforesaid doctrine, was their own property; therefore, in opposing them, the savages were invading their just rights, infringing the immutable laws of nature, and counteracting the will of heaven: therefore, they were guilty of impiety, burglary, and trespass on the case: therefore, they were hardened offenders against God and man: therefore, they ought to be exterminated.

But a more irresistible right than either that I have mentioned, and one which will be the most readily admitted by my reader, provided he be blessed with bowels of charity and philanthropy, is the right acquired by civilization. All the world knows the lamentable state in which these poor savages were found. Not only deficient in the comforts of life, but what is still worse, most piteously and unfortunately blind to the miseries of their situation. But no sooner did the benevolent inhabitants of Europe behold their sad condition, than they immediately went to work to ameliorate and improve it. They introduced among them rum, gin, brandy, and the other comforts of life—and it is astonishing to read how soon the poor savages learned to estimate those blessings; they likewise made known to them a thousand remedies, by which the most inveterate diseases are alleviated and healed; and that they might comprehend the benefits and enjoy the comforts of these medicines, they previously introduced among them the diseases which they were calculated to cure. By these and a variety of other methods was the condition of these poor savages wonderfully improved; they acquired a thousand wants, of which they had before been ignorant; and as he has most sources of happiness who has most wants to be gratified, they were doubtlessly rendered a much happier race of beings.

But the most important branch of civilization, and which

has most strenuously been extolled by the zealous and pious fathers of the Romish Church, is the introduction of the Christian faith. It was truly a sight that might well inspire horror, to behold these savages tumbling among the dark mountains of paganism, and guilty of the most horrible ignorance of religion. It is true, they neither stole nor defrauded; they were sober, frugal, continent, and faithful to their word; but though they acted right habitually, it was all in vain, unless they acted so from precept. The new comers, therefore, used every method to induce them to embrace and practise the true religion—except indeed that of setting them the example.

But notwithstanding all these complicated labors for their good, such was the unparalleled obstinacy of these stubborn wretches, that they ungratefully refused to acknowledge the strangers as their benefactors, and persisted in disbelieving the doctrines they endeavored to inculcate; most insolently alleging, that, from their conduct, the advocates of Christianity did not seem to believe in it themselves. Was not this too much for human patience?—would not one suppose that the benign visitants from Europe, provoked at their incredulity, and discouraged by their stiff-necked obstinacy, would forever have abandoned their shores, and consigned them to their original ignorance and misery? But no: so zealous were they to effect the temporal comfort and eternal salvation of these pagan infidels, that they even proceeded from the milder means of persuasion to the more painful and troublesome one of persecution—let loose among them whole troops of fiery monks and furious bloodhounds—purified them by fire and sword, by stake and fagot; in consequence of which indefatigable measures the cause of Christian love and charity was so rapidly advanced, that in a few years not one fifth of the number of unbelievers existed in South America that were found there at the time of its discovery.

What stronger right need the European settlers advance to the country than this? Have not whole nations of uninformed savages been made acquainted with a thousand imperious wants and indispensable comforts, of which they were before wholly ignorant? Have they not been literally hunted and smoked out of the dens and lurking-places of ignorance and infidelity, and absolutely scourged into the right path? Have not the temporal things, the vain baubles and filthy lucre of this world, which were too apt to engage their worldly and selfish thoughts, been benevolently taken from them; and have they not, instead thereof, been taught to set their affections on things above? And, finally, to use the words of a reverend Spanish father, in a letter to his superior in Spain, "can any one have the presumption to say that these savage Pagans have yielded anything more than an inconsiderable recompense to their benefactors, in surrendering to them a little pitiful tract of this dirty sublunary planet in exchange for a glorious inheritance in the kingdom of heaven?"

Here, then, are three complete and undeniable sources of right established, any one of which was more than ample to establish a property in the newly-discovered regions of America. Now, so it has happened in certain parts of this delightful quarter of the globe, that the right of discovery has been so strenuously asserted, the influence of cultivation so industriously extended, and the progress of salvation and civilization so zealously prosecuted, that, what with their attendant wars, persecutions, oppressions, diseases, and other partial evils that often hang on the skirts of great benefits, the savage aborigines have, somehow or another, been utterly annihilated; and this all at once brings me to a fourth right, which is worth all the others put together. For the original claimants to the soil being all dead and buried, and no one remaining to inherit or dispute the soil, the Spaniards, as the next immediate occupants, entered upon the possession as clearly as the hangman succeeds to the clothes of the malefactor; and as they have Blackstone,* and all the learned expounders of the law on their side, they may set all actions of ejectment at defiance; and this last right may be entitled the RIGHT BY EXTERMINATION, or, in other words, the RIGHT BY GUNPOWDER.

But lest any scruples of conscience should remain on this head, and to settle the question of right forever, his holiness Pope Alexander VI. issued a bull, by which he generously granted the newly-discovered quarter of the globe to the Spaniards and Portuguese; who, thus having law and gospel on

* Bl. Com. b. ii. c. 1.

their side, and being inflamed with great spiritual zeal, showed the Pagan savages neither favor nor affection, but prosecuted the work of discovery, colonization, civilization, and extermination with ten times more fury than ever.

Thus were the European worthies who first discovered America clearly entitled to the soil; and not only entitled to the soil, but likewise to the eternal thanks of these infidel savages, for having come so far, endured so many perils by sea and land, and taken such unwearied pains, for no other purpose but to improve their forlorn, uncivilized, and heathenish condition—for having made them acquainted with the comforts of life—for having introduced among them the light of religion—and, finally, for having hurried them out of the world, to enjoy its reward!

But as argument is never so well understood by us selfish mortals as when it comes home to ourselves, and as I am particularly anxious that this question should be put to rest forever, I will suppose a parallel case, by way of arousing the candid attention of my readers.

Let us suppose, then, that the inhabitants of the moon, by astonishing advancement in science, and by profound insight into that lunar philosophy, the mere flickerings of which have of late years dazzled the feeble optics, and addled the shallow brains of the good people of our globe—let us suppose, I say, that the inhabitants of the moon, by these means, had arrived at such a command of their *energies*, such an enviable state of *perfectibility*, as to control the elements, and navigate the boundless regions of space. Let us suppose a roving crew of these soaring philosophers, in the course of an aërial voyage of discovery among the stars, should chance to alight upon this outlandish planet.

And here I beg my readers will not have the uncharitableness to smile, as is too frequently the fault of volatile readers, when perusing the grave speculations of philosophers. I am far from indulging in any sportive vein at present; nor is the supposition I have been making so wild as many may deem it. It has long been a very serious and anxious question with me, and many a time and oft, in the course of my overwhelming cares and contrivances for the welfare and protection of this my native planet, have I lain awake whole nights debating in my mind, whether it were most probable we should first discover and civilize the moon, or the moon discover and civilize our globe. Neither would the prodigy of sailing in the air and cruising among the stars be a whit more astonishing and incomprehensible to us than was the European mystery of navigating floating castles, through the world of waters, to the simple natives. We have already discovered the art of coasting along the aërial shores of our planet, by means of balloons, as the savages had of venturing along their seacoasts in canoes; and the disparity between the former and the aërial vehicles of the philosophers from the moon might not be greater than that between the bark canoes of the savages and the mighty ships of their discoverers. I might here pursue an endless chain of similar speculations; but as they would be unimportant to my subject, I abandon them to my reader, particularly if he be a philosopher, as matters well worthy of his attentive consideration.

To return, then, to my supposition; let us suppose that the aërial visitants I have mentioned, possessed of vastly superior knowledge to ourselves; that is to say, possessed of superior knowledge in the art of extermination—riding on hyppogriffs—defended with impenetrable armor—armed with concentrated sunbeams, and provided with vast engines, to hurl enormous moonstones: in short, let us suppose them, if our vanity will permit the supposition, as superior to us in knowledge, and consequently in power, as the Europeans were to the Indians, when they first discovered them. All this is very possible; it is only our self-sufficiency that makes us think otherwise; and I warrant the poor savages, before they had any knowledge of the white men, armed in all the terrors of glittering steel and tremendous gunpowder, were as perfectly convinced that they themselves were the wisest, the most virtuous, powerful, and perfect of created beings, as are, at this present moment, the lordly inhabitants of old England, the volatile populace of France, or even the self-satisfied citizens of this most enlightened republic.

Let us suppose, moreover, that the aërial voyagers, finding this planet to be nothing but a howling wilderness, inhabited by us, poor savages and wild beasts, shall take formal possession of it, in the name of his most gracious and philosophic excellency, the man in the moon. Finding, however, that their numbers are incompetent to hold it in complete subjection, on account of the ferocious barbarity of its inhabitants they shall take our worthy President, the King of England, the Emperor of Hayti, the mighty Bonaparte, and the great King of Bantam, and returning to their native planet, shall carry them to court as were the Indian chiefs led about as spectacles in the courts of Europe.

Then making such obeisance as the etiquette of the court requires, they shall address the puissant man in the moon, in, as near as I can conjecture, the following terms:—

"Most serene and mighty Potentate, whose dominions extend as far as eye can reach, who rideth on the Great Bear, useth the sun as a looking-glass, and maintaineth unrivalled control over tides, madmen, and sea-crabs. We, thy liege subjects, have just returned from a voyage of discovery, in the course of which we have landed and taken possession of that obscure little dirty planet, which thou beholdest rolling at a distance. The five uncouth monsters, which we have brought into this august presence, were once very important chiefs among their fellow-savages, who are a race of beings totally destitute of the common attributes of humanity; and differing in everything from the inhabitants of the moon, inasmuch as they carry their heads upon their shoulders, instead of under their arms—have two eyes instead of one—are utterly destitute of tails, and of a variety of unseemly complexions, particularly of horrible whiteness, instead of pea-green.

"We have moreover found these miserable savages sunk into a state of the utmost ignorance and depravity, every man shamelessly living with his own wife, and rearing his own children, instead of indulging in that community of wives enjoined by the law of nature, as expounded by the philosophers of the moon. In a word, they have scarcely a gleam of true philosophy among them, but are, in fact, utter heretics, ignoramuses, and barbarians. Taking compassion, therefore, on the sad condition of these sublunary wretches, we have endeavored, while we remained on their planet, to introduce among them the light of reason, and the comforts of the moon. We have treated them to mouthfuls of moonshine, and draughts of nitrous oxide, which they swallowed with incredible voracity, particularly the females; and we have likewise endeavored to instil into them the precepts of lunar philosophy. We have insisted upon their renouncing the contemptible shackles of religion and common sense, and adoring the profound, omnipotent, and all-perfect energy, and the ecstatic, immutable, immovable perfection. But such was the unparalleled obstinacy of these wretched savages, that they persisted in cleaving to their wives, and adhering to their religion, and absolutely set at naught the sublime doctrines of the moon—nay, among other abominable heresies, they even went so far as blasphemously to declare, that this ineffable planet was made of nothing more nor less than green cheese!"

At these words, the great man in the moon (being a very profound philosopher) shall fall into a terrible passion, and possessing equal authority over things that do not belong to him, as did whilom his holiness the Pope, shall forthwith issue a formidable bull, specifying, "That, whereas a certain crew of Lunatics have lately discovered, and taken possession of a newly-discovered planet called *the earth;* and that, whereas it is inhabited by none but a race of two-legged animals that carry their heads on their shoulders instead of under their arms, cannot talk the lunatic language, have two eyes instead of one, are destitute of tails, and of a horrible whiteness, instead of pea-green: therefore, and for a variety of other excellent reasons, they are considered incapable of possessing any property in the planet they infest, and the right and title to it are confirmed to its original discoverers. And furthermore, the colonists who are now about to depart to the aforesaid planet are authorized and commanded to use every means to convert these infidel savages from the darkness of Christianity, and make them thorough and absolute lunatics."

In consequence of this benevolent bull, our philosophic benefactors go to work with hearty zeal. They seize upon our fertile territories, scourge us from our rightful possessions, relieve us from our wives; and when we are unreasonable enough to complain, they will turn upon us and say: Miserable barbarians! ungrateful wretches! have we not come thousands of miles to improve your worthless planet; have we not fed you with moonshine; have we not intoxicated you with nitrous oxide;

does not our moon give you light every night; and have you the baseness to murmur when we claim a pitiful return for all these benefits? But finding that we not only persist in absolute contempt of their reasoning and disbelief in their philosophy, but even go so far as daringly to defend our property, their patience shall be exhausted, and they shall resort to their superior powers of argument: hunt us with hyppogriffs, transfix us with concentrated sunbeams, demolish our cities with moon-stones; until having, by main force, converted us to the true faith, they shall graciously permit us to exist in the torrid deserts of Arabia, or the frozen regions of Lapland, there to enjoy the blessings of civilization and the charms of lunar philosophy, in much the same manner as the reformed and enlightened savages of this country are kindly suffered to inhabit the inhospitable forests of the north, or the impenetrable wildernesses of South America.

Thus, I hope, I have clearly proved, and strikingly illustrated, the right of the early colonists to the possession of this country; and thus is this gigantic question completely vanquished: so, having manfully surmounted all obstacles, and subdued all opposition, what remains but that I should forthwith conduct my readers into the city which we have been so long in a manner besieging? But hold; before I proceed another step, I must pause to take breath, and recover from the excessive fatigue I have undergone, in preparing to begin this most accurate of histories. And in this I do but imitate the example of a renowned Dutch tumbler of antiquity, who took a start of three miles for the purpose of jumping over a hill, but having run himself out of breath by the time he reached the foot, sat himself quietly down for a few moments to blow, and then walked over it at his leisure.

Book II

TREATING OF THE FIRST SETTLEMENT OF THE PROVINCE OF NIEUW-NEDERLANDTS

CHAPTER I

In Which Are Contained Divers Reasons Why a Man Should Not Write in a Hurry; Also, of Master Hendrick Hudson, His Discovery of a Strange Country—and How He Was Magnificently Rewarded by the Munificence of Their High Mightinesses

MY great-great-grandfather, by the mother's side, Hermanus Van Clattercop, when employed to build the large stone church at Rotterdam, which stands about three hundred yards to your left after you turn off from the Boomkeys, and which is so conveniently constructed, that all the zealous Christians of Rotterdam prefer sleeping through a sermon there to any other church in the city—my great-grandfather, I say, when employed to build that famous church, did in the first place send to Delft for a box of long pipes; then having purchased a new spitting-box and a hundred-weight of the best Virginia, he sat himself down, and did nothing for the space of three months but smoke most laboriously. Then did he spend full three months more in trudging on foot, and voyaging in trekschuit, from Rotterdam to Amsterdam—to Delft—to Haerlem—to Leyden—to the Hague, knocking his head and breaking his pipe against every church in his road. Then did he advance gradually nearer and nearer to Rotterdam, until he came in full sight of the identical spot whereon the church was to be built. Then did he spend three months longer in walking round it and round it, contemplating it, first from one point of view, and then from another—now would he be paddled by it on the canal—now would he peep at it through a telescope from the other side of the Meuse, and now would he take a bird's-eye glance at it from the top of one of those gigantic windmills which protect the gates of the city. The good folks of the place were on the tiptoe of expectation and impatience; notwithstanding all the turmoil of my great-great-grandfather, not a symptom of the church was yet to be seen; they even began to fear it would never be brought into the world, but that its great projector would lie down and die in labor of the mighty plan he had conceived. At length, having occupied twelve good months in puffing and paddling, and talking and walking—having travelled over all Holland, and even taken a peep into France and Germany—having smoked five hundred and ninety-nine pipes, and three hundred-weight of the best Virginia tobacco—my great-great-grandfather gathered together all that knowing and industrious class of citizens who prefer attending to anybody's business sooner than their own, and having pulled off his coat and five pair of breeches, he advanced sturdily up and laid the corner-stone of the church, in presence of the whole multitude—just at the commencement of the thirteenth month.

In a similar manner, and with the example of my worthy ancestor full before my eyes, have I proceeded in writing this most authentic history. The honest Rotterdamers no doubt thought my great-great-grandfather was doing nothing at all to the purpose, while he was making such a world of prefatory bustle about the building of his church—and many of the ingenious inhabitants of this fair city will unquestionably suppose that all the preliminary chapters, with the discovery, population, and final settlement of America, were totally irrelevant and superfluous—and that the main business, the history of New York, is not a jot more advanced than if I had never taken up my pen. Never were wise people more mistaken in their conjectures: in consequence of going to work slowly and deliberately, the church came out of my grandfather's hands one of the most sumptuous, goodly, and glorious edifices in the known world—excepting that, like our magnificent capitol, at Washington, it was begun on so grand a scale that the good folks could not afford to finish more than the wing of it. So, likewise, I trust, if ever I am able to finish this work on the plan I have commenced (of which, in simple truth, I sometimes have my doubts), it will be found that I have pursued the latest rules of my art, as exemplified in the writings of all the great American historians, and wrought a very large history out of a small subject—which, nowadays, is considered one of the great triumphs of historic skill. To proceed, then, with the thread of my story.

In the ever-memorable year of our Lord, 1609, on a Saturday morning, the five-and-twentieth day of March, old style, did that "worthy and irrecoverable discoverer (as he has justly been called), Master Henry Hudson," set sail from Holland in a stout vessel called the Half-Moon, being employed by the Dutch East India Company, to seek a northwest passage to China.

Henry (or, as the Dutch historians call him, Hendrick) Hudson was a seafaring man of renown, who had learned to smoke tobacco under Sir Walter Raleigh, and is said to have been the first to introduce it into Holland, which gained him much popularity in that country, and caused him to find great favor in the eyes of their High Mightinesses, the Lords States General, and also of the honorable West India Company. He was a short, square, brawny old gentleman, with a double chin, a mastiff mouth, and a broad copper nose, which was supposed in those days to have acquired its fiery hue from the constant neighborhood of his tobacco-pipe.

He wore a true Andrea Ferrara, tucked in a leathern belt, and a commodore's cocked hat on one side of his head. He was remarkable for always jerking up his breeches when he gave out his orders, and his voice sounded not unlike the brattling of a tin trumpet—owing to the number of hard northwesters which he had swallowed in the course of his seafaring.

Such was Hendrick Hudson, of whom we have heard so much, and know so little; and I have been thus particular in his description for the benefit of modern painters and statuaries, that they may represent him as he was—and not, according to their common custom with modern heroes, make him look like Cæsar, or Marcus Aurelius, or the Apollo of Belvidere.

As chief mate and favorite companion, the commodore chose master Robert Juet, of Limehouse, in England. By some his name has been spelled *Chewit*, and ascribed to the circumstances of his having been the first man that ever chewed tobacco; but this I believe to be a mere flippancy; more especially as certain of his progeny are living at this day, who write their names Juet. He was an old comrade and early schoolmate of the great Hudson, with whom he had often played truant and sailed chip boats in a neighboring pond, when they were little boys: from whence it is said that the commodore first derived his bias towards a seafaring life. Certain it is that the old people about Limehouse declared Robert Juet to be an unlucky urchin, prone to mischief, that would one day or other come to the gallows.

He grew up, as boys of that kind often grow up, a rambling, heedless varlet, tossed about in all quarters of the world—meeting with more perils and wonders than did Sinbad the Sailor, without growing a whit more wise, prudent, or ill-natured. Under every misfortune, he comforted himself with a quid of tobacco, and the truly philosophic maxim, that "it will be all the same thing a hundred years hence." He was skilled in the art of carving anchors and true lover's knots on the bulk-heads and quarter-railings, and was considered a great wit on board ship, in consequence of his playing pranks on everybody around, and now and then even making a wry face at old Hendrick, when his back was turned.

To this universal genius are we indebted for many particulars concerning this voyage; of which he wrote a history, at the request of the commodore, who had an unconquerable aversion to writing himself, from having received so many floggings about it when at school. To supply the deficiencies of master Juet's journal, which is written with true log-book brevity, I have availed myself of divers family traditions, handed down from my great-great-grandfather, who accompanied the expedition in the capacity of cabin-boy.

From all that I can learn, few incidents worthy of remark happened in the voyage; and it mortifies me exceedingly that I have to admit so noted an expedition into my work, without making any more of it.

Suffice it to say, the voyage was prosperous and tranquil; the crew, being a patient people, much given to slumber and vacuity, and but little troubled with the disease of thinking—a malady of the mind, which is the sure breeder of discontent. Hudson had laid in abundance of gin and sourkrout, and every man was allowed to sleep quietly at his post unless the wind blew. True it is, some slight disaffection was shown on two or three occasions, at certain unreasonable conduct of Commodore Hudson. Thus, for instance, he forbore to shorten sail when the wind was light, and the weather serene, which was considered among the most experienced Dutch seamen as certain *weather-breeders*, or prognostics that the weather would change for the worse. He acted, moreover, in direct contradiction to that ancient and sage rule of the Dutch navigators, who always took in sail at night, put the helm a-port, and turned in—by which precaution they had a good night's rest, were sure of knowing where they were the next morning, and stood but little chance of running down a continent in the dark. He likewise prohibited the seamen from wearing more than five jackets and six pair of breeches, under pretence of rendering them more alert; and no man was permitted to go aloft and hand in sails with a pipe in his mouth, as is the invariable Dutch custom at the present day. All these grievances, though they might ruffle for a moment the constitutional tranquillity of the honest Dutch tars, made but transient impression; they ate hugely, drank profusely, and slept immeasurably; and being under the especial guidance of Providence, the ship was safely conducted to the coast of America; where, after sundry unimportant touchings and standings off and on, she at length, on the fourth day of September, entered that majestic bay which at this day expands its ample bosom before the city of New York, and which had never before been visited by any European.*

* True it is—and I am not ignorant of the fact—that in a certain apocryphal book of voyages, compiled by one Hakluyt, is to be found a letter written to Francis the First, by one Giovanne, or John Verazzani, on which some writers are inclined to found a belief that this delightful bay had been visited nearly a century previous to the voyage of the enterprising Hudson. Now this (albeit it has met with the countenance of certain very judicious and learned men) I hold in utter disbelief, and that for various good and substantial reasons: *First*, Because on strict examination it will be found, that the description given by this Verazzani applies about as well to the bay of New York as it does to my nightcap. *Secondly*, Because that this John Verazzani, for whom I already begin to feel a most bitter enmity, is a native of Florence; and everybody knows the crafty wiles of these losel Florentines, by which they filched away the laurels from the brows of the immortal Colon (vulgarly called Columbus), and bestowed them on their officious townsman, Amerigo Vespucci; and I make no doubt they are equally ready to rob the illustrious Hudson of the credit of discovering this beautiful island, adorned by the city of New York, and placing it beside their usurped discovery of South America. And, *thirdly*, I award my decision in favor of the pretensions of Hendrick Hudson, inasmuch as his expedition

It has been traditionary in our family, that when the great navigator was first blessed with a view of this enchanting island, he was observed, for the first and only time in his life, to exhibit strong symptoms of astonishment and admiration. He is said to have turned to master Juet, and uttered these remarkable words, while he pointed towards this paradise of the new world —"See! there!"—and thereupon, as was always his way when he was uncommonly pleased, he did puff out such clouds of dense tobacco-smoke, that in one minute the vessel was out of sight of land, and master Juet was fain to wait until the winds dispersed this impenetrable fog.

It was indeed—as my great-great-grandfather used to say—though in truth I never heard him, for he died, as might be expected, before I was born—"It was indeed a spot on which the eye might have revelled forever, in ever new and never-ending beauties." The island of Mannahata spread wide before them, like some sweet vision of fancy, or some fair creation of industrious magic. Its hills of smiling green swelled gently one above another, crowned with lofty trees of luxuriant growth; some pointing their tapering foliage towards the clouds, which were gloriously transparent; and others loaded with a verdant burden of clambering vines, bowing their branches to the earth, that was covered with flowers. On the gentle declivities of the hills were scattered in gay profusion, the dog-wood, the sumach, and the wild brier, whose scarlet berries and white blossoms glowed brightly among the deep green of the surrounding foliage; and here and there a curling column of smoke, rising from the little glens that opened along the shore, seemed to promise the weary voyagers a welcome at the hands of their fellow-creatures. As they stood gazing with entranced attention on the scene before them, a red man, crowned with feathers, issued from one of these glens, and after contemplating in wonder the gallant ship, as she sat like a stately swan swimming on a silver lake, sounded the war-whoop, and bounded into the woods like a wild deer, to

sailed from Holland, being truly and absolutely a Dutch enterprise; and though all the proofs in the world were introduced on the other side, I would set them at naught, as undeserving my attention. If these three reasons be not sufficient to satisfy every burgher of this ancient city, all I can say is, they are degenerate descendants from their venerable Dutch ancestors, and totally unworthy the trouble of convincing. Thus, therefore, the title of Hendrick Hudson to his renowed discovery is fully vindicated.

the utter astonishment of the phlegmatic Dutchmen, who had never heard such a noise, or witnessed such a caper in their whole lives.

Of the transactions of our adventurers with the savages, and how the latter smoked copper pipes, and ate dried currants; how they brought great store of tobacco and oysters; how they shot one of the ship's crew, and how he was buried, I shall say nothing; being that I consider them unimportant to my history. After tarrying a few days in the bay, in order to refresh themselves after their seafaring, our voyagers weighed anchor, to explore a mighty river which emptied into the bay. This river, it is said, was known among the savages by the name of the *Shatemuck*; though we are assured in an excellent little history published in 1674, by John Josselyn, Gent., that it was called the *Mohegan*,* and master Richard Bloome, who wrote some time afterwards, asserts the same—so that I very much incline in favor of the opinion of these two honest gentlemen. Be this as it may, up this river did the adventurous Hendrick proceed, little doubting but it would turn out to be the much looked-for passage to China!

The journal goes on to make mention of divers interviews between the crew and the natives, in the voyage up the river; but as they would be impertinent to my history, I shall pass over them in silence, except the following dry joke, played off by the old commodore and his school-fellow, Robert Juet, which does such vast credit to their experimental philosophy, that I cannot refrain from inserting it. "Our master and his mate determined to try some of the chiefe men of the countrey, whether they had any treacherie in them. So they tooke them downe into the cabin, and gave them so much wine and aqua vitæ, that they were all merrie; and one of them had his wife with him, which sate so modestly, as any of our countrey women would do in a strange place. In the end, one of them was drunke, which had been aborde of our ship all the time that we had been there, and that was strange to them, for they could not tell how to take it." †

Having satisfied himself by this ingenious experiment, that

* This river is likewise laid down in Ogilvy's map as Manhattan—Noordt Montaigne and Mauritius river.

† Juet's Journ. Purch. Pil.

the natives were an honest, social race of jolly roysters, who had no objection to a drinking-bout and were very merry in their cups, the old commodore chuckled hugely to himself, and thrusting a double quid of tobacco in his cheek, directed master Juet to have it carefully recorded, for the satisfaction of all the natural philosophers of the university of Leyden—which done, he proceeded on his voyage, with great self-complacency. After sailing, however, above an hundred miles up the river, he found the watery world around him began to grow more shallow and confined, the current more rapid, and perfectly fresh—phenomena not uncommon in the ascent of rivers, but which puzzled the honest Dutchmen prodigiously. A consultation was therefore called, and having deliberated full six hours, they were brought to a determination by the ship's running aground—whereupon they unanimously concluded, that there was but little chance of getting to China in this direction. A boat, however, was despatched to explore higher up the river, which, on its return, confirmed the opinion; upon this the ship was warped off and put about, with great difficulty, being, like most of her sex, exceedingly hard to govern; and the adventurous Hudson, according to the account of my great-great-grandfather, returned down the river—with a prodigious flea in his ear!

Being satisfied that there was little likelihood of getting to China, unless, like the blind man, he returned from whence he set out, and took a fresh start, he forthwith recrossed the sea to Holland, where he was received with great welcome by the honorable East India Company, who were very much rejoiced to see him come back safe—with their ship; and at a large and respectable meeting of the first merchants and burgomasters of Amsterdam, it was unanimously determined, that, as a munificent reward for the eminent services he had performed, and the important discovery he had made, the great river Mohegan should be called after his name!—and it continues to be called Hudson river unto this very day.

CHAPTER II

Containing an Account of a Mighty Ark Which Floated, Under the Protection of St. Nicholas, from Holland to Gibbet Island—the Descent of the Strange Animals Therefrom—a Great Victory, and a Description of the Ancient Village of Communipaw

THE delectable accounts given by the great Hudson, and master Juet, of the country they had discovered, excited not a little talk and speculation among the good people of Holland. Letters-patent were granted by government to an association of merchants, called the West India Company, for the exclusive trade on Hudson river, on which they erected a trading-house, called Fort Aurania, or Orange, from whence did spring the great city of Albany. But I forbear to dwell on the various commercial and colonizing enterprises which took place—among which was that of Mynheer Adrian Block, who discovered and gave a name to Block Island, since famous for its cheese—and shall barely confine myself to that which gave birth to this renowned city.

It was some three or four years after the return of the immortal Hendrick, that a crew of honest, Low-Dutch colonists set sail from the city of Amsterdam for the shores of America. It is an irreparable loss to history, and a great proof of the darkness of the age, and the lamentable neglect of the noble art of book-making, since so industriously cultivated by knowing sea-captains, and learned supercargoes, that an expedition so interesting and important in its results should be passed over in utter silence. To my great-great-grandfather am I again indebted for the few facts I am enabled to give concerning it—he having once more embarked for this country, with a full determination, as he said, of ending his days here, and of begetting a race of Knickerbockers that should rise to be great men in the land.

The ship in which these illustrious adventurers set sail was called the *Goede Vrouw*, or good woman, in compliment to the wife of the President of the West India Company, who was allowed by everybody (except her husband) to be a sweet-tempered lady—when not in liquor. It was in truth a most gallant vessel, of the most approved Dutch construction, and made by the ablest ship-carpenters of Amsterdam, who, it is well known, always model their ships after the fair forms of their country-women. Accordingly it had one hundred feet in the beam, one hundred feet in the kneel, and one hundred feet from the bottom of the stern-post to the tafferel. Like the beauteous model, who was declared to be the greatest belle in Amsterdam, it was full in the bows, with a pair of enormous cat-heads, a copper bottom, and withal a most prodigious poop!

The architect, who was somewhat of a religious man, far from decorating the ship with pagan idols, such as Jupiter, Neptune, or Hercules (which heathenish abominations, I have no doubt, occasion the misfortunes and shipwreck of many a noble vessel)—he, I say on the contrary, did laudably erect for a head, a goodly image of St. Nicholas, equipped with a low, broad-brimmed hat, a huge pair of Flemish trunk-hose, and a pipe that reached to the end of the bowsprit. Thus gallantly furnished, the stanch ship floated sideways, like a majestic goose, out of the harbor of the great city of Amsterdam, and all the bells, that were not otherwise engaged, rang a triple bob-major on the joyful occasion.

My great-great-grandfather remarks, that the voyage was uncommonly prosperous, for, being under the especial care of the ever-revered St. Nicholas, the *Goede Vrouw* seemed to be endowed with qualities unknown to common vessels. Thus she made as much leeway as headway, could get along very nearly as fast with the wind ahead as when it was a-poop—and was particularly great in a calm; in consequence of which singular advantages she made out to accomplish her voyage in a very few months, and came to anchor at the mouth of the Hudson, a little to the east of Gibbet Island.

Here, lifting up their eyes, they beheld, on what is at present called the Jersey shore, a small Indian village, pleasantly embowered in a grove of spreading elms, and the natives all collected on the beach, gazing in stupid admiration at the *Goede Vrouw*. A boat was immediately despatched to enter into a treaty with them, and approaching the shore, hailed them through a trumpet, in the most friendly terms; but so horribly confounded were these poor savages at the tremendous and uncouth sound of the Low-Dutch language, that they one and all took to their heels, and scampered over the Bergen hills; nor did they stop until they had buried themselves, head and ears, in the marshes on the other side, where they all miserably perished to a man; and their bones, being collected and decently covered by the Tammany Society of that day, formed that singular mound called RATTLESNAKE HILL, which rises out of the centre of the salt marshes a little to the east of the Newark Causeway.

Animated by this unlooked-for victory, our valiant heroes sprang ashore in triumph, took possession of the soil as conquerors, in the name of their High Mightinesses the Lords States General; and, marching fearlessly forward, carried the village of COMMUNIPAW by storm, notwithstanding that it was vigorously defended by some half a score of old squaws and pappooses. On looking about them they were so transported with the excellencies of the place, that they had very little doubt the blessed St. Nicholas had guided them thither, as the very spot whereon to settle their colony. The softness of the soil was wonderfully adapted to the driving of piles; the swamps and marshes around them afforded ample opportunties for the constructing of dykes and dams; the shallowness of the shore was peculiarly favorable to the building of docks; in a word, this spot abounded with all the requisities for the foundation of a great Dutch city. On making a faithful report, therefore, to the crew of the *Goede Vrouw*, they one and all determined that this was the destined end of their voyage. Accordingly they descended from the *Goede Vrouw*, men, women, and children, in goodly groups, as did the animals of yore from the ark, and formed themselves into a thriving settlement, which they called by the Indian name COMMUNIPAW.

As all the world is doubtless perfectly acquainted with Communipaw, it may seem somewhat superfluous to treat of it in the present work; but my readers will please to recollect, notwithstanding it is my chief desire to satisfy the present age, yet I write likewise for posterity, and have to consult the understanding and curiosity of some half a score of centuries yet to come, by which time, perhaps, were it not for this invaluable history, the great Communipaw, like Babylon, Carthage, Nineveh, and other great cities, might be perfectly extinct—sunk and forgotten in its own mud—its inhabitants turned into oysters,* and even its situation a fertile subject of learned controversy and hard-headed investigation among indefatigable historians. Let me then piously rescue from oblivion the humble relics of a place, which was the egg from whence was hatched the mighty city of New York!

Communipaw is at present but a small village, pleasantly situated, among rural scenery, on that beauteous part of the Jersey shore which was known in ancient legends by the name of Pavonia,† and commands a grand prospect of the superb bay of New York. It is within but half an hour's sail of the latter place, provided you have a fair wind, and may be distinctly seen from the city. Nay, it is a well-known fact, which I can testify from my own experience, that on a clear, still summer evening, you may hear, from the Battery of New York, the obstreperous peals of broad-mouthed laughter of the Dutch Negroes at Communipaw, who, like most other Negroes, are famous for their risible powers. This is peculiarly the case on Sunday evenings, when, it is remarked by an ingenious and observant philosopher, who has made great discoveries in the neighborhood of this city, that they always laugh loudest, which he attributes to the circumstance of their having their holiday clothes on.

These Negroes, in fact, like the monks of the dark ages, engross all the knowledge of the place, and being infinitely more adventurous and more knowing than their masters, carry on all the foreign trade; making frequent voyages to town in canoes loaded with oysters, buttermilk, and cabbages. They are great astrologers, predicting the different changes of weather almost as accurately as an almanac; they are moreover exquisite performers on three-stringed fiddles; in whistling they almost boast the far-famed powers of Orpheus's lyre, for not a horse or an ox in the place, when at the plough or before the wagon, will budge a foot until he hears the well-known whistle of his black driver and companion. And from their amazing skill at casting up accounts upon their fingers, they are regarded with as much veneration as were the disciples of Pythagoras of yore, when initiated into the sacred quaternary of numbers.

* Men by inaction degenerate into oysters.—*Kaimes.*

† Pavonia, in the ancient maps, is given to a tract of country extending from about Hoboken to Amboy.

As to the honest burghers of Communipaw, like wise men and sound philosophers, they never look beyond their pipes, nor trouble their heads about any affairs out of their immediate neighborhood; so that they live in profound and enviable ignorance of all the troubles, anxieties, and revolutions of this distracted planet. I am even told that many among them do verily believe that Holland, of which they have heard so much from tradition, is situated somewhere on Long Island—that *Spiking-devil* and *the Narrows* are the two ends of the world—that the country is still under the dominion of their High Mightinesses—and that the city of New York still goes by the name of Nieuw Amsterdam. They meet every Saturday afternoon at the only tavern in the place, which bears as a sign a square-headed likeness of the Prince of Orange, where they smoke a silent pipe, by way of promoting social conviviality, and invariably drink a mug of cider to the success of Admiral Van Tromp, who they imagine is still sweeping the British channel, with a broom at his mast-head.

Communipaw, in short, is one of the numerous little villages in the vicinity of this most beautiful of cities, which are so many strongholds and fastnesses, whither the primitive manners of our Dutch forefathers have retreated, and where they are cherished with devout and scrupulous strictness. The dress of the original settlers is handed down inviolate, from father to son: the identical broad-brimmed hat, broad-skirted coat, and broad-bottomed breeches, continue from generation to generation; and several gigantic knee-buckles of massy silver are still in wear, that made gallant display in the days of the patriarchs of Communipaw. The language likewise continues unadulterated by barbarous innovations; and so critically correct is the village schoolmaster in his dialect, that his reading of a Low-Dutch psalm has much the same effect on the nerves as the filing of a handsaw.

CHAPTER III

In Which Is Set Forth the True Art of Making a Bargain—Together with the Miraculous Escape of a Great Metropolis in a Fog—and the Biography of Certain Heroes of Communipaw

HAVING, in the trifling digression which concluded the last chapter, discharged the filial duty which the city of New York owed to Communipaw, as being the mother settlement, and having given a faithful picture of it as it stands at present, I return with a soothing sentiment of self-approbation, to dwell upon its early history. The crew of the *Goede Vrouw* being soon reinforced by fresh importations from Holland, the settlement went jollily on, increasing in magnitude and prosperity. The neighboring Indians in a short time became accustomed to the uncouth sound of the Dutch language, and an intercourse gradually took place between them and the new comers. The Indians were much given to long talks, and the Dutch to long silence; in this particular, therefore, they accommodated each other completely. The chiefs would make long speeches about the big bull, the Wabash, and the Great Spirit, to which the others would listen very attentively, smoke their pipes, and grunt *yah, myn-her*—whereat the poor savages were wondrously delighted. They instructed the new settlers in the best art of curing and smoking tobacco, while the latter, in return, made them drunk with true Hollands—and then taught them the art of making bargains.

A brisk trade for furs was soon opened; the Dutch traders were scrupulously honest in their dealings, and purchased by weight, establishing it as an invariable table of avoirdupois, that the hand of a Dutchman weighed one pound, and his foot two pounds. It is true, the simple Indians were often puzzled by the great disproportion between bulk and weight, for let them place a bundle of furs, never so large, in one scale, and a Dutchman put his hand or foot in the other, the bundle was sure to kick the beam; never was a package of furs known to weigh more than two pounds in the market of Communipaw!

This is a singular fact—but I have it direct from my great-grandfather, who had risen to considerable importance in the colony, being promoted to the office of weigh-master, on account of the uncommon heaviness of his foot.

The Dutch possessions in this part of the globe began now to assume a very thriving appearance, and were comprehended under the general title of Nieuw Nederlandts, on account, as the sage Vander Donck observes, of their great resemblance to the Dutch Netherlands—which indeed was truly remarkable, excepting that the former were rugged and mountainous, and the latter level and marshy. About this time the tranquillity of the Dutch colonists was doomed to suffer a temporary interruption. In 1614, Captain Sir Samuel Argal, sailing under a commission from Dale, governor of Virginia, visited the Dutch settlements on Hudson River and demanded their submission to the English crown and Virginian dominion. To this arrogant demand, as they were in no condition to resist it, they submitted for the time, like discreet and reasonable men.

It does not appear that the valiant Argal molested the settlement of Communipaw; on the contrary, I am told that when his vessel first hove in sight, the worthy burghers were seized with such a panic, that they fell to smoking their pipes with astonishing vehemence; insomuch that they quickly raised a cloud, which, combining with the surrounding woods and marshes, completely enveloped and concealed their beloved village, and overhung the fair regions of Pavonia—so that the terrible Captain Argal passed on, totally unsuspicious that a sturdy little Dutch settlement lay snugly couched in the mud, under cover of all this pestilent vapor. In commemoration of this fortunate escape, the worthy inhabitants have continued to smoke, almost without intermission, unto this very day; which is said to be the cause of the remarkable fog which often hangs over Communipaw of a clear afternoon.

Upon departure of the enemy, our worthy ancestors took full six months to recover their wind and get over the consternation into which they had been thrown. They then called a council of safety to smoke over the state of the province. At this council presided one Oloffe Van Kortlandt, a personage who was held in great reverence among the sages of Communipaw for the variety and darkness of his knowledge. He had originally been one of a set of peripatetic philosophers who passed much of their time sunning themselves on the side of the great canal of Amsterdam in Holland; enjoying, like Diogenes, a free and unencumbered estate in sunshine. His name Kortlandt (Shortland or Lackland) was supposed, like that of the illustrious Jean Sansterre, to indicate that he had *no land;* but he insisted, on the contrary, that he had great landed estates somewhere in Terra Incognita; and he had come out to the new world to look after them. He was the first great land-speculator that we read of in these parts.

Like all land-speculators, he was much given to dreaming. Never did anything extraordinary happen at Communipaw but he declared that he had previously dreamt it, being one of those infallible prophets who predict events after they have come to pass. This supernatural gift was as highly valued among the burghers of Pavonia as among the enlightened nations of antiquity. The wise Ulysses was more indebted to his sleeping than his waking moments for his most subtle achievements, and seldom undertook any great exploit without first soundly sleeping upon it; and the same may be said of Oloffe Van Kortlandt, who was thence aptly denominated Oloffe the Dreamer.

As yet his dreams and speculations had turned to little personal profit; and he was as much a lack-land as ever. Still he carried a high head in the community; if his sugar-loaf hat was rather the worse for wear, he set it off with a taller cock's-tail; if his shirt was none of the cleanest, he puffed it out the more at the bosom; and if the tail of it peeped out of a hole in his breeches, it at least proved that it really had a tail and was not mere ruffle.

The worthy Van Kortlandt, in the council in question, urged the policy of emerging from the swamps of Communipaw and seeking some more eligible site for the seat of empire. Such, he said, was the advice of the good St. Nicholas, who had appeared to him in a dream the night before; and whom he had known by his broad hat, his long pipe, and the resemblance which he bore to the figure on the bow of the *Goede Vrouw*.

Many have thought this dream was a mere invention of Oloffe Van Kortlandt, who, it is said, had ever regarded Communipaw with an evil eye because he had arrived there after all the land had been shared out, and who was anxious to change the seat of empire to some new place, where he might be present at the distribution of "town lots." But we must not give heed to such insinuations, which are too apt to be advanced against those worthy gentlemen engaged in laying out towns, and in other land-speculations. For my own part, I am disposed to place the same implicit faith in the vision of Oloffe the Dreamer that was manifested by the honest burghers of Communipaw, who one and all agreed that an expedition should be forthwith fitted out to go on a voyage of discovery in quest of a new seat of empire.

This perilous enterprise was to be conducted by Oloffe himself; who chose as lieutenants or coadjutors Mynheers Abraham Hardenbroeck, Jacobus Van Zandt, and Winant Ten Broeck—three indubitably great men, but of whose history, although I have made diligent inquiry, I can learn but little previous to their leaving Holland. Nor need this occasion much surprise; for adventurers, like prophets, though they make great noise abroad, have seldom much celebrity in their own countries; but this much is certain, that the overflowings and offscourings of a country are invariably composed of the richest parts of the soil. And here I cannot help remarking how convenient it would be to many of our great men and great families of doubtful origin, could they have the privilege of the heroes of yore, who, whenever their origin was involved in obscurity, modestly announced themselves descended from a god—and who never visited a foreign country but what they told some cock-and-bull stories about their being kings and princes at home. This venal trespass on the truth, though it has been occasionally played off by some pseudo-marquis, baronet, and other illustrious foreigner, in our land of good-natured credulity, has been completely discountenanced in this skeptical, matter-of-fact age; and I even question whether any tender virgin, who was accidentally and unaccountably enriched with a bantling, would save her character at parlor firesides and evening tea-parties by ascribing the phenomenon to a swan, a shower of gold, or a river god.

Had I the benefit of mythology and classic fable above alluded to, I should have furnished the first of the trio with a pedigree equal to that of the proudest hero of antiquity. His name, Van Zandt, that is to say, *from the sand*, or, in common parlance, from the dirt, gave reason to suppose that, like Triptolemus, Themes, the Cyclops, and the Titans, he had sprung from Dame Terra, or the earth! This supposition is strongly corroborated by his size, for it is well known that all the progeny of mother earth were of a gigantic stature; and Van Zandt, we are told, was a tall, raw-boned man, above six feet high, with an astonishingly hard head. Nor is this origin of the illustrious Van Zandt a whit more improbable or repugnant to belief than what is related and universally admitted of certain of our greatest, or rather richest men; who, we are told with the utmost gravity, did originally spring from a dunghill!

Of the second of the trio but faint accounts have reached to this time, which mention that he was a sturdy, obstinate, worrying, bustling little man; and, from being usually equipped in an old pair of buckskins, was familiarly dubbed Harden Broeck: that is to say, Hard in the Breech, or, as it was generally rendered, Tough Breeches.

Ten Broeck completed this junto of adventurers. It is a singular but ludicrous fact—which, were I not scrupulous in recording the whole truth, I should almost be tempted to pass over in silence as incompatible with the gravity and dignity of history—that this worthy gentleman should likewise have been nicknamed from what in modern times is considered the most ignoble part of the dress. But in truth the small-clothes seems to have been a very dignified garment in the eyes of our venerated ancestors, in all probability from its covering that part of the body which has been pronounced "the seat of honor."

The name of Ten Broeck, or, as it was sometimes spelled, Tin Broeck, has been indifferently translated into Ten Breeches and Tin Breeches. Certain elegant and ingenious writers on the subject declare in favor of *Tin*, or rather *Thin* Breeches; whence they infer that the original bearer of it was a poor but merry rogue, whose galligaskins were none of the soundest, and who, peradventure, may have been the author of that truly philosophical stanza:—

> "Then why should we quarrel for riches,
> Or any such glittering toys;
> A light heart and *thin pair of breeches*,
> Will go through the world, my brave boys!"

The more accurate commentators, however, declare in favor of the other reading, and affirm that the worthy in question was a burly, bulbous man, who, in sheer ostentation of his venerable progenitors, was the first to introduce into the settlement the ancient Dutch fashion of ten pair of breeches.

Such was the trio of coadjutors chosen by Oloffe the Dreamer to accompany him in this voyage into unknown realms; as to the names of his crews, they have not been handed down by history.

Having, as I before observed, passed much of his life in the open air, among the peripatetic philosophers of Amsterdam, Oloffe had become familiar with the aspect of the heavens, and could as accurately determine when a storm was brewing or a squall rising, as a dutiful husband can foresee, from the brow of his spouse, when a tempest is gathering about his ears. Having pitched upon a time for his voyage when the skies appeared propitious, he exhorted all his crews to take a good night's rest, wind up their family affairs, and make their wills; precautions taken by our forefathers even in after-times when they became more adventurous, and voyaged to Haverstraw, or Kaatskill, or Groodt Esopus, or any other far country, beyond the great waters of the Tappaan Zee.

CHAPTER IV

How the Heroes of Communipaw Voyaged to Hell-Gate, and How They Were Received There

AND now the rosy blush of morn began to mantle in the east, and soon the rising sun, emerging from amidst golden and purple clouds, shed his blithesome rays on the tin weathercocks of Communipaw. It was that delicious season of the year, when nature, breaking from the chilling thraldom of old winter, like a blooming damsel from the tyranny of a sordid old father, threw herself, blushing with ten thousand charms, into the arms of youthful spring. Every tufted copse and blooming grove resounded with the notes of hymeneal love. The very insects, as they sipped the dew that gemmed the tender grass of the meadows, joined in the joyous epithalamium—the virgin bud timidly put forth its blushes, "the voice of the turtle was heard in the land," and the heart of man dissolved away in tenderness. Oh!

sweet Theocritus! had I thine oaten reed, wherewith thou erst did charm the gay Sicilian plains; or, oh! gentle Bion! thy pastoral pipe, wherein the happy swains of the Lesbian isle so much delighted, then might I attempt to sing, in soft Bucolic or negligent Idyllium, the rural beauties of the scene; but having nothing, save this jaded goosequill, wherewith to wing my flight, I must fain resign all poetic disportings of the fancy and pursue my narrative in humble prose; comforting myself with the hope, that, though it may not steal so sweetly upon the imagination of my reader, yet it may commend itself with virgin modesty to his better judgment, clothed in the chaste and simple garb of truth.

No sooner did the first rays of cheerful Phœbus dart into the windows of Communipaw, than the little settlement was all in motion. Forth issued from his castle the sage Van Kortlandt, and seizing a conch shell, blew a far-resounding blast, that soon summoned all his lusty followers. Then did they trudge resolutely down to the water-side, escorted by a multitude of relatives and friends, who all went down, as the common phrase expresses it, "to see them off." And this shows the antiquity of those long family processions, often seen in our city, composed of all ages, sizes, and sexes, laden with bundles and bandboxes, escorting some bevy of country cousins, about to depart for home in a market-boat.

The good Oloffe bestowed his forces in a squadron of three canoes, and hoisted his flag on board a little round Dutch boat, shaped not unlike a tub, which had formerly been the jolly-boat of the *Goede Vrouw*. And now, all being embarked, they bade farewell to the gazing throng upon the beach, who continued shouting after them, even when out of hearing, wishing them a happy voyage, advising them to take good care of themselves not to get drowned—with an abundance other of those sage and invaluable cautions, generally given by landsmen to such as go down to the sea in ships, and adventure upon the deep waters. In the meanwhile the voyagers cheerily urged their course across the crystal bosom of the bay, and soon left behind them the green shores of ancient Pavonia.

And first they touched at two small islands which lay nearly opposite Communipaw, and which are said to have been brought into existence about the time of the great irruption of the Hudson, when it broke through the Highlands and made its way to the ocean.* For in this tremendous uproar of the waters, we are told that many huge fragments of rock and land were rent from the mountains and swept down by this runaway river, for sixty or seventy miles; where some of them ran aground on the shoals just opposite Communipaw, and formed the identical islands in question, while others drifted out to sea, and were never heard of more! A sufficient proof of the fact is, that the rock which forms the bases of these islands is exactly similar to that of the Highlands, and, moreover, one of our philosophers, who has diligently compared the agreement of their respective surfaces, has even gone so far as to assure me, in confidence, that Gibbet Island was originally nothing more nor less than a wart on Anthony's nose.†

Leaving these wonderful little isles, they next coasted by Governor's Island, since terrible from its frowning fortress and grinning batteries. They would by no means, however, land upon this island, since they doubted much it might be the abode of demons and spirits, which in those days did greatly abound throughout this savage and pagan country.

Just at this time a shoal of jolly porpoises came rolling and tumbling by, turning up their sleek sides to the sun, and spouting up the briny element in sparkling showers. No sooner did the sage Oloffe mark this, than he was greatly rejoiced. "This," exclaimed he, "if I mistake not, augurs well: the porpoise is a fat, well-conditioned fish—a burgomaster among fishes—his looks betoken ease, plenty, and prosperity; I greatly admire this round fat fish, and doubt not but this is a happy omen of the success of our undertaking." So saying, he directed his squadron to steer in the track of these alderman fishes.

*It is a matter long since established by certain of our philosophers—that is to say, having been often advanced, and never contradicted, it has grown to be pretty nigh equal to a settled fact—that the Hudson was originally a lake dammed up by the mountains of the Highlands. In process of time, however, becoming very mighty and obstreperous, and the mountain waxing pursy, dropsical, and weak in the back, by reason of their extreme old age, it suddenly rose upon them, and after a violent struggle effected its escape. This is said to have come to pass in very remote time, probably before that rivers had lost the art of running uphill. The foregoing is a theory in which I do not pretend to be skilled, notwithstanding that I do fully give it my belief.

† A promontory in the Highlands.

Turning, therefore, directly to the left, they swept up the strait vulgarly called the East River. And here the rapid tide which courses through this strait, seizing on the gallant tub in which Commodore Van Kortlandt had embarked, hurried it forward with a velocity unparalleled in a Dutch boat, navigated by Dutchmen; insomuch that the good commodore, who had all his life long been accustomed only to the drowsy navigation of canals, was more than ever convinced that they were in the hands of some supernatural power, and that the jolly porpoises were towing them to some fair haven that was to fulfil all their wishes and expectations.

Thus borne away by the resistless current, they doubled that boisterous point of land since called Corlear's Hook,* and leaving to the right the rich winding cove of the Wallabout, they drifted into a magnificent expanse of water, surrounded by pleasant shores, whose verdure was exceedingly refreshing to the eye. While the voyagers were looking around them, on what they conceived to be a serene and sunny lake, they beheld at a distance a crew of painted savages, busily employed in fishing, who seemed more like the genii of this romantic region—their slender canoe lightly balanced like a feather on the undulating surface of the bay.

At sight of these the hearts of the heroes of Communipaw were not a little troubled. But as good-fortune would have it, at the bow of the commodore's boat was stationed a very valiant man, named Hendrick Kip (which, being interpreted, means *chicken*, a name given him in token of his courage). No sooner did he behold these varlet heathens than he trembled with excessive valor, and although a good half-mile distant, he seized a musketoon that lay at hand, and turning away his head, fired it most intrepidly in the face of the blessed sun. The blundering weapon recoiled and gave the valiant Kip an ignominious kick, which laid him prostrate with uplifted heels in the bottom of the boat. But such was the effect of this tremendous fire, that the wild men of the woods, struck with consternation, seized hastily upon their paddles, and shot away into one of the deep inlets of the Long Island shore.

This signal victory gave new spirits to the voyagers; and in

* Properly spelt *hoeck* (i. e. a point of land).

honor of the achievement they gave the name of the valiant Kip to the surrounding bay, and it has continued to be called Kip's Bay from that time to the present. The heart of the good Van Kortlandt—who, having no land of his own, was a great admirer of other people's—expanded to the full size of a pepper-corn at the sumptuous prospect of rich unsettled country around him, and falling into a delicious revery, he straightway began to riot in the possession of vast meadows of salt marsh and interminable patches of cabbages. From this delectable vision he was all at once awakened by the sudden turning of the tide, which would soon have hurried him from this land of promise, had not the discreet navigator given signal to steer for shore; where they accordingly landed hard by the rocky heights of Bellevue—that happy retreat, where our jolly aldermen eat for the good of the city, and fatten the turtle that are sacrificed on civic solemnities.

Here, seated on the greensward, by the side of a small stream that ran sparkling among the grass, they refreshed themselves after the toils of the seas, by feasting lustily on the ample stores which they had provided for this perilous voyage. Thus having well fortified their deliberative powers, they fell into an earnest consultation, what was farther to be done. This was the first council-dinner ever eaten at Bellevue by Christian burghers; and here, as tradition relates, did originate the great family feud between the Hardenbroecks and the Tenbroecks, which afterwards had a singular influence on the building of the city. The sturdy Hardenbroeck, whose eyes had been wondrously delighted with the salt marshes which spread their reeking bosoms along the coast, at the bottom of Kip's Bay, counselled by all means to return thither, and found the intended city. This was strenuously opposed by the unbending Ten Broeck, and many testy arguments passed between them. The particulars of this controversy have not reached us, which is ever to be lamented; this much is certain, that the sage Oloffe put an end to the dispute by determining to explore still farther in the route which the mysterious porpoises had so clearly pointed out; whereupon the sturdy Tough Breeches abandoned the expedition, took possession of a neighboring hill, and in a fit of great wrath peopled all that tract of country, which has continued to be inhabited by the Hardenbroecks unto this very day.

By this time the jolly Phœbus, like some wanton urchin sporting on the side of a green hill, began to roll down the declivity of the heavens; and now, the tide having once more turned in their favor, the Pavonians again committed themselves to its discretion, and coasting along the western shores, were borne towards the straits of Blackwell's Island.

And here the capricious wanderings of the current occasioned not a little marvel and perplexity to these illustrious mariners. Now would they be caught by the wanton eddies, and, sweeping round a jutting point, would wind deep into some romantic little cove, that indented the fair island of Manna hatta; now were they hurried narrowly by the very bases of impending rocks, mantled with the flaunting grape-vine, and crowned with groves which threw a broad shade on the waves beneath; and anon they were borne away into the mid-channel and wafted along with a rapidity that very much discomposed the sage Van Kortlandt, who, as he saw the land swiftly receding on either side, began exceedingly to doubt that *terra firma* was giving them the slip.

Wherever the voyagers turned their eyes, a new creation seemed to bloom around. No signs of human thrift appeared to check the delicious wildness of nature, who here revelled in all her luxuriant variety. Those hills, now bristled, like the fretful porcupine, with rows of poplars (vain upstart plants! minions of wealth and fashion!), were then adorned with the vigorous natives of the soil: the lordly oak, the generous chestnut, the graceful elm—while here and there the tulip-tree reared its majestic head, the giant of the forest. Where now are seen the gay retreats of luxury—villas half buried in twilight bowers, whence the amorous flute oft breathes the sighings of some city swain—there the fish-hawk built his solitary nest on some dry tree that overlooked his watery domain. The timid deer fed undisturbed along those shores now hallowed by the lovers' moonlight walk, and printed by the slender foot of beauty; and a savage solitude extended over those happy regions, where now are reared the stately towers of the Joneses, the Schermerhornes, and the Rhinelanders.

Thus gliding in silent wonder through these new and unknown scenes, the gallant squadron of Pavonia swept by the foot of a promontory, which strutted forth boldly into the waves, and seemed to frown upon them as they brawled against its base. This is the bluff well known to modern mariners by the name of Gracie's Point, from the fair castle which, like an elephant, it carries upon its back. And here broke upon their view a wild and varied prospect, where land and water were beauteously intermingled, as though they had combined to heighten and set off each other's charms. To the right lay the sedgy point of Blackwell's Island, drest in the fresh garniture of living green—beyond it stretched the pleasant coast of Sundswick, and the small harbor well known by the name of Hallet's Cove—a place infamous in latter days, by reason of its being the haunt of pirates who infest these seas, robbing orchards and watermelon patches, and insulting gentlemen navigators, when voyaging in their pleasure-boats. To the left a deep bay, or rather creek, gracefully receded between shores fringed with forests, and forming a kind of vista, through which were beheld the sylvan regions of Haerlem, Morrisania, and East Chester. Here the eye reposed with delight on a richly wooded country, diversified by tufted knolls, shadowy intervals, and waving lines of upland, swelling above each other, while over the whole the purple mists of spring diffused a hue of soft voluptuousness.

Just before them the grand course of the stream, making a sudden bend, wound among embowered promontories and shores of emerald verdure, that seemed to melt into the wave. A character of gentleness and mild fertility prevailed around. The sun had just descended, and the thin haze of twilight, like a transparent veil drawn over the bosom of virgin beauty, heightened the charms which it half concealed.

Ah! witching scenes of foul delusion. Ah! hapless voyagers, gazing with simple wonder on these Circean shores! Such, alas! are they, poor easy souls, who listen to the seductions of a wicked world—treacherous are its smiles! fatal its caresses. He who yields to its enticements launches upon a whelming tide, and trusts his feeble bark among the dimpling eddies of a whirlpool! And thus it fared with the worthies of Pavonia, who, little mistrusting the guileful scene before them, drifted quietly on, until they were aroused by an uncommon tossing and agitation of their vessels. For now the late dimpling current began to brawl around them, and the waves to boil and foam with horrific fury. Awakened as if from a dream, the astonished Oloffe bawled aloud to put about, but his words were lost amid the roaring of the waters. And now ensued a scene of direful consternation. At one time they were borne with dreadful velocity among tumultuous breakers; at another, hurried down boisterous rapids. Now they were nearly dashed upon the Hen and Chickens (infamous rocks!—more voracious than Scylla and her whelps); and anon they seemed sinking into yawning gulfs, that threatened to entomb them beneath the waves. All the elements combined to produce a hideous confusion. The waters raged, the winds howled; and as they were hurried along, several of the astonished mariners beheld the rocks and trees of the neighboring shores driving through the air!

At length the mighty tub of Commodore Van Kortlandt was drawn into the vortex of that tremendous whirlpool called the Pot, where it was whirled about in giddy mazes, until the senses of the good commander and his crew were overpowered by the horror of the scene, and the strangeness of the revolution.

How the gallant squadron of Pavonia was snatched from the jaws of this modern Charybdis, has never been truly made known, for so many survived to tell the tale, and, what is still more wonderful, told it in so many different ways, that there has ever prevailed a great variety of opinions on the subject.

As to the commodore and his crew, when they came to their senses, they found themselves stranded on the Long Island shore. The worthy commodore, indeed, used to relate many and wonderful stories of his adventures in this time of peril: how that he saw spectres flying in the air, and heard the yelling of hobgoblins, and put his hand into the pot when they were whirled round, and found the water scalding hot, and beheld several uncouth-looking beings seated on rocks and skimming it with huge ladles; but particularly he declared with great exultation, that he saw the losel porpoises, which had betrayed them into this peril, some broiling on the Gridiron, and others hissing on the Frying-pan!

These, however, were considered by many as mere fantasies of the commodore, while he lay in a trance; especially as he was known to be given to dreaming; and the truth of them has never been clearly ascertained. It is certain, however, that to the accounts of Oloffe and his followers may be traced the various traditions handed down of this marvellous strait: as how the devil has been seen there, sitting astride of the Hog's Back and playing on the fiddle—how he broils fish there before a storm; and many other stories in which we must be cautious of putting too much faith. In consequence of all these terrific circumstances, the Pavonian commander gave this pass the name of *Helle-gat*, or, as it has been interpreted, *Hell-Gate*; * which it continues to bear at the present day.

CHAPTER V

How the Heroes of Communipaw Returned Somewhat Wiser Than They Went—and How the Sage Oloffe Dreamed a Dream—and the Dream That He Dreamed

THE darkness of night had closed upon this disastrous day, and a doleful night was it to the shipwrecked Pavonians, whose ears were incessantly assailed with the raging of the elements, and the howling of the hobgoblins that infested this perfidious strait. But when the morning dawned, the horrors of the preceding evening had passed away; rapids, breakers, and whirlpools had disappeared; the stream again ran smooth and dimpling, and having changed its tide, rolled gently back, towards the quarter where lay their much-regretted home.

The woe-begone heroes of Communipaw eyed each other with rueful countenances; their squadron had been totally dis-

* This is a narrow strait in the Sound, at the distance of six miles above New York. It is dangerous to shipping, unless under the care of skilful pilots, by reason of numerous rocks, shelves, and whirlpools. These have received sundry appellations, such as the Gridiron, Frying-pan, Hog's Back, Pot, &c., and are very violent and turbulent at certain times of tide. Certain mealy-mouthed men, of squeamish consciences, who are loth to give the Devil his due, have softened the above characteristic name into *Hurl*-gate, forsooth! Let those take care how they venture into the Gate, or they may be hurled into the Pot before they are aware of it. The name of this strait, as given by our author, is supported by the map in Vander Donck's history, published in 1656—by Ogilvie's History of America, 1671—as also by a journal still extant, written in the 16th century, and to be found in Hazard's State Papers. And an old MS. written in French, speaking of various alterations in names about this city, observes, "*De Helle-gat*, trou d'Enfer, ils ont fait *Hell-gate*, Porte d'Enfer."

persed by the late disaster. Some were cast upon the western shore, where, headed by one Ruleff Hopper, they took possession of all the country lying about the six-mile stone; which is held by the Hoppers at this present writing.

The Waldrons were driven by stress of weather to a distant coast, where, having with them a jug of genuine Hollands, they were enabled to conciliate the savages, setting up a kind of tavern; whence, it is said, did spring the fair town of Haerlem, in which their descendants have ever since continued to be reputable publicans. As to the Suydams, they were thrown upon the Long Island coast, and may still be found in those parts. But the most singular luck attended the great Ten Broeck, who, falling overboard, was miraculously preserved from sinking by the multitude of his nether garments. Thus buoyed up, he floated on the waves like a merman, or like an angler's dobber, until he landed safely on a rock, where he was found the next morning, busily drying his many breeches in the sunshine.

I forbear to treat of the long consultation of Oloffe with his remaining followers, in which they determined that it would never do to found a city in so diabolical a neighborhood. Suffice it in simple brevity to say, that they once more committed themselves, with fear and trembling, to the briny elements, and steered their course back again through the scenes of their yesterday's voyage, determined no longer to roam in search of distant sites, but to settle themselves down in the marshy regions of Pavonia.

Scarce, however, had they gained a distant view of Communipaw, when they were encountered by an obstinate eddy, which opposed their homeward voyage. Weary and dispirited as they were, they yet tugged a feeble oar against the stream; until, as if to settle the strife, half a score of potent billows rolled the tub of Commodore Van Kortlandt high and dry on the long point of an island which divided the bosom of the bay.

Some pretend that these billows were sent by old Neptune to strand the expedition on a spot whereon was to be founded his stronghold in this western world; others, more pious, attribute everything to the guardianship of the good St. Nicholas; and after-events will be found to corroborate this opinion. Oloffe Van Kortlandt was a devout trencherman. Every repast was a kind of religious rite with him; and his first thought on finding him once more on dry ground, was, how he should contrive to celebrate his wonderful escape from Hell-gate and all its horrors by a solemn banquet. The stores which had been provided for the voyage by the good housewives of Communipaw were nearly exhausted, but, in casting his eyes about, the commodore beheld that the shore abounded with oysters. A great store of these was instantly collected; a fire was made at the foot of a tree; all hands fell to roasting and broiling and stewing and frying, and a sumptuous repast was soon set forth. This is thought to be the origin of those civic feasts with which, to the present day, all our public affairs are celebrated, and in which the oyster is ever sure to play an important part.

On the present occasion, the worthy Van Kortlandt was observed to be particularly zealous in his devotions to the trencher; for having the cares of the expedition especially committed to his care, he deemed it incumbent on him to eat profoundly for the public good. In proportion as he filled himself to the very brim with the dainty viands before him, did the heart of this excellent burgher rise up towards his throat, until he seemed crammed and almost choked with good eating and good-nature. And at such times it is, when a man's heart is in his throat, that he may more truly be said to speak from it, and his speeches abound with kindness and good fellowship. Thus having swallowed the last possible morsel, and washed it down with a fervent potation, Oloffe felt his heart yearning, and his whole frame in a manner dilating with unbounded benevolence. Everything around him seemed excellent and delightful; and laying his hands on each side of his capacious periphery, and rolling his half-closed eyes around on the beautiful diversity of land and water before him, he exclaimed, in a fat half-smothered voice, "What a charming prospect!" The words died away in his throat—he seemed to ponder on the fair scene for a moment—his eyelids heavily closed over their orbs—his head drooped upon his bosom—he slowly sank upon the green turf, and a deep sleep stole gradually over him.

And the sage Oloffe dreamed a dream—and lo, the good St. Nicholas came riding over the tops of the trees, in that self-same wagon wherein he brings his yearly presents to children, and he descended hard by where the heroes of Communipaw had made their late repast. And he lit his pipe by the fire, and sat himself down and smoked; and as he smoked, the smoke from his pipe ascended into the air and spread like a cloud overhead. And Oloffe bethought him, and he hastened and climbed up to the top of one of the tallest trees, and saw that the smoke spread over a great extent of country; and as he considered it more attentively, he fancied that the great volume of smoke assumed a variety of marvellous forms, where in dim obscurity he saw shadowed out palaces and domes and lofty spires, all of which lasted but a moment, and then faded away, until the whole rolled off, and nothing but the green woods were left. And when St. Nicholas had smoked his pipe, he twisted it in his hatband, and laying his finger beside his nose, gave the astonished Van Kortlandt a very significant look; then, mounting his wagon, he returned over the tree-tops and disappeared.

And Van Kortlandt awoke from his sleep greatly instructed; and he aroused his companions and related to them his dream, and interpreted it, that it was the will of St. Nicholas that they should settle down and build the city here; and that the smoke of the pipe was a type how vast would be the extent of the city, inasmuch as the volumes of its smoke would spread over a wide extent of country. And they all with one voice assented to this interpretation, excepting Mynheer Ten Broeck, who declared the meaning to be that it would be a city wherein a little fire would occasion a great smoke, or, in other words, a very vaporing little city—both which interpretations have strangely come to pass!

The great object of their perilous expedition, therefore, being thus happily accomplished, the voyagers returned merrily to Communipaw—where they were received with great rejoicings. And here, calling a general meeting of all the wise men and the dignitaries of Pavonia, they related the whole history of their voyage, and of the dream of Oloffe Van Kortlandt. And the people lifted up their voices and blessed the good St. Nicholas; and from that time forth the sage Van Kortlandt was held in more honor than ever, for his great talent at dreaming, and was pronounced a most useful citizen and a right good man—when he was asleep.

CHAPTER VI

Containing an Attempt at Etymology—and of the Founding of the Great City of New Amsterdam

THE original name of the island, whereon the squadron of Communipaw was thus propitiously thrown, is a matter of some dispute, and has already undergone considerable vitiation—a melancholy proof of the instability of all sublunary things, and the vanity of all our hopes of lasting fame; for who can expect his name will live to posterity, when even the names of mighty islands are thus soon lost in contradiction and uncertainty!

The name most current at the present day, and which is likewise countenanced by the great historian Vander Donck, is MANHATTAN; which is said to have originated in a custom among the squaws, in the early settlement, of wearing men's hats, as is still done among many tribes. "Hence," as we are told by an old governor who was somewhat of a wag, and flourished almost a century since, and had paid a visit to the wits of Philadelphia—"hence arose the appellation of man-hat-on, first given to the Indians, and afterwards to the island"—a stupid joke! but well enough for a governor.

Among the more venerable sources of information on this subject is that valuable history of the American possessions, written by Master Richard Blome, in 1687, wherein it is called Manhadaes and Manahanent; nor must I forget the excellent little book, full of precious matter, of that authentic historian John Josselyn, Gent., who expressly calls it Manadaes.

Another etymology, still more ancient, and sanctioned by the countenance of our ever-to-be-lamented Dutch ancestors, is that found in certain letters still extant,* which passed between the early governors and their neighboring powers, wherein it is called indifferently Monhattoes, Munhatos, and Manhattoes, which are evidently unimportant variations of the same name; for our wise forefathers set little store by those niceties either in orthography or orthoepy, which form the sole study and ambition of many learned men and women of this hypercritical age. This last name is said to be derived from the great Indian spirit

* *Vide* Hazard's Col. Stat. Pap.

Manetho, who was supposed to make this island his favorite abode, on account of its uncommon delights. For the Indian traditions affirm that the bay was once a translucid lake, filled with silver and golden fish, in the midst of which lay this beautiful island, covered with every variety of fruits and flowers; but that the sudden irruption of the Hudson laid waste these blissful scenes, and Manetho took his flight beyond the great waters of Ontario.

These, however, are very fabulous legends, to which very cautious credence must be given; and though I am willing to admit the last-quoted orthography of the name as very fit for prose, yet is there another which I peculiarly delight in, as at once poetical, melodious, and significant, and which we have on the authority of master Juet; who, in his account of the voyage of the great Hudson, calls this MANNA-HATA, that is to say, the island of manna, or, in other words, a land flowing with milk and honey.

Still, my deference to the learned obliges me to notice the opinion of the worthy Dominie Heckwelder, which ascribes the name to a great drunken bout held on the island by the Dutch discoverers, whereat they made certain of the natives most ecstatically drunk for the first time in their lives; who, being delighted with their jovial entertainment, gave the place the name of Mannahattanink, that is to say, The Island of Jolly Topers: a name which it continues to merit to the present day.*

CHAPTER VII

How the People of Pavonia Migrated from Communipaw to the Island of Manna-hata—and How Oloffe the Dreamer Proved Himself a Great Land-speculator

IT having been solemnly resolved that the seat of empire should be removed from the green shores of Pavonia to the pleasant island of Manna-hata, everybody was anxious to embark under the standard of Oloffe the Dreamer, and to be among the first sharers of the promised land. A day was appointed for the grand migra-

* MSS. of the Rev. John Heckwelder, in the archives of the New York Historical Society.

tion, and on that day little Communipaw was in a buzz and a bustle like a hive in swarming-time. Houses were turned inside out and stripped of the venerable furniture which had come from Holland; all the community, great and small, black and white, man, woman, and child, was in commotion, forming lines from the houses to the water-side, like lines of ants from an ant-hill; everybody laden with some article of household furniture; while busy housewives plied backwards and forwards along the lines, helping everything forward by the nimbleness of their tongues.

By degrees a fleet of boats and canoes were piled up with all kinds of household articles: ponderous tables; chests of drawers resplendent with brass ornaments; quaint corner-cupboards; beds and bedsteads; with any quantity of pots, kettles, frying-pans, and Dutch ovens. In each boat embarked a whole family, from the robustious burgher down to the cats and dogs and little Negroes. In this way they set off across the mouth of the Hudson, under the guidance of Oloffe the Dreamer, who hoisted his standard on the leading boat.

This memorable migration took place on the first of May, and was long cited in tradition as the *grand moving*. The anniversary of it was piously observed among the "sons of the pilgrims of Communipaw," by turning their houses topsy-turvy and carrying all the furniture through the streets, in emblem of the swarming of the parent-hive; and this is the real origin of the universal agitation and "moving" by which this most restless of cities is literally turned out of doors on every May-day.

As the little squadron from Communipaw drew near to the shores of Manna-hata, a sachem, at the head of a band of warriors, appeared to oppose their landing. Some of the most zealous of the pilgrims were for chastising this insolence with powder and ball, according to the approved mode of discoverers; but the sage Oloffe gave them the significant sign of St. Nicholas, laying his finger beside his nose and winking hard with one eye; whereupon his followers perceived that there was something sagacious in the wind. He now addressed the Indians in the blandest terms; and made such tempting display of beads, hawks'-bells, and red blankets, that he was soon permitted to land, and a great land-speculation ensued. And here let me give the true story of the original purchase of the site of this renowned city, about which so much has been said and written. Some affirm that the first cost was but sixty guilders. The learned Dominie Heckwelder records a tradition * that the Dutch discoverers bargained for only so much land as the hide of a bullock would cover; but that they cut the hide in strips no thicker than a child's finger, so as to take in a large portion of land, and to take in the Indians into the bargain. This, however, is an old fable which the worthy Dominie may have borrowed from antiquity. The true version is, that Oloffe Van Kortlandt bargained for just so much land as a man could cover with his nether garments. The terms being concluded, he produced his friend Mynheer Ten Broeck as the man whose breeches were to be used in measurement. The simple savages, whose ideas of a man's nether garments had never expanded beyond the dimensions of a breech-clout, stared with astonishment and dismay as they beheld this bulbous-bottomed burgher peeled like an onion, and breeches after breeches spread forth over the land until they covered the actual site of this venerable city.

This is the true history of the adroit bargain by which the island of Manhattan was bought for sixty guilders; and in corrboration of it I will add, that Mynheer Ten Breeches, for his services on this memorable occasion, was elevated to the office of land-measurer; which he ever afterwards exercised in the colony.

CHAPTER VIII

Of the Founding and Naming of the New City; of the City Arms; and of the Direful Feud Between Ten Breeches and Tough Breeches

THE land being thus fairly purchased of the Indians, a circumstance very unusual in the history of colonization, and strongly illustrative of the honesty of our Dutch progenitors, a stockade fort and trading-house were forthwith erected on an eminence in front of the place where the good St. Nicholas had appeared in a vision to Oloffe the Dreamer, and which, as has already been observed, was the identical place at present known as the Bowling Green.

* MSS. of the Rev. John Heckwelder; New York Historical Society.

Around this fort a progeny of little Dutch-built houses, with tiled roofs and weathercocks, soon sprang up, nestling themselves under its walls for protection, as a brood of half-fledged chickens nestle under the wings of the mother hen. The whole was surrounded by an enclosure of strong palisadoes, to guard against any sudden irruption of the savages. Outside of these extended the cornfields and cabbage-gardens of the community, with here and there an attempt at a tobacco-plantation; all covering those tracts of country at present called Broadway, Wall Street, William Street, and Pearl Street.

I must not omit to mention, that, in portioning out the land, a goodly "bowerie," or farm, was allotted to the sage Oloffe in consideration of the service he had rendered to the public by his talent at dreaming; and the site of his "bowerie" is known by the name of Kortlandt (or Cortlandt) Street to the present day.

And now the infant settlement having advanced in age and stature, it was thought high time it should receive an honest Christian name. Hitherto it had gone by the original Indian name Manna-hata, or, as some will have it, "The Manhattoes"; but this was now decried as savage and heathenish, and as tending to keep up the memory of the pagan brood that originally possessed it. Many were the consultations held upon the subject, without coming to a conclusion, for though everybody condemned the old name, nobody could invent a new one. At length, when the council was almost in despair, a burgher, remarkable for the size and squareness of his head, proposed that they should call it New Amsterdam. The proposition took everybody by surprise; it was so striking, so apposite, so ingenious. The name was adopted by acclamation, and New Amsterdam the metropolis was thenceforth called. Still, however, the early authors of the province continued to call it by the general appellation of "The Manhattoes," and the poets fondly clung to the euphonious name of Manna-hata; but those are a kind of folk whose tastes and notions should go for nothing in matters of this kind.

Having thus provided the embryo city with a name, the next was to give it an armorial bearing or device, as some cities have a rampant lion, others a soaring eagle—emblematical, no doubt, of the valiant and high-flying qualities of the inhabitants; so, after mature deliberation, a sleek beaver was emblazoned on the city standard, as indicative of the amphibious origin, and patient, persevering habits of the New Amsterdammers.

The thriving state of the settlement and the rapid increase of houses soon made it necessary to arrange some plan upon which the city should be built; but at the very first consultation held on the subject, a violent discussion arose; and I mention it with much sorrowing as being the first altercation on record in the councils of New Amsterdam. It was, in fact, a breaking forth of the grudge and heart-burning that had existed between those two eminent burghers, Mynheers Tenbroeck and Hardenbroeck, ever since their unhappy dispute on the coast of Bellevue. The great Hardenbroeck had waxed very wealthy and powerful, from his domains, which embraced the whole chain of Apulean mountains that stretched along the gulf of Kip's Bay, and from part of which his descendants have been expelled in latter ages by the powerful clans of the Joneses and the Schermerhornes.

An ingenious plan for the city was offered by Mynheer Hardenbroeck, who proposed that it should be cut up and intersected by canals, after the manner of the most admired cities in Holland. To this Mynheer Tenbroeck was diametrically opposed, suggesting, in place thereof, that they should run out docks and wharves, by means of piles driven into the bottom of the river, on which the town should be built. "By these means," said he triumphantly, "shall we rescue a considerable space of territory from these immense rivers, and build a city that shall rival Amsterdam, Venice, or any amphibious city in Europe." To this proposition, Hardenbroeck (or Tough Breeches) replied, with a look of as much scorn as he could possibly assume. He cast the utmost censure upon the plan of his antagonist, as being preposterous and against the very order of things, as he would leave to every true Hollander. "For what," said he, "is a town without canals?—it is like a body without veins and arteries, and must perish for want of a free circulation of the vital fluid." Ten Breeches, on the contrary, retorted with a sarcasm upon his antagonist, who was somewhat of an arid, dry-boned habit: he remarked, that as to the circulation of the blood being necessary to existence, Mynheer Tough Breeches was a living contradiction to his own assertion: for everybody knew there had not a drop of blood circulated through his wind-dried carcase for good ten years, and yet there was not a greater busybody in the whole colony. Personalities have seldom much effect in making converts in argument; nor have I ever seen a man convinced of error by being convicted of deformity. At least, such was not the case at present. If Ten Breeches was very happy in sarcasm, Tough Breeches, who was a sturdy little man, and never gave up the last word, rejoined with increasing spirit; Ten Breeches had the advantage of the greatest volubility, but Tough Breeches had that invaluable coat of mail in argument, called obstinancy. Ten Breeches had, therefore, the most mettle, but Tough Breeches the best bottom; so that, though Ten Breeches made a dreadful clattering about his ears, and battered and belabored him with hard words and sound arguments, yet Tough Breeches hung on most resolutely to the last. They parted, therefore, as is usual in all arguments where both parties are in the right, without coming to any conclusion; but they hated each other most heartily forever after, and a similar breach with that between the houses of Capulet and Montague did ensue between the families of Ten Breeches and Tough Breeches.

I would not fatigue my reader with these dull matters of fact, but that my duty as a faithful historian requires that I should be particular; and in truth, as I am now treating of the critical period when our city, like a young twig, first received the twists and turns which have since contributed to give it its present picturesque irregularity, I cannot be too minute in detailing their first causes.

After the unhappy altercation I have just mentioned, I do not find that anything farther was said on the subject worthy of being recorded. The council, consisting of the largest and oldest heads in the community, met regularly once a week, to ponder on this momentous subject; but, either they were deterred by the war of words they had witnessed, or they were naturally averse to the exercise of the tongue, and the consequent exercise of the brains—certain it is, the most profound silence was maintained—the question as usual lay on the table—the members quietly smoked their pipes, making but few laws, without ever enforcing any—and in the mean time the affairs of the settlement went on—as it pleased God.

As most of the council were but little skilled in the mystery of combining pot-hooks and hangers, they determined most judiciously not to puzzle either themselves or posterity with voluminous records. The secretary, however, kept the minutes of the council, with tolerable precision, in a large vellum folio, fastened with massy brass clasps; the journal of each meeting consisted but of two lines, stating in Dutch, that "the council sat this day, and smoked twelve pipes, on the affairs of the colony." By which it appears that the first settlers did not regulate their time by hours, but pipes, in the same manner as they measure distances in Holland at this very time: an admirably exact measurement, as a pipe in the mouth of a true-born Dutchman is never liable to those accidents and irregularities that are continually putting our clocks out of order.

In this manner did the profound council of New Amsterdam smoke, and doze, and ponder, from week to week, month to month, and year to year, in what manner they should construct their infant settlement; meanwhile, the town took care of itself, and like a sturdy brat which is suffered to run about wild, unshackled by clouts and bandages, and other abominations by which your notable nurses and sage old women cripple and disfigure the children of men, increased so rapidly in strength and magnitude, that before the honest burgomasters had determined upon a plan, it was too late to put it in execution—whereupon they wisely abandoned the subject altogether.

CHAPTER IX

How the City of New Amsterdam Waxed Great Under the Protection of St. Nicholas and the Absence of Laws and Statutes—How Oloffe the Dreamer Began to Dream of an Extension of Empire, and of the Effect of His Dreams

THERE is something exceedingly delusive in thus looking back through the long vista of departed years, and catching a glimpse of the fairy realms of antiquity. Like a landscape melting into distance, they receive a thousand charms from their very obscurity, and the fancy delights to fill up their outlines with graces and excellences of its own creation. Thus loom on my imagination those happier days of our city, when as yet New Amsterdam was a mere pastoral town, shrouded in groves of sycamores and willows, and surrounded by trackless forests and wide-spreading waters, that seemed to shut out all the cares and vanities of a wicked world.

In those days did this embryo city present the rare and noble spectacle of a community governed without laws; and thus being left to its own course, and the fostering care of Providence, increased as rapidly as though it had been burdened with a dozen panniers full of those sage laws usually heaped on the backs of young cities—in order to make them grow. And in this particular I greatly admire the wisdom and sound knowledge of human nature, displayed by the sage Oloffe the Dreamer and his fellow-legislators. For my part, I have not so bad an opinion of mankind as many of my brother philosophers. I do not think poor human nature so sorry a piece of workmanship as they would make it out to be; and as far as I have observed, I am fully satisfied that man, if left to himself, would about as readily go right as wrong. It is only this eternally sounding in his ears that it is his duty to go right, which makes him go the very reverse. The noble independence of his nature revolts at this intolerable tyranny of law, and the perpetual interference of officious morality, which are ever besetting his path with finger-posts and directions to "keep to the right, as the law directs"; and like a spirited urchin, he turns directly contrary, and gallops through mud and mire, over hedges and ditches, merely to show that he is a lad of spirit, and out of his leading-strings. And these opinions are amply substantiated by what I have above said of our worthy ancestors; who never being be-preached and be-lectured, and guided and governed by statutes and laws and by-laws, as are their more enlightened descendants, did one and all demean themselves honestly and peaceably, out of pure ignorance, or, in other words, because they knew no better.

Nor must I omit to record one of the earliest measures of this infant settlement, inasmuch as it shows the piety of our forefathers, and that, like good Christians, they were always ready to serve God, after they had first served themselves. Thus, having quietly settled themselves down, and provided for their own comfort, they bethought themselves of testifying their gratitude to the great and good St. Nicholas, for his protecting care, in guiding them to this delectable abode. To this end they built a fair and goodly chapel within the fort, which they consecrated to his name; whereupon he immediately took the town of New Amsterdam under his peculiar patronage, and he has ever since been, and I devoutly hope will ever be, the tutelar saint of this excellent city.

At this early period was instituted that pious ceremony, still religiously observed in all our ancient families of the right breed, of hanging up a stocking in the chimney on St. Nicholas eve; which stocking is always found in the morning miraculously filled; for the good St. Nicholas has ever been a great giver of gifts, particularly to children.

I am moreover told that there is a little legendary book, somewhere extant, written in Low Dutch, which says, that the image of this renowned saint, which whilom graced the bowsprit of the *Goede Vrouw*, was elevated in front of this chapel, in the centre of what in modern days is called the Bowling Green —on the very spot, in fact, where he appeared in vision to Oloffe the Dreamer. And the legend further treats of divers miracles wrought by the mighty pipe which the saint held in his mouth, a whiff of which was a sovereign cure for indigestion—an invaluable relic in this colony of brave trencher-men. As, however, in spite of the most diligent search, I cannot lay my hands upon this little book, I must confess that I entertain considerable doubt on the subject.

Thus benignly fostered by the good St. Nicholas, the infant city thrived apace. Hordes of painted savages, it is true, still lurked about the unsettled parts of the island. The hunter still pitched his bower of skins and bark beside the rills that ran through the cool and shady glens, while here and there might be seen, on some sunny knoll, a group of Indian wigwams, whose smoke arose above the neighboring trees, and floated in the transparent atmosphere. A mutual good-will, however, existed between these wandering beings and the burghers of New Amsterdam. Our benevolent forefathers endeavored as much as possible to ameliorate their situation, by giving them gin, rum, and glass beads, in exchange for their peltries; for it seems the kind-hearted Dutchmen had conceived a great friendship for their savage neighbors, on account of their being pleasant men to trade with, and little skilled in the art of making a bargain.

Now and then a crew of these half-human sons of the forest would make their appearance in the streets of New Amsterdam, fantastically painted and decorated with beads and flaunting feathers, sauntering about with an air of listless indifference—sometimes in the marketplace, instructing the little Dutch boys in the use of the bow and arrow—at other times, inflamed with liquor, swaggering and whooping and yelling about the town like so many fiends, to the great dismay of all the good wives, who would hurry their children into the house, fasten the doors, and throw water upon the enemy from the garret windows. It is worthy of mention here, that our forefathers were very particular in holding up these wild men as excellent domestic examples—and for reasons that may be gathered from the history of master Ogilby, who tells us, that "for the least offence the bridegroom soundly beats his wife and turns her out of doors, and marries another, insomuch that some of them have every year a new wife." Whether this awful example had any influence or not, history does not mention; but it is certain that our grandmothers were miracles of fidelity and obedience.

True it is, that the good understanding between our ancestors and their savage neighbors was liable to occasional interruptions, and I have heard my grandmother, who was a very wise old woman, and well versed in the history of these parts, tell a long story of a winter's evening, about a battle between the New Amsterdammers and the Indians, which was known by the name of the *Peach War*, and which took place near a peach orchard, in a dark glen, which for a long while went by the name of Murderer's Valley.

The legend of this sylvan war was long current among the nurses, old wives, and other ancient chroniclers of the place; but time and improvement have almost obliterated both the tradition and the scene of battle; for what was once the blood-stained valley is now in the centre of this populous city, and known by the name of *Dey Street*.

I know not whether it was to this "Peach war," and the

acquisitions of Indian land which may have grown out of it, that we may ascribe the first seeds of the spirit of "annexation" which now began to manifest themselves. Hitherto the ambition of the worthy burghers had been confined to the lovely island of Manna-hata; and Spiten Devil on the Hudson, and Hell-gate on the Sound, were to them the pillars of Hercules, the *ne plus ultra* of human enterprise. Shortly after the Peach war, however, a restless spirit was observed among the New Amsterdammers, who began to cast wistful looks upon the wild lands of their Indian neighbors; for, somehow or other, wild Indian land always looks greener in the eyes of settlers than the land they occupy. It is hinted that Oloffe the Dreamer encouraged these notions; having, as has been shown, the inherent spirit of a land speculator, which had been wonderfully quickened and expanded since he had become a landholder. Many of the common people, who had never before owned a foot of land, now began to be discontented with the town lots which had fallen to their shares; others, who had snug farms and tobacco-plantations, found they had not sufficient elbow-room, and began to question the rights of the Indians to the vast regions they pretended to hold—while the good Oloffe indulged in magnificent dreams of foreign conquest and great patroonships in the wilderness.

The result of these dreams were certain exploring expeditions, sent forth in various directions, to "sow the seeds of empire," as it was said. The earliest of these were conducted by Hans Reinier Oothout, an old navigator, famous for the sharpness of his vision, who could see land when it was quite out of sight to ordinary mortals, and who had a spy-glass covered with a bit of tarpauling, with which he could spy up the crookedest river quite to its head-waters. He was accompanied by Mynheer Ten Breeches, as land-measurer, in case of any dispute with the Indains.

What was the consequence of these exploring expeditions? In a little while we find a frontier post or trading-house called Fort Nassau, established far to the south on Delaware River; another, called Fort Goed Hoep (or Good Hope), on the Varsche, or Fresh, or Connecticut River, and another, called Fort Aurania (now Albany), away up the Hudson River; while the boundaries of the province kept extending on every side, nobody knew whither, far into the regions of Terra Incognita.

Of the boundary feuds and troubles which the ambitious little province brought upon itself by these indefinite expansions of its territory, we shall treat at large in the after-pages of this eventful history; sufficient for the present is it to say that the swelling importance of the New Netherlands awakened the attention of the mother-country, who, finding it likely to yield much revenue and no trouble, began to take that interest in its welfare which knowing people evince for rich relations.

But as this opens a new era in the fortunes of New Amsterdam, I will here put an end to this second book of my history, and will treat of the maternal policy of the mother-country in my next.

Book III

IN WHICH IS RECORDED THE GOLDEN REIGN OF WOUTER VAN TWILLER

CHAPTER I

Of the Renowned Wouter Van Twiller, His Unparalleled Virtues—as Likewise His Unutterable Wisdom in the Law-case of Wandle Schoonhoven and Barent Bleecker—and the Great Admiration of the Public Thereat

GRIEVOUS and very much to be commiserated is the task of the feeling historian, who writes the history of his native land. If it fall to his lot to be the recorder of calamity or crime, the mournful page is watered with his tears; nor can he recall the most prosperous and blissful era, without a melancholy sigh at the reflection that it has passed away forever! I know not whether it be owing to an immoderate love for the simplicity of former times, or to that certain tenderness of heart incident to all sentimental historians; but I candidly confess that I cannot look back on the happier days of our city, which I now describe, without great dejection of spirit. With faltering hand do I withdraw the curtain of oblivion, that veils the modest merit of our venerable ancestors, and as their figures rise to my mental vision, humble myself before their mighty shades.

Such are my feelings when I revisit the family mansion of the Knickerbockers, and spend a lonely hour in the chamber where hang the portraits of my forefathers, shrouded in dust, like the forms they represent. With pious reverence do I gaze on the countenances of those renowned burghers, who have preceded me in the steady march of existence—whose sober and temperate blood now meanders through my veins, flowing slower and slower in its feeble conduits, until its current shall soon be stopped forever!

These, I say to myself, are but frail memorials of the mighty men who flourished in the days of the patriarchs; but who, alas, have long since mouldered in that tomb towards which my steps are insensibly and irresistibly hastening! As I pace the darkened chamber and lose myself in melancholy musings, the shadowy images around me almost seem to steal once more into existence—their countenances to assume the animation of life—their eyes to pursue me in every movement! Carried away by the delusions of fancy, I almost imagine myself surrounded by the shades of the departed, and holding sweet converse with the worthies of antiquity! Ah, hapless Diedrich! born in a degenerate age, abandoned to the buffetings of fortune—a stranger and a weary pilgrim in thy native land—blest with no weeping wife, nor family of helpless children, but doomed to wander neglected through those crowded streets, and elbowed by foreign upstarts from those fair abodes where once thine ancestors held sovereign empire!

Let me not, however, lose the historian in the man, nor suffer the doting recollections of age to overcome me, while dwelling with fond garrulity on the virtuous days of the patriarchs—on those sweet days of simplicity and ease, which never more will dawn on the lovely island of Manna-hata.

These melancholy reflections have been forced from me by the growing wealth and importance of New Amsterdam, which, I plainly perceive, are to involve it in all kinds of perils and disasters. Already, as I observed at the close of my last book, they had awakened the attentions of the mother-country. The usual mark of protection shown by mother-countries to wealthy colonies was forthwith manifested; a governor being sent out to rule over the province, and squeeze out of it as much revenue as possible. The arrival of a governor of course put an end to the protectorate of Oloffe the Dreamer. He appears, however, to have dreamt to some purpose during his sway, as we find him afterwards living as a patroon on a great landed estate on the banks of the Hudson; having virtually forfeited all right to his ancient appellation of Kortlandt or Lackland.

It was in the year of our Lord 1629 that Mynheer Wouter Van Twiller was appointed governor of the province of Nieuw Nederlandts, under the commission and control of their High

Mightinesses the Lords States General of the United Netherlands, and the privileged West India Company.

This renowned old gentleman arrived at New Amsterdam in the merry month of June, the sweetest month in all the year; when dan Apollo seems to dance up the transparent firmament—when the robin, the thrush, and a thousand other wanton songsters, make the woods to resound with amorous ditties, and the luxurious little boblincon revels among the clover-blossoms of the meadows—all which happy coincidence persuaded the old dames of New Amsterdam, who were skilled in the art of foretelling events, that this was to be a happy and prosperous administration.

The renowned Wouter (or Walter) Van Twiller was descended from a long line of Dutch burgomasters, who had successively dozed away their lives, and grown fat upon the bench of magistracy in Rotterdam; and who had comported themselves with such singular wisdom and propriety, that they were never either heard or talked of—which, next to being universally applauded, should be the object of ambition of all magistrates and rulers. There are two opposite ways by which some men make a figure in the world: one, by talking faster than they think, and the other, by holding their tongues and not thinking at all. By the first, many a smatterer acquires the reputation of a man of quick parts; by the other, many a dunderpate, like the owl, the stupidest of birds, comes to be considered the very type of wisdom. This, by the way, is a casual remark, which I would not, for the universe, have it thought I apply to Governor Van Twiller. It is true he was a man shut up within himself, like an oyster, and rarely spoke, except in monosyllables; but then it was allowed he seldom said a foolish thing. So invincible was his gravity that he was never known to laugh or even to smile through the whole course of a long and prosperous life. Nay, if a joke were uttered in his presence, that set light-minded hearers in a roar, it was observed to throw him into a state of perplexity. Sometimes he would deign to inquire into the matter, and when, after much explanation, the joke was made as plain as a pike-staff, he would continue to smoke his pipe in silence, and at length, knocking out the ashes, would exclaim, "Well! I see nothing in all that to laugh about."

With all his reflective habits, he never made up his mind on a subject. His adherents accounted for this by the astonishing magnitude of his ideas. He conceived every subject on so grand a scale that he had not room in his head to turn it over and examine both sides of it. Certain it is, that, if any matter were propounded to him on which ordinary mortals would rashly determine at first glance, he would put on a vague, mysterious look, shake his capacious head, smoke some time in profound silence, and at length observe, that "he had his doubts about the matter"; which gained him the reputation of a man slow of belief and not easily imposed upon. What is more, it gained him a lasting name; for to this habit of the mind has been attributed his surname of Twiller; which is said to be a corruption of the original Twijfler, or, in plain English, *Doubter*.

The person of this illustrious old gentleman was formed and proportioned, as though it had been moulded by the hands of some cunning Dutch statuary, as a model of majesty and lordly grandeur. He was exactly five feet six inches in height, and six feet five inches in circumference. His head was a perfect sphere, and of such stupendous dimensions, that Dame Nature, with all her sex's ingenuity, would have been puzzled to construct a neck capable of supporting it; wherefore she wisely declined the attempt, and settled it firmly on the top of his backbone, just between the shoulders. His body was oblong and particularly capacious at bottom; which was wisely ordered by Providence, seeing that he was a man of sedentary habits, and very averse to the idle labor of walking. His legs were short, but sturdy in proportion to the weight they had to sustain; so that when erect he had not a little the appearance of a beer-barrel on skids. His face, that infallible index of the mind, presented a vast expanse, unfurrowed by any of those lines and angles which disfigure the human countenance with what is termed expression. Two small gray eyes twinkled feebly in the midst, like two stars of lesser magnitude in a hazy firmament, and his full-fed cheeks, which seemed to have taken toll of everything that went into his mouth, were curiously mottled and streaked with dusky red, like a spitzenberg apple.

His habits were as regular as his person. He daily took his four stated meals, appropriating exactly an hour to each; he smoked and doubted eight hours, and he slept the remaining twelve of the four-and-twenty. Such was the renowned Wouter Van Twiller—a true philosopher, for his mind was either elevated above, or tranquilly settled below, the cares and perplexities of this world. He had lived in it for years, without feeling the least curiosity to know whether the sun revolved round it, or it round the sun; and he had watched, for at least half a century, the smoke curling from his pipe to the ceiling, without once troubling his head with any of those numerous theories by which a philosopher would have perplexed his brain, in accounting for its rising above the surrounding atmosphere.

In his council he presided with great state and solemnity. He sat in a huge chair of solid oak, hewn in the celebrated forest of the Hague, fabricated by an experienced timmerman of Amsterdam, and curiously carved about the arms and feet, into exact imitations of gigantic eagle's claws. Instead of a sceptre, he swayed a long Turkish pipe, wrought with jasmin and amber, which had been presented to a stadtholder of Holland at the conclusion of a treaty with one of the petty Barbary powers. In this stately chair would he sit, and this magnificent pipe would he smoke, shaking his right knee with a constant motion, and fixing his eye for hours together upon a little print of Amsterdam, which hung in a black frame against the opposite wall of the council-chamber. Nay, it has even been said, that when any deliberation of extraordinary length and intricacy was on the carpet, the renowned Wouter would shut his eyes for full two hours at a time, that he might not be disturbed by external objects; and at such times the internal commotion of his mind was evinced by certain regular guttural sounds, which his admirers declared were merely the noise of conflict, made by his contending doubts and opinions.

It is with infinite difficulty I have been enabled to collect these biographical anecdotes of the great man under consideration. The facts respecting him were so scattered and vague, and divers of them so questionable in point of authenticity, that I have had to give up the search after many, and decline the admission of still more, which would have tended to heighten the coloring of his portrait.

I have been the more anxious to delineate fully the person

and habits of Wouter Van Twiller, from the consideration that he was not only the first, but also the best governor that ever presided over this ancient and respectable province; and so tranquil and benevolent was his reign, that I do not find throughout the whole of it a single instance of any offender being brought to punishment—a most indubitable sign of a merciful governor, and a case unparalleled, excepting in the reign of the illustrious King Log, from whom, it is hinted, the renowned Van Twiller was a lineal descendant.

The very outset of the career of this excellent magistrate was distinguished by an example of legal acumen, that gave flattering presage of a wise and equitable administration. The morning after he had been installed in office, and at the moment that he was making his breakfast from a prodigious earthen dish, filled with milk and Indian pudding, he was interrupted by the appearance of Wandle Schoonhoven, a very important old burgher of New Amsterdam, who complained bitterly of one Barent Bleecker, inasmuch as he refused to come to a settlement of accounts, seeing that there was a heavy balance in favor of the said Wandle. Governor Van Twiller, as I have already observed, was a man of few words; he was likewise a mortal enemy to multiplying writings—or being disturbed at his breakfast. Having listened attentively to the statement of Wandle Schoonhoven, giving an occasional grunt, as he shovelled a spoonful of Indian pudding into his mouth—either as a sign that he relished the dish, or comprehended the story—he called unto him his constable, and pulling out of his breeches-pocket a huge jack-knife, dispatched it after the defendant as a summons, accompanied by his tobacco-box as a warrant.

This summary process was as effectual in those simple days as was the seal-ring of the great Haroun Alraschid among the true believers. The two parties being confronted before him, each produced a book of accounts, written in a language and character that would have puzzled any but a High-Dutch commentator, or a learned decipherer of Egyptian obelisks. The sage Wouter took them one after the other, and having poised them in his hands, and attentively counted over the number of leaves, fell straightway into a very great doubt, and smoked for half an hour without saying a word; at length, laying his finger beside his nose, and shutting his eyes for a moment, with the air of a man who has just caught a subtle idea by the tail, he slowly took his pipe from his mouth, puffed forth a column of tobacco-smoke, and with marvellous gravity and solemnity pronounced, that, having carefully counted over the leaves and weighed the books, it was found, that one was just as thick and as heavy as the other: therefore, it was the final opinion of the court that the accounts were equally balanced: therefore, Wandle should give Barent a receipt, and Barent should give Wandle a receipt, and the constable should pay the costs.

This decision, being straighway made known, diffused general joy throughout New Amsterdam, for the people immediately perceived that they had a very wise and equitable magistrate to rule over them. But its happiest effect was, that not another lawsuit took place throughout the whole of his administration; and the office of constable fell into such decay, that there was not one of those losel scouts known in the province for many years. I am the more particular in dwelling on this transaction, not only because I deem it one of the most sage and righteous judgments on record, and well worthy the attention of modern magistrates, but because it was a miraculous event in the history of the renowned Wouter—being the only time he was ever known to come to a decision in the whole course of his life.

CHAPTER II

Containing Some Account of the Grand Council of New Amsterdam, as also Divers Especial Good Philosophical Reasons Why an Alderman Should Be Fat—with Other Particulars Touching the State of the Province

IN treating of the early governors of the province, I must caution my readers against confounding them, in point of dignity and power, with those worthy gentlemen who are whimsically denominated governors in this enlightened republic—a set of unhappy victims of popularity, who are, in fact, the most dependent, hen-pecked beings in the community; doomed to bear the secret goadings and corrections of their own party, and the sneers and revilings of the whole world beside; set up, like geese at Christmas holidays, to be pelted and shot at by every whipster and vagabond in the land. On the contrary, the Dutch governors enjoyed that uncontrolled authority vested in all commanders of distant colonies or territories. They were, in a manner, absolute despots in their little domains, lording it, if so disposed, over both law and gospel, and accountable to none but the mother-country; which it is well known is astonishingly deaf to all complaints against its governors, provided they discharge the main duty of their station—squeezing out a good revenue. This hint will be of importance, to prevent my readers from being seized with doubt and incredulity, whenever, in the course of this authentic history, they encounter the uncommon circumstance of a governor acting with independence, and in opposition to the opinions of the multitude.

To assist the doubtful Wouter in the arduous business of legislation, a board of magistrates was appointed, which presided immediately over the police. This potent body consisted of a schout or bailiff, with powers between those of the present mayor and sheriff; five burgermeesters, who were equivalent to aldermen; and five schepens, who officiated as scrubs, subdevils, or bottle-holders to the burgermeesters, in the same manner as do assistant aldermen to their principals at the present day—it being their duty to fill the pipes of the lordly burgermeesters, hunt the markets for delicacies for corporation dinners, and to discharge such other little offices of kindness as were occasionally required. It was, moreover, tacitly understood, though not specifically enjoined, that they should consider themselves as butts for the blunt wits of the burgermeesters, and should laugh most heartily at all their jokes; but this last was a duty as rarely called in action in those days as it is at present, and was shortly remitted, in consequence of the tragical death of a fat little schepen, who actually died of suffocation in an unsuccessful effort to force a laugh at one of burgermeester Van Zandt's best jokes.

In return for these humble services, they were permitted to say yes and *no* at the council-board, and to have that enviable privilege, the run of the public kitchen—being graciously permitted to eat, and drink, and smoke, at all those snug junketings and public gormandizings for which the ancient magistrates were equally famous with their modern successors. The post of schepen, therefore, like that of assistant aldermen, was eagerly coveted by all your burghers of a certain description, who have a huge relish for good feeding, and an humble ambition to be great men in a small way—who thirst after a little brief authority, that shall render them the terror of the alms-house and the bridewell—that shall enable them to lord it over obsequious poverty, vagrant vice, outcast prostitution, and hunger-driven dishonesty—that shall give to their beck a houndlike pact of catchpolls and bumbailiffs—tenfold greater rogues than the culprits they hunt down! My readers will excuse this sudden warmth, which I confess is unbecoming of a grave historian—but I have a mortal antipathy to catchpolls, bumbailiffs, and little-great men.

The ancient magistrates of this city corresponded with those of the present time no less in form, magnitude, and intellect, than in prerogative and privilege. The burgomasters, like our aldermen, were generally chosen by weight—and not only the weight of the body, but likewise the weight of the head. It is a maxim practically observed in all honest, plain-thinking, regular cities, that an alderman should be fat—and the wisdom of this can be proved to a certainty. That the body is in some measure an image of the mind, or rather that the mind is moulded to the body, like melted lead to the clay in which it is cast, has been insisted on by many philosophers, who have made human nature their peculiar study; for, as a learned gentleman of our own city observes, "there is a constant relation between the moral character of all intelligent creatures and their physical constitution, between their habits and the structure of their bodies." Thus we see that a lean, spare, diminutive body is generally accompanied by a petulant, restless, meddling mind: either the mind wears down the body, by its continual motion, or else the body, not affording the mind sufficient house-room, keeps it continually in a state of fretfulness, tossing and worrying about from the uneasiness of its situation. Whereas your round, sleek, fat, unwieldy periphery is ever attended by a mind like itself, tranquil, torpid, and at ease; and we may always observe, that your well-fed, robustious burghers are in general very tenacious of their ease and comfort, being great enemies to noise, discord, and disturbance—and surely none are more likely to study the public tranquillity than those who are so careful of their own. Who ever hears of fat men heading a riot, or herding together in turbulent mobs?—no—no; it is your lean, hungry men who are continually worrying society, and setting the whole community by the ears.

The divine Plato, whose doctrines are not sufficiently attended to by philosophers of the present age, allows to every man three souls: one, immortal and rational, seated in the brain, that it may overlook and regulate the body; a second, consisting of the surly and irascible passions which, like belligerent powers, lie encamped around the heart; a third, mortal and sensual, destitute of reason, gross and brutal in its propensities, and enchained in the belly, that it may not disturb the divine soul by its ravenous howlings. Now, according to this excellent theory, what can be more clear than that your fat alderman is most likely to have the most regular and well-conditioned mind. His head is like a huge spherical chamber, containing a prodigious mass of soft brains, whereon the rational soul lies softly and snugly couched, as on a feather-bed; and the eyes, which are the windows of the bed-chamber, are usually half closed, that its slumberings may not be disturbed by external objects. A mind thus comfortably lodged, and protected from disturbance, is manifestly most likely to perform its functions with regularity and ease. By dint of good feeding, moreover, the mortal and malignant soul, which is confined in the belly, and which, by its raging and roaring, puts the irritable soul in the neighborhood of the heart in an intolerable passion, and thus renders men crusty and quarrelsome when hungry, is completely pacified, silenced, and put to rest—whereupon a host of honest, good-fellow qualities and kind-hearted affections, which had lain perdue, slyly peeping out of the loop-holes of the heart, finding this cerberus asleep, do pluck up their spirits, turn out one and all in their holiday suits, and gambol up and down the diaphragm—disposing their possessor to laughter, good-humor, and a thousand friendly offices towards his fellow-mortals.

As a board of magistrates, formed on this principle, think

but very little, they are the less likely to differ and wrangle about favorite opinions; and as they generally transact business upon a hearty dinner, they are naturally disposed to be lenient and indulging in the administration of their duties. Charlemagne was conscious of this, and therefore ordered in his cartularies, that no judge should hold a court of justice, except in the morning, on an empty stomach. A pitiful rule, which I can never forgive, and which I warrant bore hard upon all the poor culprits in the kingdom. The more enlightened and humane generation of the present day have taken an opposite course, and have so managed that the aldermen are the best-fed men in the community; feasting lustily on the fat things of the land, and gorging so heartily on oysters and turtles, that in process of time they acquire the activity of the one, and the form, the waddle, and the green fat of the other. The consequence is, as I have just said, these luxurious feastings do produce such a dulcet equanimity and repose of the soul, rational and irrational, that their transactions are proverbial for unvarying monotony; and the profound laws which they enact in their dozing moments, amid the labors of digestion, are quietly suffered to remain as dead letters, and never enforced, when awake. In a word, your fair, round-bellied burgomaster, like a full-fed mastiff, dozes quietly at the house-door, always at home, and always at hand to watch over its safety; but as to electing a lean, meddling candidate to the office, as has now and then been done, I would as lief put a greyhound to watch the house, or a race-horse to draw an ox-wagon.

The burgomasters, then, as I have already mentioned, were wisely chosen by weight, and the schepens, or assistant aldermen, were appointed to attend upon them and help them eat; but the latter, in the course of time, when they had been fed and fattened into sufficient bulk of body and drowsiness of brain, became very eligible candidates for the burgomasters' chairs, having fairly eaten themselves into office, as a mouse eats his way into a comfortable lodgment in a goodly, blue-nosed, skimmed-milk, New-England cheese.

Nothing could equal the profound deliberations that took place between the renowned Wouter and these his worthy compeers, unless it be the sage divans of some of our modern corporations. They would sit for hours, smoking and dozing over public affairs, without speaking a word to interrupt that perfect stillness so necessary to deep reflection. Under the sober sway of Wouter Van Twiller and these his worthy coadjutors, the infant settlement waxed vigorous apace, gradually emerging from the swamps and forests, and exhibiting that mingled appearance of town and country, customary in new cities, and which at this day may be witnessed in the city of Washington —that immense metropolis, which makes so glorious an appearance on paper.

It was a pleasing sight, in those times, to behold the honest burgher, like a patriarch of yore, seated on the bench at the door of his whitewashed house, under the shade of some gigantic sycamore or overhanging willow. Here would he smoke his pipe of a sultry afternoon, enjoying the soft southern breeze, and listening with silent gratulation to the clucking of his hens, the cackling of his geese, and the sonorous grunting of his swine —that combination of farm-yard melody which may truly be said to have a silver sound, inasmuch as it conveys a certain assurance of profitable marketing.

The modern spectator, who wanders through the streets of this populous city, can scarcely form an idea of the different appearance they presented in the primitive days of the Doubter. The busy hum of multitudes, the shouts of revelry, the rumbling equipages of fashion, the rattling of accursed carts, and all the spirit-grieving sounds of brawling commerce, were unknown in the settlement of New Amsterdam. The grass grew quietly in the highways; the bleating sheep and frolicsome calves sported about the verdant ridge, where now the Broadway loungers take their morning stroll; the cunning fox or ravenous wolf skulked in the woods, where now are to be seen the dens of Gomez and his righteous fraternity of money-brokers; and flocks of vociferous geese cackled about the fields where now the great Tammany wigwam and the patriotic tavern of Martling echo with the wranglings of the mob.

In these good times did a true and enviable equality of rank and property prevail, equally removed from the arrogance of wealth, and the servility and heart-burnings of repining poverty; and, what in my mind is still more conducive to tranquillity and harmony among friends, a happy equality of intellect was likewise to be seen. The minds of the good burghers of New Amsterdam seemed all to have been cast in one mould, and to be those honest, blunt minds, which, like certain manufactures, are made by the gross, and considered as exceedingly good for common use.

Thus it happens that your true dull minds are generally preferred for public employ, and especially promoted to city honors; your keen intellects, like razors, being considered too sharp for common service. I know that it is common to rail at the unequal distribution of riches, as the great source of jealousies, broils, and heart-breakings; whereas, for my part, I verily believe it is the sad inequality of intellect that prevails, that embroils communities more than anything else; and I have remarked that your knowing people, who are so much wiser than anybody else, are eternally keeping society in a ferment. Happily for New Amsterdam, nothing of the kind was known within its walls; the very words of learning, education, taste, and talents were unheard of; a bright genius was an animal unknown, and a blue-stocking lady would have been regarded with as much wonder as a horned frog or a fiery dragon. No man, in fact, seemed to know more than his neighbor, nor any man to know more than an honest man ought to know, who has nobody's business to mind but his own; the parson and the council clerk were the only men that could read in the community, and the sage Van Twiller always signed his name with a cross.

Thrice happy and ever to be envied little Burgh! existing in all the security of harmless insignificance—unnoticed and unenvied by the world, without ambition, without vainglory, without riches, without learning, and all their train of carking cares; and as of yore, in the better days of man, the deities were wont to visit him on earth and bless his rural habitations, so, we are told, in the sylvan days of New Amsterdam, the good St. Nicholas would often make his appearance in his beloved city, of a holiday afternoon, riding jollily among the tree-tops, or over the roofs of the houses, now and then drawing forth magnificent presents from his breeches pockets, and dropping them down the chimneys of his favorites. Whereas, in these degenerate days of iron and brass, he never shows us the light of his countenance, nor ever visits us, save one night in the year, when he rattles down the chimneys of the descendants of patriarchs, confining his presents merely to the children, in token of the degeneracy of the parents.

Such are the comfortable and thriving effects of a fat government. The province of the New Netherlands, destitute of wealth, possessed a sweet tranquillity that wealth could never purchase. There were neither public commotions, nor private quarrels; neither parties, nor sects, nor schisms; neither persecutions, nor trials, nor punishments; nor were there counsellors, attorneys, catchpolls, or hangmen. Every man attended to what little business he was lucky enough to have, or neglected it if he pleased, without asking the opinion of his neighbor. In those days nobody meddled with concerns above his comprehension; nor thrust his nose into other people's affairs; nor neglected to correct his own conduct, and reform his own character, in his zeal to pull to pieces the characters of others; but, in a word, every respectable citizen ate when he was not hungry, drank when he was not thirsty, and went regularly to bed when the sun set and the fowls went to roost, whether he was sleepy or not; all which tended so remarkably to the population of the settlement, that I am told every dutiful wife throughout New Amsterdam made a point of enriching her husband with at least one child a year, and very often a brace—this superabundance of good things clearly constituting the true luxury of life, according to the favorite Dutch maxim, that, "more than enough constitutes a feast." Everything, therefore, went on exactly as it should do, and in the usual words employed by historians to express the welfare of a country, "the profoundest *tranquillity* and *repose* reigned throughout the province."

CHAPTER III

How the Town of New Amsterdam Arose Out of Mud, and Came to be Marvellously Polished and Polite—Together with a Picture of the Manners of Our Great-great-grandfathers

MANIFOLD are the tastes and dispositions of the enlightened *literati*, who turn over the pages of history. Some there be whose hearts are brimful of the yeast of courage, and whose bosoms do work, and swell, and foam, with untried valor, like a barrel of new cider, or a train-band captain, fresh from under the hands of his tailor. This doughty class of readers can be satisfied with nothing but bloody battles, and horrible encounters; they must be continually storming forts, sacking cities, springing mines, marching up to the muzzles of cannon, charging bayonet through every page, and revelling in gunpowder and carnage. Others, who are of a less martial, but equally ardent imagination, and who, withal, are a little given to the marvellous, will dwell with wondrous satisfaction on descriptions of prodigies, unheard-of events, hair-breadth escapes, hardy adventures, and all those astonishing narrations which just amble along the boundary line of possibility. A third class, who, not to speak slightly of them, are of a lighter turn, and skim over the records of past times, as they do over the edifying pages of a novel, merely for relaxation and innocent amusement, do singularly delight in treasons, executions, Sabine rapes, Tarquin outrages, conflagrations, murders, and all the other catalogue of hideous crimes, which, like cayenne in cookery, do give a pungency and flavor to the dull detail of history. While a fourth class, of more philosophic habits, do diligently pore over the musty chronicles of time, to investigate the operations of the human kind, and watch the gradual changes in men and manners, effected by the progress of knowledge, the vicissitudes of events, or the influence of situation.

If the three first classes find but little wherewithal to solace themselves in the tranquil reign of Wouter Van Twiller, I entreat them to exert their patience for a while, and bear with the tedious picture of happiness, prosperity, and peace, which my duty as a faithful historian obliges me to draw; and I promise them, that, as soon as I can possibly alight on anything horrible, uncommon, or impossible, it shall go hard, but I will make it afford them entertainment. This being premised, I turn with great complacency to the fourth class of my readers, who are men, or, if possible, women after my own heart; grave, philosophical, and investigating; fond of analyzing characters, of taking a start from first causes, and so hunting a nation down, through all the mazes of innovation and improvement. Such will naturally be anxious to witness the first development of the newly-hatched colony, and the primitive manners and customs prevalent among its inhabitants, during the halcyon reign of Van Twiller, or the Doubter.

I will not grieve their patience, however, by describing minutely the increase and improvement of New Amsterdam. Their own imaginations will doubtless present to them the good burghers, like so many painstaking and persevering beavers, slowly and surely pursuing their labors: they will behold the prosperous transformation from the rude log hut to the stately Dutch mansion, with brick front, glazed windows, and tiled roof; from the tangled thicket to the luxuriant cabbage-garden; and from the skulking Indian to the ponderous burgomaster. In a word, they will picture to themselves the steady, silent, and undeviating march of prosperity, incident to a city destitute of pride or ambition, cherished by a fat government, and whose citizens do nothing in a hurry.

The sage council, as has been mentioned in a preceding chapter, not being able to determine upon any plan for the building of their city—the cows, in a laudable fit of patriotism, took it under their peculiar charge, and, as they went to and from pasture, established paths through the bushes, on each side of which the good folks built their houses—which is one cause of the rambling and picturesque turns and labyrinths which distinguish certain streets of New York at this very day.

The houses of the higher class were generally constructed of wood, excepting the gable end which was of small, black and yellow Dutch bricks, and always faced on the street, as our ancestors, like their descendants, were very much given to outward show, and were noted for putting the best leg foremost. The house was always furnished with abundance of large doors and small windows on every floor, the date of its erection was curiously designated by iron figures on the front, and on the top of the roof was perched a fierce little weathercock, to let the family into the important secret which way the wind blew.

These, like the weathercocks on the tops of our steeples, pointed so many different ways, that every man could have a wind to his mind—the most stanch and loyal citizens, however, always went according to the weathercock on the top of the governor's house, which was certainly the most correct, as he had a trusty servant employed every morning to climb up and set it to the right quarter.

In those good days of simplicity and sunshine, a passion for cleanliness was the leading principle in domestic economy, and the universal test of an able housewife—a character which formed the utmost ambition of our unenlightened grandmothers. The front-door was never opened, except on marriages, funerals, New-Year's days, the festival of St. Nicholas, or some such great occasion. It was ornamented with a gorgeous brass knocker, curiously wrought, sometimes in the device of a dog, and sometimes of a lion's head, and was daily burnished with such religious zeal, that it was ofttimes worn out by the very precautions taken for its preservation. The whole house was constantly in a state of inundation, under the discipline of mops and brooms and scrubbing-brushes; and the good housewives of those days were a kind of amphibious animal, delighting exceedingly to be dabbling in water—insomuch that an historian of the day gravely tells us, that many of his townswomen grew to have webbed fingers like unto a duck; and some of them, he had little doubt, could the matter be examined into, would be found to have the tails of mermaids—but this I look upon to be a mere sport of fancy, or, what is worse, a wilful misrepresentation.

The grand parlor was the sanctum sanctorum, where the passion for cleaning was indulged without control. In this sacred apartment no one was permitted to enter, excepting the mistress and her confidential maid, who visited it, once a week, for the purpose of giving it a thorough cleaning, and putting things to rights—always taking the precaution of leaving their shoes at the door, and entering devoutly on their stocking-feet. After scrubbing the floor, sprinkling it with fine white sand, which was curiously stroked into angles and curves and rhomboids with a broom—after washing the windows, rubbing and polishing the furniture, and putting a new bunch of evergreens in the fireplace—the window-shutters were again closed to keep out the flies, and the room carefully locked up until the revolution of time brought round the weekly cleaning-day.

As to the family, they always entered in at the gate, and most generally lived in the kitchen. To have seen a numerous household assembled round the fire, one would have imagined that he was transported back to those happy days of primeval simplicity, which float before our imaginations like golden visions. The fire-places were of a truly patriarchal magnitude, where the whole family, old and young, master and servant, black and white, nay, even the very cat and dog, enjoyed a community of privilege, and had each a right to a corner. Here the old burgher would sit in perfect silence, puffing his pipe, looking in the fire with half-shut eyes, and thinking of nothing for hours together; the goede vrouw, on the opposite side, would employ herself diligently in spinning yarn, or knitting stockings. The young folks would crowd around the hearth, listening with breathless attention to some old crone of a Negro, who was the oracle of the family, and who, perched like a raven in a corner of the chimney, would croak forth for a long winter afternoon a string of incredible stories about New-England witches—grisly ghosts, horses without heads—and hair-breadth escapes, and bloody encounters among the Indians.

In those happy days a well-regulated family always rose with the dawn, dined at eleven, and went to bed at sunset. Dinner was invariably a private meal, and the fat old burghers showed incontestable signs of disapprobation and uneasiness at being surprised by a visit from a neighbor on such occasions. But though our worthy ancestors were thus singularly averse to giving dinners, yet they kept up the social bands of intimacy by occasional banquetings, called tea-parties.

These fashionable parties were generally confined to the higher classes, or noblesse, that is to say, such as kept their own cows, and drove their own wagons. The company commonly assembled at three o'clock, and went away about six, unless it was in winter-time, when the fashionable hours were a little earlier, that the ladies might get home before dark. The tea-table was crowned with a huge earthen dish, well stored with slices of fat pork, fried brown, cut up into morsels, and swimming in gravy. The company being seated round the genial board, and each furnished with a fork, evinced their dexterity in launching at the fattest pieces in this mighty dish—in much the same manner as sailors harpoon porpoises at sea, or our Indians spear salmon in the lakes. Sometimes the table was graced with immense apple-pies, or saucers full of preserved peaches and pears; but it was always sure to boast an enormous dish of balls of sweetened dough, fried in hog's fat, and called doughnuts, or olykoeks—a delicious kind of cake, at present scarce known in this city, except in genuine Dutch families.

The tea was served out of a majestic Delft tea-pot, ornamented with paintings of fat little Dutch shepherds and shepherdesses tending pigs, with boats sailing in the air, and houses built in the clouds, and sundry other ingenious Dutch fantasies. The beaux distinguished themselves by their adroitness in replenishing this pot from a huge copper tea-kettle, which would have made the pigmy macaronies of these degenerate days sweat merely to look at it. To sweeten the beverage, a lump of sugar was laid beside each cup, and the company alternately nibbled and sipped with great decorum, until an improvement was introduced by a shrewd and economic old lady, which was to suspend a large lump directly over the tea-table, by a string from the ceiling, so that it could be swung from mouth to mouth—an ingenious expedient, which is still kept up by some families in Albany, but which prevails without exception in Communipaw, Bergen, Flatbush, and all our uncontaminated Dutch villages.

At these primitive tea-parties the utmost propriety and dignity of deportment prevailed. No flirting nor coquetting—no gambling of old ladies, nor hoyden chattering and romping of young ones—no self-satisfied struttings of wealthy gentlemen, with their brains in their pockets, nor amusing conceits and monkey divertisements of smart young gentlemen, with no brains at all. On the contrary, the young ladies seated themselves demurely in their rush-bottom chairs, and knit their own woollen stockings; nor ever opened their lips excepting to say *yah Mynheer*, or, *yah ya Vrouw*, to any question that was asked them; behaving in all things like decent, well-educated damsels. As to the gentlemen, each of them tranquilly smoked his pipe, and seemed lost in contemplation of the blue and white tiles with which the fireplaces were decorated; wherein sundry passages of Scripture were piously portrayed: Tobit and his dog figured to great advantage; Haman swung conspicuously on his gibbet; and Jonah appeared most manfully bouncing out of the whale, like Harlequin through a barrel of fire.

The parties broke up without noise and without confusion. They were carried home by their own carriages, that is to say, by the vehicles nature had provided them, excepting such of the wealthy as could afford to keep a wagon. The gentlemen gallantly attended their fair ones to their respective abodes, and took leave of them with a hearty smack at the door: which, as it was an established piece of etiquette, done in perfect simplicity and honesty of heart, occasioned no scandal at that time, nor should it at the present—if our great-grandfathers approved of the custom, it would argue a great want of deference in their descendants to say a word against it.

CHAPTER IV

Containing Further Particulars of the Golden Age, and What Constituted a Fine Lady and Gentleman in the Days of Walter the Doubter

IN this dulcet period of my history, when the beauteous island of Manna-hata presented a scene, the very counterpart of those glowing pictures drawn of the golden reign of Saturn, there was, as I have before observed, a happy ignorance, an honest simplicity prevalent among its inhabitants, which, were I even able to depict, would be but little understood by the degenerate age for which I am doomed to write. Even the female sex, those arch innovators upon the tranquillity, the honesty, and gray-beard customs of society, seemed for a while to conduct themselves with incredible sobriety and comeliness.

Their hair, untortured by the abominations of art, was scrupulously pomatumed back from their foreheads with a candle, and covered with a little cap of quilted calico, which fitted exactly to their heads. Their petticoats of linsey-woolsey were striped with a variety of gorgeous dyes—though I must confess these gallant garments were rather short, scarce reaching below the knee, but then they made up in the number, which generally equalled that of the gentleman's small-clothes; and what is still more praiseworthy, they were all of their own manufacture—of which circumstance, as may well be supposed, they were not a little vain.

These were the honest days in which every woman stayed at home, read the Bible, and wore pockets—ay, and that too of a goodly size, fashioned with patchwork into many curious devices, and ostentatiously worn on the outside. These, in fact, were convenient receptacles, where all good housewives carefully stored away such things as they wished to have at hand; by which means they often came to be incredibly crammed; and I remember there was a story current, when I was a boy, that the lady of Wouter Van Twiller once had occasion to empty her right pocket in search of a wooden ladle, when the contents filled a couple of corn-baskets, and the utensil was discovered lying among some rubbish in one corner—but we must not give too much faith to all these stories, the anecdotes of those remote periods being very subject to exaggeration.

Besides these notable pockets, they likewise wore scissors and pin-cushions suspended from their girdles by red ribands, or, among the more opulent and showy classes, by brass, and even silver chains—indubitable tokens of thrifty housewives and industrious spinsters. I cannot say much in vindication of the shortness of the petticoats; it doubtless was introduced for the purpose of giving the stockings a chance to be seen, which were generally of blue worsted, with magnificent red clocks—or, perhaps, to display a well-turned ankle, and a neat, though serviceable foot, set off by a high-heeled leathern shoe, with a large and splendid silver buckle. Thus we find that the gentle sex in all ages have shown the same disposition to infringe a little upon the laws of decorum, in order to betray a lurking beauty, or gratify an innocent love of finery.

From the sketch here given, it will be seen that our good grandmothers differed considerably in their ideas of a fine figure from their scantily dressed descendants of the present day. A fine lady, in those times, waddled under more clothes, even on a fair summer's day, than would have clad the whole bevy of a modern ball-room. Nor were they the less admired by the gentlemen in consequence thereof. On the contrary, the greatness of a lover's passion seemed to increase in proportion to the magnitude of its object—and a voluminous damsel, arrayed in a dozen of petticoats, was declared by a Low-Dutch sonneteer of the province to be radiant as a sun-flower, and luxuriant as a full-blown cabbage. Certain it is, that in those days the heart of a lover could not contain more than one lady at a time; whereas the heart of a modern gallant has often room enough to accommodate half a dozen. The reason of which I conclude to be, that either the hearts of the gentlemen have grown larger, or the persons of the ladies smaller: this, however, is a question for physiologists to determine.

But there was a secret charm in these petticoats, which, no doubt, entered into the consideration of the prudent gallants. The wardrobe of a lady was in those days her only fortune; and she who had a good stock of petticoats and stockings was as absolutely an heiress as is a Kamtchatka damsel with a store of bearskins, or a Lapland belle with a plenty of reindeer. The ladies, therefore, were very anxious to display these powerful attractions to the greatest advantage; and the best rooms in the house, instead of being adorned with caricatures of dame Nature, in water-colors and needle-work, were always hung round with abundance of homespun garments, the manufacture and the property of the females—a piece of laudable ostentation that still prevails among the heiresses of our Dutch villages.

The gentlemen, in fact, who figured in the circles of the gay world in these ancient times, corresponded, in most particulars, with the beauteous damsels whose smiles they were ambitious to deserve. True it is, their merits would make but a very inconsiderable impression upon the heart of a modern fair: they neither drove their curricles, nor sported their tandems, for as yet those gaudy vehicles were not even dreamt of; neither did they distinguish themselves by their brilliancy at the table, and their consequent rencontres with watchmen, for our forefathers were of too pacific a disposition to need those guardians of the night, every soul throughout the town being sound asleep before nine o'clock. Neither did they establish their claims to gentility at the expense of their tailors, for as yet those offenders against the pockets of society, and the tranquillity of all aspiring young gentlemen, were unknown in New Amsterdam; every good housewife made the clothes of her husband and family, and even the goede vrouw of Van Twiller himself thought it no disparagement to cut out her husband's linsey-woolsey galligaskins.

Not but what there were some two or three youngsters who

manifested the first dawning of what is called fire and spirit; who held all labor in contempt; skulked about docks and market-places; loitered in the sunshine; squandered what little money they could procure at hustlecap and chuck-farthing; swore, boxed, fought cocks, and raced their neighbors' horses; in short, who promised to be the wonder, the talk, and abomination of the town, had not their stylish career been unfortunately cut short by an affair of honor with a whipping-post.

Far other, however, was the truly fashionable gentleman of those days: his dress, which served for both morning and evening, street and drawing-room, was a linsey-woolsey coat, made, perhaps, by the fair hands of the mistress of his affections, and gallantly bedecked with abundance of large brass buttons; half a score of breeches heightened the proportions of his figure; his shoes were decorated by enormous cooper buckles; a low-crowned broad-rimmed hat overshadowed his burly visage; and his hair dangled down his back in a prodigious queue of eel-skin.

Thus equipped, he would manfully sally forth, with pipe in mouth, to besiege some fair damsel's obdurate heart—not such a pipe, good reader, as that which Acis did sweetly tune in praise of his Galatea, but one of true Delft manufacture, and furnished with a charge of fragrant tobacco. With this would he resolutely set himself down before the fortress, and rarely failed, in the process of time, to smoke the fair enemy into a surrender, upon honorable terms.

Such was the happy reign of Wouter Van Twiller, celebrated in many a long-forgotten song as the real golden age, the rest being nothing but counterfeit copper-washed coin. In that delightful period, a sweet and holy calm reigned over the whole province. The burgomaster smoked his pipe in peace; the substantial solace of his domestic cares, after her daily toils were done, sat soberly at the door, with her arms crossed over her apron of snowy white, without being insulted with ribald street-walkers or vagabond boys—those unlucky urchins who do so infest our streets, displaying, under the roses of youth, the thorns and briers of iniquity. Then it was that the lover with ten breeches, and the damsel with petticoats of half a score, indulged in all the innocent endearments of virtuous love, without fear and without reproach; for what had that virtue to fear, which was defended by a shield of good linsey-woolseys, equal at least to the seven bull-hides of the invincible Ajax?

Ah, blissful and never to be forgotten age! when everything was better than it has ever been since, or ever will be again—when Buttermilk Channel was quite dry at low water—when the shad in the Hudson were all salmon—and when the moon shone with a pure and resplendent whiteness, instead of that melancholy yellow light which is the consequence of her sickening at the abominations she every night witnesses in this degenerate city!

Happy would it have been for New Amsterdam could it always have existed in this state of blissful ignorance and lowly simplicity; but, alas! the days of childhood are too sweet to last! Cities, like men, grow out of them in time, and are doomed alike to grow into the bustle, the cares, and miseries of the world. Let no man congratulate himself, when he beholds the child of his bosom or the city of his birth increasing in magnitude and importance—let the history of his own life teach him the dangers of the one, and this excellent little history of Manna-hata convince him of the calamities of the other.

CHAPTER V

Of the Founding of Fort Aurania—of the Mysteries of the Hudson—of the Arrival of the Patroon Killian Van Rensellaer; His Lordly Descent upon the Earth, and His Introduction of Club-law

IT has already been mentioned, that, in the early times of Oloffe the Dreamer, a frontier-post, or trading-house, called Fort Aurania, had been established on the upper waters of the Hudson, precisely on the site of the present venerable city of Albany; which was at that time considered at the very end of the habitable world. It was, indeed, a remote possession, with which, for a long time, New Amsterdam held but little intercourse. Now and then the "Company's Yacht," as it was called, was sent to the fort with supplies, and to bring away the peltries which had been purchased of the Indians. It was like an expedition to the Indias, or the North Pole, and always made great talk in the settlement. Sometimes an adventurous burgher would accompany the expedition, to the great uneasiness of his friends; but, on his return, had so many stories to tell of storms and tempests on the Tappan Zee, of hobgoblins in the Highlands and at the Devil's Dans Kammer, and of all the other wonders and perils with which the river abounded in those early days, that he deterred the less adventurous inhabitants from following his example.

Matters were in this state, when, one day, as Walter the Doubter and his burgermeesters were smoking and pondering over the affairs of the province, they were roused by the report of a cannon. Sallying forth, they beheld a strange vessel at anchor in the bay. It was unquestionably of Dutch build, broad-bottomed and high-pooped, and bore the flag of their High Mightinesses at the mast-head.

After a while, a boat put off for land, and a stranger stepped on shore—a lofty, lordly kind of man, tall, and dry, with a meagre face, furnished with huge moustaches. He was clad in Flemish doublet and hose, and an insufferably tall hat, with a cocktail feather. Such was the patroon Killian Van Rensellaer, who had come out from Holland to found a colony or patroonship on a great tract of wild land, granted to him by their High Mightinesses the Lords States General, in the upper regions of the Hudson.

Killian Van Rensellaer was a nine days' wonder in New Amsterdam; for he carried a high head, looked down upon the portly, short-legged burgomasters, and owned no allegiance to the governor himself; boasting that he held his patroonship directly from the Lords States General.

He tarried but a short time in New Amsterdam, merely to beat up recruits for his colony. Few, however, ventured to enlist for those remote and savage regions; and when they embarked, their friends took leave of them as if they should never see them more, and stood gazing with tearful eye as the stout, round-sterned little vessel ploughed and splashed its way up the Hudson, with great noise and little progress, taking nearly a day to get out of sight of the city.

And now, from time to time, floated down tidings to the Manhattoes of the growing importance of this new colony. Every account represented Killian Van Rensellaer as rising in importance and becoming a mighty patroon in the land. He had received more recruits from Holland. His patroonship of Rensellaerwick lay immediately below Fort Aurania, and extended for several miles on each side of the Hudson, beside embracing the mountainous region of the Helderberg. Over all this he claimed to hold separate jurisdiction, independent of the colonial authorities of New Amsterdam.

All these assumptions of authority were duly reported to Governor Van Twiller and his council, by dispatches from Fort Aurania; at each new report the governor and his counsellors looked at each other, raised their eyebrows, gave an extra puff or two of smoke, and then relapsed into their usual tranquillity.

At length tidings came that the patroon of Rensellaerwick had extended his usurpations along the river, beyond the limits granted him by their High Mightinesses; and that he had even seized upon a rocky island in the Hudson, commonly known by the name of Bearn or Bear's Island, where he was erecting a fortress, to be called by the lordly name of Rensellaerstein.

Wouter Van Twiller was roused by this intelligence. After consulting with his burgomasters, he dispatched a letter to the patroon of Rensellaerwick, demanding by what right he had seized upon this island, which lay beyond the bounds of his patroonship. The answer of Killian Van Rensellaer was in his own lordly style, *"By wapen recht!"*—that is to say, by the right of arms, or, in common parlance, by club-law. This answer plunged the worthy Wouter in one of the deepest doubts he had in the whole course of his administration; in the mean time, while Wouter doubted, the lordly Killian went on to finish his fortress of Rensellaerstein, about which I foresee I shall have something to record in a future chapter of this most eventful history.

CHAPTER VI

In Which the Reader Is Beguiled into a Delectable Walk, Which Ends Very Differently from What It Commenced

IN the year of our Lord one thousand eight hundred and four, on a fine afternoon in the glowing month of September, I took my customary walk upon the Battery, which is at once the pride and bulwark of this ancient and impregnable city of New York. The ground on which I trod was hallowed by recollections of the past; and as I slowly wandered through the long alley of poplars, which, like so many birch brooms standing on end, diffused a melancholy and lugubrious shade, my imagination drew a contrast between the surrounding scenery and what it was in the classic days of our forefathers. Where the government house by name, but the custom-house by occupation, proudly reared its brick walls and wooden pillars, there whilom stood the low, but substantial, red-tiled mansion of the renowned Wouter Van Twiller. Around it the mighty bulwarks of Fort Amsterdam frowned defiance to every absent foe; but, like many a whiskered warrior and gallant militia captain, confined their martial deeds to frowns alone. The mud breastworks had long been levelled with the earth, and their site converted into the green lawns and leafy alleys of the Battery; where the gay apprentice sported his Sunday coat, and the laborious mechanic, relieved from the dirt and drudgery of the week, poured his weekly tale of love into the half-averted ear of the sentimental chambermaid. The capacious bay still presented the same expansive sheet of water, studded with islands, sprinkled with fishing-boats, and bounded by shores of picturesque beauty. But the dark forests which once clothed those shores had been violated by the savage hand of cultivation, and their tangled mazes, and impenetrable thickets, had degenerated into teeming orchards and waving fields of grain. Even Governor's Island, once a smiling garden, appertaining to the sovereigns of the province, was now covered with fortifications, inclosing a tremendous block-house—so that this once peaceful island resembled a fierce little warrior in a big cocked hat, breathing gunpowder and defiance to the world!

For some time did I indulge in a pensive train of thought;

contrasting, in sober sadness, the present day with the hallowed years behind the mountains; lamenting the melancholy progress of improvement, and praising the zeal with which our worthy burghers endeavored to preserve the wrecks of venerable customs, prejudices, and errors from the overwhelming tide of modern innovation—when, by degrees, my ideas took a different turn, and I insensibly awakened to an enjoyment of the beauties around me.

It was one of those rich autumnal days which heaven particularly bestows upon the beauteous island of Manna-hata and its vicinity—not a floating cloud obscured the azure firmament—the sun, rolling in glorious splendor through his ethereal course, seemed to expand his honest Dutch countenance into an unusual expression of benevolence, as he smiled his evening salutation upon a city which he delights to visit with his most bounteous beams—the very winds seemed to hold in their breaths in mute attention, lest they should ruffle the tranquillity of the hour—and the waveless bosom of the bay presented a polished mirror, in which nature beheld herself and smiled. The standard of our city, reserved, like a choice handkerchief, for days of gala, hung motionless on the flag-staff, which forms the handle of a gigantic churn; and even the tremulous leaves of the poplar and the aspen ceased to vibrate to the breath of heaven. Everything seemed to acquiesce in the profound repose of nature. The formidable eighteen-pounders slept in the embrazures of the wooden batteries, seemingly gathering fresh strength to fight the battles of their country on the next fourth of July; the solitary drum on Governor's Island forgot to call the garrison to their *shovels;* the evening gun had not yet sounded its signal for all the regular well-meaning poultry throughout the country to go to roost; and the fleet of canoes, at anchor between Gibbet Island and Communipaw, slumbered on their rakes, and suffered the innocent oysters to lie for a while unmolested in the soft mud of their native banks! My own feelings sympathized with the contagious tranquillity, and I should infallibly have dozed upon one of those fragments of benches, which our benevolent magistrates have provided for the benefit of convalescent loungers, had not the extraordinary inconvenience of the couch set all repose at defiance.

In the midst of this slumber of the soul, my attention was attracted to a black speck, peering above the western horizon, just in the rear of Bergen steeple: gradually it augments and overhangs the would-be cities of Jersey, Harsimus, and Hoboken, which, like three jockeys, are starting on the course of existence, and jostling each other at the commencement of the race. Now it skirts the long shore of ancient Pavonia, spreading its wide shadows from the high settlements of Weehawk quite to the lazaretto and quarantine erected by the sagacity of our police, for the embarrassment of commerce; now it climbs the serene vault of heaven, cloud rolling over cloud, shrouding the orb of day, darkening the vast expanse, and bearing thunder and hail and tempest in its bosom. The earth seems agitated at the confusion of the heavens; the late waveless mirror is lashed into furious waves that roll in hollow murmurs to the shore; the oyster-boats that erst sported in the placid vicinity of Gibbet Island, now hurry affrighted to the land; the poplar writhes and twists and whistles in the blast; torrents of drenching rain and sounding hail deluge the Battery walks; the gates are thronged by apprentices, servant-maids, and little Frenchmen, with pocket-handkerchiefs over their hats, scampering from the storm; the late beauteous prospect presents one scene of anarchy and wild uproar, as though old Chaos had resumed his reign, and was hurling back into one vast turmoil the conflicting elements of nature.

Whether I fled from the fury of the storm, or remained boldly at my post, as our gallant train-band captains who march their soldiers through the rain without flinching, are points which I leave to the conjecture of the reader. It is possible he may be a little perplexed also to know the reason why I introduced this tremendous tempest to disturb the serenity of my work. On this latter point I will gratuitously instruct his ignorance. The panorama view of the Battery was given merely to gratify the reader with a correct description of that celebrated place and the parts adjacent; secondly, the storm was played off, partly to give a little bustle and life to this tranquil part of my work, and to keep my drowsy readers from falling asleep, and partly to serve as an overture to the tempestuous times which are about to assail the pacific province of Nieuw Nederlandts, and which overhang the slumbrous administration of the renowned Wouter Van Twiller.

It is thus the experienced playwright puts all the fiddles, the French-horns, the kettle-drums, and trumpets of his orchestra in requisition, to usher in one of those horrible and brimstone uproars called Melodrames—and it is thus he discharges his thunder, his lightning, his rosin, and saltpetre, preparatory to the rising of a ghost or the murdering of a hero. We will now proceed with our history.

Whatever may be advanced by philosophers to the contrary, I am of opinion, that, as to nations, the old maxim, that "honesty is the best policy," is a sheer and ruinous mistake. It might have answered well enough in the honest times when it was made; but in these degenerate days, if a nation pretends to rely merely upon the justice of its dealings, it will fare something like the honest man who fell among thieves, and found his honesty a poor protection against bad company. Such, at least, was the case with the guileless government of the New Netherlands; which, like a worthy unsuspicious old burgher, quietly settled itself down in the city of New Amsterdam, as into a snug elbow-chair, and fell into a comfortable nap, while, in the mean time, its cunning neighbors stepped in and picked its pockets. In a word, we may ascribe the commencement of all the woes of this great province, and its magnificent metropolis, to the tranquil security, or, to speak more accurately, to the unfortunate honesty of its government. But as I dislike to begin an important part of my history towards the end of a chapter, and as my readers, like myself, must doubtless be exceedingly fatigued with the long walk we have taken, and the tempest we have sustained, I hold it meet we shut up the book, smoke a pipe, and, having thus refreshed our spirits, take a fair start in a new chapter.

CHAPTER VII

Faithfully Describing the Ingenious People of Connecticut and Thereabouts—Showing, Moreover, the True Meaning of Liberty of Conscience, and a Curious Device Among These Sturdy Barbarians to Keep Up a Harmony of Intercourse, and Promote Population

THAT my readers may the more fully comprehend the extent of the calamity, at this very moment impending over the honest, unsuspecting province of Nieuw Nederlandts, and its dubious governor, it is necessary that I should give some account of a horde of strange barbarians, bordering upon the eastern frontier.

Now so it came to pass, that, many years previous to the time of which we are treating, the sage cabinet of England had adopted a certain national creed, a kind of public walk of faith, or rather a religious turnpike, in which every loyal subject was directed to travel to Zion—taking care to pay the *toll-gatherers* by the way.

Albeit a certain shrewd race of men, being very much given to indulge their own opinions on all manner of subjects (a propensity exceedingly offensive to your free governments of Europe), did most presumptuously dare to think for themselves in matters of religion, exercising what they considered a natural and unextinguishable right—the liberty of conscience.

As, however, they possessed that ingenuous habit of mind which always thinks aloud, which rides cock-a-hoop on the tongue, and is forever galloping into other people's ears, it naturally followed that their liberty of conscience likewise implied *liberty of speech*, which being freely indulged, soon put the country in a hubbub, and aroused the pious indignation of the vigilant fathers of the church.

The usual methods were adopted to reclaim them, which in those days were considered efficacious in bringing back stray sheep to the fold; that is to say, they were coaxed, they were admonished, they were menaced, they were buffeted—line upon line, precept upon precept, lash upon lash, here a little and there a great deal, were exhorted without mercy and without success—until the worthy pastors of the church, wearied out by their unparalleled stubbornness, were driven, in the excess of their tender mercy, to adopt the Scripture text, and literally to "heap live embers on their heads."

Nothing, however, could subdue that independence of the tongue which has ever distinguished this singular race, so that, rather than subject that heroic member to further tyranny, they one and all embarked for the wilderness of America, to enjoy, unmolested, the inestimable right of talking. And, in fact, no sooner did they land upon the shore of this free-spoken country, than they all lifted up their voices, and made such a clamor of tongues, that we are told they frightened every bird and beast out of the neighborhood, and struck such mute terror into certain fish, that they have been called *dumb-fish* ever since.

This may appear marvellous, but it is nevertheless true; in proof of which I would observe, that the dumb-fish has ever since become an object of superstitious reverence, and forms the Saturday's dinner of every true Yankee.

The simple aborigines of the land for a while contemplated these strange folk in utter astonishment; but discovering that they wielded harmless though noisy weapons, and were a lively, ingenious, good-humored race of men, they became very friendly and sociable, and gave them the name of *Yanokies*, which in the Mais-Teusaeg (or Massachusett) language signifies *silent men* —a waggish appellation, since shortened into the familiar epithet of YANKEES, which they retain unto the present day.

True it is, and my fidelity as an historian will not allow me to pass over the fact, that, having served a regular apprenticeship in the school of persecution, these ingenious people soon showed that they had become masters of the art. The great majority were of one particular mode of thinking in matters of religion; but, to their great surprise and indignation, they found that divers papists, quakers, and anabaptists were springing up among them, and all claiming to use the liberty of speech. This was at once pronounced a daring abuse of the liberty of conscience, which they now insisted was nothing more than the liberty to think as one pleased in matters of religion—provided one thought right; for otherwise it would be giving a latitude to damnable heresies. Now as they, the majority, were convinced that they alone thought right, it consequently followed, that whoever thought different from them thought wrong—and whoever thought wrong, and obstinately persisted in not being convinced and converted, was a flagrant violator of the inestimable liberty of conscience, and a corrupt and infectious member of the body politic, and deserved to be lopped off and cast into the fire. The consequence of all which was a fiery persecution of divers sects, and especially of quakers.

Now I'll warrant there are hosts of my readers, ready at once to lift up their hands and eyes, with that virtuous indignation with which we contemplate the faults and errors of our neighbors, and to exclaim at the preposterous idea of convincing the mind by tormenting the body, and establishing the doctrine of charity and forbearance by intolerant persecution. But in simple truth what are we doing at this very day, and in this very enlightened nation, but acting upon the very same principle in our political controversies? Have we not within but a few years released ourselves from the shackles of a government which cruelly denied us the privilege of governing ourselves, and using in full latitude that invaluable member, the tongue? and are we not at this very moment striving our best to tyrannize over the opinions, tie up the tongues, and ruin the fortunes of one another? What are our great political societies, but mere political inquisitions—our pot-house committees, but little tribunals of denunciation—our newspapers, but mere whipping-posts and pillories, where unfortunate individuals are pelted with rotten eggs—and our council of appointment, but a grand *auto da fé* where culprits are annually sacrificed for their political heresies?

Where, then, is the difference in principle between our measures and those you are so ready to condemn among the people I am treating of? There is none; the difference is merely circumstantial. Thus we *denounce*, instead of banishing—we *libel*, instead of scourging—we *turn out of office*, instead of hanging—and where they burnt an offender in proper person, we either tar and feather, or *burn him in effigy*—this political persecution being, somehow or other, the grand palladium of our liberties, and an incontrovertible proof that this is *a free country!*

But nothwithstanding the fervent zeal with which this holy war was prosecuted against the whole race of unbelievers, we do not find that the population of this new colony was in any wise hindered thereby; on the contrary, they multiplied to a degree which would be incredible to any man unacquainted with the marvellous fecundity of this growing country.

This amazing increase may, indeed, be partly ascribed to a singular custom prevalent among them, commonly known by the name of *bundling*—a superstitious rite observed by the young people of both sexes, with which they usually terminated their festivities, and which was kept up with religious strictness by the more bigoted part of the community. This ceremony was likewise, in those primitive times, considered as an indispensable preliminary to matrimony, their courtships commencing where ours usually finish—by which means they acquired that intimate acquaintance with each other's good qualities before marriage, which has been pronounced by philosophers the sure basis of a happy union. Thus early did this cunning and ingenious people display a shrewdness of making a bargain, which has ever since distinguished them—and a strict adherence to the good old vulgar maxim about "buying a pig in a poke."

To this sagacious custom, therefore, do I chiefly attribute the unparalleled increase of the Yanokie or Yankee race; for it is a certain fact, well authenticated by court records and parish registers, that, wherever the practice of bundling prevailed, there was an amazing number of sturdy brats annually born unto the State, without the license of the law, or the benefit of clergy. Neither did the irregularity of their birth operate in the least to their disparagement. On the contrary, they grew up a long-sided, raw-boned, hardy race of whoreson whalers, woodcutters, fishermen, and peddlers, and strapping corn-fed wenches—who by their united efforts tended marvellously towards peopling those notable tracts of country called Nantucket, Piscataway, and Cape Cod.

CHAPTER VIII

How These Singular Barbarians Turned Out to Be Notorious Squatters—How They Built Air-castles, and Attempted to Initiate the Nederlanders into the Mystery of Bundling

IN the last chapter I have given a faithful and unprejudiced account of the origin of that singular race of people inhabiting the country eastward of the Nieuw Nederlandts; but I have yet to mention certain peculiar habits which rendered them exceedingly annoying to our ever-honored Dutch ancestors.

The most prominent of these was a certain rambling propensity, with which, like the sons of Ishmael, they seem to have been gifted by heaven, and which continually goads them on to shift their residence from place to place, so that a Yankee farmer is in a constant state of migration, *tarrying* occasionally here and there, clearing lands for other people to enjoy, building houses for others to inhabit, and in a manner may be considered the wandering Arab of America.

His first thought, on coming to years of manhood, is to *settle* himself in the world—which means nothing more nor less than to begin his rambles. To this end he takes unto himself for a wife some buxom country heiress, passing rich in red ribbons, glass beads, and mock tortoise-shell combs, with a white gown and morocco shoes for Sunday, and deeply skilled in the mystery of making apple-sweetmeats, long sauce, and pumpkin-pie.

Having thus provided himself, like a peddler with a heavy knapsack, wherewith to regale his shoulders through the journey of life, he literally sets out on the peregrination. His whole family, household-furniture, and farming-utensils are hoisted into a covered cart, his own and his wife's wardrobe packed up in a firkin—which done, he shoulders axe, takes staff in hand, whistles "Yankee doodle," and trudges off to the woods, as confident of the protection of Providence, and relying as cheerfully upon his own resources, as ever did a patriarch of yore when he journeyed into a strange country of the Gentiles. Having buried himself in the wilderness, he builds himself a log hut, clears away a cornfield and potato-patch, and, Providence smiling upon his labors, is soon surrounded by a snug farm and some half a score of flaxen-headed urchins, who, by their size, seem to have sprung all at once out of the earth, like a crop of toadstools.

But it is not the nature of this most indefatigable of speculators to rest contented with any state of sublunary enjoyment: *improvement* is his darling passion; and having thus improved his lands, the next care is to provide a mansion worthy the residence of a landholder. A huge palace of pine boards immediately springs up in the midst of the wilderness, large enough for a parish church, and furnished with windows of all dimensions, but so rickety and flimsy withal, that every blast gives it a fit of the ague.

By the time the outside of this mighty air-castle is completed, either the funds or the zeal of our adventurer is exhausted, so that he barely manages to furnish one room within, where the whole family burrow together—while the rest of the house is devoted to the curing of pumpkins, or storing of carrots and potatoes, and is decorated with fanciful festoons of dried apples and peaches. The outside, remaining unpainted, grows venerably black with time; the family wardrobe is laid under contribution for old hats, petticoats, and breeches, to stuff into the broken windows, while the four winds of heaven keep up a whistling and howling about this aërial palace, and play as many unruly gambols as they did of yore in the cave of old Æolus.

The humble log hut, which whilom nestled this *improving* family snugly within its narrow but comfortable walls, stands hard by, in ignominious contrast, degraded into a cow-house or pig-sty; and the whole scene reminds one forcibly of a fable, which I am surprised has never been recorded, of an aspiring snail, who abandoned his humble habitation, which he had long filled with great respectability, to crawl into the empty shell of a lobster—where he would no doubt have resided with great style and splendor, the envy and the hate of all the painstaking snails in the neighborhood, had he not perished with cold in one corner of his stupendous mansion.

Being thus completely settled, and, to use his own words, "to rights," one would imagine that he would begin to enjoy the comforts of his situation—to read newspapers, talk politics, neglect his own business, and attend to the affairs of the nation, like a useful and patriotic citizen; but now it is that his wayward disposition begins again to operate. He soon grows tired of a spot where there is no longer any room for improvement—sells his farm, air-castle, petticoat windows and all, reloads his cart, shoulders his axe, puts himself at the head of his family, and wanders away in search of new lands—again to fell trees—again to clear cornfields—again to build a shingle palace, and again to sell off and wander. Such were the people of Connecticut, who bordered upon the eastern frontier of New Netherlands; and my readers may easily imagine what uncomfortable neighbors this light-hearted but restless tribe must have been to our tranquil progenitors. If they cannot, I would ask them if they have ever known one of our regular, well-organized Dutch families, whom it hath pleased heaven to afflict with the neighborhood of a French boarding-house? The honest old burgher cannot take his afternoon's pipe on the bench before his door, but he is persecuted with the scraping of fiddles, the chattering of women, and the squalling of children; he cannot sleep at night for the horrible melodies of some amateur, who chooses to serenade the moon, and display his terrible proficiency in *execution*, on the clarionet, hautboy, or some other soft-toned instrument; nor can he leave the street-door open, but his house is defiled by the unsavory visits of a troop of pup-dogs, who even sometimes carry their loathsome ravages into the *sanctum sanctorum*, the parlor!

If my readers have ever witnessed the sufferings of such a family, so situated, they may form some idea how our worthy ancestors were distressed by their mercurial neighbors of Connecticut.

Gangs of these marauders, we are told, penetrated into the New Netherland settlements, and threw whole villages into consternation by their unparalleled volubility and their intolerable inquisitiveness—two evil habits hitherto unknown in those parts, or only known to be abhorred; for our ancestors were noted as being men of truly Spartan taciturnity, and who neither knew nor cared aught about anybody's concerns but their own. Many enormities were committed on the highways, where several unoffending burghers were brought to a stand, and tortured with questions and guesses—which outrages occasioned as much vexation and heart-burning as does the modern right of search on the high seas.

Great jealousy did they likewise stir up, by their intermeddling and successes among the divine sex; for, being a race of brisk, likely, pleasant-tongued varlets, they soon seduced the light affections of the simple damsels from their ponderous Dutch gallants. Among other hideous customs, they attempted to introduce among them that of *bundling*, which the Dutch lasses of the Nederlandts, with that eager passion for novelty and foreign fashions natural to their sex, seemed very well inclined to follow, but that their mothers, being more experienced in the world, and better acquainted with men and things, strenuously discountenanced all such outlandish innovations.

But what chiefly operated to embroil our ancestors with these strange folk, was an unwarrantable liberty which they occasionally took of entering in hordes into the territories of the New Netherlands, and settling themselves down, without leave or license, to *improve* the land, in the manner I have before noticed. This unceremonious mode of taking possession of *new land* was technically termed *squatting*, and hence is derived the appellation of *squatters*—a name odious in the ears of all great landholders, and which is given to those enterprising worthies who seize upon land first, and take their chance to make good their title to it afterwards.

All these grievances, and many others which were constantly accumulating, tended to form that dark and portentous cloud, which, as I observed in a former chapter, was slowly gathering over the tranquil province of New Netherlands. The pacific cabinet of Van Twiller, however, as will be perceived in the sequel, bore them all with a magnanimity that redounds to their immortal credit, becoming by passive endurance inured to this increasing mass of wrongs—like that mighty man of old, who, by dint of carrying about a calf from the time it was born, continued to carry it without difficulty when it had grown to be an ox.

CHAPTER IX

How the Fort Goed Hoop Was Fearfully Beleaguered—How the Renowned Wouter Fell into a Profound Doubt, and How He Finally Evaporated

BY this time my readers must fully perceive what an arduous task I have undertaken—exploring a little kind of Herculaneum of history, which had lain nearly for ages buried under the rubbish of years, and almost totally forgotten—raking up the limbs and fragments of disjointed facts, and endeavoring to put them scrupulously together, so as to restore them to their original form and connection—now lugging forth the character of an almost forgotten hero, like a mutilated statue, now deciphering a half-defaced inscription, and now lighting upon a mouldering manuscript, which, after painful study, scarce repays the trouble of perusal.

In such case, how much has the reader to depend upon the honor and probity of his author, lest, like a cunning antiquarian, he either impose upon him some spurious fabrication of his own for a precious relic of antiquity, or else dress up the dismembered fragment with such false trappings, that it is scarcely possible to distinguish the truth from the fiction with which it is enveloped. This is a grievance which I have more than once had to lament, in the course of my wearisome researches among the works of my fellow-historians, who have strangely disguised and distorted the facts respecting this country; and particularly respecting the great province of New Netherlands; as will be perceived by any who will take the trouble to compare their romantic effusions, tricked out in the meretricious gauds of fable, with this authentic history.

I have had more vexations of the kind to encounter, in those parts of my history which treat of the transactions on the eastern border, than in any other, in consequence of the troops of historians who have infested these quarters, and have shown the honest people of Nieuw Nederlandts no mercy in their works. Among the rest, Mr. Benjamin Trumbull arrogantly declares, that "the Dutch were always mere intruders." Now, to this I shall make no other reply than to proceed in the steady narration of my history, which will contain not only proofs that the Dutch had clear title and possession in the fair valleys of the Connecticut, and that they were wrongfully dispossessed thereof, but likewise, that they have been scandalously maltreated ever since by the misrepresentations of the crafty historians of New England. And in this I shall be guided by a spirit of truth and impartiality, and a regard to immortal fame; for I would not wittingly dishonor my work by a single falsehood, misrepresentation, or prejudice, though it should gain our forefathers the whole country of New England.

I have already noticed, in a former chapter of my history, that the territories of the Nieuw Nederlandts extended on the east, quite to the Varsche or fresh, or Connecticut river. Here, at an early period, had been established a frontier post on the bank of the river, and called Fort Goed Hoop, not far from the site of the present fair city of Hartford. It was placed under the command of Jacobus Van Curlet, or Curlis, as some historians will have it—a doughty soldier, of that stomachful class famous for eating all they kill. He was long in the body and short in the limb, as though a tall man's body had been mounted on a little man's legs. He made up for this turnspit construction by striding to such an extent, that you would have sworn he had on the seven-leagued boots of Jack the Giant-killer; and so high did he tread on parade, that his soldiers were sometimes alarmed lest he should trample himself under foot.

But notwithstanding the erection of this fort and the appointment of this ugly little man of war as commander, the Yankees continued the interlopings hinted at in my last chapter, and at length had the audacity to *squat* themselves down within the jurisdiction of Fort Goed Hoop.

The long-bodied Van Curlet protested with great spirit against these unwarrantable encroachments, couching his protest in Low Dutch, by way of inspiring more terror, and forthwith dispatched a copy of the protest to the governor at New Amsterdam, together with a long and bitter account of the aggressions of the enemy. This done, he ordered his men, one and all, to be of good cheer, shut the gate of the fort, smoked three pipes, went to bed, and awaited the result with a resolute and intrepid tranquillity, that greatly animated his adherents, and no doubt struck sore dismay and affright into the hearts of the enemy.

Now it came to pass, that about this time the renowned Wouter Van Twiller, full of years and honors, and council-dinners, had reached that period of life and faculty which, according to the great Gulliver, entitles a man to admission into the ancient order of Struldbruggs. He employed his time in smoking his Turkish pipe, amid an assemblage of sages, equally enlightened and nearly as venerable as himself, and who, for their silence, their gravity, their wisdom, and their cautious averseness to coming to any conclusion in business, are only to be equalled by certain profound corporations which I have known in my time. Upon reading the protest of the gallant Jacobus Van Curlet, therefore, his excellency fell straightway into one of the deepest doubts that ever he was known to encounter; his capacious head gradually drooped on his chest, he closed his eyes, and inclined his ear to one side, as if listening with great attention to the discussion that was going on in his belly—and which all who knew him declared to be the huge court-house or council-chamber of his thoughts, forming to his head what the house of representatives does to the Senate. An inarticulate sound, very much resembling a snore, occasionally escaped him; but the nature of this internal cogitation was never known, as he never opened his lips on the subject to man, woman, or child. In the mean time, the protest of Van Curlet lay quietly on the table, where it served to light the pipes of the venerable sages assembled in council; and in the great smoke which they raised, the gallant Jacobus, his protest, and his mighty Fort Goed Hoop were soon as completely beclouded and forgotten as is a question of emergency swallowed up in the speeches and resolutions of a modern session of Congress.

There are certain emergencies when your profound legislators and sage deliberative councils are mightily in the way of a nation, and when an ounce of hare-brained decision is worth a pound of sage doubt and cautious discussion. Such, at least, was the case at present; for, while the renowned Wouter Van Twiller was daily battling with his doubts, and his resolution growing weaker and weaker in the contest, the enemy pushed farther and farther into his territories, and assumed a most formidable appearance in the neighborhood of Fort Goed Hoop. Here they founded the mighty town of *Pyquag*, or, as it has since been called, *Weathersfield*, a place which, if we may credit the assertions of that worthy historian, John Josselyn, Gent., "hath been infamous by reason of the witches therein." And so daring did these men of Pyquag become, that they extended those plantations of onions, for which their town is illustrious, under the very noses of the garrison of Fort Goed Hoop, insomuch that the honest Dutchmen could not look toward that quarter without tears in their eyes.

This crying injustice was regarded with proper indignation by the gallant Jacobus Van Curlet. He absolutely trembled with the violence of his choler and the exacerbations of his valor, which were the more turbulent in their workings from the length of the body in which they were agitated. He forthwith proceeded to strengthen his redoubts, heighten his breastworks, deepen his fosse, and fortify his position with a double row of abatis; after which he dispatched a fresh courier with accounts of his perilous situation.

The courier chosen to bear the dispatches was a fat, oily, little man, as being less liable to be worn out, or to lose leather on the journey; and to insure his speed, he was mounted on the fleetest wagon-horse in the garrison, remarkable for length of limb, largeness of bone, and hardness of trot, and so tall, that the little messenger was obliged to climb on his back by means of his tail and crupper. Such extraordinary speed did he make, that he arrived at Fort Amsterdam in a little less than a month, though the distance was full two hundred pipes, or about one hundred and twenty miles.

With an appearance of great hurry and business, and smoking a short travelling-pipe, he proceeded on a long swing-trot through the muddy lanes of the metropolis, demolishing whole batches of dirt-pies, which the little Dutch children were making in the road; and for which kind of pastry the children of this city have ever been famous. On arriving at the governor's house, he climbed down from his steed, roused the gray-headed doorkeeper, old Skaats, who, like his lineal descendant and faithful representative, the venerable crier of our court, was nodding at his post, rattled at the door of the council-chamber, and startled the members as they were dozing over a plan for establishing a public market.

At that very moment a gentle grunt, or rather a deep-drawn snore, was heard from the chair of the governor; a whiff of smoke was at the same instant observed to escape from his lips, and a light cloud to ascend from the bowl of his pipe. The council, of course, supposed him engaged in deep sleep, for the good of the community, and according to custom in all such cases established, every man bawled out silence, when, of a sudden, the door flew open, and the little courier straddled into the apartment, cased to the middle in a pair of Hessian boots, which he had got into for the sake of expedition. In his right hand he held forth the ominous dispatches, and with his left he grasped firmly the waistband of his galligaskins, which had unfortunately given way in the exertion of descending from his horse. He stumped resolutely up to the governor, and with more hurry than perspicuity delivered his message. But fortunately his ill tidings came too late to ruffle the tranquillity of this most tranquil of rulers. His venerable excellency had just breathed and smoked his last —his lungs and his pipe having been exhausted together, and his peaceful soul having escaped in the last whiff that curled from his tobacco-pipe. In a word, the renowned Walter the Doubter, who had so often slumbered with his contemporaries, now slept with his fathers, and Wilhelmus Kieft governed in his stead.

Book IV

CONTAINING THE CHRONICLES OF THE REIGN OF WILLIAM THE TESTY

CHAPTER I

Showing the Nature of History in General; Containing Furthermore the Universal Acquirements of William the Testy, and How a Man May Learn So Much as to Render Himself Good for Nothing

WHEN the lofty Thucydides is about to enter upon his description of the plague that desolated Athens, one of his modern commentators assures the reader, that the history is now going to be exceeding solemn, serious, and pathetic, and hints, with that air of chuckling gratulation with which a good dame draws forth a choice morsel from a cupboard to regale a favorite, that this plague will give his history a most agreeable variety.

In like manner did my heart leap within me, when I came to the dolorous dilemma of Fort Goed Hoop, which I at once perceived to be the forerunner of a series of great events and entertaining disasters. Such are the true subjects for the historic pen. For what is history, in fact, but a kind of Newgate calendar, a register of the crimes and miseries that man has inflicted on his fellowman? It is a huge libel on human nature, to which we industriously add page after page, volume after volume, as if we were building up a monument to the honor, rather than the infamy of our species. If we turn over the pages of these chronicles that man has written of himself, what are the characters dignified by the appellation of great, and held up to the admiration of posterity? Tyrants, robbers, conquerors, renowned only for the magnitude of their misdeeds, and the stupendous wrongs and miseries they have inflicted on mankind—warriors, who have hired themselves to the trade of blood, not from motives of virtuous patriotism, or to protect the injured and defenceless, but merely to gain the vaunted glory of being adroit and successful in massacring their fellow-beings! What are the great events that constitute a glorious era?—The fall of empires; the desolation of happy countries; splendid cities smoking in their ruins; the proudest works of art tumbled in the dust; the shrieks and groans of whole nations ascending unto heaven!

It is thus the historian may be said to thrive on the miseries of mankind, like birds of prey which hover over the field of battle to fatten on the mighty dead. It was observed by a great projector of inland lock-navigation, that rivers, lakes, and oceans were only formed to feed canals. In like manner I am tempted to believe that plots, conspiracies, wars, victories, and massacres are ordained by Providence only as food for the historian.

It is a source of great delight to the philosopher, in studying the wonderful economy of nature, to trace the mutual dependencies of things, how they are created reciprocally for each other, and how the most noxious and apparently unnecessary animal has its uses. Thus those swarms of flies, which are so often execrated as useless vermin, are created for the sustenance of spiders; and spiders, on the other hand, are evidently made to devour flies. So those heroes, who have been such scourges to the world, were bounteously provided as themes for the poet and historian, while the poet and the historian were destined to record the achievements of heroes!

These, and many similar reflections, naturally arose in my mind as I took up my pen to commence the reign of William Kieft: for now the stream of our history, which hitherto has rolled in a tranquil current, is about to depart forever from its peaceful haunts, and brawl through many a turbulent and rugged scene.

As some sleek ox, sunk in the rich repose of a clover-field, dozing and chewing the cud, will bear repeated blows before it raises itself, so the province of Nieuw Nederlandts, having waxed fat under the drowsy reign of the Doubter, needed cuffs and kicks to rouse it into action. The reader will now witness the manner in which a peaceful community advances towards a state of war; which is apt to be like the approach of a horse to a drum, with much prancing and little progress, and too often with the wrong end foremost.

Wilhelmus Kieft, who in 1634 ascended the gubernatorial chair (to borrow a favorite though clumsy appellation of modern phraseologists), was of a lofty descent, his father being inspector of wind-mills in the ancient town of Saardam; and our hero, we are told, when a boy, made very curious investigations into the nature and operation of these machines, which was one reason why he afterwards came to be so ingenious a governor. His name, according to the most authentic etymologists, was a corruption of Kyver, that is to say, a *wrangler* or *scolder*, and expressed the characteristic of his family, which, for nearly two centuries, had kept the windy town of Saardam in hot water, and produced more tartars and brimstones than any ten families in the place; and so truly did he inherit this family peculiarity, that he had not been a year in the government of the province, before he was universally denominated William the Testy. His appearance answered to his name. He was a brisk, wiry, waspish little old gentleman; such a one as may now and then be seen stumping about our city in a broad-skirted coat with huge buttons, a cocked hat stuck on the back of his head, and a cane as high as his chin. His face was broad, but his features were sharp; his cheeks were scorched into a dusky red by two fiery little gray eyes; his nose turned up, and the corners of his mouth turned down, pretty much like the muzzle of an irritable pug-dog.

I have heard it observed by a profound adept in human physiology, that if a woman waxes fat with the progress of years, her tenure of life is somewhat precarious, but if haply she withers as she grows old, she lives forever. Such promised to be the case with William the Testy, who grew tough in proportion as he dried. He had withered, in fact, not through the process of years, but through the tropical fervor of his soul, which burnt like a vehement rush-light in his bosom, inciting him to incessant broils and bickerings. Ancient traditions speak much of his learning, and of the gallant inroads he had made into the dead languages, in which he had made captive a host of Greek nouns and Latin verbs, and brought off rich booty in ancient saws and apothegms, which he was wont to parade in his public harangues, as a triumphant general of yore his *spolia opima*. Of metaphysics he knew enough to confound all hearers and himself into the bargain. In logic, he knew the whole family of syllogisms and dilemmas, and was so proud of his skill that he never suffered even a self-evident fact to pass unargued. It was observed, however, that he seldom got into an argument without getting into a perplexity, and then into a passion with his adversary for not being convinced gratis.

He had, moreover, skirmished smartly on the frontiers of several of the sciences, was fond of experimental philosophy, and prided himself upon inventions of all kinds. His abode, which he had fixed at a Bowerie or country-seat at a short distance from the city, just at what is now called Dutch Street, soon abounded with proofs of his ingenuity: patent smoke-jacks that required a horse to work them; Dutch ovens that roasted meat without fire; carts that went before the horses; weather-cocks that turned against the wind; and other wrong-headed contrivances that astonished and confounded all beholders. The house, too, was beset with paralytic cats and dogs, the subjects of his experimental philosophy; and the yelling and yelping of the latter unhappy victims of science, while aiding in the pursuit of knowledge, soon gained for the place the name of "Dog's Misery," by which it continues to be known even at the present day.

It is in knowledge as in swimming: he who flounders and splashes on the surface makes more noise, and attracts more attention, than the pearl-diver who quietly dives in quest of treasures to the bottom. The vast acquirements of the new governor were the theme of marvel among the simple burghers of New Amsterdam; he figured about the place as learned a man as a Bonze at Pekin, who has mastered one half of the Chinese alphabet, and was unanimously pronounced a "universal genius!"

I have known in my time many a genius of this stamp; but, to speak my mind freely, I never knew one who, for the ordinary purposes of life, was worth his weight in straw. In this respect, a little sound judgment and plain common sense is worth all the sparkling genius that ever wrote poetry or invented theories. Let us see how the universal acquirements of William the Testy aided him in the affairs of government.

CHAPTER II

How William the Testy Undertook to Conquer by Proclamation —How He Was a Great Man Abroad, but a Little Man in His Own House

NO sooner had this bustling little potentate been blown by a whiff of fortune into the seat of government than he called his council together to make them a speech on the state of affairs.

Caius Gracchus, it is said, when he harangued the Roman populace, modulated his tone by an oratorical flute or pitch-pipe; Wilhelmus Kieft, not having such an instrument at hand, availed himself of that musical organ or trump which nature has implanted in the midst of a man's face: in other words, he preluded his address by a sonorous blast of the nose—a preliminary flourish much in vogue among public orators.

He then commenced by expressing his humble sense of his utter unworthiness of the high post to which he had been appointed; which made some of the simple burghers wonder why he undertook it, not knowing that it is a point of etiquette with a public orator never to enter upon office without declaring himself unworthy to cross the threshold. He then proceeded in a manner highly classic and erudite to speak of government generally, and of the governments of ancient Greece in particular, together with the wars of Rome and Carthage, and the rise and fall of sundry outlandish empires which the worthy burghers had never read nor heard of. Having thus, after the manner of your learned orator, treated of things in general, he came, by a natural, roundabout transition, to the matter in hand, namely, the daring aggressions of the Yankees.

As my readers are well aware of the advantage a potentate has of handling his enemies as he pleases in his speeches and bulletins, where he has the talk all on his own side, they may rest assured that William the Testy did not let such an opportunity escape of giving the Yankees what is called "a taste of his quality." In speaking of their inroads into the territories of their High Mightinesses, he compared them to the Gauls who desolated Rome, the Goths and Vandals who overran the fairest plains of Europe; but when he came to speak of the unparalleled audacity with which they of Weathersfield had advanced their patches up to the very walls of Fort Goed Hoop, and threatened to smother the garrison in onions, tears of rage started into his eyes, as though he nosed the very offence in question.

Having thus wrought up his tale to a climax, he assumed a most belligerent look, and assured the council that he had devised an instrument, potent in its effects, and which he trusted would soon drive the Yankees from the land. So saying, he thrust his hand into one of deep pockets of his broad-skirted coat and drew forth, not an infernal machine, but an instrument in writing, which he laid with great emphasis upon the table.

The burghers gazed at it for a time in silent awe, as a wary housewife does at a gun, fearful it may go off halfcocked. The document in question had a sinister look, it is true; it was crabbed in text, and from a broad red ribbon dangled the great seal of the province, about the size of a buckwheat pancake. Still, after all, it was but an instrument in writing. Herein, however, existed the wonder of the invention. The document in question was a PROCLAMATION, ordering the Yankees to depart instantly from the territories of their High Mightinesses, under pain of suffering all the forfeitures and punishments in such case made and provided. In was on the moral effect of this formidable instrument that Wilhelmus Kieft calculated, pledging his valor as a governor that, once fulminated against the Yankees, it would, in less than two months, drive every mother's son of them across the borders.

The council broke up in perfect wonder; and nothing was talked of for some time among the old men and women of New Amsterdam but the vast genius of the governor, and his new and cheap mode of fighting by proclamation.

As to Wilhelmus Kieft, having dispatched his proclamation to the frontiers, he put on his cocked hat and corduroy small-clothes, and mounting a tall raw-boned charger, trotted out to his rural retreat of Dog's Misery. Here, like the good Numa, he reposed from the toils of state, taking lessons in government, not from the nymph Egeria, but from the honored wife of his bosom; who was one of that class of females sent upon the earth a little after the flood, as a punishment for the sins of mankind, and commonly known by the appellation of *knowing women*. In fact, my duty as an historian obliges me to make known a circumstance which was a great secret at the time, and consequently was not a subject of scandal at more than half the tea-tables in New Amsterdam, but which, like many other great secrets, has leaked out in the lapse of years—and this was, that Wilhelmus the Testy, though one of the most potent little men that ever breathed, yet submitted at home to a species of government, neither laid down in Aristotle nor Plato, in short, it partook of the nature of a pure, unmixed tyranny, and is familiarly denominated *petticoat government*—an absolute sway, which, although exceedingly common in these modern days, was very rare among the ancients, if we may judge from the rout made about the domestic economy of honest Socrates; which is the only ancient case on record.

The great Kieft, however, warded off all the sneers and sarcasms of his particular friends, who are ever ready to joke with a man on sore points of the kind, by alleging that it was a government of his own election, to which he submitted through choice, adding at the same time a profound maxim which he had found in an ancient author, that "he who would aspire to *govern*, should first learn to *obey*."

CHAPTER III

In Which Are Recorded the Sage Projects of a Ruler of Universal Genius—the Art of Fighting by Proclamation—and How That the Valiant Jacobus Van Curlet Came to Be Foully Dishonored at Fort Goed Hoop

NEVER was a more comprehensive, a more expeditious, or, what is still better, a more economical measure devised, than this of defeating the Yankees by proclamation—an expedient, likewise, so gentle and humane, there were ten chances to one in favor of its succeeding; but then there was one chance to ten that it would not succeed—as the ill-natured fates would have it, that single chance carried the day! The proclamation was perfect in all its parts, well constructed, well written, well sealed, and well published; all that was wanting to insure its effect was, that the Yankees should stand in awe of it; but, provoking to relate, they treated it with the most absolute contempt, applied it to an unseemly purpose; and thus did the first warlike proclamation come to a shameful end—a fate which I am credibly informed has befallen but too many of its successors.

So far from abandoning the country, those varlets continued their encroachments, squatting along the green banks of the Varsche river, and founding Hartford, Stamford, New Haven, and other border-towns. I have already shown how the onion patches of Pyquag were an eye-sore to Jacobus Van Curlet and his garrison; but now these moss-troopers increased in their atrocities, kidnapping hogs, impounding horses, and sometimes grievously ribroasting their owners. Our worthy forefathers could scarcely stir abroad without danger of being out-jockeyed in horse-flesh, or taken in in bargaining; while, in their absence, some daring Yankee peddler would penetrate to their household, and nearly ruin the good housewives with tin ware and wooden bowls.*

I am well aware of the perils which environ me in this part of my history. While raking with curious hand but pious heart, among the mouldering remains of former days, anxious to draw therefrom the honey of wisdom, I may fare somewhat like that valiant worthy, Samson, who, in meddling with the carcass of a dead lion, drew a swarm of bees about his ears. Thus, while narrating the many misdeeds of the Yanokie or Yankee race, it is ten chances to one but I offend the morbid sensibilities of cer-

* The following cases in point appear in Hazard's Collection of State Papers.

"In the meantime, they of Hartford have not onely usurped and taken in the lands of Connecticott, although unrighteously and against the lawes of nations but have hindered our nation in sowing theire own purchased broken up lands, but have also sowed them with corne in the night, which the Nederlanders had broken up and intended to sowe: and have beaten the servants of the high and mighty the honored companie, which where laboring upon theire master's lands, from theire lands, with sticks and plow staves in hostile manner laming, and among the rest, struck Ever Duckings [Evert Duyckink] a hole in his head, with a stick, so that the bloode ran downe very strongly downe upon his body."

"Those of Hartford sold a hogg, that belonged to the honored companie, under pretence that it had eaten of theire grounde grass, when they had not any foot of inheritance. They proffered the hogg for 5*s*. if the commissioners would have given 5*s*. for damage; which the commissioners denied, because noe man's own hogg (as men used to say) can trespass upon his owne master's grounde."

tain of their unreasonable descendants, who may fly out and raise such a buzzing about this unlucky head of mine, that I shall need the tough hide of an Achilles, or an Orlando Furioso, to protect me from their stings.

Should such be the case, I should deeply and sincerely lament—not my misfortune in giving offence, but the wrong-headed perverseness of an ill-natured generation, in taking offence at anything I say. That their ancestors did use my ancestors ill is true, and I am very sorry for it. I would, with all my heart, the fact were otherwise; but as I am recording the sacred events of history, I'd not bate one nail's breadth of the honest truth, though I were sure the whole edition of my work would be bought up and burnt by the common hangman of Connecticut. And in sooth, now that these testy gentlemen have drawn me out, I will make bold to go farther, and observe that this is one of the grand purposes for which we impartial historians are sent into the world—to redress wrongs and render justice on the heads of the guilty. So that, though a powerful nation may wrong its neighbors with temporary impunity, yet sooner or later an historian springs up, who wreaks ample chastisement on it in return.

Thus these moss-troopers of the east little thought, I'll warrant it, while they were harassing the inoffensive province of Nieuw Nederlandts, and driving its unhappy governor to his wit's end, that an historian would ever arise, and give them their own, with interest. Since, then, I am but performing my bounden duty as an historian, in avenging the wrongs of our revered ancestors, I shall make no further apology; and, indeed, when it is considered that I have all these ancient borderers of the east in my power, and at the mercy of my pen, I trust that it will be admitted I conduct myself with great humanity and moderation.

It was long before William the Testy could be persuaded that his much-vaunted war-measure was ineffectual; on the contrary, he flew in a passion whenever it was doubted, swearing that, though slow in operation, yet when it once began to work, it would soon purge the land of these invaders. When convinced, at length, of the truth, like a shrewd physician he attributed the failure to the quantity, not the quality of the medicine, and resolved to double the dose. He fulminated, therefore, a second proclamation, more vehement than the first, forbidding all intercourse with these Yankee intruders, ordering the Dutch burghers on the frontiers to buy none of their pacing horses, measly pork, apple-sweetmeats, Weathersfield onions, or wooden bowls, and to furnish them with no supplies of gin, gingerbread, or sourkrout.

Another interval elapsed, during which the last proclamation was as little regarded as the first; and the non-intercourse was especially set at naught by the young folks of both sexes, if we may judge by the active bundling which took place along the borders.

At length, one day the inhabitants of New Amsterdam were aroused by a furious barking of dogs, great and small, and beheld, to their surprise, the whole garrison of Fort Goed Hoop straggling into town all tattered and wayworn, with Jacobus Van Curlet at their head, bringing the melancholy intelligence of the capture of Fort Goed Hoop by the Yankees.

The fate of this important fortress is an impressive warning to all military commanders. It was neither carried by storm nor famine; nor was it undermined; nor bombarded; nor set on fire by red-hot shot; but was taken by a stratagem no less singular than effectual, and which can never fail of success, whenever an opportunity occurs of putting it in practice.

It seems that the Yankees had received intelligence that the garrison of Jacobus Van Curlet had been reduced nearly one eighth by the death of two of his most corpulent soldiers, who had overeaten themselves on fat salmon caught in the Varsche river. A secret expedition was immediately set on foot to surprise the fortress. The crafty enemy, knowing the habits of the garrison to sleep soundly after they had eaten their dinners and smoked their pipes, stole upon them at the noontide of a sultry summer's day, and surprised them in the midst of their slumbers.

In an instant the flag of their High Mightinesses was lowered, and the Yankee standard elevated in its stead, being a dried codfish, by way of a spread eagle. A strong garrison was appointed, of long-sided, hard-fisted Yankees, with Weathersfield onions for cockades and feathers. As to Jacobus Van Curlet and his men, they were seized by the nape of the neck, conducted to the gate, and one by one dismissed by a kick in the crupper, as Charles XII. dismissed the heavy-bottomed Russians at the battle of Narva; Jacobus Van Curlet receiving two kicks in consideration of his official dignity.

CHAPTER IV

Containing the Fearful Wrath of William the Testy, and the Alarm of New Amsterdam—How the Governor Did Strongly Fortify the City—of the Rise of Antony the Trumpeter, and the Windy Addition to the Armorial Bearings of New Amsterdam

LANGUAGE cannot express the awful ire of William the Testy on hearing of the catastrophe at Fort Goed Hoop. For three good hours his rage was too great for words, or rather the words were too great for him (being a very small man), and he was nearly choked by the misshapen, nine-cornered Dutch oaths and epithets which crowded at once into his gullet. At length his words found vent, and for three days he kept up a constant discharge, anathematizing the Yankees, man, woman, and child, for a set of dieven, schobbejacken, deugenieten, twistzoekeren, blaes-kaken, loosen-schalken, kakken-bedden, and a thousand other names, of which, unfortunately for posterity, history does not make mention. Finally, he swore that he would have nothing more to do with such a squatting, bundling, guessing, questioning, swapping, pumpkin-eating, molasses-daubing, shingle-splitting, cider-watering, horse-jockeying, notion-peddling crew; that they might stay at Fort Goed Hoop and rot, before he would dirty his hands by attempting to drive them away: in proof of which he ordered the new-raised troops to be marched forthwith into winter-quarters, although it was not as yet quite midsummer. Great despondency now fell upon the city of New Amsterdam. It was feared that the conquerors of Fort Goed Hoop, flushed with victory and apple-brandy, might march on to the capital, take it by storm, and annex the whole province to Connecticut. The name of Yankee became as terrible among the Nieuw Nederlanders as was that of Gaul among the ancient Romans; insomuch that the good wives of the Manhattoes used it as a bugbear wherewith to frighten their unruly children.

Everybody clamored around the governor, imploring him to put the city in a complete posture of defence; and he listened to their clamors. Nobody could accuse William the Testy of being idle in time of danger, or at any other time. He was never idle, but then he was often busy to very little purpose. When a youngling, he had been impressed with the words of Solomon, "Go to the ant, thou sluggard, observe her ways and be wise"; in conformity to which he had ever been of a restless, ant-like turn, hurrying hither and thither, nobody knew why or wherefore, busying himself about small matters with an air of great importance and anxiety, and toiling at a grain of mustard-seed in the full conviction that he was moving a mountain. In the present instance, he called in all his inventive powers to his aid, and was continually pondering over plans, making diagrams, and worrying about with a troop of workmen and projectors at his heels. At length, after a world of consultation and contrivance, his plans of defence ended in rearing a great flag-staff in the centre of the fort, and perching a wind-mill on each bastion.

These warlike preparations in some measure allayed the public alarm, especially after an additional means of securing the safety of the city had been suggested by the governor's lady. It has already been hinted in this most authentic history, that in the domestic establishment of William the Testy "the gray mare was the better horse"; in other words, that his wife "ruled the roast," and in governing the governor, governed the province, which might thus be said to be under petticoat government.

Now it came to pass, that about this time there lived in the Manhattoes a jolly, robustious trumpeter, named Antony Van Corlear, famous for his long wind; and who, as the story goes, could twang so potently upon his instrument, that the effect upon all within hearing was like that ascribed to the Scotch bagpipe when it sings right lustily i' the nose.

This sounder of brass was moreover a lusty bachelor, with a pleasant, burly visage, a long nose, and huge whiskers. He had his little *bowerie*, or retreat, in the country, where he led a roistering life, giving dances to the wives and daughters of the burghers of the Manhattoes, insomuch that he became a prodigious favorite with all the women, young and old. He is said to have been the first to collect that famous toll levied on the fair sex at Kissing Bridge, on the highway to Hellgate.*

To this sturdy bachelor the eyes of all the women were turned in this time of darkness and peril, as the very man to second and carry out the plans of defence of the governor. A kind of petticoat council was forthwith held at the government house, at which the governor's lady presided; and this lady, as has been hinted, being all potent with the governor, the result of these councils was the elevation of Antony the Trumpeter to the post of commandant of wind-mills and champion of New Amsterdam.

The city being thus fortified and garrisoned, it would have done one's heart good to see the governor snapping his fingers and fidgeting with delight, as the trumpeter strutted up and down the ramparts, twanging defiance to the whole Yankee race, as does a modern editor to all the principalities and powers on the other side of the Atlantic. In the hands of Antony Van Corlear this windy instrument appeared to him as potent as the horn of the paladin Astolpho, or even the more classic horn of Alecto; nay, he had almost the temerity to compare it with the rams' horns celebrated in holy writ, at the very sound of which the walls of Jericho fell down.

Be all this as it may, the apprehensions of hostilities from the east gradually died away. The Yankees made no further invasion; nay, they declared they had only taken possession of Fort Goed Hoop as being erected within their territories. So far from manifesting hostility, they continued to throng to New Amsterdam with the most innocent countenances imaginable, filling the market with their notions, being as ready to trade with the Nederlanders as ever, and not a whit more prone to get to the windward of them in a bargain.

The old wives of the Manhattoes, who took tea with the governor's lady, attributed all this affected moderation to the awe inspired by the military preparations of the governor, and the windy prowess of Antony the Trumpeter.

There were not wanting illiberal minds, however, who

* The bridge here mentioned by Mr. Knickerbocker still exists; but it is said that the toll is seldom collected nowadays, excepting on sleighing-parties, by the descendants of the patriarchs, who still preserve the traditions of the city.

sneered at the governor for thinking to defend his city as he governed it, by mere wind; but William Kieft was not to be jeered out of his wind-mills: he had seen them perched upon the ramparts of his native city of Saardam, and was persuaded they were connected with the great science of defence; nay, so much piqued was he by having them made a matter of ridicule, that he introduced them into the arms of the city, where they remain to this day, quartered with the ancient beaver of the Manhattoes, an emblem and memento of his policy.

I must not omit to mention that certain wise old burghers of the Manhattoes, skilful in expounding signs and mysteries, after events have come to pass, consider this early intrusion of the wind-mill into the escutcheon of our city, which before had been wholly occupied by the beaver, as portentous of its after fortune, when the quiet Dutchman would be elbowed aside by the enterprising Yankee, and patient industry overtopped by windy speculation.

CHAPTER V

Of the Jurisprudence of William the Testy, and His Admirable Expedients for the Suppression of Poverty

AMONG the wrecks and fragments of exalted wisdom, which have floated down the stream of time from venerable antiquity, and been picked up by those humble but industrious wights who ply along the shores of literature, we find a shrewd ordinance of Charondas the Locrian legislator. Anxious to preserve the judicial code of the State from the additions and amendments of country members and seekers of popularity, he ordained that, whoever proposed a new law should do it with a halter about his neck; whereby, in case his proposition were rejected, they just hung him up—and there the matter ended.

The effect was, that for more than two hundred years there was but one trifling alteration in the judicial code; and legal matters were so clear and simple that the whole race of lawyers starved to death for want of employment. The Locrians, too, being freed from all incitement to litigation, lived very lovingly together, and were so happy a people that they make scarce any figure in history; it being only your litigious, quarrelsome, rantipole nations who make much noise in the world.

I have been reminded of these historical facts in coming to treat of the internal policy of William the Testy. Well would it have been for him had he in the course of his universal acquirements stumbled upon the precaution of the good Charondas, or had he looked nearer home at the protectorate of Oloffe the Dreamer, when the community was governed without laws. Such legislation, however, was not suited to the busy, meddling mind of William the Testy. On the contrary, he conceived that the true wisdom of legislation consisted in the multiplicity of laws. He accordingly had great punishments for great crimes, and little punishments for little offences. By degrees the whole surface of society was cut up by ditches and fences, and quickset hedges of the law, and even the sequestered paths of private life so beset by petty rules and ordinances, too numerous to be remembered, that one could scarce walk at large without the risk of letting off a spring-gun or falling into a man-trap.

In a little while the blessings of innumerable laws became apparent; a class of men arose to expound and confound them. Petty courts were instituted to take cognizance of petty offences, pettifoggers began to abound; and the community was soon set together by the ears.

Let me not be thought as intending anything derogatory to the profession of the law, or to the distinguished members of that illustrious order. Well am I aware that we have in this ancient city innumerable worthy gentlemen, the knights-errant of modern days, who go about redressing wrongs and defending the defenceless, not for the love of filthy lucre, nor the selfish cravings of renown, but merely for the pleasure of doing good. Sooner would I throw this trusty pen into the flames, and cork up my ink-bottle forever, than infringe even for a nail's breadth upon the dignity of these truly benevolent champions of the distressed. On the contrary, I allude merely to those caitiff scouts who, in these latter days of evil, infest the skirts of the profession, as did the recreant Cornish knights of yore the honorable order of chivalry—who, under its auspices, commit flagrant wrongs—who thrive by quibbles, by quirks and chicanery, and like vermin increase the corruption in which they are engendered.

Nothing so soon awakens the malevolent passions as the facility of gratification. The courts of law would never be so crowded with petty, vexatious, and disgraceful suits, were it not for the herds of pettifoggers. These tamper with the passions of the poorer and more ignorant classes, who, as if poverty were not a sufficient misery in itself, are ever ready to imbitter it by litigation. These, like quacks in medicine, excite the malady to profit by the cure, and retard the cure to augment the fees. As the quack exhausts the constitution, the pettifogger exhausts the purse; and as he who has once been under the hands of a quack is forever after prone to dabble in drugs, and poison himself with infallible prescriptions, so the client of the pettifogger is ever after prone to embroil himself with his neighbors, and impoverish himself with successful lawsuits. My readers will excuse this digression into which I have been unwarily betrayed; but I could not avoid giving a cool and unprejudiced account of an abomination too prevalent in this excellent city, and with the effects of which I am ruefully acquainted: having been nearly ruined by a lawsuit which was decided against me; and my ruin having been completed by another, which was decided in my favor.

To return to our theme. There was nothing in the whole range of moral offences against which the jurisprudence of William the Testy was more strenuously directed than the crying sin of poverty. He pronounced it the root of all evil, and determined to cut it up, root and branch, and extirpate it from the land. He had been struck, in the course of his travels in the old countries of Europe, with the wisdom of those notices posted up in country towns, that "any vagrant found begging there would be put in the stocks," and he had observed that no beggars were to be seen in these neighborhoods; having doubtless thrown off their rag and their poverty, and become rich under the terror of the law. He determined to improve upon this hint. In a little while a new machine, of his own invention, was erected hard by Dog's Misery. This was nothing more nor less than a gibbet, of a very strange, uncouth, and unmatchable construction, far more efficacious, as he boasted, than the stocks, for the punishment of poverty. It was for altitude not a whit inferior to that of Haman so renowned in Bible history; but the marvel of the contrivance was, that the culprit, instead of being suspended by the neck, according to venerable custom, was hoisted by the waistband, and kept dangling and sprawling between heaven and earth for an hour or two at a time—to the infinite entertainment and edification of the respectable citizens who usually attend exhibitions of the kind.

It is incredible how the little governor chuckled at beholding caitiff vagrants and sturdy beggars thus swinging by the crupper, and cutting antic gambols in the air. He had a thousand pleasantries and mirthful conceits to utter upon these occasions. He called them his dandlelions—his wild-fowl—his high-fliers—his spread-eagles—his goshawks—his scare-crows—and finally, his *gallowsbirds;* which ingenious appellation, though originally confined to worthies who had taken the air in this strange manner, has since grown to be a cant name given to all candidates for legal elevation. This punishment, moreover, if we may credit the assertions of certain grave etymologists, gave the first hint for a kind of harnessing, or strapping, by which our forefathers braced up their multifarious breeches, and which has of late years been revived, and continues to be worn at the present day.

Such was the punishment of all petty delinquents, vagrants and beggars and others detected in being guilty of poverty in a small way; as to those who had offended on a great scale, who had been guilty of flagrant misfortunes and enormous backslidings of the purse, and who stood convicted of large debts, which they were unable to pay, William Kieft had them straightway inclosed within the stone walls of a prison, there to remain until they should reform and grow rich. This notable expedient, however, does not appear to have been more efficacious under William the Testy than in more modern days: it being found that the longer a poor devil was kept in prison the poorer he grew.

CHAPTER VI

Projects of William the Testy for Increasing the Currency—He Is Outwitted by the Yankees—the Great Oyster War

NEXT to his projects for the suppression of poverty may be classed those of William the Testy, for increasing the wealth of New Amsterdam. Solomon, of whose character for wisdom the little governor was somewhat emulous, had made gold and silver as plenty as the stones in the streets of Jerusalem. William Kieft could not pretend to vie with him as to the precious metals, but he determined, as an equivalent, to flood the streets of New Amsterdam with Indian money. This was nothing more nor less than strings of beads wrought of clams, periwinkles, and other shell-fish, and called seawant or wampum. These had formed a native currency among the simple savages, who were content to take them of the Dutchmen in exchange for peltries. In an unlucky moment, William the Testy, seeing this money of easy production, conceived the project of making it the current coin of the province. It is true it had an intrinsic value among the Indians, who used it to ornament their robes and moccasins, but among the honest burghers it had no more intrinsic value than those rags which form the paper currency of modern days. This consideration, however, had no weight with William Kieft. He began by paying all the servants of the company, and all the debts of government, in strings of wampum. He sent emissaries to sweep the shores of Long Island, which was the Ophir of this modern Solomon, and abounded in shell-fish. These were transported in loads to New Amsterdam, coined into Indian money, and launched into circulation.

And now, for a time, affairs went on swimmingly; money became as plentiful as in the modern days of paper currency, and, to use the popular phrase, "a wonderful impulse was given to public prosperity." Yankee traders poured into the province, buying everything they could lay their hands on, and paying the worthy Dutchmen their own price—in Indian money. If the latter, however, attempted to pay the Yankees in the same coin for their tin ware and wooden bowls, the case was altered; nothing would do but Dutch guilders and such like "metallic currency."

What was worse, the Yankees introduced an inferior kind of wampum made of oyster-shells, with which they deluged the province, carrying off in exchange all the silver and gold, the Dutch herrings, and Dutch cheeses: thus early did the knowing men of the east manifest their skill in bargaining the New Amsterdammers out of the oyster, and leaving them the shell.*

It was a long time before William the Testy was made sensible how completely his grand project of finance was turned against him by his eastern neighbors; nor would he probably have ever found it out, had not tidings been brought him that the Yankees had made a descent upon Long Island, and had established a kind of mint at Oyster Bay, where they were coining up all the oyster-banks.

Now this was making a vital attack upon the province in a double sense, financial and gastronomical. Ever since the council-dinner of Oloffe the Dreamer at the founding of New Amsterdam, at which banquet the oyster figured so conspicuously, this divine shell-fish has been held in a kind of superstitious reverence at the Manhattoes; as witness the temples erected to its cult in every street and lane and alley. In fact, it is the standard luxury of the place, as is the terrapin at Philadelphia, the soft crab at Baltimore, or the canvas-back at Washington.

The seizure of Oyster Bay, therefore, was an outrage not merely on the pockets, but the larders of the New Amsterdammers; the whole community was aroused, and an oyster crusade was immediately set on foot against the Yankees. Every stout trencherman hastened to the standard; nay, some of the most corpulent Burgomasters and Schepens joined the expedition as a

* In a manuscript record of the province, dated 1659, Library of the New York Historical Society, is the following mention of Indian money:

"*Seawant* alias wampum. Beads manufactured from the *Quahaug* or *wilk*: a shell-fish formerly abounding on our coasts, but lately of more rare occurrence, of two colors, black and white; the former twice the value of the latter. Six beads of the white and three of the black for an English penny. The seawant depreciates from time to time. The New-England people make use of it as a means of barter, not only to carry away the best cargoes which we send thither, but to accumulate a large quantity of beavers and other furs; by which the company is defrauded of her revenues, and the merchants disappointed in making returns with that speed with which they might wish to meet their engagements; while their commissioners and the inhabitants remain overstocked with seawant—a sort of currency of no value except with the New Netherland savages, &c."

corps de reserve, only to be called into action when the sacking commenced.

The conduct of the expedition was intrusted to a valiant Dutchman, who for size and weight might have matched with Colbrand the Danish champion, slain by Guy of Warwick. He was famous throughout the province for strength of arm and skill at quarter-staff, and hence was named Stoffel Brinkerhoff, or rather Brinkerhoofd, that is to say Stoffel the head-breaker.

This sturdy commander, who was a man of few words but vigorous deeds, led his troops resolutely on through Nineveh, and Babylon, and Jericho, and Patch-hog, and other Long Island towns, without encountering any difficulty of note; though it is said that some of the burgomasters gave out at Hardscramble Hill and Hungry Hollow, and that others lost heart and turned back at Pusspanick. With the rest he made good his march until he arrived in the neighborhood of Oyster Bay.

Here he was encountered by a host of Yankee warriors, headed by Preserved Fish, and Habakkuk Nutter, and Return Strong, and Zerubbabel Fisk, and Determined Cock! at the sound of whose names Stoffel Brinkerhoff verily believed the whole parliament of Praise-God Barebones had been let loose upon him. He soon found, however, that they were merely the "selectmen" of the settlement, armed with no weapon but the tongue, and disposed only to meet him on the field of argument. Stoffel had but one mode of arguing, that was, with the cudgel; but he used it with such effect that he routed his antagonists, broke up the settlement, and would have driven the inhabitants into the sea if they had not managed to escape across the Sound to the mainland by the Devil's stepping-stones, which remain to this day monuments of this great Dutch victory over the Yankees.

Stoffel Brinkerhoff made great spoil of oysters and clams, coined and uncoined, and then set out on his return to the Manhattoes. A grand triumph, after the manner of the ancients, was prepared for him by William the Testy. He entered new Amsterdam as a conqueror, mounted on a Narraganset pacer. Five dried codfish on poles, standards taken from the enemy, were borne before him, and an immense store of oysters and clams, Weathersfield onions, and Yankee "notions" formed the *spolia opima;* while several coiners of oyster-shells were led captive to grace the hero's triumph.

The procession was accompanied by a full band of boys and Negroes, performing on the popular instruments of rattle-bones and clam-shells, while Antony Van Corlear sounded his trumpet from the ramparts.

A great banquet was served up in the stadt-house from the clams and oysters taken from the enemy; while the governor sent the shells privately to the mint, and had them coined into Indian money, with which he paid his troops.

It is moreover said that the governor, calling to mind the practice among the ancients to honor their victorious general with public statues, passed a magnanimous decree, by which every tavern-keeper was permitted to paint the head of Stoffel Brinkerhoff upon his sign!

CHAPTER VII

Growing Discontents of New Amsterdam Under the Government of William the Testy

IT has been remarked by the observant writer of the Stuyvesant manuscript, that under the administration of William Kieft the disposition of the inhabitants of New Amsterdam experienced an essential change, so that they became very meddlesome and factious. The unfortunate propensity of the little governor to experiment and innovation, and the frequent exacerbations of his temper, kept his council in a continual worry; and the council being to the people at large what yeast or leaven is to a batch, they threw the whole community in a ferment; and the people at large being to the city what the mind is to the body, the unhappy commotions they underwent operated most disastrously upon New Amsterdam—insomuch that, in certain of their paroxysms of consternation and perplexity, they begat several of the most crooked, distorted, and abominable streets, lanes, and alleys, with which this metropolis is disfigured.

The fact was, that about this time the community, like Balaam's ass, began to grow more enlightened than its rider, and to show a disposition for what is called "self-government." This restive propensity was first evinced in certain popular meetings, in which the burghers of New Amsterdam met to talk and smoke over the complicated affairs of the province, gradually obfuscating themselves with politics and tobacco-smoke. Hither resorted those idlers and squires of low degree who hang loose on society and are blown about by every wind of doctrine. Cobblers abandoned their stalls to give lessons on political economy; blacksmiths suffered their fires to go out while they stirred up the fires of faction; and even tailors, though said to be the ninth parts of humanity, neglected their own measures to criticize the measures of government.

Strange! that the science of government, which seems to be so generally understood, should invariably be denied to the only one called upon to exercise it. Not one of the politicans in question, but, take his word for it, could have administered affairs ten times better than William the Testy.

Under the instructions of these political oracles the good people of New Amsterdam soon became exceedingly enlightened, and, as a matter of course, exceedingly discontented. They gradually found out the fearful error in which they had indulged, of thinking themselves the happiest people in creation, and were convinced that, all circumstances to the contrary notwithstanding, they were a very unhappy, deluded, and consequently ruined people!

We are naturally prone to discontent, and avaricious after imaginary causes of lamentation. Like lubberly monks we belabor our own shoulders, and take a vast satisfaction in the music of our own groans. Nor is this said by way of paradox; daily experience shows the truth of these observations. It is almost impossible to elevate the spirits of a man groaning under ideal calamities; but nothing is easier than to render him wretched, though on the pinnacle of felicity; as it would be an Herculean task to hoist a man to the top of a steeple, though the merest child could topple him off thence.

I must not omit to mention that these popular meetings were generally held at some noted tavern, these public edifices possessing what in modern times are thought the true fountains of political inspiration. The ancient Greeks deliberated upon a matter when drunk, and reconsidered it when sober. Mob-politicians in modern times dislike to have two minds upon a subject, so they both deliberate and act when drunk; by this means a world of delay is spared; and as it is universally allowed that a man when drunk sees double, it follows conclusively that he sees twice as well as his sober neighbors.

CHAPTER VIII

Of the Edict of William the Testy Against Tobacco—of the Pipe-plot, and the Rise of Feuds and Parties

WILHELMUS KIEFT, as has already been observed, was a great legislator on a small scale, and had a microscopic eye in public affairs. He had been greatly annoyed by the factious meeting of the good people of New Amsterdam, but, observing that on these occasions the pipe was ever in their mouth, he began to think that the pipe was at the bottom of the affair, and that there was some mysterious affinity between politics and tobacco-smoke. Determined to strike at the root of the evil, he began forthwith to rail at tobacco, as a noxious, nauseous weed, filthy in all its uses; and as to smoking, he denounced it as a heavy tax upon the public pocket—a vast consumer of time, a great encourager of idleness, and a deadly bane to the prosperity and morals of the people. Finally he issued an edict, prohibiting the smoking of tobacco throughout the New Netherlands. Ill-fated Kieft! Had he lived in the present age and attempted to check the unbounded license of the press, he could not have struck more sorely upon the sensibilities of the million. The pipe, in fact, was the great organ of reflection and deliberation of the New Netherlander. It was his constant companion and solace: was he gay, he smoked; was he sad, he smoked; his pipe was never out of his mouth; it was a part of his physiognomy; without it his best friends would not know him. Take away his pipe? You might as well take away his nose!

The immediate effect of the edict of William the Testy was a popular commotion. A vast multitude, armed with pipes and tobacco-boxes, and an immense supply of ammunition, sat themselves down before the governor's house, and fell to smoking with tremendous violence. The testy William issued forth like a wrathful spider, demanding the reason of this lawless fumigation. The sturdy rioters replied by lolling back in their seats, and puffing away with redoubled fury, raising such a murky cloud that the governor was fain to take refuge in the interior of his castle.

A long negotiation ensued through the medium of Antony the Trumpeter. The governor was at first wrathful and unyielding, but was gradually smoked into terms. He concluded by permitting the smoking of tobacco, but he abolished the fair long pipes used in the days of Wouter Van Twiller, denoting ease, tranquillity, and sobriety of deportment; these he condemned as incompatible with the despatch of business, in place whereof he substituted little captious short pipes, two inches in length, which, he observed, could be stuck in one corner of the mouth, or twisted in the hat-band, and would never be in the way. Thus ended this alarming insurrection, which was long known by the name of The Pipe-Plot, and which, it has been somewhat quaintly observed, did end, like most plots and seditions, in mere smoke.

But mark, oh, reader! the deplorable evils which did afterwards result. The smoke of these villainous little pipes, continually ascending in a cloud about the nose, penetrated into and befogged the cerebellum, dried up all the kindly moisture of the brain, and rendered the people who use them as vaporish and testy as the governor himself. Nay, what is worse, from being goodly, burly, sleek-conditioned men, they became, like our Dutch yeomanry who smoke short pipes, a lantern-jawed, smoke-dried, leathern-hided race.

Nor was this all. From this fatal schism in tobacco-pipes we may date the rise of parties in the Nieuw Nederlands. The rich and self-important burghers who had made their fortunes, and could afford to be lazy, adhered to the ancient fashion, and formed a kind of aristocracy known as the *Long Pipes;* while the lower order, adopting the reform of William Kieft as more convenient in their handicraft employments, were branded with the plebeian name of *Short Pipes*.

A third party sprang up, headed by the descendants of Robert Chewit, the companion of the great Hudson. These discarded pipes altogether and took to chewing tobacco; hence they were called *Quids*—an appellation since given to those political mongrels, which sometimes spring up between two great parties, as a mule is produced between a horse and an ass.

And here I would note the great benefit of party distinctions in saving the people at large the trouble of thinking. Hesiod divides mankind into three classes—those who think for themselves, those who think as others think, and those who do not think at all. The second class comprises the great mass of society; for most people require a set creed and a file-leader. Hence the origin of party: which means a large body of people, some few of whom think, and all the rest talk. The former take the lead and discipline the latter; prescribing what they must say, what they must approve, what they must hoot at, whom they must support, but, above all, whom they must hate; for no one can be a right good partisan, who is not a thorough-going hater.

The enlightened inhabitants of the Manhattoes, therefore, being divided into parties, were enabled to hate each other with great accuracy. And now the great business of politics went bravely on, the long pipes and short pipes assembling in separate beer-houses, and smoking at each other with implacable vehemence, to the great support of the State and profit of the tavern-keepers. Some, indeed, went so far as to bespatter their adversaries with those odoriferous little words which smell so strong in the Dutch language, believing, like true politicians, that they served their party, and glorified themselves in proportion as they bewrayed their neighbors. But, however they might differ among themselves, all parties agreed in abusing the governor, seeing that he was not a governor of their choice, but appointed by others to rule over them.

Unhappy William Kieft! exclaims the sage writer of the Stuyvesant manuscript, doomed to contend with enemies too knowing to be entrapped, and to reign over a people too wise to be governed. All his foreign expeditions were baffled and set at naught by the all-pervading Yankees; all his home measures were canvassed and condemned by "numerous and respectable meetings" of pot-house politicans.

In the multitude of counsellors, we are told, there is safety; but the multitude of counsellors was a continual source of perplexity to William Kieft. With a temperament as hot as an old radish, and a mind subject to perpetual whirlwinds and tornadoes, he never failed to get into a passion with every one who undertook to advise him. I have observed, however, that your passionate little men, like small boats with large sails, are easily upset or blown out of their course; so was it with William the Testy, who was prone to be carried away by the last piece of advice blown into his ear. The consequence was, that, though a projector of the first class, yet by continually changing his projects he gave none a fair trial; and by endeavoring to do everything, he in sober truth did nothing.

In the mean time, the sovereign people got into the saddle, showed themselves, as usual, unmerciful riders; spurring on the little governor with harangues and petitions, and thwarting him with memorials and reproaches, in much the same way as holiday apprentices manage an unlucky devil of a hack-horse—so that Wilhelmus Kieft was kept at a worry or a gallop throughout the whole of his administration.

CHAPTER IX

Of the Folly of Being Happy in Time of Prosperity—of Troubles to the South Brought on by Annexation—of the Secret Expedition of Jan Jansen Alpendam, and His Magnificient Reward

IF we could but get a peep at the tally of dame Fortune, where like a vigilant landlady she chalks up the debtor and creditor accounts of thoughtless mortals, we should find that every good is checked off by an evil, and that, however we may apparently revel scot-free for a season, the time will come when we must ruefully pay off the reckoning. Fortune in fact is a pestilent shrew, and withal an inexorable creditor; and though for a time she may be all smiles and courtesies and indulge us in long credits, yet sooner or later she brings up her arrears with a vengeance, and washes out her scores with our tears. "Since," says good old Boetius, "no man can retain her at his pleasure; what are her favors but sure prognostications of approaching trouble and calamity?"

This is the fundamental maxim of that sage school of philosophers, the croakers, who esteem it true wisdom to doubt and despond when other men rejoice, well knowing that happiness is at best but transient—that, the higher one is elevated on the see-saw balance of fortune, the lower must be his subsequent depression—that he who is on the uppermost round of a ladder has most to suffer from a fall, while he who is at the bottom runs very little risk of breaking his neck by tumbling to the top.

Philosophical readers of this stamp must have doubtless indulged in dismal forebodings all through the tranquil reign of Walter the Doubter, and considered it what Dutch seamen call a weather-breeder. They will not be surprised, therefore, that the foul weather which gathered during his days should now be rattling from all quarters on the head of William the Testy.

The origin of some of these troubles may be traced quite back to the discoveries and annexations of Hans Reinier Oothout, the explorer, and Wynant Ten Breeches, the land-measurer, made in the twilight days of Oloffe the Dreamer; by which the territories of the Nieuw Nederlands were carried far to the south, to Delaware river and parts beyond. The consequence was, many disputes and brawls with the Indians, which now and then reached the drowsy ears of Walter the Doubter and his council, like the muttering of distant thunder from behind the mountains, without, however, disturbing their repose. It was not till the time of William the Testy that the thunderbolt reached the Manhattoes. While the little governor was diligently protecting his eastern boundaries from the Yankees, word was brought him of the irruption of a vagrant colony of Swedes in the south, who had landed on the banks of the Delaware and displayed the banner of the redoubtable virago Queen Christina, and taken possession of the country in her name. These had been guided in their expedition by one Peter Minuits, or Minnewits, a renegade Dutchman, formerly in the service of their High Mightinesses, but who now declared himself governor of all the surrounding country, to which was given the name of the province of New Sweden.

It is an old saying that "a little pot is soon hot," which was the case with William the Testy. Being a little man, he was soon in a passion, and once in a passion, he soon boiled over. Summoning his council on the receipt of this news, he belabored the

Swedes in the longest speech that had been heard in the colony since the wordy warfare of Ten Breeches and Tough Breeches. Having thus taken off the fire-edge of his valor, he resorted to his favorite measure of proclamation, and despatched a document of the kind, ordering the renegade Minnewits and his gang of Swedish vagabonds to leave the country immediately, under pain of the vengeance of their High Mightinesses the Lords States General, and of the potentates of the Manhattoes.

This strong measure was not a whit more effectual than its predecessors, which had been thundered against the Yankees; and William Kieft was preparing to follow it up with something still more formidable, when he received intelligence of other invaders on his southern frontier, who had taken possession of the banks of the Schuylkill, and built a fort there. They were represented as a gigantic, gunpowder race of men, exceedingly expert at boxing, biting, gouging, and other branches of the rough-and-tumble mode of warfare, which they had learned from their prototypes and cousins-german, the Virginians, to whom they have ever borne considerable resemblance. Like them, too, they were great roisters, much given to revel on hoe-cake and bacon, mint-julep and apple-toddy; whence their newly formed colony had already acquired the name of Merryland, which, with a slight modification, it retains to the present day.

In fact, the Merrylanders and their cousins, the Virginians, were represented to William Kieft as offsets from the same original stock as his bitter enemies the Yanokie, or Yankee tribes of the east, having both come over to this country for the liberty of conscience, or, in other words, to live as they pleased: the Yankees taking to praying and money-making, and converting quakers; and the Southerners to horse-racing and cock-fighting, and breeding Negroes.

Against these new invaders Wilhelmus Kieft immediately despatched a naval armament of two sloops and thirty men, under Jan Jansen Alpendam, who was armed to the very teeth with one of the little governor's most powerful speeches, written in vigorous Low Dutch.

Admiral Alpendam arrived without accident in the Schuylkill, and came upon the enemy just as they were engaged in a great "barbecue," a kind of festivity or carouse much practised in

Merryland. Opening upon them with the speech of William the Testy, he denounced them as a pack of lazy, canting, julep-tippling, cock-fighting, horse-racing, slave-trading, tavern-hunting, Sabbath-breaking, mulatto-breeding upstarts, and concluded by ordering them to evacuate the country immediately: to which they laconically replied in plain English, "they'd see him d—d first!"

Now, this was a reply on which neither Jan Jansen Alpendam nor Wilhelmus Kieft had made any calculation. Finding himself, therefore, totally unprepared to answer so terrible a rebuff with suitable hostility, the admiral concluded his wisest course would be to return home and report progress. He accordingly steered his course back to New Amsterdam, where he arrived safe, having accomplished this hazardous enterprise at small expense of treasure and no loss of life. His saving policy gained him the universal appellation of the Saviour of his Country; and his services were suitably rewarded by a shingle monument, erected by subscription on the top of Flattenbarrack Hill, where it immortalized his name for three whole years, when it fell to pieces and was burnt for firewood.

CHAPTER X

Troublous Times on the Hudson—How Killian Van Rensellaer Erected a Feudal Castle, and How He Introduced Club-law into the Province

ABOUT this time the testy little governor of the New Netherlands appears to have had his hands full, and with one annoyance and the other to have been kept continually on the bounce. He was on the very point of following up the expedition of Jan Jansen Alpendam by some belligerent measures against the marauders of Merryland, when his attention was suddenly called away by belligerent troubles springing up in another quarter, the seeds of which had been sown in the tranquil days of Walter the Doubter.

The reader will recollect the deep doubt into which that most pacific governor was thrown on Killian Van Rensellaer's taking possession of Bearn Island by *wapen recht*. While the governor doubted and did nothing, the lordly Killian went on to complete his sturdy little castellum of Rensellaerstein, and to garrison it with a number of his tenants from the Helderberg, a mountain region famous for the hardest heads and hardest fists in the province. Nicholas Koorn, a faithful squire of the patroon, accustomed to strut at his heels, wear his cast-off clothes, and imitate his lofty bearing, was established in this post as wacht-meester. His duty it was to keep an eye on the river, and oblige every vessel that passed, unless on the service of their High Mightinesses, to strike its flag, lower its peak, and pay toll to the lord of Rensellaerstein.

This assumption of sovereign authority within the territories of the Lords States General, however it might have been tolerated by Walter the Doubter, had been sharply contested by William the Testy on coming into office; and many written remonstrances had been addressed by him to Killian Van Rensellaer, to which the latter never deigned a reply. Thus, by degrees, a sore place, or, in Hibernian parlance, a *raw*, had been established in the irritable soul of the little governor, insomuch that he winced at the very name of Rensellaerstein.

Now it came to pass, that, on a fine sunny day, the Company's yacht, the Half-Moon, having been on one of its stated visits to Fort Aurania, was quietly tiding it down the Hudson. The commander, Govert Lockerman, a veteran Dutch skipper of few words but great bottom, was seated on the high poop, quietly smoking his pipe under the shadow of the proud flag of Orange, when, on arriving abreast of Bearn Island, he was saluted by a stentorian voice from the shore, "Lower thy flag, and be d—d to thee!"

Govert Lockerman, without taking his pipe out of his mouth, turned up his eye from under his broad-brimmed hat to see who hailed him thus discourteously. There, on the ramparts of the fort, stood Nicholas Koorn, armed to the teeth, flourishing a brass-hilted sword, while a steeple-crowned hat and cock's tail-feather, formerly worn by Killian Van Rensellaer himself, gave an inexpressible loftiness to his demeanor.

Govert Lockerman eyed the warrior from top to toe, but was not to be dismayed. Taking the pipe slowly out of his mouth, "To whom should I lower my flag?" demanded he. "To the high and mighty Killian Van Rensellaer, the lord of Rensellaerstein!" was the reply.

"I lower it to none but the Prince of Orange and my masters the Lords States General." So saying, he resumed his pipe and smoked with an air of dogged determination.

Bang! went a gun from the fortress; the ball cut both sail and rigging. Govert Lockerman said nothing, but smoked the more doggedly.

Bang! went another gun; the shot whistled close astern.

"Fire, and be d—d," cried Govert Lockerman, cramming a new charge of tobacco into his pipe, and smoking with still increasing vehemence.

Bang! went a third gun. The shot passed over his head, tearing a hole in the "princely flag of Orange."

This was the hardest trial of all for the pride and patience of Govert Lockerman. He maintained a stubborn, though swelling silence; but his smothered rage might be perceived by the short vehement puffs of smoke emitted from his pipe, by which he might be tracked for miles, as he slowly floated out of shot and out of sight of Bearn Island. In fact he never gave vent to his passion until he got fairly among the highlands of the Hudson; when he let fly whole volleys of Dutch oaths, which are said to linger to this very day among the echoes of the Dunderberg, and to give particular effect to the thunder-storms in that neighborhood.

It was the sudden apparition of Govert Lockerman at Dog's Misery, bearing in his hand the tattered flag of Orange, that arrested the attention of William the Testy, just as he was devising a new expedition against the marauders of Merryland. I will not pretend to describe the passion of the little man when he heard of the outrage of Rensellaerstein. Suffice it to say, in the first transports of his fury, he turned Dog's Misery topsy-turvy; kicked every cur out of doors, and threw the cats out of the window; after which, his spleen being in some measure relieved, he went into a council of war with Govert Lockerman, the skipper, assisted by Antony Van Corlear, the Trumpeter.

CHAPTER XI

Of the Diplomatic Mission of Antony the Trumpeter to the Fortress of Rensellaerstein—and How He Was Puzzled by a Cabalistic Reply

THE eyes of all New Amsterdam were now turned to see what would be the end of this direful feud between William the Testy and the patroon of Rensellaerwick; and some, observing the consultations of the governor with the skipper and the trumpeter, predicted warlike measures by sea and land. The wrath of William Kieft, however, though quick to rise, was quick to evaporate. He was a perfect brush-heap in a blaze, snapping and crackling for a time, and then ending in smoke. Like many other valiant potentates, his first thoughts were all for war, his sober second thoughts for diplomacy.

Accordingly, Govert Lockerman was once more despatched up the river in the Company's yacht, the Goed Hoop, bearing Antony the Trumpeter as ambassador, to treat with the belligerent powers of Rensellaerstein. In the fulness of time the yacht arrived before Bearn Island, and Antony the Trumpeter, mounting the poop, sounded a parley to the fortress. In a little while the steeple-crowned hat of Nicholas Koorn, the wacht-meester, rose above the battlements, followed by his iron visage, and ultimately his whole person, armed, as before, to the very teeth; while, one by one, a whole row of Helderbergers reared their round burly heads above the wall, and beside each pumpkin-head peered the end of a rusty musket. Nothing daunted by this formidable array, Antony Van Corlear drew forth and read with audible voice a missive from William the Testy, protesting against the usurpation of Bearn Island, and ordering the garrison to quit the premises, bag and baggage, on pain of the vengeance of the potentate of the Manhattoes.

In reply, the wacht-meester applied the thumb of his right hand to the end of his nose, and the thumb of his left hand to the little finger of the right, and spreading each hand like a fan, made an aërial flourish with his fingers. Antony Van Corlear was sorely perplexed to understand this sign, which seemed to him something mysterious and masonic. Not liking to betray his ignorance, he again read with a loud voice the missive of William the Testy, and again Nicholas Koorn applied the thumb of his right hand to the end of his nose, and the thumb of his left hand to the little finger of the right, and repeated this kind of nasal weather-cock. Antony Van Corlear now persuaded himself that this was some short-hand sign or symbol, current in diplomacy, which, though unintelligible to a new diplomat, like himself, would speak volumes to the experienced intellect of William the Testy; considering his embassy therefore at an end, he sounded his trumpet with great complacency, and set sail on his return down the river, every now and then practising this mysterious sign of the wacht-meester, to keep it accurately in mind.

Arrived at New Amsterdam he made a faithful report of his embassy to the governor, accompanied by a manual exhibition of the response of Nicholas Koorn. The governor was equally perplexed with his embassy. He was deeply versed in the mysteries of freemasonry; but they threw no light on the matter. He knew every variety of windmill and weather-cock, but was not a whit the wiser as to the aërial sign in question. He had even dabbled in Egyptian hieroglyphics and the mystic symbols of the obelisks, but none furnished a key to the reply of Nicholas Koorn. He called a meeting of his council. Antony Van Corlear stood forth in the midst, and putting the thumb of his right hand to his nose, and the thumb of his left hand to the finger of the right, he gave a faithful facsimile of the portentous sign. Having a nose of unusual dimensions, it was as if the reply had been put in capitals; but all in vain: the worthy burgomasters were equally perplexed with the governor. Each one put his thumb to the end of his nose, spread his fingers like a fan, imitated the motion of Antony Van Corlear, and then smoked in dubious silence. Several times was Antony obliged to stand forth like a fugleman and repeat the sign, and each time a circle of nasal weather-cocks might be seen in the council-chamber.

Perplexed in the extreme, William the Testy sent for all the soothsayers, and fortune-tellers and wise men of the Manhattoes, but none could interpret the mysterious reply of Nicholas Koorn. The council broke up in sore perplexity. The matter got abroad, and Antony Van Corlear was stopped at every corner to repeat the signal to a knot of anxious newsmongers, each of whom departed with his thumb to his nose and his fingers in the air, to carry the story home to his family. For several days, all business was neglected in New Amsterdam; nothing was talked of but the diplomatic mission of Antony the Trumpeter—nothing was to be seen but knots of politicians with their thumbs to their noses. In the mean time the fierce feud between William the Testy and Killian Van Rensellaer, which at first had menaced deadly warfare, gradually cooled off, like many other war-questions, in the prolonged delays of diplomacy.

Still to this early affair of Rensellaerstein may be traced the remote origin of those windy wars in modern days which rage in the bowels of the Helderberg, and have wellnigh shaken the great patroonship of the Van Rensellaers to its foundation; for we are told that the bully boys of the Helderberg, who served under Nicholas Koorn the wacht-meester, carried back to their mountains the hieroglyphic sign which had so sorely puzzled Antony Van Corlear and the sages of the Manhattoes; so that to the present day the thumb to the nose and the fingers in the air is apt to be the reply of the Helderbergers whenever called upon for any long arrears of rent.

CHAPTER XII

Containing the Rise of the Great Amphictyonic Council of the Pilgrims, with the Decline and Final Extinction of William the Testy

IT was asserted by the wise men of ancient times, who had a nearer opportunity of ascertaining the fact, that at the gate of Jupiter's palace lay two huge tuns, one filled with blessings, the other with misfortunes; and it would verily seem as if the latter had been completely overturned and left to deluge the unlucky province of Nieuw Nederlands: for about this time, while harassed and annoyed from the south and the north, incessant forays were made by the border-chivalry of Connecticut upon the pigsties and hen-roosts of the Nederlanders. Every day or two some broad-bottomed express-rider, covered with mud and mire, would come floundering into the gate of New Amsterdam, freighted with some new tale of aggression from the frontier; whereupon Antony Van Corlear, seizing his trumpet, the only substitute for a newspaper in those primitive days, would sound the tidings from the ramparts with such doleful notes and disastrous cadence as to throw half the old women in the city into hysterics; all which tended greatly to increase his popularity; there being nothing for which the public are more grateful than being frequently treated to a panic—a secret well known to the modern editors.

But, oh ye powers! into what a paroxysm of passion did each new outrage of the Yankees throw the choleric little governor! Letter after letter, protest after protest, bad Latin, worse English, and hideous Low Dutch, were incessantly fulminated upon them, and the four-and-twenty letters of the alphabet, which formed his standing army, were worn out by constant campaigning. All, however, was ineffectual; even the recent victory at Oyster Bay, which had shed such a gleam of sunshine between the clouds of his foul-weather reign, was soon followed by a more fearful gathering up of those clouds, and indignations of more portentous tempest; for the Yankee tribe on the banks of the Connecticut, finding on this memorable occasion their incompetency to cope, in fair fight, with the sturdy chivalry of the Manhattoes, had called to their aid all the ten tribes of their brethren who inhabit the east country, which from them has derived the name of Yankee-land. This call was promptly responded to. The consequence was a great confederacy of the tribes of Massachusetts, Connecticut, New Plymouth, and New Haven, under the title of the "United Colonies of New England"; the pretended object of which was mutual defence against the savages, but the real object the subjugation of the Nieuw Nederlands.

For, to let the reader into one of the great secrets of history, the Nieuw Nederlands had long been regarded by the whole Yankee race as the modern land of promise, and themselves as the chosen and peculiar people destined, one day or other, by hook or by crook, to get possession of it. In truth, they are a wonderful and all-prevalent people, of that class who only require an inch to gain an ell, or a halter to gain a horse. From the time they first gained a foothold on Plymouth Rock, they began to migrate, progressing and progressing from place to place, and land to land, making a little here and a little there, and controverting the old proverb, that a rolling stone gathers no moss. Hence they have facetiously received the nickname of THE PILGRIMS: that is to say, a people who are always seeking a better country than their own.

The tidings of this great Yankee league struck William Kieft with dismay, and for once in his life he forgot to bounce on receiving a disagreeable piece of intelligence. In fact, on turning over in his mind all that he had read at the Hague about leagues and combinations, he found that this was a counterpart of the Amphictyonic league, by which the states of Greece attained such power and supremacy; and the very idea made his heart quake for the safety of his empire at the Manhattoes.

The affairs of the confederacy were managed by an annual council of delegates held at Boston, which Kieft denominated the Delphos of this truly classic league. The very first meeting gave evidence of hostility to the Nieuw Nederlanders, who were charged, in their dealings with the Indians, with carrying on a traffic in "guns, powther and shott—a trade damnable and injurious to the colonists." It is true the Connecticut traders were fain to dabble a little in this damnable traffic; but then they always dealt in what were termed Yankee guns, ingeniously calculated to burst in the pagan hands which used them.

The rise of this potent confederacy was a death-blow to the glory of William the Testy, for from that day forward he never held up his head, but appeared quite crestfallen. It is true, as the grand council augmented in power, and the league, rolling onward, gathered about the red hills of New Haven, threatening to overwhelm the Nieuw Nederlands, he continued occasionally to fulminate proclamations and protests, as a shrewd sea-captain fires his guns into a water-spout; but alas! they had no more effect than so many blank cartridges.

Thus end the authenticated chronicles of the reign of William the Testy; for henceforth, in the troubles, perplexities, and confusion of the times, he seems to have been totally overlooked, and to have slipped forever through the fingers of scrupulous history. It is a matter of deep concern that such obscurity should hang over his latter days; for he was in truth a mighty and great-little man, and worthy of being utterly renowned, seeing that he was the first potentate that introduced into this land the art of fighting by proclamation, and defending a country by trumpeters and wind-mills.

It is true, that certain of the early provincial poets, of whom there were great numbers in the Nieuw Nederlands, taking advantage of his mysterious exit, have fabled, that, like Romulus, he was translated to the skies, and forms a very fiery little star, somewhere on the left claw of the Crab; while others, equally fanciful, declare that he had experienced a fate similar to that of the good king Arthur, who, we are assured by ancient bards, was carried away to the delicious abodes of fairy-land, where he still exists in pristine worth and vigor, and will one day or an other return to restore the gallantry, the honor, and the immaculate probity, which prevailed in the glorious days of the Round Table.*

All these, however, are but pleasing fantasies, the cobweb visions of those dreaming varlets, the poets, to which I would not have my judicious readers attach any credibility. Neither am I disposed to credit an ancient and rather apocryphal historian, who asserts that the ingenious Wilhelmus was annihilated by the blowing down of one of his wind-mills; nor a writer of latter times, who affirms that he fell a victim to an experiment in natural history, having the misfortune to break his neck from a garret-window of the stadthouse in attempting to catch swallows by sprinkling salt upon their tails. Still less do I put my faith in the tradition that he perished at sea in conveying home to Holland a treasure of golden ore, discovered somewhere among the haunted regions of the Catskill mountains.†

* The old Welsh bards believed that King Arthur was not dead, but carried awaie by the fairies into some pleasant place, where he sholde remaine for a time, and then returne againe and reigne in as great authority as ever.—HOLLINSHED.

The Britons suppose that he shall come yet and conquere all Britaigne, for certes, this is the prophicye of Merlyn—He say'd that his deth shall be doubteous; and said soth for men thereof yet have doubte and shullen for ever more—for men wyt not whether that he lyveth or is dede.—DR. LEEW, CHRON.

† Diedrich Knickerbocker, in his scrupulous search after truth, is sometimes too fastidious in regard to facts which border a little on the marvellous. The story of the golden ore rests on something better than mere tradition. The venerable Adrian Van der Donck, Doctor of Laws, in his description of the New Netherlands, asserts it from his own observation

The most probable account declares, that, what with the constant troubles on his frontiers, the incessant schemings and projects going on in his own pericranium, the memorials, petitions, remonstrances, and sage pieces of advice of respectable meetings of the sovereign people, and the refractory disposition of his councillors, who were sure to differ from him on every point, and uniformly to be in the wrong, his mind was kept in a furnace-heat, until he became as completely burnt out as a Dutch family-pipe which has passed through three generations of hard smokers. In this manner did he undergo a kind of animal combustion, consuming away like a farthing rush-light: so that when grim death finally snuffed him out, there was scarce left enough of him to bury!

Some have supposed that the mineral in question was not gold, but pyrites; but we have the assertion of Adrian Van der Donck, an eyewitness, and the experiment of Johannes de la Montagne, a learned doctor of medicine, on the golden side of the question. Cornelius Van Tienhooven, also, at that time secretary of the New Netherlands, declared in Holland that he had tested several specimens of the mineral, which proved satisfactory.*

It would appear, however, that these golden treasures of the Kaatskill always brought ill luck: as is evidenced in the fate of Arent Corsen

as an eye-witness. He was present, he says, in 1645, at a treaty between Governor Kieft and the Mohawk Indians, in which one of the latter, in painting himself for the ceremony, used a pigment, the weight and shining appearance of which excited the curiosity of the governor and Mynheer Van der Donck. They obtained a lump, and gave it to be proved by a skilful doctor of medicine, Johannes de la Montagne, one of the councillors of the New Netherlands. It was put into a crucible, and yielded two pieces of gold, worth about three guilders. All this, continues Adrian Van der Donck, was kept secret. As soon as peace was made with the Mohawks, an officer and a few men were sent to the mountain (in the region of the Kaatskill), under the guidance of an Indian, to search for the precious mineral. They brought back a bucket full of ore; which, being submitted to the crucible, proved as productive as the first. William Kieft now thought the discovery certain. He sent a confidential person, Arent Corsen, with a bag full of the mineral, to New Haven, to take passage in an English ship for England, thence to proceed to Holland. The vessel sailed at Christmas, but never reached her port. All on board perished.

In the year 1647, Wilhelmus Kieft himself embarked on board the Princess, taking with him specimens of the supposed mineral. The ship was never heard of more!

* See Van der Donck's "Description of the New Netherlands." Collect. New York Hist. Society, Vol. I. p. 161.

and Wilhelmus Kieft, and the wreck of the ships in which they attempted to convey the treasure across the ocean. The golden mines have never since been explored, but remain among the mysteries of the Kaatskill mountains, and under the protection of the goblins which haunt them.

Book V

CONTAINING THE FIRST PART OF THE REIGN OF PETER STUYVESANT, AND HIS TROUBLES WITH THE AMPHICTYONIC COUNCIL

CHAPTER I

In Which the Death of a Great Man Is Shown to Be No Very Inconsolable Matter of Sorrow—and How Peter Stuyvesant Acquired a Great Name from the Uncommon Strength of His Head

TO a profound philosopher like myself, who am apt to see clear through a subject, where the penetration of ordinary people extends but halfway, there is no fact more simple and manifest than that the death of a great man is a matter of very little importance. Much as we may think of ourselves, and much as we may excite the empty plaudits of the million, it is certain that the greatest among us do actually fill but an exceeding small space in the world; and it is equally certain, that even that small space is quickly supplied when we leave it vacant. "Of what consequence is it," said Pliny, "that individuals appear, or make their exit? the world is a theatre whose scenes and actors are continually changing." Never did philosopher speak more correctly; and I only wonder that so wise a remark could have existed so many ages, and mankind not have laid it more to heart. Sage follows on in the footsteps of sage; one hero just steps out of his triumphal car, to make way for the hero who comes after him; and of the proudest monarch it is merely said, that "he slept with his fathers, and his successor reigned in his stead."

The world, to tell the private truth, cares but little for their loss, and if left to itself would soon forget to grieve; and though a nation has often been figuratively drowned in tears on the death of a great man, yet it is ten to one if an individual tear has been shed on the occasion, excepting from the forlorn pen of some hungry author. It is the historian, the biographer, and the poet, who have the whole burden of grief to sustain—who—kind souls!—like undertakers in England, act the part of chief mourners—who inflate a nation with sighs it never heaved, and deluge it with tears it never dreamt of shedding. Thus, while the patriotic author is weeping and howling, in prose, in blank verse, and in rhyme, and collecting the drops of public sorrow into his volume, as into a lachrymal vase, it is more than probable his fellow-citizens are eating and drinking, fiddling and dancing, as utterly ignorant of the bitter lamentations made in their name as are those men of straw, John Doe and Richard Roe, of the plaintiffs for whom they are generously pleased to become sureties.

The most glorious hero that ever desolated nations might have mouldered into oblivion among the rubbish of his own monument, did not some historian take him into favor, and benevolently transmit his name to posterity; and much as the valiant William Kieft worried, and bustled, and turmoiled, while he had the destinies of a whole colony in his hand, I question seriously whether he will not be obliged to this authentic history for all his future celebrity.

His exit occasioned no convulsion in the city of New Amsterdam nor its vicinity: the earth trembled not, neither did any stars shoot from their spheres; the heavens were not shrouded in black, as poets would fain persuade us they have been, on the death of a hero; the rocks (hard-hearted varlets!) melted not into tears, nor did the trees hang their heads in silent sorrow; and as to the sun, he lay abed the next night just as long, and showed as jolly a face when he rose as he ever did on the same day of the month in any year, either before or since. The good people of New Amsterdam, one and all, declared that he had been a very busy, active, bustling little governor; that he was "the father of his country"; that he was "the noblest work of God"; that "he was a man, take him for all in all, they ne'er should look upon his like again"; together with sundry other civil and affectionate speeches regularly said on the death of all great men: after which they smoked their pipes, thought no more about him, and Peter Stuyvesant succeeded to his station.

Peter Stuyvesant was the last, and, like the renowned Wouter Van Twiller, the best of our ancient Dutch governors. Wouter having surpassed all who preceded him, and Peter, or Piet, as he was sociably called by the old Dutch burghers, who were ever prone to familiarize names, having never been equalled by any successor. He was in fact the very man fitted by nature to retrieve the desperate fortunes of her beloved province, had not the fates, those most potent and unrelenting of all ancient spinsters, destined them to inextricable confusion.

To say merely that he was a hero, would be doing him great injustice: he was in truth a combination of heroes; for he was of a sturdy, raw-boned make, like Ajax Telamon, with a pair of round shoulders that Hercules would have given his hide for (meaning his lion's hide) when he undertook to ease old Atlas of his load. He was, moreover, as Plutarch describes Coriolanus, not only terrible for the force of his arm, but likewise of his voice, which sounded as though it came out of a barrel; and, like the self-same warrior, he possessed a sovereign contempt for the sovereign people, and an iron aspect, which was enough of itself to make the very bowels of his adversaries quake with terror and dismay. All this martial excellency of appearance was inexpressibly heightened by an accidental advantage, with which I am surprised that neither Homer nor Virgil have graced any of their heroes. This was nothing less than a wooden leg, which was the only prize he had gained in bravely fighting the battles of his country, but of which he was so proud, that he was often heard to declare he valued it more than all his other limbs put together; indeed so highly did he esteem it, that he had it gallantly enchased and relieved with silver devices, which caused it to be related in divers histories and legends that he wore a silver leg.*

Like that choleric warrior Achilles, he was somewhat subject to extempore bursts of passion, which were rather unpleasant to his favorites and attendants, whose perceptions he was apt to quicken, after the manner of his illustrious imitator, Peter the Great, by anointing their shoulders with his walking-staff.

Though I cannot find that he had read Plato, or Aristotle,

* See the histories of Masters Josselyn and Blome.

or Hobbes, or Bacon, or Algernon Sydney, or Tom Paine, yet did he sometimes manifest a shrewdness and sagacity in his measures, that one would hardly expect from a man who did not know Greek, and had never studied the ancients. True it is, and I confess it with sorrow, that he had an unreasonable aversion to experiments, and was fond of governing his province after the simplest manner; but then he contrived to keep it in better order than did the erudite Kieft, though he had all the philosophers, ancient and modern, to assist and perplex him. I must likewise own that he made but very few laws; but then, again, he took care that those few were rigidly and impartially enforced; and I do not know but justice, on the whole, was as well administered as if there had been volumes of sage acts and statutes yearly made, and daily neglected and forgotten.

He was, in fact, the very reverse of his predecessors, being neither tranquil and inert, like Walter the Doubter, nor restless and fidgeting, like William the Testy—but a man, or rather a governor, of such uncommon activity and decision of mind, that he never sought nor accepted the advice of others—depending bravely upon his single head, as would a hero of yore upon his single arm, to carry him through all difficulties and dangers. To tell the simple truth, he wanted nothing more to complete him as a statesman than to think always right; for no one can say but that he always acted as he thought. He was never a man to flinch when he found himself in a scrape, but to dash forward through thick and thin, trusting, by hook or by crook, to make all things straight in the end. In a word, he possessed, in an eminent degree, that great quality in a statesman, called perseverance by the polite, but nicknamed obstinacy by the vulgar—a wonderful salve for official blunders, since he who perseveres in error without flinching gets the credit of boldness and consistency, while he who wavers in seeking to do what is right gets stigmatized as a trimmer. This much is certain; and it is a maxim well worthy the attention of all legislators, great and small, who stand shaking in the wind, irresolute which way to steer, that a ruler who follows his own will pleases himself, while he who seeks to satisfy the wishes and whims of others runs great risk of pleasing nobody. There is nothing, too, like putting down one's foot resolutely when in doubt, and letting things take their course. The clock that stands still points right twice in the four-and-twenty hours, while others may keep going continually and be continually going wrong.

Nor did this magnanimous quality escape the discernment of the good people of Nieuw Nederlands; on the contrary, so much were they struck with the independent will and vigorous resolution displayed on all occasions by their new governor, that they universally called him Hard-Koppig Piet, or Peter the Headstrong—a great compliment to the strength of his understanding.

If, from all that I have said, thou dost not gather, worthy reader, that Peter Stuyvesant was a tough, sturdy, valiant, weather-beaten, mettlesome, obstinate, leathern-sided, lion-hearted, generous-spirited old governor, either I have written to but little purpose, or thou art very dull at drawing conclusions.

This most excellent governor commenced his administration on the 29th of May, 1647—a remarkably stormy day, distinguished in all the almanacs of the time which have come down to us by the name of *Windy Friday*. As he was very jealous of his personal and official dignity, he was inaugurated into office with great ceremony—the goodly oaken chair of the renowned Wouter Van Twiller being carefully preserved for such occasions, in like manner as the chair and stone were reverentially preserved at Schone, in Scotland, for the coronation of the Caledonian monarchs.

I must not omit to mention that the tempestuous state of the elements, together with its being that unlucky day of the week termed "hanging-day," did not fail to excite much grave speculation and divers very reasonable apprehensions among the more ancient and enlightened inhabitants; and several of the sager sex, who were reputed to be not a little skilled in the mystery of astrology and fortune-telling, did declare outright that they were omens of a disastrous administration—an event that came to be lamentably verified, and which proves beyond dispute the wisdom of attending to those preternatural intimations furnished by dreams and visions, the flying of birds, falling of stones, and cackling of geese, on which the sages and rulers of ancient times placed such reliance; or to those shooting of stars, eclipses of the moon, howlings of dogs, and flarings of candles, carefully noted and interpreted by the oracular sibyls of our day

—who, in my humble opinion, are the legitimate inheritors and preservers of the ancient science of divination. This much is certain, that Governor Stuyvesant succeeded to the chair of state at a turbulent period; when foes thronged and threatened from without; when anarchy and stiff-necked opposition reigned rampant within; when the authority of their High Mightinesses the Lords States General, though supported by economy and defended by speeches, protests, and proclamations, yet tottered to its very centre; and when the great city of New Amsterdam, though fortified by flag-staffs, trumpeters, and wind-mills, seemed, like some fair lady of easy virtue, to lie open to attack, and ready to yield to the first invader.

CHAPTER II

Showing How Peter the Headstrong Bestirred Himself Among the Rats and Cobwebs on Entering into Office—His Interview with Antony the Trumpeter, and His Perilous Meddling with the Currency

THE very first movements of the great Peter, on taking the reins of government, displayed his magnanimity, though they occasioned not a little marvel and uneasiness among the people of the Manhattoes. Finding himself constantly interrupted by the opposition, and annoyed by the advice of his privy council, the members of which had acquired the unreasonable habit of thinking and speaking for themselves during the preceding reign, he determined at once to put a stop to such grievous abominations. Scarcely, therefore, had he entered upon his authority, than he turned out of office all the meddlesome spirits of the factious cabinet of William the Testy; in place of whom he chose unto himself counsellors from those fat, somniferous, respectable burghers who had flourished and slumbered under the easy reign of Walter the Doubter. All these he caused to be furnished with abundance of fair long pipes, and to be regaled with frequent corporation dinners, admonishing them to smoke, and eat, and sleep for the good of the nation, while he took the burden of government upon his own shoulders—an arrangement to which they all gave hearty acquiescence.

Nor did he stop here, but made a hideous rout among the inventions and expedients of his learned predecessor—rooting up his patent gallows, where caitiff vagabonds were suspended by the waistband—demolishing his flag-staffs and wind-mills, which, like mighty giants, guarded the ramparts of New Amsterdam—pitching to the duyvel whole batteries of quaker guns—and, in a word, turning topsy-turvy the whole philosophic, economic, and wind-mill system of the immortal sage of Saardam.

The honest folk of New Amsterdam began to quake now for the fate of their matchless champion, Antony the Trumpeter, who had acquired prodigious favor in the eyes of the women, by means of his whiskers and his trumpet. Him did Peter the Headstrong cause to be brought into his presence, and eyeing him for a moment from head to foot, with a countenance that would have appalled anything else than a sounder of brass—"Pr'ythee, who and what art thou?" said he. "Sire," replied the other, in no wise dismayed, "for my name, it is Antony Van Corlear; for my parentage, I am the son of my mother; for my profession, I am champion and garrison of this great city of New Amsterdam." "I doubt me much," said Peter Stuyvesant, "that thou art some scurvy costard-monger knave. How didst thou acquire this paramount honor and dignity?" "Marry, sir," replied the other, "like many a great man before me, simply *by sounding my own trumpet*." "Ay, is it so?" quoth the governor; "why, then let us have a relish of thy art." Whereupon the good Antony put his instrument to his lips, and sounded a charge with such a tremendous outset, such a delectable quaver, and such a triumphant cadence, that it was enough to make one's heart leap out of one's mouth only to be within a mile of it. Like as a war-worn charger, grazing in peaceful plains, starts at a strain of martial music, pricks up his ears, and snorts, and paws, and kindles at the noise, so did the heroic Peter joy to hear the clangor of the trumpet; for of him might truly be said, what was recorded of the renowned St. George of England, "there was nothing in all the world that more rejoiced his heart than to hear the pleasant sound of war, and see the soldiers brandish forth their steeled weapons." Casting his eye more kindly, therefore, upon the sturdy Van Corlear, and finding him to be a jovial varlet, shrewd in his discourse, yet of great discretion and immeasurable wind, he straightway conceived a vast kindness for him, and discharging him from the troublesome duty of garrisoning, defending, and alarming the city, ever after retained him about his person, as his chief favorite, confidential envoy, and trusty squire. Instead of disturbing the city with disastrous notes, he was instructed to play so as to delight the governor while at his repasts, as did the minstrels of yore in the days of glorious chivalry—and on all public occasions to rejoice the ears of the people with warlike melody—thereby keeping alive a noble and martial spirit.

But the measure of the valiant Peter which produced the greatest agitation in the community, was his laying his hand upon the currency. He had old-fashioned notions in favor of gold and silver, which he considered the true standards of wealth and mediums of commerce; and one of his first edicts was, that all duties to government should be paid in those precious metals, and that seawant, or wampum, should no longer be a legal tender.

Here was a blow at public prosperity! All those who speculated on the rise and fall of this fluctuating currency, found their calling at an end; those, too, who had hoarded Indian money by barrels full, found their capital shrunk in amount; but, above all, the Yankee traders, who were accustomed to flood the market with newly coined oyster-shells, and to abstract Dutch merchandise in exchange, were loud-mouthed in decrying this "tampering with the currency." It was clipping the wings of commerce; it was checking the development of public prosperity; trade would be at an end; goods would moulder on the shelves; grain would rot in the granaries; grass would grow in the market-place. In a word, no one who has not heard the outcries and howlings of a modern Tarshish, at any check upon "paper-money," can have any idea of the clamor against Peter the Headstrong, for checking the circulation of oyster-shells.

In fact, trade did shrink into narrower channels; but then the stream was deep as it was broad; the honest Dutchmen sold less goods; but then they got the worth of them, either in silver and gold, or in codfish, tin ware, apple-brandy, Weathersfield onions, wooden bowls, and other articles of Yankee barter. The ingenious people of the east, however, indemnified themselves another way for having to abandon the coinage of oyster-shells; for about this time we are told that wooden nutmegs made their first appearance in New Amsterdam, to the great annoyance of the Dutch housewives.

NOTE

From a manuscript record of the province; Lib. N. Y. Hist. Society. —We have been unable to render your inhabitants wiser and prevent their being further imposed upon than to declare absolutely and peremptorily that henceforward seawant shall be bullion—not longer admissible in trade, without any value, as it is indeed. So that every one may be upon his guard to barter no longer away his wares and merchandises for these bubbles—at least not to accept them at a higher rate, or in a larger quantity, than as they may want them in their trade with the savages.

In this way your English [Yankee] neighbors shall no longer be enabled to draw the best wares and merchandises from our country for nothing—the beavers and furs not excepted. This has indeed long since been insufferable, although it ought chiefly to be imputed to the imprudent penuriousness of our own merchants and inhabitants, who, it is to be hoped, shall through the abolition of this seawant become wiser and more prudent.

27th January, 1662.

Seawant falls into disrepute; duties to be paid in silver coin.

CHAPTER III

How the Yankee League Waxed More and More Potent; and How It Outwitted the Good Peter in Treaty-making

NOW it came to pass, that, while Peter Stuyvesant was busy regulating the internal affairs of his domain, the great Yankee league, which had caused such tribulation to William the Testy, continued to increase in extent and power. The grand Amphictyonic council of the league was held at Boston, where it spun a web, which threatened to link within it all the mighty principalities and powers of the east. The object proposed by this formidable combination was, mutual protection and defence against their savage neighbors; but all the world knows the real aim was to form a grand crusade against the Nieuw Nederlands, and to get possession of the city of the Manhattoes—as devout an object of enterprise and ambition to the Yankees as was ever the capture of Jerusalem to ancient crusaders.

In the very year following the inauguration of Governor Stuyvesant, a grand deputation departed from the city of Providence (famous for its dusty streets and beauteous women) in behalf of the plantation of Rhode Island, praying to be admitted into the league.

The following minute of this deputation appears in the ancient records of the council.*

"Mr. Will. Cottington and Captain Partridg of Rhoode Island presented this insewing request to the commissioners in wrighting—

"Our request and motion is in behalfe of Rhoode Iland, that wee the Ilanders of Roode-Iland may be rescauied into combination with all the united colonyes of New England in a firme and perpetual league of friendship and amity of ofence and defence, mutuall advice and succor upon all just occasions for our mutuall safety and wellfair, etc. WILL COTTINGTON,

"ALICXSANDER PARTRIDG."

There was certainly something in the very physiognomy of this document that might well inspire apprehension. The name of Alexander, however misspelt, has been warlike in every age; and though its fierceness is in some measure softened by being coupled with the gentle cognomen of Partridge, still, like the color of scarlet, it bears an exceeding great resemblance to the sound of a trumpet. From the style of the letter, moreover, and the soldier-like ignorance of orthography displayed by the noble Captain Alicxsander Partridg in spelling his own name, we may picture to ourselves this mighty man of Rhodes, strong in arms, potent in the field, and as great a scholar as though he had been educated among that learned people of Thrace, who, Aristotle assures us, could not count beyond the number four.

The result of this great Yankee league was augmented audacity on the part of the moss-troopers of Connecticut—pushing their encroachments farther and farther into the territories of their High Mightinesses, so that even the inhabitants of New

* Haz. Col. Stat. Pap.

Amsterdam began to draw short breath and to find themselves exceedingly cramped for elbow-room.

Peter Stuyvesant was not a man to submit quietly to such intrusions; his first impulse was to march at once to the frontier and kick these squatting Yankees out of the country; but, bethinking himself in time that he was now a governor and legislator, the policy of the statesman for once cooled the fire of the old soldier, and he determined to try his hand at negotiation. A correspondence accordingly ensued between him and the grand council of the league; and it was agreed that commissioners from either side should meet at Hartford, to settle boundaries, adjust grievances, and establish a "perpetual and happy peace."

The commissioners on the part of the Manhattoes were chosen, according to immemorial usage of that venerable metropolis, from among the "wisest and weightiest" men of the community, that is to say, men with the oldest heads and heaviest pockets. Among these sages the veteran navigator, Hans Reinier Oothout, who had made such extensive discoveries during the time of Oloffe the Dreamer, was looked up to as an oracle in all matters of the kind; and he was ready to produce the very spy-glass with which he first spied the mouth of the Connecticut river from his mast-head; and all the world knows the discovery of the mouth of a river gives prior right to all the lands drained by its waters.

It was with feelings of pride and exultation that the good people of the Manhattoes saw two of the richest and most ponderous burghers departing on this embassy—men whose word on 'change was oracular, and in whose presence no poor man ventured to appear without taking off his hat: when it was seen, too, that the veteran Reinier Oothout accompanied them with his spy-glass under his arm, all the old men and old women predicted that men of such weight, with such evidence, would leave the Yankees no alternative but to pack up their tin kettles and wooden wares, put wife and children in a cart, and abandon all the lands of their High Mightinesses, on which they had squatted.

In truth, the commissioners sent to Hartford by the league seemed in no wise calculated to compete with men of such capacity. They were two lean Yankee lawyers, litigious-looking varlets, and evidently men of no substance, since they had no rotundity in the belt, and there was no jingling of money in their pockets; it is true, they had longer heads than the Dutchmen; but if the heads of the latter were flat at top, they were broad at bottom, and what was wanting in height of forehead was made up by a double chin.

The negotiation turned as usual upon the good old corner-stone of original discovery—according to the principle that he who first sees a new country has an unquestionable right to it. This being admitted, the veteran Oothout, at a concerted signal, stepped forth in the assembly with the identical tarpauling spy-glass in his hand, with which he had discovered the mouth of the Connecticut, while the worthy Dutch commissioners lolled back in their chairs, secretly chuckling at the idea of having for once got the weather-gage of the Yankees; but what was their dismay when the latter produced a Nantucket whaler with a spy-glass twice as long, with which he discovered the whole coast, quite down to the Manhattoes, and so crooked, that he had spied with it up the whole course of the Connecticut river. This principle pushed home, therefore, the Yankees had a right to the whole country bordering on the Sound; nay, the city of New Amsterdam was a mere Dutch squatting-place on their territories.

I forbear to dwell upon the confusion of the worthy Dutch commissioners at finding their main pillar of proof thus knocked from under them; neither will I pretend to describe the consternation of the wise men at the Manhattoes when they learned how their commissioner had been out-trumped by the Yankees, and how the latter pretended to claim to the very gates of New Amsterdam.

Long was the negotiation protracted, and long was the public mind kept in a state of anxiety. There are two modes of settling boundary questions when the claims of the opposite are irreconcilable. One is by an appeal to arms, in which case the weakest party is apt to lose its right, and get a broken head into the bargain; the other mode is by compromise, or mutual concession—that is to say, one party cedes half of its claims, and the other party half of its rights; he who grasps most gets most, and the whole is pronounced an equitable division, "perfectly honorable to both parties."

The latter mode was adopted in the present instance. The Yankees gave up claims to vast tracts of the Nieuw Nederlands which they had never seen, and all right to the land of Mannahata and the city of New Amsterdam, to which they had no right at all; while the Dutch, in return, agreed that the Yankees should retain possession of the frontier places where they had squatted, and of both sides of the Connecticut river.

When the news of this treaty arrived at New Amsterdam, the whole city was in an uproar of exultation. The old women rejoiced that there was to be no war, the old men that their cabbage-gardens were safe from invasion; while the political sages pronounced the treaty a great triumph over the Yankees, considering how much they had claimed, and how little they had been "fobbed off with."

And now my worthy reader is, doubtless, like the great and good Peter, congratulating himself with the idea that his feelings will no longer be harassed by afflicting details of stolen horses, broken heads, impounded hogs, and all the other catalogue of heart-rending cruelties that disgraced these border wars. But if he should indulge in such expectations, it is a proof that he is but little versed in the paradoxical ways of cabinets; to convince him of which, I solicit his serious attention to my next chapter, wherein I will show that Peter Stuyvesant has already committed a great error in politics, and, by effecting a peace, has materially hazarded the tranquillity of the province.

CHAPTER IV

Containing Divers Speculations on War and Negotiations—Showing That a Treaty of Peace Is a Great National Evil

IT was the opinion of that poetical philosopher, Lucretius, that war was the original state of man, whom he described as being primitively a savage beast of prey, engaged in a constant state of hostility with his own species, and that this ferocious spirit was tamed and ameliorated by society. The same opinion has been advocated by Hobbes,* nor have there been wanting many other philosophers to admit and defend.

* Hobbes's Leviathan. Part i, ch. 13.

For my part, though prodigiously fond of these valuable speculations, so complimentary to human nature, yet, in this instance, I am inclined to take the proposition by halves, believing with Horace,* that, though war may have been originally the favorite amusement and industrious employment of our progenitors, yet, like many other excellent habits, so far from being ameliorated, it has been cultivated and confirmed by refinement and civilization, and increases in exact proportion as we approach towards that state of perfection which is the *ne plus ultra* of modern philosophy.

The first conflict between man and man was the mere exertion of physical force, unaided by auxiliary weapons; his arm was his buckler, his fist was his mace, and a broken head the catastrophe of his encounters. The battle of unassisted strength was succeeded by the more rugged one of stones and clubs, and war assumed a sanguinary aspect. As man advanced in refinement, as his faculties expanded, and as his sensibilities became more exquisite, he grew rapidly more ingenious and experienced in the art of murdering his fellow-beings. He invented a thousand devices to defend and to assault: the helmet, the cuirass, and the buckler, the sword, the dart, and the javelin, prepared him to elude the wound as well as to launch the blow. Still urging on, in the career of philanthropic invention, he enlarges and heightens his powers of defence and injury:—The Aries, the Scorpio, the Balista, and the Catapulta, give a horror and sublimity to war, and magnify its glory, by increasing its desolation. Still insatiable, though armed with machinery that seemed to reach the limits of destructive invention, and to yield a power of injury commensurate even with the desires of revenge—still deeper researches must be made in the diabolical arcana. With furious zeal he dives into the bowels of the earth; he toils midst poisonous minerals and deadly salts—the sublime discovery of gunpowder blazes upon the world—and finally the dreadful art of fighting by proclamation seems to endow the demon of war with ubiquity and omnipotence!

* Quum prorepserunt primis animalia terris,
Mutuum ac turpe pecus, glandem atque cubilia propter,
Unguibus et pugnis, dein fustibus, atque ita porro
Pugnabant armis, quæ post fabricaverat usus.

Hor. Sat. L. i. S. 3.

This, indeed, is grand!—this, indeed, marks the powers of mind, and bespeaks that divine endowment of reason, which distinguishes us from the animals, our inferiors. The unenlightened brutes content themselves with the native force which Providence has assigned them. The angry bull butts with his horns, as did his progenitors before him; the lion, the leopard, and the tiger seek only with their talons and their fangs to gratify their sanguinary fury; and even the subtle serpent darts the same venom, and uses the same wiles, as did his sire before the flood. Man alone, blessed with the inventive mind, goes on from discovery to discovery—enlarges and multiplies his powers of destruction—arrogates the tremendous weapons of Deity itself, and tasks creation to assist him in murdering his brother-worm!

In proportion as the art of war has increased in improvement has the art of preserving peace advanced in equal ratio; and as we have discovered, in this age of wonders and inventions, that proclamation is the most formidable engine in war, so have we discovered the no less ingenious mode of maintaining peace by perpetual negotiations.

A treaty, or, to speak more correctly, a negotiation, therefore, according to the acceptation of experienced statesmen, learned in these matters, is no longer an attempt to accommodate differences, to ascertain rights, and to establish an equitable exchange of kind offices, but a contest of skill between two powers, which shall over-reach and take in the other. It is a cunning endeavor to obtain by peaceful manœuvre, and the chicanery of cabinets, those advantages which a nation would otherwise have wrested by force of arms—in the same manner as a conscientious highwayman reforms and becomes a quiet and praiseworthy citizen, contenting himself with cheating his neighbor out of that property he would formerly have seized with open violence.

In fact, the only time when two nations can be said to be in a state of perfect amity is, when a negotiation is open, and a treaty pending. Then, when there are no stipulations entered into, no bonds to restrain the will, no specific limits to awaken the captious jealousy of right implanted in our nature, when each party has some advantage to hope and expect from the other, then it is that the two nations are wonderfully gracious and friendly—their ministers professing the highest mutual regard, exchanging billets-doux, making fine speeches, and indulging in all those little diplomatic flirtations, coquetries, and fondlings, that do so marvellously tickle the good-humor of the respective nations. Thus it may paradoxically be said, that there is never so good an understanding between two nations as when there is a little misunderstanding—and that so long as they are on no terms at all, they are on the best terms in the world!

I do not by any means pretend to claim the merit of having made the above discovery. It has, in fact, long been secretly acted upon by certain enlightened cabinets, and is, together with divers other notable theories, privately copied out of the commonplace book of an illustrious gentleman, who has been member of congress, and enjoyed the unlimited confidence of heads of departments. To this principle may be ascribed the wonderful ingenuity shown of late years in protracting and interrupting negotiations. Hence the cunning measure of appointing as ambassador some political pettifogger skilled in delays, sophisms, and misapprehensions, and dexterous in the art of baffling argument—or some blundering statesman, whose errors and misconstructions may be a plea for refusing to ratify his engagements. And hence, too, that most notable expedient, so popular with our government, of sending out a brace of ambassadors—between whom, having each an individual will to consult, character to establish, and interest to promote, you may as well look for unanimity and concord as between two lovers with one mistress, two dogs with one bone, or two naked rogues with one pair of breeches. This disagreement, therefore, is continually breeding delays and impediments, in consequence of which the negotiation goes on swimmingly—inasmuch as there is no prospect of its ever coming to a close. Nothing is lost by these delays and obstacles but time; and in a negotiation, according to the theory I have exposed, all time lost is in reality so much time gained:—with what delightful paradoxes does modern political economy abound!

Now all that I have here advanced is so notoriously true, that I almost blush to take up the time of my readers with treating of matters which must many a time have stared them in the face. But the proposition to which I would most earnestly call their attention is this, that, though a negotiation be the most harmonizing of all national transactions, yet a treaty of peace is a great political evil, and one of the most fruitful sources of war.

I have rarely seen an instance of any special contract between individuals that did not produce jealousies, bickerings, and often downright ruptures between them; nor did I ever know of a treaty between two nations that did not occasion continual misunderstandings. How many worthy country neighbors have I known, who, after living in peace and good-fellowship for years, have been thrown into a state of distrust, cavilling, and animosity, by some ill-starred agreement about fences, runs of water, and stray cattle! And how many well-meaning nations, who would otherwise have remained in the most amicable disposition towards each other, have been brought to swords' points about the infringement or misconstruction of some treaty, which in an evil hour they had concluded, by way of making their amity more sure!

Treaties at best are but complied with so long as interest requires their fulfilment; consequently they are virtually binding on the weaker party only, or, in plain truth, they are not binding at all. No nation will wantonly go to war with another if it has nothing to gain thereby, and therefore needs no treaty to restrain it from violence; and if it have anything to gain, I much question, from what I have witnessed of the righteous conduct of nations, whether any treaty could be made so strong that it could not thrust the sword through—nay, I would hold ten to one, the treaty itself would be the very source to which resort would be had to find a pretext for hostilities.

Thus, therefore, I conclude—that, though it is the best of all policies for a nation to keep up a constant negotiation with its neighbors, yet it is the summit of folly for it ever to be beguiled into a treaty; for then comes on nonfulfilment and infraction, then remonstrance, then altercation, then retaliation, then recrimination, and finally open war. In a word, negotiation is like courtship, a time of sweet words, gallant speeches, soft looks, and endearing caresses—but the marriage ceremony is the signal for hostilities.

If my painstaking reader be not somewhat perplexed by the ratiocination of the foregoing passage, he will perceive, at a glance, that the Great Peter, in concluding a treaty with his eastern neighbors, was guilty of lamentable error in policy. In fact, to this unlucky agreement may be traced a world of bickerings and heart-burnings, between the parties, about fancied or pretended infringements of treaty-stipulations; in all which the Yankees were prone to indemnify themselves by a "dig into the sides" of the New Netherlands. But, in sooth, these border feuds, albeit they gave great annoyance to the good burghers of Mannahata, were so pitiful in their nature, that a grave historian like myself, who grudges the time spent in anything less than the revolutions of states and fall of empires, would deem them unworthy of being inscribed on his page. The reader is, therefore, to take it for granted, though I scorn to waste, in the detail, that time which my furrowed brow and trembling hand inform me is invaluable, that all the while the Great Peter was occupied in those tremendous and bloody contests which I shall shortly rehearse; there was a continued series of little, dirty, snivelling scourings, broils, and maraudings, kept up on the eastern frontiers by the moss-troopers of Connecticut. But, like that mirror of chivalry, the sage and valorous Don Quixote, I leave these petty contests for some future Sancho Panza of an historian, while I reserve my prowess and my pen for achievements of higher dignity; for at this moment I hear a direful and portentous note issuing from the bosom of the great council of the league, and resounding throughout the regions of the east, menacing the fame and fortunes of Peter Stuyvesant. I call, therefore, upon the reader to leave behind him all the paltry brawls of the Connecticut borders, and to press forward with me to the relief of our favorite hero, who, I foresee, will be wofully beset by the implacable Yankees in the next chapter.

CHAPTER V

How Peter Stuyvesant Was Grievously Belied by the Great Council of the League; and How He Sent Antony the Trumpeter to Take to the Council a Piece of His Mind

THAT the reader may be aware of the peril at this moment menacing Peter Stuyvesant and his capital, I must remind him of the old charge advanced in the council of the league in the time of William the Testy, that the Nederlanders were carrying on a trade "damnable and injurious to the colonists," in furnishing the savages with "guns, powther, and shott." This, as I then suggested, was a crafty device of the Yankee confederacy to have a snug cause of war *in petto*, in case any favorable opportunity should present of attempting the conquest of the New Nederlands: the great object of Yankee ambition.

Accordingly we now find, when every other ground of complaint had apparently been removed by treaty, this nefarious charge revived with tenfold virulence, and hurled like a thunderbolt at the very head of Peter Stuyvesant; happily his head, like that of the great bull of the Wabash, was proof against such missiles.

To be explicit, we are told that, in the year 1651, the great confederacy of the east accused the immaculate Peter, the soul of honor and heart of steel, of secretly endeavoring, by gifts and promises, to instigate the Narroheganset, Mohaque, and Pequot Indians, to surprise and massacre the Yankee settlements. "For," as the grand council observed, "the Indians round about for divers hundred miles cercute seeme to have drunk deepe of an intoxicating cupp, att or from the Manhattoes against the English, whoe have sought their good, both in bodily and spirituall respects."

This charge they pretended to support by the evidence of divers Indians, who were probably moved by that spirit of truth which is said to reside in the bottle, and who swore to the fact as sturdily as though they had been so many Christian troopers.

Though descended from a family which suffered much injury from the losel Yankees of those times, my great-grandfather having had a yoke of oxen and his best pacer stolen, and having received a pair of black eyes and a bloody nose in one of these border wars, and my grandfather, when a very little boy tending pigs, having been kidnapped and severely flogged by a long-sided Connecticut schoolmaster—yet I should have passed over all these wrongs with forgiveness and oblivion—I could even have suffered them to have broken Everet Ducking's head—to have kicked the doughty Jacobus Van Curlet and his ragged regiment out of doors—to have carried every hog into captivity, and depopulated every hen-roost on the face of the earth with perfect impunity—but this wanton attack upon one of the most gallant and irreproachable heroes of modern times is too much even for me to digest, and has overset, with a single puff, the patience of the historian, and the forbearance of the Dutchman.

Oh, reader, it was false! I swear to thee, it was false!—if thou hast any respect to my word—if the undeviating character for veracity, which I have endeavored to maintain throughout this work, has its due weight upon thee, thou wilt not give thy faith to this tale of slander; for I pledge my honor and my immortal fame to thee, that the gallant Peter Stuyvesant was not only innocent of this foul conspiracy, but would have suffered his right arm or even his wooden leg to consume with slow and everlasting flames, rather than attempt to destroy his enemies in any other way than open, generous warfare—beshrew those caitiff scouts, that conspired to sully his honest name by such an imputation!

Peter Stuyvesant, though haply he may never have heard of a knight-errant, had as true a heart of chivalry as ever beat at the round table of King Arthur. In the honest bosom of this heroic Dutchman dwelt the seven noble virtues of knighthood, flourishing among his hardy qualities like wild flowers among rocks. He was, in truth, a hero of chivalry struck off by nature at a single heat, and though little care may have been taken to refine her workmanship, he stood forth a miracle of her skill. In all his dealings he was headstrong perhaps, but open and above-board; if there was anything in the whole world he most loathed and despised, it was cunning and secret wile; "straight forward" was his motto; and he would at any time rather run his hard head against a stone wall than attempt to get round it.

Such was Peter Stuyvesant; and if my admiration of him has on this occasion transported my style beyond the sober gravity which becomes the philosophic recorder of historic events, I must plead as an apology, that, though a little gray-headed Dutchman, arrived almost at the down-hill of life, I still retain a lingering spark of that fire which kindles in the eye of youth when contemplating the virtues of ancient worthies. Blessed, thrice and nine times blessed be the good St. Nicholas, if I have indeed escaped that apathy which chills the sympathies of age and paralyzes every glow of enthusiasm.

The first measure of Peter Stuyvesant, on hearing of this slanderous charge would have been worthy of a man who had studied for years in the chivalrous library of Don Quixote. Drawing his sword and laying it across the table, to put him in proper tune, he took pen in hand and indited a proud and lofty letter to the council of the league, reproaching them with giving ear to the slanders of heathen savages against a Christian, a soldier, and a cavalier; declaring, that, whoever charged him with the plot in question, lied in his throat; to prove which he offered to meet the president of the council or any of his compeers, or their champion, Captain Alicxsander Partridg, that mighty man of Rhodes, in single combat—wherein he trusted to vindicate his honor by the prowess of his arm.

This missive was intrusted to his trumpeter and squire, Antony Van Corlear, that man of emergencies, with orders to travel night and day, sparing neither whip nor spur, seeing that he carried the vindication of his patron's fame in his saddle-bags.

The loyal Antony accomplished his mission with great speed and considerable loss of leather. He delivered his missive with becoming ceremony, accompanying it with a flourish of defiance on his trumpet to the whole council, ending with a significant and nasal twang full in the face of Captain Partridge, who nearly jumped out of his skin in an ecstasy of astonishment.

The grand council was composed of men too cool and practical to be put readily in a heat, or to indulge in knight-errantry; and above all to run a tilt with such a fiery hero as Peter the Headstrong. They knew the advantage, however, to have always a snug, justifiable cause of war in reserve with a neighbor, who had territories worth invading; so they devised a reply to Peter Stuyvesant, calculated to keep up the "raw" which they had established.

On receiving this answer, Antony Van Corlear remounted the Flanders mare which he always rode, and trotted merrily back to the Manhattoes, solacing himself by the way according to his wont; twanging his trumpet like a very devil, so that the sweet valleys and banks of the Connecticut resounded with the warlike melody; bringing all the folks to the windows as he passed through Hartford and Pyquag, and Middletown, and all the other border towns, ogling and winking at the women, and making aërial wind-mills from the end of his nose at their husbands, and stopping occasionally in the villages to eat pumpkin-pies, dance at country frolics, and bundle with the Yankee lasses—whom he rejoiced exceedingly with his soul-stirring instrument.

CHAPTER VI

How Peter Stuyvesant Demanded a Court of Honor—and What the Court of Honor Awarded to Him

THE reply of the grand council to Peter Stuyvesant was couched in the coolest and most diplomatic language. They assured him that "his confident denials of the barbarous plot alleged against him would weigh little against the testimony of divers sober and respectable Indians"; that "his guilt was proved to their perfect satisfaction," so that they must still require and seek due *satisfaction and security;* ending with—"so we rest, sir—Yours in ways of righteousness."

I forbear to say how the lion-hearted Peter roared and ramped at finding himself more and more entangled in the meshes thus artfully drawn round him by the knowing Yankees. Impatient, however, of suffering so gross an aspersion to rest upon his honest name, he sent a second messenger to the council, reiterating his denial of the treachery imputed to him, and offering to submit his conduct to the scrutiny of a court of honor. His offer was readily accepted; and now he looked forward with confidence to an august tribunal to be assembled at the Manhattoes, formed of high-minded cavaliers, peradventure governors and commanders of the confederate plantations, when the matter might be investigated by his peers, in a manner befitting his rank and dignity.

While he was awaiting the arrival of such high functionaries, behold, one sunshiny afternoon there rode into the great gate of the Manhattoes two lean, hungry-looking Yankees, mounted on Narraganset pacers, with saddle-bags under their bottoms, and green satchels under their arms, who looked marvellously like two pettifogging attorneys beating the hoof from one county court to another in quest of lawsuits; and, in sooth, though they may have passed under different names at the time, I have reason to suspect they were the identical varlets who had negotiated the worthy Dutch commissioners out of the Connecticut river.

It was a rule with these indefatigable missionaries never to let the grass grow under their feet. Scarce had they, therefore, alighted at the inn and deposited their saddle-bags, than they made their way to the residence of the governor. They found him, according to custom, smoking his afternoon pipe on the "stoop," or bench at the porch of his house, and announced themselves, at once, as commissioners sent by the grand council of the east to investigate the truth of certain charges advanced against him.

The good Peter took his pipe from his mouth, and gazed at them for a moment in mute astonishment. By way of expediting business, they were proceeding on the spot to put some preliminary questions—asking him, peradventure, whether he pleaded guilty or not guilty, considering him something in the light of a culprit at the bar—when they were brought to a pause by seeing him lay down his pipe and begin to fumble with his walking-staff. For a moment those present would not have given half a crown for both the crowns of the commissioners; but Peter Stuyvesant repressed his mighty wrath and stayed his hand; he scanned the varlets from head to foot, satchels and all, with a look of ineffable scorn; then strode into the house, slammed the door after him, and commanded that they should never again be admitted to his presence.

The knowing commissioners winked to each other, and made a certificate on the spot that the governor had refused to answer their interrogatories or to submit to their examination. They then proceeded to rummage about the city for two or three days, in quest of what they called evidence, perplexing Indians and old women with their cross-questioning until they had stuffed their satchels and saddle-bags with all kinds of apocryphal tales, rumors, and calumnies; with these they mounted their Narraganset pacers and travelled back to the grand council; neither did the proud-hearted Peter trouble himself to hinder their researches nor impede their departure; he was too mindful of their sacred character as envoys; but I warrant me, had they played the same tricks with William the Testy, he would have had them tucked up by the waistband and treated to an aërial gambol on his patent gallows.

CHAPTER VII

How "Drum Ecclesiastic" Was Beaten Throughout Connecticut for a Crusade Against the New Netherlands, and How Peter Stuyvesant Took Measures to Fortify His Capital

THE grand council of the east held a solemn meeting on the return of their envoys. As no advocate appeared in behalf of Peter Stuyvesant, everything went against him. His haughty refusal to submit to the questioning of the commissioners was construed into a consciousness of guilt. The contents of the satchels and saddle-bags were poured forth before the council and appeared a mountain of evidence. A pale, bilious orator took the floor, and declaimed for hours and in belligerent terms. He was one of those furious zealots who blows the bellows of faction until the whole furnace of politics is red-hot with sparks and cinders. What was it to him if he should set the house on fire, so that he might boil his pot by the blaze. He was from the borders of Connecticut; his constituents lived by marauding their Dutch neighbors, and were the greatest poachers in Christendom, excepting the Scotch border nobles. His eloquence had its effect, and it was determined to set on foot an expedition against the Nieuw Nederlands.

It was necessary, however, to prepare the public mind for this measure. Accordingly the arguments of the orator were echoed from the pulpit for several succeeding Sundays, and a crusade was preached up against Peter Stuyvesant and his devoted city.

This is the first we hear of the "drum ecclesiastic" beating up for recruits in worldly warfare in our country. It has since been called into frequent use. A cunning politician often lurks under the clerical robe; things spiritual and things temporal are strangely jumbled together, like drugs on an apothecary's shelf; and instead of a peaceful sermon, the simple seeker after righteousness has often a political pamphlet thrust down his throat, labelled with a pious text from Scripture.

And now nothing was talked of but an expedition against the Manhattoes. It pleased the populace, who had a vehement prejudice against the Dutch, considering them a vastly inferior race, who had sought the new world for the lucre of gain, not the liberty of conscience; who were mere heretics and infidels, inasmuch as they refused to believe in witches and sea-serpents, and had faith in the virtues of horse-shoes nailed to the door; ate pork without molasses; held pumpkins in contempt, and were in perpetual breach of the eleventh commandment of all true Yankees, "Thou shalt have codfish dinners on Saturdays."

No sooner did Peter Stuyvesant get wind of the storm that was brewing in the east than he set to work to prepare for it. He was not one of those economical rulers, who postpone the expense of fortifying until the enemy is at the door. There is nothing, he would say, that keeps off enemies and crows more than the smell of gunpowder. He proceeded, therefore, with all diligence, to put the province and its metropolis in a posture of defence.

Among the remnants which remained from the days of William the Testy were the militia laws—by which the inhabitants were obliged to turn out twice a year, with such military equipments as it pleased God—and were put under the command of tailors and man-milliners, who, though on ordinary occasions they might have been the meekest, most pippin-hearted little men in the world, were very devils at parade, when they had cocked hats on their heads and swords by their sides. Under the instructions of these periodical warriors, the peaceful burghers of the Manhattoes were schooled in iron war, and became so hardy in the process of time, that they could march through sun and rain, from one end of the town to the other, without flinching—and so intrepid and adroit, that they could face to the right, wheel to the left, and fire without winking or blinking.

Peter Stuyvesant, like all old soldiers who have seen service and smelt gunpowder, had no great respect for militia troops; however, he determined to give them a trial, and accordingly called for a general muster, inspection, and review. But, oh Mars and Bellona! what a turning-out was here! Here came old Roelant Cuckaburt, with a short blunderbuss on his shoulder, and a long horseman's sword trailing by his side; and Barent Dirkson, with something that looked like a copper kettle turned upside down on his head, and a couple of old horse-pistols in his belt; and Dirk Volkertson, with a long duck fowling-piece without any ramrod; and a host more, armed higgledy-piggledy—with swords, hatchets, snickersnees, crowbars, broomsticks, and what not; the officers distinguished from the rest by having their slouched hats cocked up with pins, and surmounted with cock-tail feathers.

The sturdy Peter eyed this nondescript host with some such rueful aspect as a man would eye the devil, and determined to give his feather-bed soldiers a seasoning. He accordingly put them through their manual exercise over and over again; trudged them backwards and forwards about the streets of New Amsterdam until their short legs ached and their fat sides sweated again; and finally encamped them in the evening on the summit of a hill without the city, to give them a taste of camp-life, intending the next day to renew the toils and perils of the field. But so it came to pass that in the night there fell a great and heavy rain, and melted away the army, so that in the morning, when Gaffer Phœbus shed his first beams upon the camp, scarce a warrior remained except Peter Stuyvesant and his trumpeter Van Corlear.

This awful desolation of a whole army would have appalled a commander of less nerve; but it served to confirm Peter's want of confidence in the militia system, which he thenceforward used to call, in joke—for he sometimes indulged in a joke—William the Testy's broken reed. He now took into his service a goodly number of burly, broad-shouldered, broad-bottomed Dutchmen; whom he paid in good silver and gold, and of whom he boasted, that, whether they could stand fire or not, they were at least waterproof. He fortified the city, too, with pickets and palisadoes, extending across the island from river to river, and, above all, cast up mud batteries, or redoubts, on the point of the island where it divided the beautiful bosom of the bay.

These latter redoubts, in process of time, came to be pleasantly overrun by a carpet of grass and clover, and overshadowed by wide-spreading elms and sycamores, among the branches of which the birds would build their nests and rejoice the ear with their melodious notes. Under these trees, too, the old burghers would smoke their afternoon pipe, contemplating the golden sun as he sank in the west, an emblem of the tranquil end toward which they were declining. Here, too, would the young men and maidens of the town take their evening stroll, watching the silver moonbeams as they trembled along the calm bosom of the bay, or lit up the sail of some gliding bark, and peradventure interchanging the soft vows of honest affection—for to evening strolls in this favored spot were traced most of the marriages in New Amsterdam.

Such was the origin of that renowned promenade, THE BATTERY, which, though ostensibly devoted to the stern purposes of war, has ever been consecrated to the sweet delights of peace. The scene of many a gambol in happy childhood—of many a tender assignation in riper years, of many a soothing walk in declining age—the healthful resort of the feeble invalid—the Sunday refreshment of the dusty tradesman—in fine, the ornament and delight of New York, and the pride of the lovely island of Manna-hata.

CHAPTER VIII

How the Yankee Crusade Against the New Netherlands Was Baffled by the Sudden Outbreak of Witchcraft Among the People of the East

HAVING thus provided for the temporary security of New Amsterdam, and guarded it against any sudden surprise, the gallant Peter took a hearty pinch of snuff, and snapping his fingers, set the great council of Amphictyons and their champion, the redoubtable Alicxsander Partridg, at defiance. In the mean time the moss-troopers of Connecticut, the warriors of New Haven and Hartford, and Pyquag, otherwise called Weathersfield, famous for its onions and its witches, and of all the other border-towns, were in a prodigious turmoil, furbishing up their rusty weapons, shouting aloud for war, and anticipating easy conquests, and glorious rummaging of the fat little Dutch villages.

In the midst of these warlike preparations, however, they received the chilling news that the colony of Massachusetts refused to back them in this righteous war. It seems that the gallant conduct of Peter Stuyvesant, the generous warmth of his vindication, and the chivalrous spirit of his defiance, though lost upon the grand council of the league, had carried conviction to the general court of Massachusetts, which nobly refused to believe him guilty of the villainous plot laid at his door.*

The defection of so important a colony paralyzed the councils of the league, some such dissension arose among its members as prevailed of yore in the camp of the brawling warriors of Greece, and in the end the crusade against the Manhattoes was abandoned.

It is said that the moss-troopers of Connecticut were sorely disappointed; but well for them that their belligerent cravings were not gratified: for by my faith, whatever might have been the ultimate result of a conflict with all the powers of the east, in the interim the stomachful heroes of Pyquag would have been choked with their own onions, and all the border-towns of Connecticut would have had such a scouring from the lion-hearted Peter and his robustious myrmidons, that I warrant me they would not have had the stomach to squat on the land or invade the hen-roost of a Nederlander for a century to come.

But it was not merely the refusal of Massachusetts to join in their unholy crusade that confounded the councils of the league; for about this time broke out in the New-England provinces the awful plague of witchcraft, which spread like pestilence through the land. Such a howling abomination could not be suffered to remain long unnoticed; it soon excited the fiery indignation of those guardians of the commonwealth who whilom had evinced such active benevolence in the conversion of Quakers and Anabaptists. The grand council of the league publicly set their faces against the crime, and bloody laws were enacted against all "solem conversing or compacting with the divil by way of conjuracion or the like." † Strict search, too, was made after witches, who were easily detected by devil's pinches—by being able to weep but three tears, and those out of the left eye—and by having a most suspicious predilection for black cats and broom-

* Hazard's State Papers.

† New Plymouth record.

sticks! What is particularly worthy of admiration is, that this terrible art, which has baffled the studies and researches of philosophers, astrologers, theurgists, and other sages, was chiefly confined to the most ignorant, decrepit, and ugly old women in the community, with scarce more brains than the broomsticks they rode upon.

When once an alarm is sounded, the public, who dearly love to be in a panic, are always ready to keep it up. Raise but the cry of yellow fever, and immediately every headache, indigestion, and overflowing of the bile is pronounced the terrible epidemic; cry out mad dog, and every unlucky cur in the street is in jeopardy: so in the present instance, whoever was troubled with colic or lumbago was sure to be bewitched—and woe to any unlucky old woman living in the neighborhood!

It is incredible the number of offences that were detected, "for every one of which," says the reverend Cotton Mather, in that excellent work the History of New England, "we have such a sufficient evidence, that no reasonable man in this whole country ever did question them; *and it will be unreasonable to do it in any other.*" *

Indeed, that authentic and judicious historian John Josselyn, Gent., furnishes us with unquestionable facts on this subject. "There are none," observes he, "that beg in this country, but there be witches too many—bottle-bellied witches, and others, that produce many strange apparitions, if you will believe report, of a shallop at sea manned with women—and of a ship and great red horse standing by the main-mast; the ship being in a small cove to the eastward, vanished of a sudden," etc.

The number of delinquents, however, and their magical devices, were not more remarkable than their diabolical obstinacy. Though exhorted in the most solemn, persuasive, and affectionate manner to confess themselves guilty, and be burnt for the good of religion and the entertainment of the public, yet did they most pertinaciously persist in asserting their innocence. Such incredible obstinacy was in itself deserving of immediate punishment, and was sufficient proof, if proof were necessary, that they were in league with the devil, who is perverseness itself. But their judges were just and merciful, and were determined to

* Mather's Hist. New Eng. B. 6, ch. 7.

punish none that were not convicted on the best of testimony; not that they needed any evidence to satisfy their own minds—for, like true and experienced judges, their minds were perfectly made up, and they were thoroughly satisfied of the guilt of the prisoners before they proceeded to try them—but still something was necessary to convince the community at large—to quiet those prying quidnuncs who should come after them—in short, the world must be satisfied. Oh, the world—the world!—all the world knows the world of trouble the world is eternally occasioning! The worthy judges therefore, were driven to the necessity of sifting, detecting, and making evident as noonday, matters which were at the commencement all clearly understood and firmly decided upon in their own pericraniums—so that it may truly be said, that the witches were burnt to gratify the populace of the day, but were tried for the satisfaction of the whole world that should come after them!

Finding, therefore, that neither exhortation, sound reason, nor friendly entreaty had any avail on these hardened offenders, they resorted to the more urgent arguments of torture; and having thus absolutely wrung the truth from their stubborn lips, they condemned them to undergo the roasting due unto the heinous crimes they had confessed. Some even carried their perverseness so far as to expire under the torture, protesting their innocence to the last; but these were looked upon as thoroughly and absolutely possessed by the devil; and the pious by-standers only lamented that they had not lived a little longer, to have perished in the flames.

In the city of Ephesus, we are told that the plague was expelled by stoning a ragged old beggar to death, whom Apollonius pointed out as being the evil spirit that caused it, and who actually showed himself to be a demon, by changing into a shagged dog. In like manner, and by measures equally sagacious, a salutary check was given to this growing evil. The witches were all burnt, banished, or panic-struck, and in a little while there was not an ugly old woman to be found throughout New England—which is doubtless one reason why all the young women there are so handsome. Those honest folk who had suffered from their incantations gradually recovered, excepting such as had been afflicted with twitches and aches, which, however, assumed the less alarming aspects of rheumatisms, sciatics, and lumbagos; and the good people of New England, abandoning the study of the occult sciences, turned their attention to the more profitable hocus-pocus of trade, and soon became expert in the legerdemain art of turning a penny. Still, however, a tinge of the old leaven is discernible, even unto this day, in their characters: witches occasionally start up among them in different disguises, as physicians, civilians, and divines. The people at large show a keenness, a cleverness, and a profundity of wisdom, that savors strongly of witchcraft; and it has been remarked, that, whenever any stones fall from the moon, the greater part of them is sure to tumble into New England!

CHAPTER IX

Which Records the Rise and Renown of a Military Commander, Showing That a Man, Like a Bladder, May Be Puffed Up to Greatness by Mere Wind; Together with the Catastrophe of a Veteran and His Queue

WHEN treating of these tempestuous times, the unknown writer of the Stuyvesant manuscript breaks out into an apostrophe in praise of the good St. Nicholas, to whose protecting care he ascribes the dissensions which broke out in the council of the league, and the direful witchcraft which filled all Yankee land as with Egyptian darkness.

A portentous gloom, says he, hung lowering over the fair valleys of the East: the pleasant banks of the Connecticut no longer echoed to the sounds of rustic gayety; grisly phantoms glided about each wild brook and silent glen; fearful apparitions were seen in the air; strange voices were heard in solitary places; and the border-towns were so occupied in detecting and punishing losel witches, that, for a time, all talk of war was suspended, and New Amsterdam and its inhabitants seemed to be totally forgotten.

I must not conceal the fact that at one time there was some danger of this plague of witchcraft extending into the New Netherlands; and certain witches, mounted on broomsticks, are said to have been seen whisking in the air over some of the Dutch villages near the borders; but the worthy Nederlanders took the precaution to nail horse-shoes to their doors, which it is well known are effectual barriers against all diabolical vermin of the kind. Many of those horse-shoes may be seen at this very day on ancient mansions and barns, remaining from the days of the patriarchs: nay, the custom is still kept up among some of our legitimate Dutch yeomanry, who inherit from their forefathers a desire to keep witches and Yankees out of the country.

And now the great Peter, having no immediate hostility to apprehend from the east, turned his face, with characteristic vigilance, to his southern frontiers. The attentive reader will recollect that certain freebooting Swedes had become very troublesome in this quarter in the latter part of the reign of William the Testy, setting at naught the proclamations of that veritable potentate, and putting his admiral, the intrepid Jan Jansen Alpendam, to a perfect nonplus. To check the incursions of these Swedes, Peter Stuyvesant now ordered a force to that frontier, giving the command of it to General Jacobus Van Poffenburgh, an officer who had risen to great importance during the reign of Wilhelmus Kieft. He had, if histories speak true, been second in command to the doughty Van Curlet, when he and his warriors were inhumanly kicked out of Fort Goed Hoop by the Yankees. In that memorable affair Van Poffenburgh is said to have received more kicks in a certain honorable part than any of his comrades, in consequence of which, on the resignation of Van Curlet, he had been promoted to his place, being considered a hero who had seen service, and suffered in his country's cause.

It is tropically observed by honest old Socrates, that heaven infuses into some men at their birth a portion of intellectual gold, into others of intellectual silver, while others are intellectually furnished with iron and brass. Of the last class was General Van Poffenburgh; and it would seem as if dame Nature, who will sometimes be partial, had given him brass enough for a dozen ordinary braziers. All this he had contrived to pass off upon William the Testy for genuine gold; and the little governor would sit for hours and listen to his gunpowder stories of exploits, which left those of Tirante the White, Don Belianis of Greece, or St. George and the Dragon quite in the background. Having been promoted by William Kieft to the command of his whole disposable forces, he gave importance to his station by the grandiloquence of his bulletins, always styling himself Commander-in-chief of the Armies of the New Netherlands, though in sober truth, these armies were nothing more than a handful of hen-stealing, bottle-bruising ragamuffins.

In person he was not very tall, but exceedingly round; neither did his bulk proceed from his being fat, but windy, being blown up by a prodigious conviction of his own importance, until he resembled one of those bags of wind given by Æolus, in an incredible fit of generosity, to that vagabond warrior Ulysses. His windy endowments had long excited the admiration of Antony Van Corlear, who is said to have hinted more than once to William the Testy, that in making Van Poffenburgh a general he had spoiled an admirable trumpeter.

As it is the practice in ancient story to give the reader a description of the arms and equipments of every noted warrior, I will bestow a word upon the dress of this redoubtable commander. It comported with his character, being so crossed and slashed, and embroidered with lace and tinsel, that he seemed to have as much brass without as nature had stored away within. He was swathed, too, in a crimson sash, of the size and texture of a fishing-net—doubtless to keep his swelling heart from bursting through his ribs. His face glowed with furnace-heat from between a huge pair of well-powdered whiskers; and his valorous soul seemed ready to bounce out of a pair of large, glassy, blinking eyes, projecting like those of a lobster.

I swear to thee, worthy reader, if history and tradition belie not this warrior, I would give all the money in my pocket to have seen him accoutred *cap-à-pie*—booted to the middle, sashed to the chin, collared to the ears, whiskered to the teeth, crowned with an overshadowing cocked hat, and girded with a leathern belt ten inches broad, from which trailed a falchion, of a length that I dare not mention. Thus equipped, he strutted about, as bitter-looking a man of war as the far-famed More, of More-hall, when he sallied forth to slay the dragon of Wantley. For what says the ballad?

"Had you but seen him in this dress,
How fierce he looked and how big,
You would have thought him for to be

Some Egyptian porcupig.
He frighted all—cats, dogs, and all,
Each cow, each horse, and each hog;
For fear they did flee, for they took him to be
Some strange outlandish hedge-hog."*

I must confess this general, with all his outward valor and ventosity, was not exactly an officer to Peter Stuyvesant's taste, but he stood foremost in the army list of William the Testy; and it is probable the good Peter, who was conscientious in his dealings with all men, and had his military notions of precedence, thought it but fair to give him a chance of proving his right to his dignities.

To this copper captain, therefore, was confided the command of the troops destined to protect the southern frontier; and scarce had he departed for his station than bulletins began to arrive from him, describing his undaunted march through savage deserts, over insurmountable mountains, across impassable rivers, and through impenetrable forests, conquering vast tracts of uninhabited country, and encountering more perils than did Xenophon in his far-famed retreat with his ten thousand Grecians.

Peter Stuyvesant read all these grandiloquent despatches with a dubious screwing of the mouth and shaking of the head; but Antony Van Corlear repeated these contents in the streets and market-places with an appropriate flourish upon his trumpet, and the windy victories of the general resounded through the streets of New Amsterdam.

On arriving at the southern frontier, Van Poffenburgh proceeded to erect a fortress, or stronghold, on the South or Delaware river. At first he bethought him to call it Fort Stuyvesant, in honor of the governor—a lowly kind of homage prevalent in our country among speculators, military commanders, and office-seekers of all kinds, by which our maps come to be studded with the names of political patrons and temporary great men; in the present instance, Van Poffenburgh carried his homage to the most lowly degree, giving his fortress the name of Fort Casimir, in honor, it is said, of a favorite pair of brimstone trunk-breeches of his Excellency.

As this fort will be found to give rise to important events, it

* Ballad of Dragon of Wantley.

may be worth while to notice that it was afterwards called Nieuw Amstel, and was the germ of the present flourishing town of New Castle, or, more properly speaking, No Castle, there being nothing of the kind on the premises.

His fortress being finished, it would have done any man's heart good to behold the swelling dignity with which the general would stride in and out a dozen times a day, surveying it in front and in rear, on this side and on that; how he would strut backwards and forwards, in full regimentals, on the top of the ramparts—like a vainglorious cock-pigeon, swelling and vaporing on the top of a dove-cot.

There is a kind of valorous spleen which, like wind, is apt to grow unruly in the stomachs of newly made soldiers, compelling them to box-lobby brawls and broken-headed quarrels, unless there can be found some more harmless way to give it vent. It is recorded in the delectable romance of Pierce Forest, that a young knight, being dubbed by King Alexander, did incontinently gallop into an adjacent forest and belabor the trees with such might and main, that he not merely eased off the sudden effervescence of his valor, but convinced the whole court that he was the most potent and courageous cavalier on the face of the earth. In like manner the commander of Fort Casimir, when he found his martial spirit waxing too hot within him, would sally forth into the fields and lay about him most lustily with his sabre—decapitating cabbages by platoons, hewing down lofty sunflowers, which he termed gigantic Swedes, and if, perchance, he espied a colony of big-bellied pumpkins quietly basking in the sun—"Ah! caitiff Yankees," would he roar, "have I caught ye at last?"—So saying, with one sweep of his sword he would cleave the unhappy vegetables from their chins to their waistbands; by which warlike havoc his choler being in some sort allayed, he would return into the fortress with the full conviction that he was a very miracle of military prowess.

He was a disciplinarian, too, of the first order. Woe to any unlucky soldier who did not hold up his head and turn out his toes when on parade, or who did not salute the general in proper style as he passed. Having one day, in his Bible researches, encountered the history of Absalom and his melancholy end, the general bethought him, that, in a country abounding with forests, his soldiers were in constant risk of a like catastrophe; he therefore, in an evil hour, issued orders for cropping the hair of both officers and men throughout the garrison.

Now, so it happened, that among his officers was a sturdy veteran named Keldermeester, who had cherished, through a long life, a mop of hair not a little resembling the shag of a Newfoundland dog, terminating in a queue like the handle of a frying-pan, and queued so tightly to his head that his eyes and mouth generally stood ajar, and his eyebrows were drawn up to the top of his forehead. It may naturally be supposed that the possessor of so goodly an appendage would resist with abhorrence an order condemning it to the shears. On hearing the general orders, he discharged a tempest of veteran, soldier-like oaths, and dunder and blixums—swore he would break any man's head who attempted to meddle with his tail—queued it stiffer than ever, and whisked it about the garrison as fiercely as the tail of a crocodile.

The eel-skin queue of old Keldermeester became instantly an affair of the utmost importance. The Commander-in-chief was too enlightened an officer not to perceive that the discipline of the garrison, the subordination and good order of the armies of the Nieuw Nederlands, the consequent safety of the whole province, and ultimately the dignity and prosperity of their High Mightinesses the Lords States General, imperiously demanded the docking of that stubborn queue. He decreed, therefore, that old Keldermeester should be publicly shorn of his glories in presence of the whole garrison; the old man as resolutely stood on the defensive; whereupon he was arrested, and tried by a court-martial for mutiny, desertion, and all the other list of offences noticed in the articles of war, ending with a "videlicet, in wearing an eel-skin queue, three feet long, contrary to orders." Then came on arraignments, and trials, and pleadings; and the whole garrison was in a ferment about this unfortunate queue. As it is well known that the commander of a frontier post has the power of acting pretty much after his own will, there is little doubt but that the veteran would have been hanged or shot at least, had he not luckily fallen ill of a fever, through mere chagrin and mortification—and deserted from all earthly command, with his beloved locks unviolated. His obstinacy remained unshaken to the very last moment, when he directed that he should be carried to his grave with his eel-skin queue sticking out of a hole in his coffin.

This magnanimous affair obtained the general great credit as a disciplinarian; but it is hinted that he was ever afterwards subject to bad dreams and fearful visitations in the night, when the grizzly spectrum of old Keldermeester would stand sentinel by his bedside, erect as a pump, his enormous queue strutting out like the handle.

Book VI

CONTAINING THE SECOND PART OF THE REIGN OF PETER THE HEADSTRONG, AND HIS GALLANT ACHIEVEMENTS ON THE DELAWARE

CHAPTER I

In Which Is Exhibited a Warlike Portrait of the Great Peter—of the Windy Contest of General Van Poffenburgh and General Printz, and of the Mosquito War on the Delaware

HITHERTO, most venerable and courteous reader, have I shown thee the administration of the valorous Stuyvesant, under the mild moonshine of peace, or rather the grim tranquillity of awful expectation; but now the war-drum rumbles from afar, the brazen trumpet brays its thrilling note, and the rude crash of hostile arms speaks fearful prophecies of coming troubles. The gallant warrior starts from soft repose, from golden visions and voluptuous ease, where in the dulcet, "piping time of peace" he sought sweet solace after all his toils. No more in beauty's siren lap reclined, he weaves fair garlands for his lady's brows; no more entwines with flowers his shining sword, nor through the livelong lazy summer's day chants forth his love-sick soul in madrigals. To manhood roused, he spurns the amorous flute; doffs from his brawny back the robe of peace, and clothes his pampered limbs in panoply of steel. O'er his dark brow, where late the myrtle waved, where wanton roses breathed enervate love, he rears the beaming casque and nodding plume; grasps the bright shield, and shakes the ponderous lance; or mounts with eager pride his fiery steed, and burns for deeds of glorious chivalry!

But soft, worthy reader! I would not have you imagine that any *preux chevalier*, thus hideously begirt with iron, existed in the city of New Amsterdam. This is but a lofty and gigantic mode, in which we heroic writers always talk of war, thereby to give it a noble and imposing aspect—equipping our warriors with bucklers, helms, and lances, and such like outlandish and obsolete weapons, the like of which perchance they had never seen or heard of—in the same manner that a cunning statuary arrays a modern general or an admiral in the accoutrements of a Cæsar or an Alexander. The simple truth, then, of all this oratorical flourish is this, that the valiant Peter Stuyvesant all of a sudden found it necessary to scour his rusty blade, which too long had rusted in its scabbard, and prepare himself to undergo those hardy toils of war in which his mighty soul so much delighted.

Methinks I at this moment behold him in my imagination, or rather, I behold his goodly portrait, which still hangs up in the family mansion of the Stuyvesants, arrayed in all the terrors of a true Dutch general. His regimental coat of German blue, gorgeously decorated with a goodly show of large brass buttons, reaching from his waistband to his chin; the voluminous skirts turned up at the corners and separating gallantly behind, so as to display the seat of a sumptuous pair of brimstone-colored trunk-breeches—a graceful style still prevalent among the warriors of our day, and which is in conformity to the custom of ancient heroes, who scorned to defend themselves in rear. His face rendered exceeding terrible and warlike by a pair of black mustachios; his hair strutting out on each side in stiffly pomatumed ear-locks, and descending in a rat-tail queue below his waist; a shining stock of black leather supporting his chin, and a little but fierce cocked hat, stuck with a gallant and fiery air over his left eye. Such was the chivalric port of Peter the Headstrong; and when he made a sudden halt, planted himself firmly on his solid supporter, with his wooden leg, inlaid with silver, a little in advance, in order to strengthen his position, his right hand grasping a gold-headed cane, his left resting upon the pummel of his sword, his head dressing spiritedly to the right, with a most appalling and hard-favored frown upon his brow—he presented altogether one of the most commanding, bitter-looking, and soldier-like figures that ever strutted upon canvas.—Proceed we now to inquire the cause of this warlike preparation.

In the preceding chapter we have spoken of the founding of Fort Casimir, and of the merciless warfare waged by its commander upon cabbages, sunflowers, and pumpkins, for want of better occasion to flesh his sword. Now it came to pass, that, higher up the Delaware, at his stronghold of Tinnekonk, resided one Jan Printz, who styled himself Governor of New Sweden. If history belie not this redoubtable Swede, he was a rival worthy of the windy and inflated commander of Fort Casimir, for master David Pieterzen de Vrie, in his excellent book of voyages, describes him as "weighing upwards of four hundred pounds," a huge feeder and bowser in proportion, taking three potations pottle-deep at every meal. He had a garrison after his own heart at Tinnekonk—guzzling, deep-drinking swashbucklers, who made the wild woods ring with their carousals.

No sooner did this robustious commander hear of the erection of Fort Casimir, than he sent a message to Van Poffenburgh, warning him off the land, as being within the bounds of his jurisdiction.

To this, General Van Poffenburgh replied that the land belonged to their High Mightinesses, having been regularly purchased of the natives, as discoverers from the Manhattoes, as witness the breeches of their land-measurer Ten Broeck.

To this the governor rejoined that the land had previously been sold by the Indians to the Swedes, and consequently was under the petticoat government of her Swedish majesty, Christina; and woe be to any mortal that wore breeches who should dare to meddle even with the hem of her sacred garment.

I forbear to dilate upon the war of words which was kept up for some time by these windy commanders; Van Poffenburgh, however, had served under William the Testy, and was a veteran in this kind of warfare. Governor Printz, finding he was not to be dislodged by these long shots, now determined upon coming to closer quarters. Accordingly, he descended the river in great force and fume, and erected a rival fortress just one Swedish mile below Fort Casimir, to which he gave the name of Helsenburg.

And now commenced a tremendous rivalry between these two doughty commanders, striving to out-strut and out-swell each other like a couple of belligerent turkey-cocks. There was a contest who should run up the tallest flag-staff and display the broadest flag; all day long there was a furious rolling of drums and twanging of trumpets in either fortress, and whichever had the wind in its favor would keep up a continual firing of cannon, to taunt its antagonist with the smell of gunpowder.

On all these points of windy warfare the antagonists were well matched; but so it happened, that, the Swedish fortress being lower down the river, all the Dutch vessels bound to Fort Casimir with supplies had to pass it. Governor Printz at once took advantage of this circumstance, and compelled them to lower their flags as they passed under the guns of his battery.

This was a deadly wound to the Dutch pride of General Van Poffenburgh, and sorely would he swell when from the ramparts of Fort Casimir he beheld the flag of their High Mightinesses struck to the rival fortress. To heighten his vexation, Governor Printz, who, as has been shown, was a huge trencherman, took the liberty of having the first rummage of every Dutch merchant-ship, and securing to himself and his guzzling garrison all the little round Dutch cheeses, all the Dutch herrings, the ginger-bread, the sweetmeats, the curious stone jugs of gin, and all the other Dutch luxuries, on their way for the solace of Fort Casimir. It is possible he may have paid to the Dutch skippers the full value of their commodities; but what consolation was this to Jacobus Van Poffenburgh and his garrison, who thus found their favorite supplies cut off, and diverted into the larders of the hostile camp? For some time this war of the cupboard was carried on to the great festivity and jollification of the Swedes, while the warriors of Fort Casimir found their hearts, or rather their stomachs, daily failing them. At length the summer heats and summer showers set in, and now, lo and behold, a great miracle was wrought for the relief of the Nederlands, not a little resembling one of the plagues of Egypt; for it came to pass that a great cloud of mosquitoes arose out of the marshy borders of the river and settled upon the fortress of Helsenburg, being, doubtless, attracted by the scent of the fresh blood of these Swedish gormandizers. Nay, it is said that the body of Jan Printz alone, which was as big and as full of blood as that of a prize-ox, was sufficient to attract the mosquitoes from every part of the country. For some time the garrison endeavored to hold out, but it was all in vain; the mosquitoes penetrated into every chink and crevice, and gave them no rest day nor night; and as to Governor Jan Printz, he moved about as in a cloud, with mosquito music in his ears, and mosquito stings to the very end of his nose. Finally the garrison was fairly driven out of the fortress, and obliged to retreat to Tinnekonk; nay, it is said that the mosquitoes followed Jan Printz even thither, and absolutely drove him out of the country; certain it is, he embarked for Sweden shortly afterwards, and Jan Claudius Risingh was sent to govern New Sweden in his stead.

Such was the famous mosquito war on the Delaware, of which General Van Poffenburgh would fain have been the hero, but the devout people of the Nieuw Nederlands always ascribed the discomfiture of the Swedes to the miraculous intervention of St. Nicholas. As to the fortress of Helsenburg, it fell to ruin; but the story of its strange destruction was perpetuated by the Swedish name of Myggen-borg, that is to say, Mosquito Castle.*

CHAPTER II

Of Jan Risingh, His Giantly Person and Crafty Deeds; and of the Catastrophe at Fort Casimir

JAN CLAUDIUS RISINGH, who succeeded to the command of New Sweden, looms largely in ancient records as a gigantic Swede, who, had he not been rather knock-kneed and splay-footed, might have served for the model of a Samson or a Hercules. He was no less rapacious than mighty, and, withal, as crafty as he was rapacious; so that there is very little doubt, that, had he lived some four or five centuries since, he would have figured as one of those wicked giants who took a cruel pleasure in pocketing beautiful princesses and distressed damsels, when gadding about the world, and locking them up in enchanted castles, without a toilet, a change of linen, or any other convenience. In consequence of which enormities they fell under the high displeasure of chivalry, and all true, loyal, and gallant knights were instucted to attack and slay outright any miscreant they might happen to find above six feet high; which is doubtless one reason why the race of large men is nearly extinct, and the generations of latter ages are so exceedingly small.

* Acrelius's History N. Sweden. For some notice of this miraculous discomfiture of the Swedes, see N. Y. His. Col., new series, Vol. I. p. 412.

Governor Risingh, notwithstanding his giantly condition, was, as I have hinted, a man of craft. He was not a man to ruffle the vanity of General Van Poffenburgh, or to rub his self-conceit against the grain. On the contrary, as he sailed up the Delaware, he paused before Fort Casimir, displayed his flag, and fired a royal salute before dropping anchor. The salute would doubtless have been returned, had not the guns been dismounted; as it was, a veteran sentinel, who had been napping at his post, and had suffered his match to go out, returned the compliment by discharging his musket with the spark of a pipe borrowed from a comrade. Governor Risingh accepted this as a courteous reply, and treated the fortress to a second salute, well knowing its commander was apt to be marvellously delighted with these little ceremonials, considering them so many acts of homage paid to his greatness. He then prepared to land with a military retinue of thirty men, a prodigious pageant in the wilderness.

And now took place a terrible rummage and racket in Fort Casimir, to receive such a visitor in proper style, and to make an imposing appearance. The main guard was turned out as soon as possible, equipped to the best advantage in the few suits of regimentals, which had to do duty by turns with the whole garrison. One tall, lank fellow appeared in a little man's coat, with the buttons between his shoulders; the skirts scarce covering his bottom; his hands hanging like spades out of the sleeves and the coat linked in front by worsted loops made out of a pair of red garters. Another had a cocked hat stuck on the back of his head, and decorated with a bunch of cock's tails; a third had a pair of rusty gaiters hanging about his heels; while a fourth, a little duck-legged fellow, was equipped in a pair of the general's cast-off breeches, which he held up with one hand while he grasped his firelock with the other. The rest were accoutred in similar style, except three ragamuffins without shirts, and with but a pair and a half of breeches between them; wherefore they were sent to the black hole, to keep them out of sight, that they might not disgrace the fortress.

His men being thus gallantly arrayed—those who lacked muskets shouldering spades and pickaxes, and every man being ordered to tuck in his shirt-tail and pull up his brogues—General Van Poffenburgh first took a sturdy draught of foaming ale, which, like the magnanimous More of More-hall,* was his invariable practice on all great occasions; this done, he put himself at their head, and issued forth from his castle, like a mighty giant, just refreshed with wine. But when the two heroes met, then began a scene of warlike parade that beggars all description. The shrewd Risingh, who had grown gray much before his time in consequence of his craftiness, saw at one glance the ruling passion of the great Van Poffenburgh, and humored him in all his valorous fantasies.

Their detachments were accordingly drawn up in front of each other; they carried arms and they presented arms; they gave the standing salute and the passing salute; they rolled their drums, they flourished their fifes, and they waved their colors; they faced to the left, and they faced to the right, and they faced to the rightabout; they wheeled forward, and they wheeled backward, and they wheeled into *echellon;* they marched and they countermarched, by grand divisions, by single divisions, and by subdivisions; by platoons, by sections, and by files; in quick time, in slow time, and in no time at all; for, having gone through all the evolutions of two great armies, including the eighteen manœuvres of Dundas; having exhausted all they could recollect or imagine of military tactics, including sundry strange and irregular evolutions, the like of which were never seen before nor since, excepting among certain of our newly raised militia—the two commanders and their respective troops came at length to a dead halt, completely exhausted by the toils of war. Never did two valiant train-band captains, or two buskined theatric heroes, in the renowned tragedies of Pizarro, Tom Thumb, or any other heroical and fighting tragedy, marshal their gallows-looking, duck-legged, heavy-heeled myrmidons with more glory and self-admiration.

These military compliments being finished, General Van Poffenburgh escorted his illustrious visitor, with great ceremony, into the Fort; attended him throughout the fortifications; showed him the horn-works, crown-works, half-moons, and vari-

* ". . . . as soon as he rose,
To make him strong and mighty,
He drank by the tale, six pots of ale,
And a quart of aqua vitæ."
Dragon of Wantley.

ous other outworks, or rather the places where they ought to be erected, and where they might be erected if he pleased; plainly demonstrating that it was a place of "great capability," and though at present but a little redoubt, yet that it was evidently a formidable fortress, in embryo. This survey over, he next had the whole garrison put under arms, exercised, and reviewed; and concluded by ordering the three bridewell birds to be hauled out of the black hole, brought up to the halberds, and soundly flogged, for the amusement of his visitor, and to convince him that he was a great disciplinarian.

The cunning Risingh, while he pretended to be struck dumb outright with the puissance of the great Van Poffenburgh, took silent note of the incompetency of his garrison—of which he gave a wink to his trusty followers, who tipped each other the wink, and laughed most obstreperously—in their sleeves.

The inspection, review, and flogging being concluded, the party adjourned to the table; for among his other great qualities, the general was remarkably addicted to huge carousals, and in one afternoon's campaign would leave more dead men on the field than he ever did in the whole course of his military career. Many bulletins of these bloodless victories do still remain on record; and the whole province was once thrown in amaze by the return of one of his campaigns, wherein it was stated, that, though, like Captain Bobadil, he had only twenty men to back him, yet in the short space of six months he had conquered and utterly annihilated sixty oxen, ninety hogs, one hundred sheep, ten thousand cabbages, one thousand bushels of potatoes, one hundred and fifty kilderkins of small beer, two thousand seven hundred and thirty-five pipes, seventy-eight pounds of sugar-plums, and forty bars of iron, besides sundry small meats, game, poultry, and garden-stuff:—an achievement unparalleled since the days of Pantagruel and his all-devouring army, and which showed that it was only necessary to let Van Poffenburgh and his garrison loose in an enemy's country, and in a little while they would breed a famine, and starve all the inhabitants.

No sooner, therefore, had the general received intimation of the visit of Governor Risingh, than he ordered a great dinner to be prepared, and privately sent out a detachment of his most experienced veterans, to rob all the hen-roosts in the neighborhood, and lay the pig-sties under contribution—a service which they discharged with such zeal and promptitude, that the garrison-table groaned under the weight of their spoils.

I wish, with all my heart, my readers could see the valiant Van Poffenburgh, as he presided at the head of the banquet; it was a sight worth beholding:—there he sat, in his greatest glory, surrounded by his soldiers, like that famous wine-bibber, Alexander, whose thirsty virtues he did most ably imitate—telling astonishing stories of his hair-breadth adventures and heroic exploits; at which, though all his auditors knew them to be incontinent lies and outrageous gasconadoes, yet did they cast up their eyes in admiration, and utter many interjections of astonishment. Nor could the general pronounce anything that bore the remotest resemblance to a joke, but the stout Risingh would strike his brawny fist upon the table till every glass rattled again, throw himself back in the chair, utter gigantic peals of laughter, and swear most horribly it was the best joke he ever heard in his life. Thus all was rout and revelry and hideous carousal within Fort Casimir; and so lustily did Van Poffenburgh ply the bottle, that in less than four short hours he made himself and his whole garrison, who all sedulously emulated the deeds of their chieftain, dead drunk, with singing songs, quaffing bumpers, and drinking patriotic toasts, none of which but was as long as a Welsh pedigree or a plea in chancery.

No sooner did things come to this pass, than Risingh and his Swedes, who had cunningly kept themselves sober, rose on their entertainers, tied them neck and heels, and took formal possession of the fort, and all its dependencies, in the name of Queen Christina of Sweden, administering at the same time an oath of allegiance to all the Dutch soldiers who could be made sober enough to swallow it. Risingh then put the fortification in order, appointed his discreet and vigilant friend Suen Schüte, otherwise called Skytte, a tall, wind-dried, water-drinking Swede, to the command, and departed, bearing with him this truly amiable garrison and its puissant commander, who, when brought to himself by a sound drubbing, bore no little resemblance to a "deboshed fish," or bloated sea-monster, caught upon dry land.

The transportation of the garrison was done to prevent the transmission of intelligence to New Amsterdam; for much as the cunning Risingh exulted in his stratagem, yet did he dread the vengeance of the sturdy Peter Stuyvesant, whose name spread as much terror in the neighborhood as did whilom that of the unconquerable Scanderbeg among his scurvy enemies the Turks.

CHAPTER III

Showing How Profound Secrets Are Often Brought to Light; with the Proceedings of Peter the Headstrong When He Heard of the Misfortunes of General Van Poffenburgh

WHOEVER first described common fame, or rumor, as belonging to the sager sex, was a very owl for shrewdness. She has in truth certain feminine qualities to an astonishing degree, particularly that benevolent anxiety to take care of the affairs of others, which keeps her continually hunting after secrets, and gadding about proclaiming them. Whatever is done openly and in the face of the world, she takes but transient notice of; but whenever a transaction is done in a corner, and attempted to be shrouded in mystery, then her goddess-ship is at her wit's end to find it out, and takes a most mischievous and lady-like pleasure in publishing it to the world.

It is this truly feminine propensity which induces her continually to be prying into the cabinets of princes, listening at the key-holes of senate-chambers, and peering through chinks and crannies, when our worthy Congress are sitting with closed doors, deliberating between a dozen excellent modes of ruining the nation. It is this which makes her so baneful to all wary statesmen and intriguing commanders—such a stumbling-block to private negotiations and secret expeditions—betraying them by means and instruments which never would have been thought of by any but a female head.

Thus it was in the case of the affair of Fort Casimir. No doubt the cunning Risingh imagined, that, by securing the garrison, he should for a long time prevent the history of its fate from reaching the ears of the gallant Stuyvesant; but his exploit was blown to the world when he least expected, and by one of the last beings he would ever have suspected of enlisting as trumpeter to the wide-mouthed deity.

This was one Dirk Schuiler (or Skulker), a kind of hanger-on to the garrison, who seemed to belong to nobody, and in a manner to be self-outlawed. He was one of those vagabond cosmopolites who shark about the world as if they had no right or business in it, and who infest the skirts of society like poachers and interlopers. Every garrison and country village has one or more scape-goats of this kind, whose life is a kind of enigma, whose existence is without motive, who comes from the Lord knows where, who lives the Lord knows how, and who seems created for no other earthly purpose but to keep up the ancient and honorable order of idleness. This vagrant philosopher was supposed to have some Indian blood in his veins, which was manifested by a certain Indian complexion and cast of countenance, but more especially by his propensities and habits. He was a tall, lank fellow, swift of foot, and long-winded. He was generally equipped in a half Indian dress, with belt, leggings, and moccasins. His hair hung in straight gallows-locks about his ears, and added not a little to his sharking demeanor. It is an old remark, that persons of Indian mixture are half civilized, half savage, and half devil—a third half being provided for their particular convenience. It is for similar reasons, and probably with equal truth, that the backwoodsmen of Kentucky are styled half man, half horse, and half alligator, by the settlers on the Mississippi, and held accordingly in great respect and abhorrence.

The above character may have presented itself to the garrison as applicable to Dirk Schuiler, whom they familiarly dubbed Gallows Dirk. Certain it is, he acknowledged allegiance to no one—was an utter enemy to work, holding it in no manner of estimation—but lounging about the fort, depending upon chance for a subsistence, getting drunk whenever he could get liquor, and stealing whatever he could lay his hands on. Every day or two he was sure to get a sound rib-roasting for some of his misdemeanors, which, however, as it broke no bones, he made very light of, and scrupled not to repeat the offence whenever another opportunity presented. Sometimes, in consquence of some flagrant villainy, he would abscond from the garrison, and be absent for a month at a time, skulking about the woods and swamps, with a long fowling-piece on his shoulder, lying in ambush for game—or squatting himself down on the edge of a pond, catching fish for hours together, and bearing no little resemblance to that notable bird of the crane family, ycleped the Mudpoke. When he thought his crimes had been forgotten or forgiven, he would sneak back to the fort with a bundle of skins, or a load of poultry, which, perchance, he had stolen, and would exchange them for liquor, with which having well soaked his carcass, he would lie in the sun and enjoy all the luxurious indolence of that swinish philosopher Diogenes. He was the terror of all the farm-yards in the country into which he made fearful inroads; and sometimes he would make his sudden appearance in the garrison at daybreak, with the whole neighborhood at his heels—like the scoundrel thief of a fox, detected in his maraudings and hunted to his hole. Such was this Dirk Schuiler; and from the total indifference he showed to the world and its concerns, and from his truly Indian stoicism and taciturnity, no one would ever have dreamt that he would have been the publisher of the treachery of Risingh.

When the carousal was going on, which proved so fatal to the brave Poffenburgh and his watchful garrison, Dirk skulked about from room to room, being a kind of privileged vagrant, or useless hound, whom nobody noticed. But though a fellow of few words, yet, like your taciturn people, his eyes and ears were always open, and in the course of his prowlings he overheard the whole plot of the Swedes. Dirk immediately settled in his own mind how he should turn the matter to his own advantage. He played the perfect jack-of-both-sides, that is to say, he made a prize of everything that came in his reach, robbed both parties, stuck the copper-bound cocked hat of the puissant Van Poffenburgh on his head, whipped a huge pair of Risingh's jack-boots under his arms, and took to his heels just before the catastrophe and confusion at the garrison.

Finding himself completely dislodged from his haunt in this quarter, he directed his flight towards his native place, New Amsterdam, whence he had formerly been obliged to abscond precipitately, in consequence of misfortune in business—that is to say, having been detected in the act of sheep-stealing. After wandering many days in the woods, toiling through swamps, fording brooks, swimming various rivers, and encountering a world of hardships that would have killed any other being but an Indian, a backwoodsman, or the devil, he at length arrived, half famished, and lank as a starved weasel, at Communipaw, where he stole a canoe, and paddled over to New Amsterdam. Immediately on landing, he repaired to Governor Stuyvesant, and, in more words than he had ever spoken before in the whole course of his life, gave an account of the disastrous affair.

On receiving these direful tidings, the valiant Peter started from his seat, dashed the pipe he was smoking against the back of the chimney, thrust a prodigious quid of tobacco into his left cheek, pulled up his galligaskins, and strode up and down the room, humming, as was customary with him when in a passion, a hideous northwest ditty. But, as I have before shown, he was not a man to vent his spleen in idle vaporing. His first measure, after the paroxysm of wrath had subsided, was to stump up-stairs to a huge wooden chest, which served as his armory, from whence he drew forth that identical suit of regimentals described in the preceding chapter. In these portentous habiliments he arrayed himself like Achilles in the armor of Vulcan, maintaining all the while an appalling silence, knitting his brows, and drawing his breath through his clenched teeth. Being hastily equipped, he strode down into the parlor and jerked down his trusty sword from over the fireplace, where it was usually suspended; but before he girded it on his thigh, he drew it from its scabbard, and as his eye coursed along the rusty blade, a grim smile stole over his iron visage; it was the first smile that had visited his countenance for five long weeks; but every one who beheld it prophesied that there would soon be warm work in the province!

Thus armed at all points, with grisly war depicted in each feature, his very cocked hat assuming an air of uncommon defiance, he instantly put himself upon the alert, and despatched Antony Van Corlear hither and thither, this way and that way, through all the muddy streets and crooked lanes of the city, summoning by sound of trumpet his trusty peers to assemble in instant council. This done, by way of expediting matters, according to the custom of people in a hurry, he kept in continual bustle, shifting from chair to chair, popping his head out of every window, and stumping up and down stairs with his wooden leg in such brisk and incessant motion, that, as we are informed by an authentic historian of the times, the continual clatter bore no small resemblance to the music of a cooper hooping a flour-barrel.

A summons so peremptory, and from a man of the governor's mettle, was not to be trifled with: the sages forthwith repaired to the council-chamber, seated themselves with the utmost tranquillity, and, lighting their long pipes, gazed with unruffled composure on his Excellency and his regimentals—being, as all counsellors should be, not easily flustered, nor taken by surprise. The governor, looking around for a moment with a lofty and soldier-like air, and resting one hand on the pommel of his sword, and flinging the other forth in a free and spirited manner, addressed them in a short but soul-stirring harangue.

I am extremely sorry that I have not the advantages of Livy, Thucydides, Plutarch, and others of my predecessors, who were furnished, as I am told, with the speeches of all their heroes, taken down in short-hand by the most accurate stenographers of the time—whereby they were enabled wonderfully to enrich their histories, and delight their readers with sublime strains of eloquence. Not having such important auxiliaries, I cannot possibly pronounce what was the tenor of Governor Stuyvesant's speech. I am bold, however, to say, from the tenor of his character, that he did not wrap his rugged subject in silks and ermines, and other sickly trickeries of phrase, but spoke forth like a man of nerve and vigor, who scorned to shrink in words from those dangers which he stood ready to encounter in very deed. This much is certain, that he concluded by announcing his determination to lead on his troops in person, and rout these costard-monger Swedes from their usurped quarters at Fort Casimir. To this hardy resolution, such of his council as were awake gave their usual signal of concurrence; and as to the rest, who had fallen asleep about the middle of the harangue (their "usual custom in the afternoon"), they made not the least objection.

And now was seen in the fair city of New Amsterdam a prodigious bustle and preparation for iron war. Recruiting parties marched hither and thither, calling lustily upon all the scrubs, the runagates, and tatterdemalions of the Manhattoes and its vicinity, who had any ambition of sixpence a day, and immortal fame into the bargain, to enlist in the cause of glory:—for I would have you note that your warlike heroes who trudge in the rear of conquerors are generally of that illustrious class of gentlemen who are equal candidates for the army or the bridewell, the halberds or the whipping-post—for whom dame Fortune has cast an even die, whether they shall make their exit by the sword or the halter, and whose deaths shall, at all events, be a lofty example to their countrymen.

But, notwithstanding all this martial rout and invitation, the ranks of honor were but scantily supplied, so averse were the peaceful burghers of New Amsterdam from enlisting in foreign broils, or stirring beyond that home which rounded all their earthly ideas. Upon beholding this, the great Peter, whose noble heart was all on fire with war and sweet revenge, determined to wait no longer for the tardy assistance of these oily citizens, but to muster up his merry men of the Hudson, who, brought up among woods, and wilds, and savage beasts, like our yeomen of Kentucky, delighted in nothing so much as desperate adventures and perilous expeditions through the wilderness. Thus resolving, he ordered his trusty squire Antony Van Corlear to have his state galley prepared and duly victualled; which being performed, he attended public service at the great church of St. Nicholas, like a true and pious governor; and then leaving peremptory orders with his council to have the chivalry of the Manhattoes marshalled out and appointed against his return, departed upon his recruiting voyage up the waters of the Hudson.

CHAPTER IV

Containing Peter Stuyvesant's Voyage Up the Hudson, and the Wonders and Delights of That Renowned River

NOW did the soft breezes of the south steal sweetly over the face of nature, tempering the panting heats of summer into genial and prolific warmth; when that miracle of hardihood and chivalric virtue, the dauntless Peter Stuyvesant, spread his canvas to the wind, and departed from the fair island of Manna-hata.

The galley in which he embarked was sumptuously adorned with pendants and streamers of gorgeous dyes, which fluttered gayly in the wind, or drooped their ends into the bosom of the stream. The bow and poop of this majestic vessel were gallantly bedight, after the rarest Dutch fashion, with figures of little pursy Cupids with periwigs on their heads, and bearing in their hands garlands of flowers, the like of which are not to be found in any book of botany, being the matchless flowers which flourished in the golden age, and exist no longer, unless it be in the imaginations of ingenious carvers of wood and discolorers of canvas.

Thus rarely decorated, in style befitting the puissant potentate of the Manhattoes, did the galley of Peter Stuyvesant launch forth upon the bosom of the lordly Hudson, which, as it rolled its broad waves to the ocean, seemed to pause for a while and swell with pride, as if conscious of the illustrious burden it sustained.

But trust me, gentlefolk, far other was the scene presented to the contemplation of the crew from that which may be witnessed at this degenerate day. Wildness and savage majesty reigned on the borders of this mighty river; the hand of cultivation had not as yet laid low the dark forest, and tamed the features of the landscape; nor had the frequent sail of commerce broken in upon the profound and awful solitude of ages. Here and there might be seen a rude wigwam perched among the cliffs of the mountains, with its curling column of smoke mounting in the transparent atmosphere—but so loftily situated that the whoopings of the savage children, gambolling on the margin of the dizzy heights, fell almost as faintly on the ear as do the notes of the lark when lost in the azure vault of heaven. Now and then, from the beetling brow of some precipice, the wild deer would look timidly down upon the splendid pageant as it passed below, and then, tossing his antlers in the air, would bound away into the thickest of the forest.

Through such scenes did the stately vessel of Peter Stuyvesant pass. Now did they skirt the bases of the rocky heights of Jersey, which spring up like everlasting walls, reaching from the waves unto the heavens, and were fashioned, if tradition may be believed, in times long past, by the mighty spirit Manetho, to protect his favorite abodes from the unhallowed eyes of mortals.

Now did they career it gayly across the vast expanse of Tappan Bay, whose wide-extended shores present a variety of delectable scenery—here the bold promontory, crowned with embowering trees, advancing into the bay—there the long woodland slope, sweeping up from the shore in rich luxuriance, and terminating in the upland precipice—while at a distance a long waving line of rocky heights threw their gigantic shades across the water. Now would they pass where some modest little interval, opening among these stupendous scenes, yet retreating as it were for protection into the embraces of the neighboring mountains, displayed a rural paradise, fraught with sweet and pastoral beauties—the velvet-tufted lawn, the bushy copse, the tinkling rivulet, stealing through the fresh and vivid verdure, on whose banks was situated some little Indian village, or, peradventure, the rude cabin of some solitary hunter.

The different periods of the revolving days seemed each, with cunning magic, to diffuse a different charm over the scene. Now would the jovial sun break gloriously from the east, blazing from the summits of the hills, and sparkling the landscape with a thousand dewy gems; while along the borders of the river were seen the heavy masses of mist, which, like midnight caitiffs disturbed at his approach, made a sluggish retreat, rolling in sullen reluctance up the mountains. At such times all was brightness, and life, and gayety—the atmosphere was of an indescribable pureness and transparency—the birds broke forth in wanton madrigals, and the freshening breezes wafted the vessel merrily on her course. But when the sun sunk amid a flood of glory in the west, mantling the heavens and the earth with a thousand gorgeous dyes, then all was calm, and silent, and magnificent. The late swelling sail hung lifelessly against the mast; the seaman, with folded arms, leaned against the shrouds, lost in that involuntary musing which the sober grandeur of nature commands in the rudest of her children. The vast bosom of the Hudson was like an unruffled mirror, reflecting the golden splendor of the heavens, excepting that now and then a bark canoe would steal across its surface, filled with painted savages, whose gay feathers glared brightly as perchance a lingering ray of the setting sun gleamed upon them from the western mountains.

But when the hour of twilight spread its majestic mists

around, then did the face of nature assume a thousand fugitive charms, which to the worthy heart that seeks enjoyment in the glorious works of its Maker are inexpressibly captivating. The mellow dubious light that prevailed just served to tinge with illusive colors the softened features of the scenery. The deceived but delighted eye sought vainly to discern in the broad masses of shade the separating line between the land and water, or to distinguish the fading objects that seemed sinking into chaos. Now did the busy fancy supply the feebleness of vision, producing with industrious craft a fairy creation of her own. Under her plastic wand the barren rocks frowned upon the watery waste in the semblance of lofty towers and high embattled castles—trees assumed the direful forms of mighty giants, and the inaccessible summits of the mountains seemed peopled with a thousand shadowy beings.

Now broke forth from the shores the notes of an innumerable variety of insects, which filled the air with a strange but not inharmonious concert, while ever and anon was heard the melancholy plaint of the whippoorwill, who, perched on some lone tree, wearied the ear of night with his incessant moanings. The mind, soothed into a hallowed melancholy, listened with pensive stillness to catch and distinguish each sound that vaguely echoed from the shore—now and then startled perchance by the whoop of some straggling savage, or by the dreary howl of a wolf, stealing forth upon his nightly prowlings.

Thus happily did they pursue their course, until they entered upon those awful defiles denominated THE HIGHLANDS, where it would seem that the gigantic Titans had erst waged their impious war with heaven, piling up cliffs on cliffs, and hurling vast masses of rock in wild confusion. But in sooth very different is the history of these cloud-capt mountains. These in ancient days, before the Hudson poured its waters from the lakes, formed one vast prison, within whose rocky bosom the omnipotent Manetho confined the rebellious spirits who repined at his control. Here, bound in adamantine chains, or jammed in rifted pines, or crushed by ponderous rocks, they groaned for many an age. At length the conquering Hudson, in its career towards the ocean, burst open their prison-house, rolling its tide triumphantly through the stupendous ruins.

Still, however, do many of them lurk about their old abodes; and these it is, according to venerable legends, that cause the echoes which resound throughout these awful solitudes—which are nothing but their angry clamors when any noise disturbs the profoundness of their repose. For when the elements are agitated by tempest, when the winds are up and the thunder rolls, then horrible is the yelling and howling of these troubled spirits, making the mountains to rebellow with their hideous uproar; for at such times it is said that they think the great Manetho is returning once more to plunge them in gloomy caverns, and renew their intolerable captivity.

But all these fair and glorious scenes were lost upon the gallant Stuyvesant; naught occupied his mind but thoughts of iron war, and proud anticipations of hardy deeds of arms. Neither did his honest crew trouble their heads with any romantic speculations of the kind. The pilot at the helm quietly smoked his pipe, thinking of nothing either past, present, or to come; those of his comrades who were not industriously smoking under the hatches were listening with open mouths to Antony Van Corlear, who, seated on the windlass, was relating to them the marvellous history of those myriads of fire-flies that sparkled like gems and spangles upon the dusky robe of night. These, according to tradition, were originally a race of pestilent sempiternous beldames, who peopled these parts long before the memory of man, being of that abominated race emphatically called *brimstones,* and who, for their innumerable sins against the children of men, and to furnish an awful warning to the beauteous sex, were doomed to infest the earth in the shape of these threatening and terrible little bugs, enduring the internal torments of that fire which they formerly carried in their hearts and breathed forth in their words, but now are sentenced to bear about forever—in their tails!

And now I am going to tell a fact, which I doubt much my readers will hesitate to believe; but if they do, they are welcome not to believe a word in this whole history, for nothing which it contains is more true. It must be known then that the nose of Antony the trumpeter was of a very lusty size, strutting boldly from his countenance like a mountain of Golconda; being sumptuously bedecked with rubies and other precious stones—the true regalia of a king of good fellows, which jolly Bacchus grants to all who bouse it heartily at the flagon. Now thus it happened, that bright and early in the morning, the good Antony, having washed his burly visage, was leaning over the quarter-railing of the galley, contemplating it in the glassy wave below. Just at this moment the illustrious sun, breaking in all its splendor from behind a high bluff of the highlands, did dart one of his most potent beams full upon the refulgent nose of the sounder of brass —the reflection of which shot straightway down, hissing-hot, into the water, and killed a mighty sturgeon that was sporting beside the vessel! This huge monster, being with infinite labor hoisted on board, furnished a luxurious repast to all the crew, being accounted of excellent flavor, excepting about the wound, where it smacked a little of brimstone; and this, on my veracity, was the first time that ever sturgeon was eaten in these parts by Christian people.*

When this astonishing miracle came to be made known to Peter Stuyvesant, and that he tasted of the unknown fish, he, as may well be supposed, marvelled exceedingly; and as a monument thereof, he gave the name of *Antony's Nose* to a stout promontory in the neighborhood; and it has continued to be called Antony's Nose ever since that time.

But hold: whither am I wandering? By the mass, if I attempt to accompany the good Peter Stuyvesant on this voyage, I shall never make an end; for never was there a voyage so fraught with marvellous incidents, nor a river so abounding with transcendent beauties, worthy of being severally recorded. Even now I have it on the point of my pen to relate how his crew were most horribly frightened, on going on shore above the highlands, by a gang of merry roistering devils, frisking and curveting on a flat rock, which projected into the river, and which is called the *Duyvel's Dans-Kamer* to this very day. But no! Diedrich Knickerbocker, it becomes thee not to idle thus in thy historic wayfaring.

Recollect that, while dwelling with the fond garrulity of age over these fairy scenes, endeared to thee by the recollections of thy youth, and the charms of a thousand legendary tales, which

* The learned Hans Megapolensis, treating of the country about Albany, in a letter which was written some time after the settlement, says: "There is in the river great plenty of sturgeon, which we Christians do not make use of, but the Indians eat them greedily."

beguiled the simple ear of thy childhood—recollect that thou art trifling with those fleeting moments which should be devoted to loftier themes. Is not Time—relentless Time!—shaking, with palsied hand, his almost exhausted hour-glass before thee? Hasten then to pursue thy weary task, lest the last sands be run ere thou hast finished thy history of the Manhattoes.

Let us, then, commit the dauntless Peter, his brave galley, and his loyal crew, to the protection of the blessed St. Nicholas; who, I have no doubt, will prosper him in his voyage, while we await his return at the great city of New Amsterdam.

CHAPTER V

Describing the Powerful Army That Assembled at the City of New Amsterdam—Together with the Interview Between Peter the Headstrong and General Van Poffenburgh, and Peter's Sentiments Touching Unfortunate Great Men

WHILE thus the enterprising Peter was coasting, with flowing sail, up the shores of the lordly Hudson, and arousing all the phlegmatic little Dutch settlements upon its borders, a great and puissant concourse of warriors was assembling at the city of New Amsterdam. And here that invaluable fragment of antiquity, the Stuyvesant manuscript, is more than commonly particular; by which means I am enabled to record the illustrious host that encamped itself in the public square in front of the fort, at present denominated the Bowling Green.

In the centre, then, was pitched the tent of the men of battle of the Manhattoes, who, being the inmates of the metropolis, composed the life-guards of the governor. These were commanded by the valiant Stoffel Brinkerhoof, who whilom had acquired such immortal fame at Oyster Bay; they displayed as a standard a beaver *rampant* on a field of orange, being the arms of the province, and denoting the persevering industry and the amphibious origin of the Nederlanders.*

* This was likewise the great seal of the New Netherlands, as may still be seen in ancient records.

On their right hand might be seen the vassals of that renowned Mynheer, Michael Paw,* who lorded it over the fair regions of ancient Pavonia, and the lands away south even unto the Navesink mountains,† and was moreover patroon of Gibbet Island. His standard was borne by his trusty squire, Cornelius Van Vorst; consisting of a huge oyster *recumbent* upon a sea-green field; being the armorial bearings of his favorite metropolis, Communipaw. He brought to the camp a stout force of warriors, heavily armed, being each clad in ten pair of linsey-woolsey breeches, and overshadowed by broad-brimmed beavers, with short pipes twisted in their hat-bands. These were the men who vegetated in the mud along the shores of Pavonia, being of the race of genuine copperheads, and were fabled to have sprung from oysters.

At a little distance was encamped the tribe of warriors who came from the neighborhood of Hell-gate. These were commanded by the Suy Dams, and the Van Dams—incontinent hard swearers, as their names betoken. They were terrible-looking fellows, clad in broad-skirted gabardines, of that curious colored cloth called thunder and lightning—and bore as a standard three devil's darning-needles, *volant*, in a flame-colored field.

Hard by was the tent of the men of battle from the marshy borders of the Waale-Boght ‡ and the country thereabouts. These were of a sour aspect, by reason that they lived on crabs, which abound in these parts. They were the first institutors of that honorable order of knighthood called *Fly-market shirks*, and, if tradition speak true, did likewise introduce the far-famed step in dancing called "double trouble." They were commanded by the fearless Jacobus Varra Vanger—and had, moreover, a jolly

* Besides what is related in the Stuyvesant MS., I have found mention made of this illustrious patroon in another manuscript, which says: "De Heer (or the squire) Michael Paw, a Dutch subject, about 10th Aug. 1630, by deed purchased Staten Island. N. B. The same Michael Paw had what the Dutch call a colonie at Pavonia, on the Jersey shore, opposite New York, and his overseer in 1636 was named Corns. Van Vorst, a person of the same name in 1769, owned Pawles Hook, and a large farm at Pavonia, and is a lineal descendant from Van Vorst.

† So called from the Navesink tribe of Indians that inhabited these parts. At present they are erroneously denominated the Neversink, or Neversunk mountains.

‡ Since corrupted into the *Wallabout;* the bay where the Navy Yard is situated.

band of Breuckelen * ferry-men, who performed a brave concerto on conch shells.

But I refrain from pursuing this minute description, which goes on to describe the warriors of Bloemen-dael, and Weehawk, and Hoboken, and sundry other places, well known in history and song; for now do the notes of martial music alarm the people of New Amsterdam, sounding afar from beyond the walls of the city. But this alarm was in a little while relieved, for lo! from the midst of a vast cloud of dust, they recognized the brimstone-colored breeches and splendid silver leg of Peter Stuyvesant, glaring in the sunbeams; and beheld him approaching at the head of a formidable army, which he had mustered along the banks of the Hudson. And here the excellent but anonymous writer of the Stuyvesant manuscript breaks out into a brave and glorious description of the forces, as they defiled through the principal gate of the city, that stood by the head of Wall Street.

First of all came the Van Brummels, who inhabit the pleasant borders of the Bronx: these were short fat men, wearing exceeding large trunk-breeches, and were renowned for feats of the trencher. They were the first inventors of suppawn, or mush and milk. Close in their rear marched the Van Vlotens, of Kaatskill, horrible quaffers of new cider, and arrant braggarts in their liquor. After them came the Van Pelts of Groodt Esopus, dexterous horsemen, mounted upon goodly switch-tailed steeds of the Esopus breed. These were mighty hunters of minks and musk-rats, whence came the word *Peltry*. Then the Van Nests of Kinderhoeck, valiant robbers of bird's-nests, as their name denotes. To these, if report may be believed, are we indebted for the invention of slap-jacks, or buckwheat-cakes. Then the Van Higginbottoms, of Wapping's creek. These came armed with ferules and birchen rods, being a race of schoolmasters, who first discovered the marvellous sympathy between the seat of honor and the seat of intellect—and that the shortest way to get knowledge into the head was to hammer it into the bottom. Then the Van Grolls of Antony's Nose, who carried their liquor in fair round little pottles, by reason they could not bouse it out of their canteens, having such rare long noses. Then the Gardeniers, of Hudson and thereabouts, distinguished by many triumphant

* Now spelt Brooklyn.

feats, such as robbing watermelon patches, smoking rabbits out of their holes, and the like, and by being great lovers of roasted pigs' tails. These were the ancestors of the renowned congressman of that name. Then the Van Hoesens, of Sing-Sing, great choristers and players upon the jews-harp. These marched two and two, singing the great song of St. Nicholas. Then the Couenhovens, of Sleepy Hollow. These gave birth to a jolly race of publicans, who first discovered the magic artifice of conjuring a quart of wine into a pint bottle. Then the Van Kortlandts, who lived on the wild banks of the Croton, and were great killers of wild ducks, being much spoken of for their skill in shooting with the long bow. Then the Van Bunschotens, of Nyack and Kakiat, who were the first that did ever kick with the left foot. They were gallant bushwhackers and hunters of raccoons by moonlight. Then the Van Winkles of Haerlem, potent suckers of eggs, and noted for running of horses, and running up of scores at taverns. They were the first that ever winked with both eyes at once. Lastly came the KNICKERBOCKERS, of the great town of Scaghtikoke, where the folk lay stones upon the houses in windy weather, lest they should be blown away. These derive their name, as some say, from *Knicker*, to shake, and *Beker*, a goblet, indicating thereby that they were sturdy toss-pots of yore; but, in truth, it was derived from *Knicker*, to nod, and *Boeken*, books: plainly meaning that they were great nodders or dozers over books. From them did descend the writer of this history.

Such was the legion of sturdy bush-beaters that poured in at the grand gate of New Amsterdam; the Stuyvesant manuscript indeed speaks of many more, whose names I omit to mention, seeing that it behooves me to hasten to matters of greater moment. Nothing could surpass the joy and martial pride of the lion-hearted Peter as he reviewed this mighty host of warriors, and he determined no longer to defer the gratification of his much-wished for revenge upon the scoundrel Swedes at Fort Casimir.

But before I hasten to record those unmatchable events which will be found in the sequel of this faithful history, let me pause to notice the fate of Jacobus Van Poffenburgh, the discomfited commander-in-chief of the armies of the New Netherlands. Such is the inherent uncharitableness of human nature, that scarcely did the news become public of his deplorable discomfiture at Fort Casimir, than a thousand scurvy rumors were set afloat in New Amsterdam, wherein it was insinuated that he had in reality a treacherous understanding with the Swedish commander; that he had long been in the practice of privately communicating with the Swedes; together with divers hints about "secret service-money." To all which deadly charges I do not give a jot more credit than I think they deserve.

Certain it is, that the general vindicated his character by the most vehement oaths and protestations, and put every man out of the ranks of honor who dared to doubt his integrity. Moreover, on returning to New Amsterdam, he paraded up and down the streets with a crew of hard swearers at his heels—sturdy bottle-companions, whom he gorged and fattened, and who were ready to bolster him through all the courts of justice—heroes of his own kidney, fierce-whiskered, broad-shouldered, colbrand-looking swaggerers—not one of whom but looked as though he could eat up an ox, and pick his teeth with the horns. These lifeguard men quarrelled all his quarrels, were ready to fight all his battles, and scowled at every man that turned up his nose at the general, as though they would devour him alive. Their conversation was interspersed with oaths like minute guns, and every bombastic rodomontade was rounded off by a thundering execration, like a patriotic toast honored with a discharge of artillery.

All these valorous vaporings had a considerable effect in convincing certain profound sages, who began to think the general a hero of unmatchable loftiness and magnanimity of soul, particularly as he was continually protesting *on the honor of a soldier*—a marvellously high-sounding asseveration. Nay, one of the members of the council went so far as to propose they should immortalize him by an imperishable statue of plaster of Paris.

But the vigilant Peter the Headstrong was not thus to be deceived. Sending privately for the commander-in-chief of all the armies, and having heard all his story, garnished with the customary pious oaths, protestations, and ejaculations—"Harkee, comrade," cried he, "though by your own account you are the most brave, upright, and honorable man in the whole province, yet do you lie under the misfortune of being damnably traduced, and immeasurably despised. Now, though it is certainly hard to punish a man for his misfortunes, and though it is very possible you are totally innocent of the crimes laid to your charge, yet as heaven, doubtless for some wise purpose, sees fit at present to withhold all proofs of your innocence, far be it from me to counteract its sovereign will. Besides, I cannot consent to venture my armies with a commander whom they despise, nor to trust the welfare of my people to a champion whom they distrust. Retire, therefore, my friend, from the irksome toils and cares of public life, with this comforting reflection, that, if guilty, you are but enjoying your just reward, and if innocent, you are not the first great and good man who has most wrongfully been slandered and maltreated in this wicked world—doubtless to be better treated in a better world, where there shall be neither error, calumny, nor persecution. In the mean time let me never see your face again, for I have a horrible antipathy to the countenances of unfortunate great men like yourself."

CHAPTER VI

In Which the Author Discourses Very Ingenuously of Himself—After Which Is to Be Found Much Interesting History About Peter the Headstrong and His Followers

AS my readers and myself are about entering on as many perils as ever a confederacy of meddlesome knights-errant wilfully ran their heads into, it is meet that, like those hardy adventurers, we should join hands, bury all differences, and swear to stand by one another, in weal or woe, to the end of the enterprise. My readers must doubtless perceive how completely I have altered my tone and deportment since we first set out together. I warrant they then thought me a crabbed, cynical, impertinent little son of a Dutchman; for I scarcely gave them a civil word, nor so much as touched my beaver, when I had occasion to address them. But as we jogged along together on the high road of my history, I gradually began to relax, to grow more courteous, and occasionally to enter into familiar discourse, until at length I came to conceive a most social, companionable kind of regard for them. This is just my way: I am always a little cold and reserved at first, particularly to people whom I neither know nor care for, and am only to be completely won by long intimacy.

Besides, why should I have been sociable to the crowd of how-d'ye-do acquaintances that flocked around me at my first appearance? Many were merely attracted by a new face; and having stared me full in the title-page, walked off without saying a word: while others lingered yawningly through the preface, and, having gratified their short-lived curiosity, soon dropped off one by one. But, more especially to try their mettle, I had recourse to an expedient, similar to one which we are told was used by that peerless flower of chivalry, King Arthur; who, before he admitted any knight to his intimacy, first required that he should show himself superior to danger or hardships, by encountering unheard-of mishaps, slaying some dozen giants, vanquishing wicked enchanters, not to say a word of dwarfs, hippogriffs, and fiery dragons. On a similar principle did I cunningly lead my readers, at the first sally, into two or three knotty chapters, where they were most wofully belabored and buffeted by a host of pagan philosophers and infidel writers. Though naturally a very grave man, yet could I scarcely refrain from smiling outright at seeing the utter confusion and dismay of my valiant cavaliers. Some dropped down dead (asleep) on the field; others threw down my book in the middle of the first chapter, took to their heels, and never ceased scampering until they had fairly run it out of sight: when they stopped to take breath, to tell their friends what troubles they had undergone, and to warn all others from venturing on so thankless an expedition. Every page thinned my ranks more and more; and of the vast multitude that first set out, but a comparatively few made shift to survive, in exceedingly battered condition, through the five introductory chapters.

What, then! would you have had me take such sunshine, faint-hearted recreants to my bosom at our first acquaintance? No, no; I reserved my friendship for those who deserved it, for those who undauntedly bore me company, in spite of difficulties, dangers, and fatigues. And now, as to those who adhere to me at present, I take them affectionately by the hand. Worthy and thrice-beloved readers! brave and well-tried comrades! who have faithfully followed my footsteps through all my wanderings—I salute you from my heart—I pledge myself to stand by you to the last, and to conduct you (so Heaven speed this trusty weapon which I now hold between my fingers) triumphantly to the end of this our stupendous undertaking.

But, hark! while we are thus talking, the city of New Amsterdam is in a bustle. The host of warriors encamped in the Bowling Green are striking their tents; the brazen trumpet of Antony Van Corlear makes the welkin to resound with portentous clangor; the drums beat; the standards of the Manhattoes, of Hell-gate, and of Michael Paw, wave proudly in the air. And now behold where the mariners are busily employed hoisting the sails of yon topsail schooner, and those clump-built sloops, which are to waft the army of the Nederlanders to gather immortal honors on the Delaware!

The entire population of the city, man, woman, and child, turned out to behold the chivalry of New Amsterdam, as it paraded the streets previous to embarkation. Many a handkerchief was waved out of the windows; many a fair nose was blown in melodious sorrow on the mournful occasion. The grief of the fair dames and beauteous damsels of Granada could not have been more vociferous on the banishment of the gallant tribe of Abencerrages than was that of the kind-hearted fair ones of New Amsterdam on the departure of their intrepid warriors. Every love-sick maiden fondly crammed the pockets of her hero with gingerbread and doughnuts; many a copper ring was exchanged, and crooked sixpence broken, in pledge of eternal constancy; and there remain extant to this day some love-verses written on that occasion, sufficiently crabbed and incomprehensible to confound the whole universe.

But it was a moving sight to see the buxom lasses, how they hung about the doughty Antony Van Corlear—for he was a jolly, rosy-faced, lusty bachelor, fond of his joke, and withal a desperate rogue among the women. Fain would they have kept him to comfort them while the army was away; for, besides what I have said of him, it is no more than justice to add, that he was a kind-hearted soul, noted for his benevolent attentions in comforting disconsolate wives during the absence of their husbands; and this made him to be very much regarded by the honest burghers of the city. But nothing could keep the valiant Antony from following the heels of the old governor, whom he loved as he did his very soul; so, embracing all the young vrouws, and giving every one of them that had good teeth and rosy lips a dozen hearty smacks, he departed, loaded with their kind wishes.

Nor was the departure of the gallant Peter among the least causes of public distress. Though the old governor was by no means indulgent to the follies and waywardness of his subjects, yet somehow or other he had become strangely popular among the people. There is something so captivating in personal bravery, that, with the common mass of mankind, it takes the lead of most other merits. The simple folk of New Amsterdam looked upon Peter Stuyvesant as a prodigy of valor. His wooden leg, that trophy of his martial encounters, was regarded with reverence and admiration. Every old burgher had a budget of miraculous stories to tell about the exploits of Hardkoppig Piet, wherewith he regaled his children of a long winter night, and on which he dwelt with as much delight and exaggeration as do our honest country yeomen on the hardy adventures of old General Putnam (or, as he is familiarly termed, *Old Put*) during our glorious Revolution. Not an individual but verily believed the old governor was a match for Beëlzebub himself; and there was even a story told, with great mystery, and under the rose, of his having shot the devil with a silver bullet one dark stormy night, as he was sailing in a canoe through Hell-gate—but this I do not record as being an absolute fact. Perish the man who would let fall a drop to discolor the pure stream of history!

Certain it is, not an old woman in New Amsterdam but considered Peter Stuyvesant as a tower of strength, and rested satisfied that the public welfare was secure so long as he was in the city. It is not surprising, then, that they looked upon his departure as a sore affliction. With heavy hearts they draggled at the heels of his troop, as they marched down to the river-side to embark. The governor, from the stern of his schooner, gave a short but truly patriarchal address to his citizens, wherein he recommended them to comport like loyal and peaceable subjects —to go to church regularly on Sundays, and to mind their business all the week besides. That the women should be dutiful and affectionate to their husbands—looking after nobody's concerns but their own—eschewing all gossipings and morning gaddings—and carrying short tongues and long petticoats. That the men should abstain from intermeddling in public concerns, intrusting the cares of government to the officers appointed to support them—staying at home, like good citizens, making money for themselves, and getting children for the benefit of their country. That the burgomasters should look well to the public interest—not oppressing the poor nor indulging the rich—not tasking their ingenuity to devise new laws, but faithfully enforcing those which were already made—rather bending their attention to prevent evil than to punish it; ever recollecting that civil magistrates should consider themselves more as guardians of public morals than rat-catchers employed to entrap public delinquents. Finally, he exhorted them, one and all, high and low, rich and poor, to conduct themselves *as well as they could*, assuring them that if they faithfully and conscientiously complied with this golden rule, there was no danger but that they would all conduct themselves well enough. This done, he gave them a paternal benediction, the sturdy Antony sounded a most loving farewell with his trumpet, the jolly crews put up a shout of triumph, and the invincible armada swept proudly down the bay.

The good people of New Amsterdam crowded down to the Battery—that blest resort, from whence so many a tender prayer has been wafted, so many a fair hand waved, so many a tearful look been cast by lovesick damsel, after the lessening bark, bearing her adventurous swain to distant climes! Here the populace watched with straining eyes the gallant squadron, as it slowly floated down the bay, and when the intervening land at the Narrows shut it from their sight, gradually dispersed with silent tongues and downcast countenances.

A heavy gloom hung over the late bustling city: the honest burghers smoked their pipes in profound thoughtfulness, casting many a wistful look to the weathercock on the church of St. Nicholas; and all the old women, having no longer the presence of Peter Stuyvesant to hearten them, gathered their children home, and barricaded the doors and windows every evening at sundown.

In the meanwhile the armada of the sturdy Peter proceeded prosperously on its voyage; and after encountering about as many storms, and water-spouts, and whales, and other horrors and phenomena as generally befall adventurous landsmen in perilous voyages of the kind, and after undergoing a severe scouring from that deplorable and unpitied malady called seasickness, the whole squadron arrived safely in the Delaware.

Without so much as dropping anchor and giving his wearied ships time to breathe, after laboring so long on the ocean, the intrepid Peter pursued his course up the Delaware, and made a sudden appearance before Fort Casimir. Having summoned the astonished garrison by a terrific blast from the trumpet of the long-winded Van Corlear, he demanded, in a tone of thunder, an instant surrender of the fort. To this demand, Suen Skytte, the wind-dried commandant, replied in a shrill, whiffling voice, which, by reason of his extreme spareness, sounded like the wind whistling through a broken bellows—"That he had no very strong reason for refusing, except that the demand was particularly disagreeable, as he had been ordered to maintain his post to the last extremity." He requested time, therefore, to consult with Governor Risingh, and proposed a truce for that purpose.

The choleric Peter, indignant at having his rightful fort so treacherously taken from him, and thus pertinaciously withheld, refused the proposed armistice, and swore by the pipe of St. Nicholas, which, like the sacred fire, was never extinguished, that unless the fort were surrendered in ten minutes, he would incontinently storm the works, make all the garrison run the gauntlet, and split their scoundrel of a commander like a pickled shad. To give this menace the greater effect, he drew forth his trusty sword, and shook it at them with such a fierce and vigorous motion, that doubtless, if it had not been exceedingly rusty, it would have lightened terror into the eyes and hearts of the enemy. He then ordered his men to bring a broadside to bear upon the fort, consisting of two swivels, three muskets, a long duck fowling-piece, and two brace of horse-pistols.

In the mean time the sturdy Van Corlear marshalled all the forces, and commenced his warlike operations. Distending his cheeks like a very Boreas, he kept up a most horrific twanging of his trumpet—the lusty choristers of Sing-Sing broke forth into a hideous song of battle—the warriors of Breuckelen and the Wallabout blew a potent and astonishing blast on their conch shells—altogether forming as outrageous a concerto as though five thousand French fiddlers were displaying their skill in a modern overture.

Whether the formidable front of war thus suddenly presented smote the garrison with sore dismay—or whether the concluding terms of the summons, which mentioned that he should surrender "at discretion," were mistaken by Suen Skytte, who, though a Swede, was a very considerate, easy-tempered man, as a compliment to his discretion, I will not take upon me to say; certain it is he found it impossible to resist so courteous a demand. Accordingly, in the very nick of time, just as the cabin-boy had gone after a coal of fire to discharge the swivel, a chamade was beat on the rampart by the only drum in the garrison, to the no small satisfaction of both parties, who, notwithstanding their great stomach for fighting, had full as good an inclination to eat a quiet dinner as to exchange black eyes and bloody noses.

Thus did this impregnable fortress once more return to the domination of their High Mightinesses. Skytte and his garrison of twenty men were allowed to march out with the honors of war; and the victorious Peter, who was as generous as brave, permitted them to keep possession of all their arms and ammunition—the same on inspection being found totally unfit for service, having long rusted in the magazine of the fortress, even before it was wrested by the Swedes from the windy Van Poffenburgh. But I must not omit to mention that the governor was so well pleased with the service of his faithful squire, Van Corlear, in the reduction of this great fortress, that he made him on the spot lord of a goodly domain in the vicinity of New Amsterdam—which goes by the name of Corlear's Hook unto this very day.

The unexampled liberality of Peter Stuyvesant towards the Swedes, occasionad great surprise in the city of New Amsterdam—nay, certain factious individuals, who had been enlightened by political meetings in the days of William the Testy, but who had not dared to indulge their meddlesome habits under the eye of their present ruler, now, emboldened by his absence, gave vent to their censures in the street. Murmurs were heard in the very council-chamber of New Amsterdam; and there is no knowing whether they might not have broken out into downright speeches and invectives, had not Peter Stuyvesant privately sent home his walking-staff, to be laid as a mace on the table of the council-chamber, in the midst of his counsellors; who, like wise men, took the hint, and forever after held their peace.

CHAPTER VII

Showing the Great Advantage That the Author Has Over His Reader in Time of Battle—Together with Divers Portentous Movements; Which Betoken That Something Terrible Is About to Happen

LIKE as a mighty alderman, when at a corporation feast the first spoonful of turtle-soup salutes his palate, feels his appetite but tenfold quickened, and redoubles his vigorous attacks upon the tureen, while his projecting eyes roll greedily round, devouring everything at table, so did the mettlesome Peter Stuyvesant feel that hunger for martial glory, which raged within his bowels, inflamed by the capture of Fort Casimir, and nothing could allay it but the conquest of all New Sweden. No sooner, therefore, had he secured his conquest, than he stumped resolutely on, flushed with success, to gather fresh laurels at Fort Christina.*

This was the grand Swedish post, established on a small river (or, as it is improperly termed, creek) of the same name; and here that crafty governor Jan Risingh lay grimly drawn up, a gray-bearded spider in the citadel of his web.

But before we hurry into the direful scenes which must attend the meeting of two such potent chieftains, it is advisable to pause for a moment, and hold a kind of warlike council. Battles should not be rushed into precipitately by the historian and his readers, any more than by the general and his soldiers. The great commanders of antiquity never engaged the enemy without previously preparing the minds of their followers by animating harangues, spiriting them up to heroic deeds, assuring them of the protection of the gods, and inspiring them with a

* At present a flourishing town, called Christiana, or Christeen, about thirty-seven miles from Philadelphia, on the post-road to Baltimore.

confidence in the prowess of their leaders. So the historian should awaken the attention and enlist the passions of his readers; and having set them all on fire with the importance of his subject, he should put himself at their head, flourish his pen, and lead them on to the thickest of the fight.

An illustrious example of this rule may be seen in that mirror of historians, the immortal Thucydides. Having arrived at the breaking out of the Peloponnesian war, one of his commentators observes that "he sounds the charge in all the disposition and spirit of Homer. He catalogues the allies on both sides. He awakens our expectations, and fast engages our attention. All mankind are concerned in the important point now going to be decided. Endeavors are made to disclose futurity. Heaven itself is interested in the dispute. The earth totters, and nature seems to labor with the great event. This is his solemn, sublime manner of setting out. Thus he magnifies a war between two, as Rapin styles them, petty states; and thus artfully he supports a little subject by treating it in a great and noble method."

In like manner, having conducted my readers into the very teeth of peril—having followed the adventurous Peter and his band into foreign regions, surrounded by foes, and stunned by the horrid din of arms—at this important moment, while darkness and doubt hang o'er each coming chapter, I hold it meet to harangue them, and prepare them for the events that are to follow.

And here I would premise one great advantage which, as historian, I possess over my reader; and this it is, that, though I cannot save the life of my favorite hero, nor absolutely contradict the event of a battle (both which liberties, though often taken by the French writers of the present reign, I hold to be utterly unworthy of a scrupulous historian), yet I can now and then make him bestow on his enemy a sturdy back-stroke sufficient to fell a giant—though, in honest truth, he may never have done anything of the kind—or I can drive his antagonist clear round and round the field, as did Homer make that fine fellow Hector scamper like a poltroon round the walls of Troy; for which, if ever they have encountered one another in the Elysian fields, I'll warrant the prince of poets has had to make the most humble apology.

I am aware that many conscientious readers will be ready to cry out "foul play!" whenever I render a little assistance to my hero, but I consider it one of those privileges exercised by historians of all ages, and one which has never been disputed. An historian is, in fact, as it were, bound in honor to stand by his hero; the fame of the latter is intrusted to his hands, and it is his duty to do the best by it he can. Never was there a general, an admiral, or any other commander, who, in giving account of any battle he had fought, did not sorely belabor the enemy; and I have no doubt that, had my heroes written the history of their own achievements, they would have dealt much harder blows than any that I shall recount. Standing forth, therefore, as the guardian of their fame, it behooves me to do them the same justice they would have done themselves; and if I happen to be a little hard upon the Swedes, I give free leave to any of their descendants, who may write a story of the State of Delaware, to take fair retaliation, and belabor Peter Stuyvesant as hard as they please.

Therefore stand by for broken heads and bloody noses! My pen hath long itched for a battle; siege after siege have I carried on without blows or bloodshed; but now I have at length got a chance, and I vow to Heaven and St. Nicholas, that, let the chronicles of the times say what they please, neither Sallust, Livy, Tacitus, Polybius, nor any other historian, did ever record a fiercer fight than that in which my valiant chieftains are now about to engage.

And you, oh most excellent readers, whom, for your faithful adherence, I could cherish in the warmest corner of my heart, be not uneasy—trust the fate of our favorite Stuyvesant with me, for by the rood, come what may, I'll stick by Hardkoppig Piet to the last. I'll make him drive about these losels vile, as did the renowned Launcelot of the Lake a herd of recreant Cornish knights; and if he does fall, let me never draw my pen to fight another battle in behalf of a brave man, if I don't make these lubberly Swedes pay for it!

No sooner had Peter Stuyvesant arrived at Fort Christina than he proceeded without delay to intrench himself, and immediately on running his first parallel, dispatched Antony Van Corlear to summon the fortress to surrender. Van Corlear was received with all due formality, hoodwinked at the portal, and conducted through a pestiferous smell of salt fish and onions to the citadel, a substantial hut built of pine logs. His eyes were here uncovered, and he found himself in the august presence of Governor Risingh. This chieftain, as I have before noted, was a very giantly man, and was clad in a coarse blue coat, strapped round the waist with a leathern belt, which caused the enormous skirts and pockets to set off with a very warlike sweep. His ponderous legs were cased in a pair of foxy-colored jackboots, and he was straddling in the attitude of the Colossus of Rhodes before a bit of broken looking-glass, shaving himself with a villainously dull razor. This afflicting operation caused him to make a series of horrible grimaces, which heightened exceedingly the grisly terrors of his visage. On Antony Van Corlear's being announced, the grim commander paused for a moment in the midst of one of his most hard-favored contortions, and after eying him askance over the shoulder, with a kind of snarling grin on his countenance, resumed his labors at the glass.

This iron harvest being reaped, he turned once more to the trumpeter, and demanded the purport of his errand. Antony Van Corlear delivered in a few words, being a kind of short-hand speaker, a long message from his Excellency, recounting the whole history of the province, with a recapitulation of grievances, and enumeration of claims, and concluding with a peremptory demand of instant surrender; which done, he turned aside, took his nose between his thumb and fingers, and blew a tremendous blast, not unlike the flourish of a trumpet of defiance—which it had doubtless learned from a long and intimate neighborhood with that melodious instrument.

Governor Risingh heard him through, trumpet and all, but with infinite impatience—leaning at times, as was his usual custom, on the pommel of his sword, and at times twirling a huge steel watch-chain, or snapping his fingers. Van Corlear having finished, he bluntly replied, that Peter Stuyvesant and his summons might go to the d—l, whither he hoped to send him and his crew of ragamuffins before supper-time. Then unsheathing his brass-hilted sword, and throwing away the scabbard—" 'Fore gad," quod he, "but I will not sheathe thee again until I make a scabbard of the smoke-dried leathern hide of this runagate

Dutchman." Then having flung a fierce defiance in the teeth of his adversary by the lips of his messenger, the latter was reconducted to the portal with all the ceremonious civility due to the trumpeter, squire, and ambassador of so great a commander; and being again unblinded, was courteously dismissed with a tweak of the nose, to assist him in recollecting his message.

No sooner did the gallant Peter receive this insolent reply than he let fly a tremendous volley of red-hot execrations, which would infallibly have battered down the fortifications, and blown up the powder-magazine about the ears of the fiery Swede, had not the ramparts been remarkably strong, and the magazine bomb-proof. Perceiving that the works withstood this terrific blast, and that it was utterly impossible (as it really was in those unphilosophic days) to carry on a war with words, he ordered his merry men all to prepare for an immediate assault. But here a strange murmur broke out among his troops, beginning with the tribe of the Van Bummels, those valiant trenchermen of the Bronx, and spreading from man to man, accompanied with certain mutinous looks and discontented murmurs. For once in his life, and only for once, did the great Peter turn pale, for he verily thought his warriors were going to falter in this hour of perilous trial, and thus to tarnish forever the fame of the province of New Netherlands.

But soon did he discover, to his great joy, that in his suspicion he deeply wronged his most undaunted army; for the cause of this agitation and uneasiness simply was, that the hour of dinner was at hand, and it would have almost broken the hearts of these regular Dutch warriors to have broken in upon the invariable routine of their habits. Besides, it was an established rule among our ancestors always to fight upon a full stomach; and to this may be doubtless attributed the circumstance that they came to be so renowned in arms.

And now are the hearty men of the Manhattoes, and their no less hearty comrades, all lustily engaged under the trees, buffeting stoutly with the contents of their wallets, and taking such affectionate embraces of their canteens and pottles as though they verily believed they were to be the last. And as I forsee we shall have hot work in a page or two, I advise my readers to do the same, for which purpose I will bring this chapter to a close—

giving them my word of honor, that no advantage shall be taken of this armistice to surprise, or in any wise molest, the honest Nederlanders while at their vigorous repast.

CHAPTER VIII

Containing the Most Horrible Battle Ever Recorded in Poetry or Prose; With the Admirable Exploits of Peter the Headstrong

NOW had the Dutchmen snatched a huge repast, and finding themselves wonderfully encouraged and animated thereby, prepared to take the field. Expectation, says the writer of the Stuyvesant manuscript—Expectation now stood on stilts. The world forgot to turn round, or rather stood still, that it might witness the affray—like a round-bellied alderman, watching the combat of two chivalrous flies upon his jerkin. The eyes of all mankind, as usual in such cases, were turned upon Fort Christina. The sun, like a little man in a crowd at a puppet-show, scampered about the heavens, popping his head here and there, and endeavoring to get a peep between the unmannerly clouds that obtruded themselves in his way. The historians filled their ink-horns; the poets went without their dinners, either that they might buy paper and goose-quills, or because they could not get anything to eat. Antiquity scowled sulkily out of its grave, to see itself outdone—while even Posterity stood mute, gazing in gaping ecstasy of retrospection on the eventful field.

The immortal deities, who whilom had seen service at the "affair" of Troy, now mounted their feather-bed clouds, and sailed over the plain, or mingled among the combatants in different disguises, all itching to have a finger in the pie. Jupiter sent off his thunderbolt to a noted coppersmith, to have it furbished up for the direful occasion. Venus vowed by her chastity to patronize the Swedes, and in semblance of a blear-eyed trull paraded the battlements of Fort Christina, accompanied by Diana, as a sergeant's widow, of cracked reputation. The noted bully, Mars, stuck two horse-pistols into his belt, shouldered a rusty firelock, and gallantly swaggered at their elbow, as a drunken corporal—while Apollo trudged in their rear, as a bandy-legged fifer, playing most villainously out of tune.

On the other side, the ox-eyed Juno, who had gained a pair of black eyes overnight, in one of her curtain-lectures with old Jupiter, displayed her haughty beauties on a baggage-wagon; Minerva, as a brawny gin-suttler, tucked up her skirts, brandished her fists, and swore most heroically, in exceeding bad Dutch (having but lately studied the language), by way of keeping up the spirits of the soldiers; while Vulcan halted as a club-footed blacksmith, lately promoted to be a captain of militia. All was silent awe, or bustling preparation: war reared his horrid front, gnashed loud his iron fangs, and shook his direful crest of bristling bayonets.

And now the mighty chieftains marshalled out their hosts. Here stood stout Risingh, firm as a thousand rocks—incrusted with stockades, and intrenched to the chin in mud batteries. His valiant soldiery lined the breastwork in grim array, each having his mustachios fiercely greased, and his hair pomatumed back, and queued so stiffly, that he grinned above the ramparts like a grisly death's-head.

There came on the intrepid Peter—his brows knit, his teeth set, his fists clenched, almost breathing forth volumes of smoke, so fierce was the fire that raged within his bosom. His faithful squire Van Corlear trudged valiantly at his heels, with his trumpet gorgeously bedecked with red and yellow ribbons, the remembrances of his fair mistresses at the Manhattoes. Then came waddling on the sturdy chivalry of the Hudson. There were the Van Wycks, and the Van Dycks, and the Ten Eycks; the Van Nesses, the Van Tassels, the Van Grolls; the Van Hœsens, the Van Giesons, and the Van Blarcoms; the Van Warts, the Van Winkles, the Van Dams; the Van Pelts, the Van Rippers, and the Van Brunts. There were the Van Hornes, the Van Hooks, the Van Bunschotens; the Van Gelders, the Van Arsdales, and the Van Bummels; the Vander Belts, the Vander Hoofs, the Vander Voorts, the Vander Lyns, the Vander Pools, and the Vander Spiegles; then came the Hoffmans, the Hooghlands, the Hoppers, the Cloppers, the Ryckmans, the Dyckmans, the Hogebooms, the Rosebooms, the Oothouts, the Quackenbosses, the Roerbacks, the Garrebrantzes, the Bensons, the Brouwers, the Waldrons, the Onderdonks, the Varra Vangers, the Schermerhorns, the Stoutenburghs, the Brinkerhoffs, the Bontecous, the Knickerbockers, the Hockstrassers, the Ten Breecheses and the Tough Breecheses, with a host more of worthies, whose names are too crabbed to be written, or if they could be written, it would be impossible for man to utter—all fortified with a mighty dinner, and, to use the words of a great Dutch poet,

"Brimful of wrath and cabbage."

For an instant the mighty Peter paused in the midst of his career, and mounting on a stump, addressed his troops in eloquent Low Dutch, exhorting them to fight like *duyvels,* and assuring them that if they conquered, they should get plenty of booty—if they fell, they should be allowed the satisfaction, while dying, of reflecting that it was in the service of their country, and after they were dead, of seeing their names inscribed in the temple of renown, and handed down, in company with all the other great men of the year, for the admiration of posterity. Finally, he swore to them, on the word of a governor (and they knew him too well to doubt it for a moment), that if he caught any mother's son of them looking pale, or playing craven, he would curry his hide till he made him run out of it like a snake in springtime. Then lugging out his trusty sabre, he brandished it three times over his head, ordered Van Corlear to sound a charge, and shouting the words "St. Nicholas and the Manhattoes!" courageously dashed forwards. His warlike followers, who had employed the interval in lighting their pipes, instantly stuck them into their mouths, gave a furious puff, and charged gallantly under cover of the smoke.

The Swedish garrison, ordered by the cunning Risingh not to fire until they could distinguish the whites of their assailants' eyes, stood in horrid silence on the covertway, until the eager Dutchmen had ascended the glacis. Then did they pour into them such a tremendous volley, that the very hills quaked around, and were terrified even unto an incontinence of water, insomuch that certain springs burst forth from their sides, which continue to run unto the present day. Not a Dutchman but would have bitten the dust beneath that dreadful fire, had not the protecting Minerva kindly taken care that the Swedes should, one and all, observe their usual custom of shutting their eyes and turning away their heads at the moment of discharge.

The Swedes followed up their fire by leaping the counterscarp, and falling tooth and nail upon the foe with furious outcries. And now might be seen prodigies of valor, unmatched in history or song. Here was the sturdy Stoffel Brinkerhoff brandishing his quarter-staff, like the giant Blanderon his oak-tree (for he scorned to carry any other weapon), and drumming a horrific tune upon the hard heads of the Swedish soldiery. There were the Van Kortlandts, posted at a distance, like the Locrain archers of yore, and plying it most potently with the long-bow, for which they were so justly renowned. On a rising knoll were gathered the valiant men of Sing-Sing, assisting marvellously in the fight, by chanting the great song of St. Nicholas; but as to the Gardeniers of Hudson, they were absent on a marauding party, laying waste the neighboring water-melon patches.

In a different part of the field were the Van Grolls of Antony's Nose, struggling to get to the thickest of the fight, but horribly perplexed in a defile between two hills, by reason of the length of their noses. So also the Van Bunschotens of Nyack and Kakiat, so renowned for kicking with the left foot, were brought to a stand for want of wind, in consequence of the hearty dinner they had eaten, and would have been put to utter rout but for the arrival of a gallant corps of voltigeurs, composed of the Hoppers, who advanced nimbly to their assistance on one foot. Nor must I omit to mention the valiant achievements of Antony Van Corlear, who, for a good quarter of an hour, waged stubborn fight with a little pursy Swedish drummer, whose hide he drummed most magnificently, and whom he would infallibly have annihilated on the spot, but that he had come into the battle with no other weapon but his trumpet.

But now the combat thickened. On came the mighty Jacobus Varra Vanger and the fighting men of the Wallabout; after them thundered the Van Pelts of Esopus, together with the Van Rippers and the Van Brunts, bearing down all before them; then the Suy Dams, and the Van Dams, pressing forward with many a blustering oath, at the head of the warriors of Hell-gate, clad in their thunder-and-lightning gabardines; and lastly, the standard-bearers and body-guard of Peter Stuyvesant, bearing the great beaver of the Manhattoes.

And now commenced the horrid din, the desperate struggle,

the maddening ferocity, the frantic desperation, the confusion and self-abandonment of war. Dutchman and Swede commingled, tugged, panted, and blowed. The heavens were darkened with a tempest of missives. Bang! went the guns; whack! went the broad-swords; thump! went the cudgels; crash! went the musket-stocks; blows, kicks, cuffs, scratches, black eyes and bloody noses swelling the horrors of the scene! Thick thwack, cut and hack, helter-skelter, higgledy-piggledy, hurly-burly, head-over-heels, rough-and-tumble! Dunder and blixum! swore the Dutchmen; splitter and splutter! cried the Swedes. Storm the works! shouted Hardkoppig Peter. Fire the mine! roared stout Risingh. Tanta-rar-ra-ra! twanged the trumpet of Antony Van Corlear until all voice and sound became unintelligible—grunts of pain, yells of fury, and shouts of triumph mingling in one hideous clamor. The earth shook as if struck with a paralytic stroke; trees shrunk aghast, and withered at the sight; rocks burrowed in the ground like rabbits; and even Christina creek turned from its course, and ran up a hill in breathless terror!

Long hung the contest doubtful; for though a heavy shower of rain, sent by the "cloud-compelling Jove," in some measure cooled their ardor, as doth a bucket of water thrown on a group of fighting mastiffs, yet did they but pause for a moment, to return with tenfold fury to the charge. Just at this juncture a vast and dense column of smoke was seen slowly rolling toward the scene of battle. The combatants paused for a moment, gazing in mute astonishment, until the wind, dispelling the murky cloud, revealed the flaunting banner of Michael Paw, the Patroon of Communipaw. That valiant chieftain came fearlessly on at the head of a phalanx of oyster-fed Pavonians and a *corps de reserve* of the Van Arsdales and Van Bummels, who had remained behind to digest the enormous dinner they had eaten. These now trudged manfully forward, smoking their pipes with outrageous vigor, so as to raise the awful cloud that has been mentioned, but marching exceedingly slow, being short of leg, and of great rotundity in the belt.

And now the deities who watched over the fortunes of the Nederlanders having unthinkingly left the field, and stepped into a neighboring tavern to refresh themselves with a pot of beer, a direful catastrophe had wellnigh ensued. Scarce had the myrmidons of Michael Paw attained the front of battle, when the Swedes, instructed by the cunning Risingh, levelled a shower of blows full at their tobacco-pipes. Astounded at this assault, and dismayed at the havoc of their pipes, these ponderous warriors gave way, and like a drove of frightened elephants broke through the ranks of their own army. The little Hoppers were borne down in the surge; the sacred banner emblazoned with the gigantic oyster of Communipaw was trampled in the dirt; on blundered and thundered the heavy-sterned fugitives, the Swedes pressing on their rear and applying their feet *a parte poste* of the Van Arsdales and the Van Bummels with a vigor that prodigiously accelerated their movements; nor did the renowned Michael Paw himself fail to receive divers grievous and dishonorable visitations of shoe-leather.

But what, oh Muse! was the rage of Peter Stuyvesant, when from afar he saw his army giving way! In the transports of his wrath he sent forth a roar, enough to shake the very hills. The men of the Manhattoes plucked up new courage at the sound, or, rather, they rallied at the voice of their leader, of whom they stood more in awe than of all the Swedes in Christendom. Without waiting for their aid, the daring Peter dashed, sword in hand, into the thickest of the foe. Then might be seen achievements worthy of the days of the giants. Wherever he went, the enemy shrank before him; the Swedes fled to right and left, or were driven, like dogs, into their own ditch; but as he pushed forward singly with headlong courage, the foe closed behind and hung upon his rear. One aimed a blow full at his heart; but the protecting power which watches over the great and good turned aside the hostile blade and directed it to a side-pocket, where reposed an enormous iron tobacco-box, endowed, like the shield of Achilles, with supernatural powers, doubtless from bearing the portrait of the blessed St. Nicholas. Peter Stuyvesant turned like an angry bear upon the foe, and seizing him, as he fled, by an immeasurable queue, "Ah, whoreson caterpillar," roared he, "here's what shall make worms' meat of thee!" So saying, he whirled his sword, and dealt a blow that would have decapitated the varlet, but that the pitying steel struck short and shaved the queue forever from his crown. At this moment an arquebusier levelled his piece from a neighboring mound, with deadly aim; but the watchful Minerva, who had just stopped to tie up her garter, seeing the peril of her favorite hero, sent old Boreas with his bellows, who, as the match descended to the pan, gave a blast that blew the priming from the touch-hole.

Thus waged the fight, when the stout Risingh, surveying the field from the top of a little ravelin, perceived his troops banged, beaten, and kicked by the invincible Peter. Drawing his falchion and uttering a thousand anathemas, he strode down to the scene of combat with some such thundering strides as Jupiter is said by Hesiod to have taken when he strode down the spheres to hurl his thunder-bolts at the Titans.

When the rival heroes came face to face, each made a prodigious start in the style of a veteran stage-champion. Then did they regard each other for a moment with the bitter aspect of two furious ram-cats on the point of a clapper-clawing. Then did they throw themselves into one attitude, then into another, striking their swords on the ground, first on the right side, then on the left; at last at it they went, with incredible ferocity. Words cannot tell the prodigies of strength and valor displayed in this direful encounter—an encounter compared to which the far-famed battles of Ajax with Hector, of Æneas with Turnus, Orlando with Rodomont, Guy of Warwick with Colbrand the Dane, or of that renowned Welsh knight, Sir Owen of the Mountains, with the giant Guylon, were all gentle sports and holiday recreations. At length the valiant Peter, watching his opportunity, aimed a blow, enough to cleave his adversary to the very chine; but Risingh, nimbly raising his sword, warded if off so narrowly, that, glancing on one side, it shaved away a huge canteen in which he carried his liquor—thence pursuing its trenchant course, it severed off a deep coat-pocket, stored with bread and cheese—which provant rolling among the armies, occasioned a fearful scrambling between the Swedes and Dutchmen, and made the general battle to wax more furious than ever.

Enraged to see his military stores laid waste, the stout Risingh, collecting all his forces, aimed a mighty blow full at the hero's crest. In vain did his fierce little cocked hat oppose its course. The biting steel clove through the stubborn ram beaver, and would have cracked the crown of any one not endowed with supernatural hardness of head; but the brittle weapon shivered in pieces on the skull of Hardkoppig Piet, shedding a thousand sparks, like beams of glory, round his grizzly visage.

The good Peter reeled with the blow, and turning up his eyes beheld a thousand suns, besides moons and stars, dancing about the firmament; at length, missing his footing, by reason of his wooden leg, down he came on his seat of honor with a crash which shook the surrounding hills, and might have wrecked his frame, had he not been received into a cushion softer than velvet, which Providence, or Minerva, or St. Nicholas, or some cow, had benevolently prepared for his reception.

The furious Risingh, in spite of the maxim, cherished by all true knights, that "fair play is a jewel," hastened to take advantage of the hero's fall; but, as he stooped to give a fatal blow, Peter Stuyvesant dealt him a thwack over the sconce with his wooden leg, which set a chime of bells ringing triple bob-majors in his cerebellum. The bewildered Swede staggered with the blow, and the wary Peter seizing a pocket-pistol, which lay hard by, discharged it full at the head of the reeling Risingh. Let not my reader mistake; it was not a murderous weapon loaded with powder and ball, but a little sturdy stone pottle charged to the muzzle with a double dram of true Dutch courage, which the knowing Antony Van Corlear carried about him by way of replenishing his valor, and which had dropped from his wallet during his furious encounter with the drummer. The hideous weapon sang through the air, and true to its course as was the fragment of a rock discharged at Hector by bully Ajax, encountered the head of the gigantic Swede with matchless violence.

This heaven-directed blow decided the battle. The ponderous pericranium of General Jan Risingh sank upon his breast; his knees tottered under him; a death-like torpor seized upon his frame, and he tumbled to the earth with such violence, that old Pluto started with affright, lest he should have broken through the roof of his infernal palace.

His fall was the signal of defeat and victory: the Swedes gave way, the Dutch pressed forward; the former took to their heels, the latter hotly pursued. Some entered with them, pell-mell, through the sally-port; others stormed the bastion, and others scrambled over the curtain. Thus in a little while the fortress of Fort Christina, which, like another Troy, had stood a siege of full ten hours, was carried by assault, without the loss of a single man on either side. Victory, in the likeness of a gigantic ox-fly, sat perched upon the cocked hat of the gallant Stuyvesant; and it was declared, by all the writers whom he hired to write the history of his expedition, that on this memorable day he gained a sufficient quantity of glory to immortalize a dozen of the greatest heroes in Christendom!

CHAPTER IX

In Which the Author and the Reader, While Reposing After the Battle, Fall into a Very Grave Discourse—After Which Is Recorded the Conduct of Peter Stuyvesant After His Victory

THANKS to St. Nicholas, we have safely finished this tremendous battle: let us sit down, my worthy reader, and cool ourselves, for I am in a prodigious sweat and agitation; truly this fighting of battles is hot work! and if your great commanders did but know what trouble they give their historians, they would not have the conscience to achieve so many horrible victories. But methinks I hear my reader complain, that throughout this boasted battle there is not the least slaughter, nor a single individual maimed, if we except the unhappy Swede, who was shorn of his queue by the trenchant blade of Peter Stuyvesant; all which, he observes, is a great outrage on probability, and highly injurious to the interest of the narration.

This is certainly an objection of no little moment, but it arises entirely from the obscurity enveloping the remote periods of time about which I have undertaken to write. Thus, though doubtless, from the importance of the object and the prowess of the parties concerned, there must have been terrible carnage, and prodigies of valor displayed before the walls of Christina, yet, notwithstanding that I have consulted every history, manuscript, and tradition, touching this memorable though long-forgotten battle, I cannot find mention made of a single man killed or wounded in the whole affair.

This is, without doubt, owing to the extreme modesty of our forefathers, who, unlike their descendants, were never prone to vaunt of their achievements; but it is a virtue which places their historian in a most embarrassing predicament; for, having promised my readers a hideous and unparalleled battle, and having worked them up into a warlike and blood-thirsty state of mind, to put them off without any havoc and slaughter would have been as bitter a disappointment as to summon a multitude of good people to attend an execution, and then cruelly balk them by a reprieve.

Had the fates only allowed me some half a score of dead men, I had been content; for I would have made them such heroes as abounded in the olden time, but whose race is now unfortunately extinct—any one of whom, if we may believe those authentic writers, the poets, could drive great armies, like sheep, before him, and conquer and desolate whole cities by his single arm.

But seeing that I had not a single life at my disposal, all that was left me was to make the most I could of my battle, by means of kicks, and cuffs, and bruises, and such like ignoble wounds. And here I cannot but compare my dilemma, in some sort, to that of the divine Milton, who, having arrayed with sublime preparation his immortal hosts against each other, is sadly put to it how to manage them, and how he shall make the end of his battle answer to the beginning, inasmuch as, being mere spirits, he cannot deal a mortal blow, nor even give a flesh wound to any of his combatants. For my part, the greatest difficulty I found was, when I had once put my warriors in a passion, and let them loose into the midst of the enemy, to keep them from doing mischief. Many a time had I to restrain the sturdy Peter from cleaving a gigantic Swede to the very waistband, or spitting half a dozen little fellows on his sword, like so many sparrows. And when I had set some hundred of missives flying in the air, I did not dare to suffer one of them to reach the ground, lest it should have put an end to some unlucky Dutchman.

The reader cannot conceive how mortifying it is to a writer thus in a manner to have his hands tied, and how many tempting opportunities I had to wink at, where I might have made as fine a death-blow as any recorded in history or song.

From my own experience I begin to doubt most potently of the authenticity of many of Homer's stories. I verily believe, that, when he had once launched one of his favorite heroes among a crowd of the enemy, he cut down many an honest fellow, without any authority for so doing, excepting that he presented a fair mark—and that often a poor fellow was sent to grim Pluto's domains, merely because he had a name that would give a sounding turn to a period. But I disclaim all such unprincipled liberties; let me but have truth and the law on my side, and no man would fight harder than myself; but since the various records I consulted did not warrant it, I had too much conscience to kill a single soldier. By St. Nicholas, but it would have been a pretty piece of business! My enemies, the critics, who I foresee will be ready enough to lay any crime they can discover at my door, might have charged me with murder outright, and I should have esteemed myself lucky to escape with no harsher verdict than manslaughter!

And now, gentle reader, that we are tranquilly sitting down here, smoking our pipes, permit me to indulge in a melancholy reflection which at this moment passes across my mind. How vain, how fleeting, how uncertain are all those gaudy bubbles after which we are panting and toiling in this world of fair delusions! The wealth which the miser has amassed with so many weary days, so many sleepless nights, a spendthrift here may squander away in joyless prodigality; the noblest monuments which pride has ever reared to perpetuate a name, the hand of time will shortly tumble into ruins; and even the brightest laurels, gained by feats of arms, may wither, and be forever blighted by the chilling neglect of mankind. "How many illustrious heroes," says the good Boëtius, "who were once the pride and glory of the age, hath the silence of historians buried in eternal oblivion!" And this it was that induced the Spartans, when they went to battle, solemnly to sacrifice to the Muses, supplicating that their achievements might be worthily recorded. Had not Homer tuned his lofty lyre, observes the elegant Cicero, the valor of Achilles had remained unsung. And such, too, after all the toils and perils he had braved, after all the gallant actions he had achieved, such too had nearly been the fate of the chivalric Peter Stuyvesant, but that I fortunately stepped in and engraved his name on the indelible tablet of history, just as the caitiff Time was silently brushing it away forever!

The more I reflect, the more I am astonished at the important character of the historian. He is the sovereign censor to decide upon the renown or infamy of his fellow-men. He is the patron of kings and conquerors, on whom it depends whether they shall live in after-ages, or be forgotten as were their ancestors before them. The tyrant may oppress while the object of his tyranny exists; but the historian possesses superior might, for his power extends even beyond the grave. The shades of departed and long-forgotten heroes anxiously bend down from above, while he writes, watching each movement of his pen, whether it shall pass by their names with neglect, or inscribe them on the deathless pages of renown. Even the drop of ink which hangs trembling on his pen, which he may either dash upon the floor, or waste in idle scrawlings—that very drop, which to him is not worth the twentieth part of a farthing, may be of incalculable value to some departed worthy, may elevate half a score, in one moment, to immortality, who would have given worlds, had they possessed them, to insure the glorious meed.

Let not my readers imagine, however, that I am indulging in vainglorious boastings, or am anxious to blazon forth the importance of my tribe. On the contrary, I shrink when I reflect on the awful responsibility we historians assume; I shudder to think what direful commotions and calamities we occasion in the world; I swear to thee, honest reader, as I am a man, I weep at the very idea! Why, let me ask, are so many illustrious men daily tearing themselves away from the embraces of their families, slighting the smiles of beauty, despising the allurements of fortune, and exposing themselves to the miseries of war? Why are kings desolating empires, and depopulating whole countries? In short, what induces all great men of all ages and countries to commit so many victories and misdeeds, and inflict so many miseries upon mankind and upon themselves, but the mere hope that some historian will kindly take them into notice, and admit them into a corner of his volume? For, in short, the mighty object of all their toils, their hardships, and privations, is nothing but *immortal fame*. And what is immortal fame?—why, half a page of dirty paper! Alas! alas! how humiliating the idea, that the renown of so great a man as Peter Stuyvesant should depend upon the pen of so little a man as Diedrich Knickerbocker!

And now, having refreshed ourselves after the fatigues and

perils of the field, it behooves us to return once more to the scene of conflict, and inquire what were the results of this renowned conquest. The fortress of Christina being the fair metropolis, and in a manner the key to New Sweden, its capture was speedily followed by the entire subjugation of the province. This was not a little promoted by the gallant and courteous deportment of the chivalric Peter. Though a man terrible in battle, yet in the hour of victory was he endued with a spirit generous, merciful, and humane. He vaunted not over his enemies, nor did he make defeat more galling by unmanly insults; for like that mirror of knightly virtue, the renowned Paladin Orlando, he was more anxious to do great actions than to talk of them after they were done. He put no man to death; ordered no houses to be burnt down; permitted no ravages to be perpetrated on the property of the vanquished; and even gave one of his bravest officers a severe admonishment with his walking-staff, for having been detected in the act of sacking a hen-roost.

He moreover issued a proclamation, inviting the inhabitants to submit to the authority of their High Mightinesses; but declaring, with unexampled clemency, that whoever refused should be lodged at the public expense, in a goodly castle provided for the purpose, and have an armed retinue to wait on them in the bargain. In consequence of these beneficent terms, about thirty Swedes stepped manfully forward and took the oath of allegiance; in reward for which they were graciously permitted to remain on the banks of the Delaware, where their descendants reside at this very day. I am told, however, by divers observant travellers, that they have never been able to get over the chapfallen looks of their ancestors, but that they still do strangely transmit from father to son manifest marks of the sound drubbing given them by the sturdy Amsterdammers.

The whole country of New Sweden, having thus yielded to the arms of the triumphant Peter, was reduced to a colony called South River, and placed under the superintendence of a lieutenant-governor, subject to the control of the supreme government of New Amsterdam. This great dignitary was called Mynheer William Beekman, or rather *Beck*-man, who derived his surname, as did Ovidious Naso of yore, from the lordly dimensions of his nose, which projected from the centre of his countenance, like the beak of a parrot. He was the great progenitor of the tribe of the Beekmans, one of the most ancient and honorable families of the province, the members of which do gratefully commemorate the origin of their dignity—not as your noble families in England would do, by having a glowing proboscis emblazoned in their escutcheon, but by one and all wearing a right goodly nose, stuck in the very middle of their faces.

Thus was this perilous enterprise gloriously terminated, with the loss of only two men: Wolfert Van Horne, a tall spare man, who was knocked overboard by the boom of a sloop in a flaw of wind; and fat Brom Van Bummel, who was suddenly carried off by an indigestion; both, however, were immortalized, as having bravely fallen in the service of their country. True it is, Peter Stuyvesant had one of his limbs terribly fractured in the act of storming the fortress; but as it was fortunately his wooden leg, the wound was promptly and effectually healed.

And now nothing remains to this branch of my history but to mention that this immaculate hero, and his victorious army, returned joyously to the Manhattoes; where they made a solemn and triumphant entry, bearing with them the conquered Risingh, and the remnant of his battered crew, who had refused allegiance; for it appears that the gigantic Swede had only fallen into a swoon, at the end of the battle, from which he was speedily restored by a wholesome tweak of the nose.

These captive heroes were lodged, according to the promise of the governor, at the public expense, in a fair and spacious castle—being the prison of state, of which Stoffel Brinkerhoff, the immortal conqueror of Oyster Bay, was appointed governor, and which has ever since remained in the possession of his descendants.*

It was a pleasant and goodly sight to witness the joy of the people of New Amsterdam, at beholding their warriors once more return from this war in the wilderness. The old women thronged round Antony Van Corlear, who gave the whole history of the campaign with matchless accuracy, saving that he took the credit of fighting the whole battle himself, and especially of vanquishing the stout Risingh—which he considered

* This castle, though very much altered and modernized, is still in being, and stands at the corner of Pearl Street, facing Coentie's slip.

himself as clearly entitled to, seeing that it was effected by his own stone pottle.

The schoolmasters throughout the town gave holiday to their little urchins, who followed in droves after the drums, with paper caps on their heads, and sticks in their breeches, thus taking the first lesson in the art of war. As to the sturdy rabble, they thronged at the heels of Peter Stuyvesant wherever he went, waving their greasy hats in the air, and shouting "Hard-koppig Piet forever!"

It was indeed a day of roaring rout and jubilee. A huge dinner was prepared at the Stadthouse in honor of the conquerors, where were assembled in one glorious constellation the great and little luminaries of New Amsterdam. There were the lordly Schout and his obsequious deputy; the burgomasters with their officious schepens at their elbows; the subaltern officers at the elbows of the schepens, and so on down to the lowest hanger-on of police: every tag having his rag at his side, to finish his pipe, drink off his heel-taps, and laugh at his flights of immortal dulness. In short—for a city feast is a city feast all the world over, and has been a city feast ever since the creation—the dinner went off much the same as do our great corporation junketings and Fourth-of-July banquets. Loads of fish, flesh, and fowl were devoured, oceans of liquor drunk, thousands of pipes smoked, and many a dull joke honored with much obstreperous fat-sided laughter.

I must not omit to mention that to this far-famed victory Peter Stuyvesant was indebted for another of his many titles; for so hugely delighted were the honest burghers with his achievements, that they unanimously honored him with the name of *Pieter de Groodt*, that is to say, Peter the Great, or, as it was translated into English by the people of New Amsterdam, for the benefit of their New England visitors, *Piet de pig*—and appellation which he maintained even unto the day of his death.

Book VII

CONTAINING THE THIRD PART OF THE REIGN OF PETER THE HEADSTRONG—HIS TROUBLES WITH THE BRITISH NATION, AND THE DECLINE AND FALL OF THE DUTCH DYNASTY

CHAPTER I

How Peter Stuyvesant Relieved the Sovereign People from the Burden of Taking Care of the Nation; with Sundry Particulars of His Conduct in Time of Peace, and of the Rise of a Great Dutch Aristocracy

THE history of the reign of Peter Stuyvesant furnishes an edifying picture of the cares and vexations inseparable from sovereignty, and a solemn warning to all who are ambitious of attaining the seat of honor. Though returning in triumph and crowned with victory, his exultation was checked on observing the abuses which had sprung up in New Amsterdam during his short absence. His walking-staff, which he had sent home to act as vicegerent, had, it is true, kept his council-chamber in order—the counsellors eying it with awe, as it lay in grim repose upon the table, and smoking their pipes in silence—but its control extended not out of doors.

The populace unfortunately had had too much their own way under the slack though fitful reign of William the Testy; and though upon the accession of Peter Stuyvesant they had felt, with the instinctive perception which mobs as well as cattle possess, that the reins of government had passed into stronger hands, yet could they not help fretting and chafing and champing upon the bit, in restive silence.

Scarcely, therefore, had he departed on his expedition against the Swedes, than the old factions of William Kieft's reign had again thrust their heads above water. Pot-house meetings were again held to "discuss the state of the nation," where cobblers, tinkers, and tailors, the self-dubbed "friends of the people," once more felt themselves inspired with the gift of legislation, and undertook to lecture on every movement of government.

Now, as Peter Stuyvesant had a singular inclination to govern the province by his individual will, his first move, on his return, was to put a stop to this gratuitous legislation. Accordingly, one evening, when an inspired cobbler was holding forth to an assemblage of the kind, the intrepid Peter suddenly made his appearance, with his ominous walking-staff in his hand, and a countenance sufficient to petrify a mill-stone. The whole meeting was thrown into confusion—the orator stood aghast, with open mouth and trembling knees, while "horror! tyranny! liberty! rights! taxes! death! destruction!" and a host of other patriotic phrases were bolted forth before he had time to close his lips. Peter took no notice of the skulking throng, but strode up to the brawling bully-ruffian, and pulling out a huge silver watch, which might have served in times of yore as a town-clock, and which is still retained by his descendants as a family curiosity, requested the orator to mend it, and set it going. The orator humbly confessed it was utterly out of his power, as he was unacquainted with the nature of its construction. "Nay, but," said Peter, "try your ingenuity, man: you see all the springs and wheels, and how easily the clumsiest hand may stop it, and pull it to pieces; and why should it not be equally easy to regulate as to stop it?" The orator declared that his trade was wholly different—that he was a poor cobbler, and had never meddled with a watch in his life—that there were men skilled in the art, whose business it was to attend to those matters; but for his part, he should only mar the workmanship and put the whole in confusion. "Why, harkee, master of mine," cried Peter—turning suddenly upon him, with a countenance that almost petrified the patcher of shoes into a perfect lapstone—"dost thou pretend to meddle with the movements of government—to regulate, and correct, and patch, and cobble a complicated machine, the principles of which are above thy comprehension, and its simplest operations too subtle for thy understanding, when thou canst not correct a trifling error in a common piece of mechanism, the whole mystery of which is open to thy inspection?—Hence with thee to the leather and stone, which are emblems of thy head; cobble thy shoes, and confine thyself to the vocation for which Heaven has fitted thee. But," elevating his voice until it made the welkin ring, "if ever I catch thee, or any of thy tribe, meddling again with the affairs of government, by St. Nicholas, but I'll have every mother's bastard of ye flayed alive, and your hides stretched for drum-heads, that ye may thenceforth make a noise to some purpose!"

This threat, and the tremendous voice in which it was uttered, caused the whole multitude to quake with fear. The hair of the orator rose on his head like his own swines' bristles, and not a knight of the thimble present but his heart died within him, and he felt as though he could have verily escaped through the eye of a needle. The assembly dispersed in silent consternation; the pseudo-statesmen, who had hitherto undertaken to regulate public affairs, were now fain to stay at home, hold their tongues, and take care of their families; and party feuds died away to such a degree, that many thriving keepers of taverns and dram-shops were utterly ruined for want of business. But though this measure produced the desired effect in putting an extinguisher on the new lights just brightening up, yet did it tend to injure the popularity of the Great Peter with the thinking part of the community, that is to say, that part which thinks for others instead of for themselves, or, in other words, who attend to everybody's business but their own. These accused the old governor of being highly aristocratical; and in truth there seems to have been some ground for such an accusation; for he carried himself with a lofty, soldier-like air, and was somewhat particular in dress, appearing, when not in uniform, in rich apparel of the antique flaundrish cut, and was especially noted for having his sound leg (which was a very comely one) always arrayed in a red stocking and high-heeled shoe.

Justice he often dispensed in the primitive patriarchal way, seated on the "stoep" before his door, under the shade of a great button-wood tree; but all visits of form and state were received with something of court ceremony in the best parlor; where Antony the Trumpeter officiated as high chamberlain. On public occasions he appeared with great pomp of equipage, and always rode to church in a yellow wagon with flaming red wheels.

These symptoms of state and ceremony, as we have hinted, were much cavilled at by the thinking (and talking) part of the community. They had been accustomed to find easy access to their former governors, and in particular had lived on terms of extreme intimacy with William the Testy; and they accused Peter Stuyvesant of assuming too much dignity and reserve, and of wrapping himself in mystery. Others, however, have pretended to discover in all this a shrewd policy on the part of the old governor. It is certainly of the first importance, say they, that a country should be governed by wise men: but then it is almost equally important that the people should think them wise; for this belief alone can produce willing subordination. To keep up, however, this desirable confidence, in rulers, the people should be allowed to see as little of them as possible. It is the mystery which envelops great men, that gives them half their greatness. There is a kind of superstitious reverence for office which leads us to exaggerate the merits of the occupant, and to suppose that he must be wiser than common men. He, however, who gains access to cabinets, soon finds out by what foolishness the world is governed. He finds that there is quackery in legislation as in everything else; that rulers have their whims and errors as well as other men, and are not so wonderfully superior as he had imagined, since even he may occasionally confute them in argument. Thus awe subsides into confidence, confidence inspires familiarity, and familiarity produces contempt. Such was the case, say they, with William the Testy. By making himself too easy of access, he enabled every scrub-politician to measure wits with him, and to find out the true dimensions not only of his person but of his mind: and thus it was that, by being familiarly scanned, he was discovered to be a very little man. Peter Stuyvesant on the contrary, say they, by conducting himself with dignity and loftiness, was looked up to with great reverence. As he never gave his reasons for anything he did, the public gave him credit for very profound ones; every movement, however intrinsically unimportant, was a matter of speculation; and his very red stockings excited some respect, as being different from the stockings of other men.

Another charge against Peter Stuyvesant was that he had a great leaning in favor of the patricians; and indeed in his time rose many of those mighty Dutch families which have taken such vigorous root, and branched out so luxuriantly in our State. Some, to be sure, were of earlier date, such as the Van Kortlandts, the Van Zandts, the Ten Broecks, the Harden Broecks, and others of Pavonian renown, who gloried in the title of "Discoverers," from having been engaged in the nautical expedition from Communipaw, in which they so heroically braved the terrors of Hell-gate and Buttermilk Channel, and discovered a site for New Amsterdam.

Others claimed to themselves the appellation of "Conquerors," from their gallant achievements in New Sweden and their victory over the Yankees at Oyster Bay. Such was that list of warlike worthies heretofore enumerated, beginning with the Van Wycks, the Van Dycks, and the Ten Eycks, and extending to the Rutgers, the Bensons, the Brinkerhoffs, and the Schermerhorns—a roll equal to the Doomsday-Book of William the Conqueror, and establishing the heroic origin of many an ancient aristocratical Dutch family. These, after all, are the only legitimate nobility and lords of the soil; these are the real "beavers of the Manhattoes"; and much does it grieve me in modern days to see them elbowed aside by foreign invaders, and more especially by those ingenious people, "the Sons of the Pilgrims"; who out-bargain them in the market, out-speculate them on the exchange, out-top them in fortune, and run up mushroom palaces so high, that the tallest Dutch family mansion has not wind enough left for its weather-cock.

In the proud days of Peter Stuyvesant, however, the good old Dutch aristocracy loomed out in all its grandeur. The burly burgher, in round-crowned flaundrish hat with brim of vast circumference, in portly gabardine and bulbous multiplicity of breeches, sat on his "stoep" and smoked his pipe in lordly silence; nor did it ever enter his brain that the active, restless Yankee, whom he saw through his half-shut eyes worrying about in dog-day heat, ever intent on the main chance, was one day to usurp control over these goodly Dutch domains. Already, however, the races regarded each other with disparaging eyes. The Yankees sneeringly spoke of the round-crowned burghers of the Manhattoes as the "Copperheads," while the latter, glorying in their own nether rotundity, and observing the slack galligaskins of their rivals, flapping like an empty sail against the mast, retorted upon them with the opprobrious appellation of "Platter-breeches."

CHAPTER II

How Peter Stuyvesant Labored to Civilize the Community—How He Was a Great Promoter of Holidays—How He Instituted Kissing on New-Year's Day—How He Distributed Fiddles Throughout the New Netherlands—How He Ventured to Reform the Ladies' Petticoats, and How He Caught a Tartar

FROM what I have recounted in the foregoing chapter I would not have it imagined that the great Peter was a tyrannical potentate, ruling with a rod of iron. On the contrary, where the dignity of office permitted, he abounded in generosity and condescension. If he refused the brawling multitude the right of misrule, he at least endeavored to rule them in righteousness. To spread abundance in the land, he obliged the bakers to give thirteen loaves to the dozen—a golden rule which remains a monument of his beneficence. So far from indulging in unreasonable austerity, he delighted to see the poor and the laboring man rejoice; and for this purpose he was a great promoter of holidays. Under his reign there was a great cracking of eggs at Paas or Easter; Whitsuntide or Pinxter also flourished in all its bloom; and never were stockings better filled on the eve of the blessed St. Nicholas.

New-Year's day, however, was his favorite festival, and was ushered in by the ringing of bells and firing of guns. On that genial day the fountains of hospitality were broken up, and the whole community was deluged with cherry-brandy, true Hollands, and mulled cider; every house was a temple of the jolly god; and many a provident vagabond got drunk out of pure economy—taking in liquor enough gratis to serve him half a year afterwards.

The great assemblage, however, was at the governor's house, whither repaired all the burghers of New Amsterdam with their wives and daughters, pranked out in their best attire. On this occasion the good Peter was devoutly observant of the pious Dutch rite of kissing the women-kind for a Happy New Year; and it is traditional that Antony the Trumpeter, who acted as gentleman usher, took toll of all who were young and handsome, as they passed through the ante-chamber. This venerable custom, thus happily introduced, was followed with such zeal by high and low, that on New-Year's day, during the reign of Peter Stuyvesant, New Amsterdam was the most thoroughly be-kissed community in all Christendom. Another great measure of Peter Stuyvesant for public improvement was the distribution of fiddles throughout the land. These were placed in the hands of veteran Negroes, who were despatched as missionaries to every part of the province. This measure, it is said, was first suggested by Antony the Trumpeter; and the effect was marvellous. Instead of those "indignation meetings" set on foot in the time of William the Testy, where men met together to rail at public abuses, groan over the evils of the times, and make each other miserable, there were joyous gatherings of the two sexes to dance and make merry. Now were instituted "quilting bees," and "husking bees," and other rural assemblages, where, under the inspiring influence of the fiddle, toil was enlivened by gayety and followed up by the dance. "Raising bees" also were frequent, where houses sprung up at the wagging of the fiddle-sticks, as the walls of Thebes sprang up of yore to the sound of the lyre of Amphion.

Jolly autumn, which pours its treasures over hill and dale, was in those days a season for the lifting of the heel as well as the heart; labor came dancing in the train of abundance, and frolic prevailed throughout the land. Happy days! when the yeomanry of the Nieuw Nederlands were merry rather than wise; and when the notes of the fiddle, those harbingers of good-humor and good-will, resounded at the close of the day from every hamlet along the Hudson!

Nor was it in rural communities alone that Peter Stuyvesant introduced his favorite engine of civilization. Under his rule the fiddle acquired that potent sway in New Amsterdam which it has ever since retained. Weekly assemblages were held, not in heated ball-rooms at midnight hours, but on Saturday afternoons, by the golden light of the sun, on the green lawn of the

Battery—with Antony the Trumpeter for master of ceremonies. Here would the good Peter take his seat under the spreading trees, among the old burghers and their wives, and watch the mazes of the dance. Here would he smoke his pipe, crack his joke, and forget the rugged toils of war in the sweet oblivious festivities of peace, giving a nod of approbation to those of the young men who shuffled and kicked most vigorously—and now and then a hearty smack, in all honesty of soul, to the buxom lass who held out longest, and tired down every competitor—infallible proof of her being the best dancer.

Once, it is true, the harmony of these meetings was in danger of interruption. A young belle, just returned from a visit to Holland, who of course led the fashions, made her appearance in not more than half a dozen petticoats, and these of alarming shortness. A whisper and a flutter ran through the assembly. The young men, of course, were lost in admiration; but the old ladies were shocked in the extreme, especially those who had marriageable daughters; the young ladies blushed and felt excessively for the "poor thing," and even the governor himself appeared to be in some kind of perturbation.

To complete the confusion of the good folks, she undertook, in the course of a jig, to describe some figures in algebra taught her by a dancing-master at Rotterdam. Unfortunately, at the highest flourish of her feet some vagabond zephyr obtruded his services, and a display of the graces took place, at which all the ladies present were thrown into great consternation; several grave country members were not a little moved, and the good Peter Stuyvesant himself was grievously scandalized.

The shortness of the females' dress, which had continued in fashion ever since the days of William Kieft, had long offended his eye; and though extremely averse to meddling with the petticoats of the ladies, yet he immediately recommended that every one should be furnished with a flounce to the bottom. He likewise ordered that the ladies, and indeed the gentlemen, should use no other step in dancing than "shuffle and turn," and "double trouble"; and forbade, under pain of his high displeasure, any young lady thenceforth to attempt what was termed "exhibiting the graces."

These were the only restrictions he ever imposed upon the

sex; and these were considered by them as tyrannical oppressions, and resisted with that becoming spirit manifested by the gentle sex whenever their privileges are invaded. In fact, Antony Van Corlear, who, as has been shown, was a sagacious man, experienced in the ways of women, took a private occasion to intimate to the governor that a conspiracy was forming among the young vrouws of New Amsterdam; and that, if the matter were pushed any further, there was danger of their leaving off petticoats altogether; whereupon the good Peter shrugged his shoulders, dropped the subject, and ever after suffered the women to wear their petticoats and cut their capers as high as they pleased—a privilege which they have jealousy maintained in the Manhattoes unto the present day.

CHAPTER III

How Troubles Thickened on the Province—How It Is Threatened by the Helderbergers, the Merrylanders, and the Giants of the Susquehanna

IN the last two chapters I have regaled the reader with a delectable picture of the good Peter and his metropolis during an interval of peace. It was, however, but a bit of blue sky in a stormy day; the clouds are again gathering up from all points of the compass, and, if I am not mistaken in my forebodings, we shall have rattling weather in the ensuing chapters.

It is with some communities as it is with certain meddlesome individuals: they have a wonderful facility at getting into scrapes; and I have always remarked that those are most prone to get in who have the least talent at getting out again. This is doubtless owing to the excessive valor of those states; for I have likewise noticed that this rampant quality is always most frothy and fussy where most confined; which accounts for its vaporing so amazingly in little states, little men and ugly little women more especially.

Such is the case with this little province of the Nieuw Nederlands; which, by its exceeding valor, has already drawn upon itself a host of enemies; has had fighting enough to satisfy a province twice its size; and is in a fair way of becoming an exceedingly forlorn, well-belabored, and woe-begone little province. All which was providentially ordered to give interest and sublimity to this pathetic history.

The first interruption to the halcyon quiet of Peter Stuyvesant was caused by hostile intelligence from the old belligerent nest of Rensellaerstein. Killian, the lordly patroon of Rensellaerwick, was again in the field, at the head of his myrmidons of the Helderberg, seeking to annex the whole of the Kaats-kill mountains to his dominions. The Indian tribes of these mountains had likewise taken up the hatchet and menaced the venerable Dutch settlement of Esopus.

Fain would I entertain the reader with the triumphant campaign of Peter Stuyvesant in the haunted regions of those mountains, but that I hold all Indian conflicts to be mere barbaric brawls, unworthy of the pen which has recorded the classic war of Fort Christina; and as to these Helderberg commotions, they are among the flatulencies which from time to time afflict the bowels of this ancient province, as with a wind-colic, and which I deem it seemly and decent to pass over in silence.

The next storm of trouble was from the south. Scarcely had the worthy Mynheer Beekman got warm in the seat of authority on the South River, than enemies began to spring up all around him. Hard by was a formidable race of savages inhabiting the gentle region watered by the Susquehanna, of whom the following mention is made by Master Hariot, in his excellent history:

"The Susquesahanocks are a giantly people, strange in proportion, behavior and attire—their voice sounding from them as out of a cave. Their tobacco-pipes were three-quarters of a yard long; carved at the great end with a bird, beare, or other device, sufficient to beat out the brains of a horse. The calfe of one of their legges measured three-quarters of a yard about; the rest of the limbs proportionable." *

These gigantic savages and smokers caused no little disquiet in the mind of Mynheer Beekman, threatening to cause a famine of tobacco in the land; but his most formidable enemy was the roaring, roistering English colony of Maryland, or, as it was anciently written, Merryland—so called because the inhabitants,

* Hariot's Journal, Purch. Pilgrims.

not having the fear of the Lord before their eyes, were prone to make merry and get fuddled with mint-julep and apple-toddy. They were, moreover, great horse-racers and cock-fighters, mighty wrestlers and jumpers, and enormous consumers of hoecake and bacon. They lay claim to be the first inventors of those recondite beverages, cock-tail, stone-fence, and sherry-cobbler, and to have discovered the gastronomical merits of terrapins, soft crabs, and canvas-back ducks.

This rantipole colony, founded by Lord Baltimore, a British nobleman, was managed by his agent, a swaggering Englishman, commonly called Fendall, that is to say, "offend all"—a name given him for his bullying propensities. These were seen in a message to Mynheer Beekman, threatening him, unless he immediately swore allegiance to Lord Baltimore as the rightful lord of the soil, to come, at the head of the roaring boys of Merryland and the giants of the Susquehanna, and sweep him and his Nederlanders out of the country.

The trusty sword of Peter Stuyvesant almost leaped from its scabbard when he received missives from Mynheer Beekman, informing him of the swaggering menaces of the bully Fendall; and as to the giantly warriors of the Susquehanna, nothing would have more delighted him than a bout, hand to hand, with half a score of them, having never encountered a giant in the whole course of his campaigns, unless we may consider the stout Risingh as such—and he was but a little one.

Nothing prevented his marching instantly to the South River and enacting scenes still more glorious than those of Fort Christina, but the necessity of first putting a stop to the increasing aggressions and inroads of the Yankees, so as not to leave an enemy in his rear; but he wrote to Mynheer Beekman to keep up a bold front and stout heart, promising, as soon as he had settled affairs in the east, that he would hasten to the south with his burly warriors of the Hudson, to lower the crests of the giants, and mar the merriment of the Merrylanders.

CHAPTER IV

How Peter Stuyvesant Adventured into the East Country, and How He Fared There

TO explain the apparently sudden movement of Peter Stuyvesant against the crafty men of the East Country, I would observe that, during his campaigns on the South River, and in the enchanted regions of the Catskill Mountains, the twelve tribes of the East had been more than usually active in prosecuting their subtle scheme for the subjugation of the Nieuw Nederlands.

Independent of the incessant maraudings among henroosts and squattings along the border, invading armies would penetrate, from time to time, into the very heart of the country. As their prototypes of yore went forth into the land of Canaan, with their wives and their children, their men-servants and their maid-servants, their flocks and herds, to settle themselves down in the land and possess it, so these chosen people of modern days would progress through the country in patriarchal style, conducting carts and wagons laden with household furniture, with women and children piled on top, and pots and kettles dangling beneath. At the tails of these vehicles would stalk a crew of long-limbed, lank-sided varlets, with axes on their shoulders and packs on their backs, resolutely bent upon "locating" themselves, as they termed it, and improving the country. These were the most dangerous kind of invaders. It is true they were guilty of no overt acts of hostility; but it was notorious that, wherever they got a footing, the honest Dutchmen gradually disappeared, retiring slowly, as do the Indians before the white men, being in some way or other talked and chaffed, and bargained and swapped, and, in plain English, elbowed out of all those rich bottoms and fertile nooks in which our Dutch yeomanry are prone to nestle themselves.

Peter Stuyvesant was at length roused to this kind of war in disguise, by which the Yankees were craftily aiming to subjugate his dominions. He was a man easily taken in, it is true, as all great-hearted men are apt to be; but if he once found it out, his wrath was terrible. He now threw diplomacy to the dogs—determined to appear no more by ambassadors, but to repair in person to the great council of the Amphictyons, bearing the sword in one hand and the olive-branch in the other, and giving them their choice of sincere and honest peace, or open and iron war.

His privy councillors were astonished and dismayed when he announced his determination. For once they ventured to remonstrate, setting forth the rashness of venturing his sacred person in the midst of a strange and barbarous people. They might as well have tried to turn a rusty weather-cock with a broken-winded bellows. In the fiery heart of the iron-headed Peter sat enthroned the five kinds of courage described by Aristotle; and had the philosopher enumerated five hundred more, I verily believe he would have possessed them all. As to that better part of valor called discretion, it was too cold-blooded a virtue for his tropical temperament.

Summoning, therefore, to his presence his trusty follower, Antony Van Corlear, he commanded him to hold himself in readiness to accompany him the following morning on this, his hazardous enterprise. Now Antony the Trumpeter was by this time a little stricken in years, but by dint of keeping up a good heart, and having never known care or sorrow (having never been married), he was still a hearty, jocund, rubicund, gamesome wag, and of great capacity in the doublet. This last was ascribed to his living a jolly life on those domains at the Hook, which Peter Stuyvesant had granted to him for his gallantry at Fort Casimir.

Be this as it may, there was nothing that more delighted Antony than this command of the great Peter, for he could have followed the stout-hearted old governor to the world's end, with love and loyalty; and he moreover still remembered the frolicking, and dancing, and bundling, and other disports of the east country, and entertained dainty recollections of numerous kind and buxom lasses, whom he longed exceedingly again to encounter.

Thus then did this mirror of hardihood set forth, with no other attendant but his trumpeter, upon one of the most perilous enterprises ever recorded in the annals of knight-errantry. For a single warrior to venture openly among a whole nation of foes—but, above all, for a plain downright Dutchman to think of negotiating with the whole council of New England!—never was there known a more desperate undertaking!—Ever since I have entered upon the chronicles of this peerless but hitherto uncelebrated chieftain, has he kept me in a state of incessant action and anxiety with the toils and dangers he is constantly encountering. Oh! for a chapter of the tranquil reign of Wouter Van Twiller, that I might repose on it as on a feather-bed!

Is it not enough, Peter Stuyvesant, that I have once already rescued thee from the machinations of these terrible Amphictyons, by bringing the powers of witchcraft to thine aid? Is it not enough, that I have followed thee undaunted, like a guardian spirit, into the midst of the horrid battle of Fort Christina?—that I have been put incessantly to my trumps to keep thee safe and sound—now warding off with my single pen the shower of dastard blows that fell upon thy rear—now narrowly shielding thee from a deadly thrust, by a mere tobacco-box—now casing thy dauntless skull with adamant, when even thy stubborn ram-beaver failed to resist the sword of the stout Risingh—and now, not merely bringing thee off alive, but triumphant, from the clutches of the gigantic Swede, by the desperate means of a paltry stone pottle? Is not all this enough, but must thou still be plunging into new difficulties, and hazarding in headlong enterprises thyself, thy trumpeter, and thy historian?

And now the ruddy-faced Aurora, like a buxom chambermaid, draws aside the sable curtains of the night, and out bounces from his bed the jolly red-haired Phœbus, startled at being caught so late in the embraces of Dame Thetis. With many a stable-boy oath he harnesses his brazen-footed steeds, and whips, and lashes, and splashes up the firmament, like a loitering coachman, half an hour behind his time. And now behold that imp of fame and prowess, the headstrong Peter, bestriding a raw-boned, switch-tailed charger, gallantly arrayed in full regimentals, and bracing on his thigh that trusty brass-hilted sword, which had wrought such fearful deeds on the banks of the Delaware.

Behold hard after him his doughty trumpeter, Van Corlear, mounted on a broken-winded, wall-eyed, calico mare, his stone pottle, which had laid low the mighty Risingh, slung under his arm, and his trumpet displayed vauntingly in his right hand, decorated with a gorgeous banner, on which is emblazoned the great beaver of the Manhattoes. See them proudly issuing out of the city-gate, like an iron-clad hero of yore, with his faithful squire at his heels, the populace following with their eyes, and shouting many a parting wish, and hearty cheering. Farewell, Hardkoppig Piet! Farewell, honest Antony! Pleasant be your wayfaring —prosperous your return! The stoutest hero that ever drew a sword, and the worthiest trumpeter that ever trod shoe-leather.

Legends are lamentably silent about the events that befell our adventurers in this their adventurous travel, excepting the Stuyvesant manuscript, which gives the substance of a pleasant little heroic poem, written on the occasion by Domine Ægidius Luyck,* who appears to have been the poet-laureate of New Amsterdam. This inestimable manuscript assures us, that it was a rare spectacle to behold the great Peter and his loyal follower hailing the morning sun, and rejoicing in the clear countenance of nature, as they pranced it through the pastoral scenes of Bloemen Dael; which, in those days, was a sweet and rural valley, beautified with many a bright wild-flower, refreshed by many a pure streamlet, and enlivened here and there by a delectable little Dutch cottage, sheltered under some sloping hill, and almost buried in embowering trees.

Now did they enter upon the confines of Connecticut, where they encountered many grievous difficulties and perils. At one place they were assailed by a troop of country squires and militia colonels, who, mounted on goodly steeds, hung upon their rear for several miles, harassing them exceedingly with guesses and questions, more especially the worthy Peter, whose silver-chased leg excited not a little marvel. At another place, hard by the renowned town of Stamford, they were set upon by a great and mighty legion of church-deacons, who imperiously demanded of them five shillings, for travelling on Sunday, and threatened to carry them captive to a neighboring church, whose steeple peered above the trees; but these the valiant Peter put to rout with little difficulty, insomuch that they bestrode their canes and galloped off in horrible confusion, leaving their cocked hats behind in the hurry of their flight. But not so easily did he escape from the hands of a crafty man of Pyquag, who, with undaunted persever-

* This Luyck was moreover rector of the Latin School in Nieuw Nederlands, 1663. There are two pieces addressed to Ægidius Luyck in D. Selyn's MSS. of poesies, upon his marriage with Judith Isendoorn. Old MS.

ance, and repeated onsets, fairly bargained him out of his goodly switch-tailed charger, leaving in place thereof a villainous, foundered Narraganset pacer.

But maugre all these hardships, they pursued their journey cheerily along the course of the soft-flowing Connecticut, whose gentle waves, says the song, roll through many a fertile vale and sunny plain—now reflecting the lofty spires of the bustling city, and now the rural beauties of the humble hamlet—now echoing with the busy hum of commerce, and now with the cheerful song of the peasant.

At every town would Peter Stuyvesant, who was noted for warlike punctilio, order the sturdy Antony to sound a courteous salutation; though the manuscript observes, that the inhabitants were thrown into great dismay when they heard of his approach. For the fame of his incomparable achievements on the Delaware had spread throughout the east country, and they dreaded lest he had come to take vengeance on their manifold transgressions.

But the good Peter rode through these towns with a smiling aspect, waving his hand with inexpressible majesty and condescension; for he verily believed that the old clothes which these ingenious people had thrust into their broken windows, and the festoons of dried apples and peaches which ornamented the fronts of their houses, were so many decorations in honor of his approach, as it was the custom in the days of chivalry to compliment renowned heroes by sumptuous displays of tapestry and gorgeous furniture. The women crowded to the doors to gaze upon him as he passed, so much does prowess in arms delight the gentle sex. The little children, too, ran after him in troops, staring with wonder at his regimentals, his brimstone breeches, and the silver garniture of his wooden leg. Nor must I omit to mention the joy which many strapping wenches betrayed at beholding the jovial Van Corlear, who had whilom delighted them so much with his trumpet, when he bore the great Peter's challenge to the Amphictyons. The kind-hearted Antony alighted from his calico mare, and kissed them all with infinite loving-kindness—and was right pleased to see a crew of little trumpeters crowding around him for his blessing, each of whom he patted on the head, bade him be a good boy, and gave him a penny to buy molasses candy.

CHAPTER V

How the Yankees Secretly Sought the Aid of the British Cabinet In Their Hostile Schemes Against the Manhattoes

NOW so it happened, that, while the great and good Peter Stuyvesant, followed by his trusty squire, was making his chivalric progress through the east country, a dark and direful scheme of war against his beloved province was forming in that nursery of monstrous projects, the British Cabinet.

This, we are confidently informed, was the result of the secret instigations of the great council of the league; who, finding themselves totally incompetent to vie in arms with the heavy-sterned warriors of the Manhattoes and their iron-headed commander, sent emissaries to the British government, setting forth in eloquent language the wonders and delights of this delicious little Dutch Canaan, and imploring that a force might be sent out to invade it by sea, while they should coöperate by land.

These emissaries arrived at a critical juncture, just as the British Lion was beginning to bristle up his mane and wag his tail; for we are assured by the anonymous writer of the Stuyvesant manuscript, that the astounding victory of Peter Stuyvesant at Fort Christina had resounded throughout Europe, and his annexation of the territory of New Sweden had awakened the jealousy of the British Cabinet for their wild lands at the south. This jealousy was brought to a head by the representations of Lord Baltimore, who declared that the territory thus annexed lay within the lands granted to him by the British crown, and he claimed to be protected in his rights. Lord Sterling, another British subject, claimed the whole of Nassau, or Long Island, once the Ophir of William the Testy, but now the kitchen-garden of the Manhattoes, which he declared to be British territory by the right of discovery, but unjustly usurped by the Nederlanders. The result of all these rumors and representations was a sudden zeal on the part of his Majesty Charles the Second, for the safety and well-being of his transatlantic possessions, and especially for the recovery of the New Netherlands, which Yankee logic had, somehow or other, proved to be a continuity of the territory taken possession of for the British crown by the

Pilgrims, when they landed on Plymouth Rock, fugitives from British oppression. All this goodly land, thus wrongfully held by the Dutchmen, he presented, in a fit of affection, to his brother, the Duke of York—a donation truly royal, since none but great sovereigns have a right to give away what does not belong to them. That this munificent gift might not be merely nominal, his Majesty ordered that an armament should be straightway dispatched to invade the city of New Amsterdam by land and water, and put his brother in complete possession of the premises.

Thus critically situated are the affairs of the New Nederlanders. While the honest burghers are smoking their pipes in sober security, and the privy councillors are snoring in the council-chamber—while Peter the Headstrong is undauntedly making his way through the east country in the confident hope by honest words and manly deeds to bring the grand council to terms—a hostile fleet is sweeping like a thunder-cloud across the Atlantic, soon to rattle a storm of war about the ears of the dozing Nederlanders, and to put the mettle of their governor to the trial.

But come what may, I here pledge my veracity, that in all warlike conflicts and doubtful perplexities he will ever acquit himself like a gallant, noble-minded, obstinate old cavalier. Forward, then, to the charge! Shine out, propitious stars, on the renowned city of the Manhattoes; and the blessing of St. Nicholas go with thee—honest Peter Stuyvesant.

CHAPTER VI

Of Peter Stuyvesant's Expedition into the East Country, Showing That Though an Old Bird, He Did Not Understand Trap

GREAT nations resemble great men in this particular, that their greatness is seldom known until they get in trouble; adversity, therefore, has been wisely denominated the ordeal of true greatness, which, like gold, can never receive its real estimation until it has passed through the furnace. In proportion, therefore, as a nation, a community, or an individual (possessing the inherent quality of greatness) is involved in perils and misfortunes, in proportion does it rise in grandeur, and even when sinking under calamity, makes, like a house on fire, a more glorious display than ever it did in the fairest period of its prosperity.

The vast empire of China, though teeming with population and imbibing and concentrating the wealth of nations, has vegetated through a succession of drowsy ages; and were it not for its internal revolutions, and the subversion of its ancient government by the Tartars, might have presented nothing but a dull detail of monotonous prosperity. Pompeii and Herculaneum might have passed into oblivion, with a herd of their contemporaries, had they not been fortunately overwhelmed by a volcano. The renowned city of Troy acquired celebrity only from its ten years' distress, and final conflagration; Paris rose in importance by the plots and massacres which ended in the exaltation of Napoleon; and even the mighty London has skulked through the records of time, celebrated for nothing of moment excepting the plague, the great fire, and Guy Faux's gunpowder plot! Thus cities and empires creep along, enlarging in silent obscurity, until they burst forth in some tremendous calamity—and snatch, as it were, immortality from the explosion!

The above principle being admitted, my reader will plainly perceive that the city of New Amsterdam and its dependent province are on the high-road to greatness. Dangers and hostilities threaten from every side, and it is really a matter of astonishment, how so small a state has been able, in so short a time, to entangle itself in so many difficulties. Ever since the province was first taken by the nose, at the Fort of Goed Hoop, in the tranquil days of Wouter Van Twiller, has it been gradually increasing in historic importance; and never could it have had a more appropriate chieftain to conduct it to the pinnacle of grandeur than Peter Stuyvesant.

This truly headstrong hero having successfully effected his daring progress through the east country, girded up his loins as he approached Boston, and prepared for the grand onslaught with the Amphictyons, which was to be the crowning achievement of the campaign. Throwing Antony Van Corlear, who, with his calico mare, formed his escort and army, a little in the advance, and bidding him be of stout heart and great wind, he placed himself firmly in his saddle, cocked his hat more fiercely over his left eye, summoned all the heroism of his soul into his countenance, and, with one arm akimbo, the hand resting on the pommel of his sword, rode into the great metropolis of the league, Antony sounding his trumpet before him in a manner to electrify the whole community.

Never was there such a stir in Boston as on this occasion; never such a hurrying hither and thither about the streets; such popping of heads out of windows; such gathering of knots in market-places. Peter Stuyvesant was a straightforward man, and prone to do everything above-board. He would have ridden at once to the great council-house of the league and sounded a parley; but the grand council knew the mettlesome hero they had to deal with, and were not for doing things in a hurry. On the contrary, they sent forth deputations to meet him on the way, to receive him in a style befitting the great potentate of the Manhattoes, and to multiply all kind of honors, and ceremonies, and formalities, and other courteous impediments in his path. Solemn banquets were accordingly given him, equal to thanksgiving feasts. Complimentary speeches were made him, wherein he was entertained with the surpassing virtues, long-sufferings, and achievements of the Pilgrim-Fathers; and it is even said he was treated to a sight of Plymouth Rock—that great cornerstone of Yankee empire.

I will not detain my readers by recounting the endless devices by which time was wasted, and obstacles and delays multiplied to the infinite annoyance of the impatient Peter. Neither will I fatigue them by dwelling on his negotiations with the grand council, when he at length brought them to business. Suffice it to say, it was like most other diplomatic negotiations: a great deal was said and very little done; one conversation led to another, one conference begot misunderstandings which it took a dozen conferences to explain, at the end of which both parties found themselves just where they had begun, but ten times less likely to come to an agreement.

In the midst of these perplexities which bewildered the brain and incensed the ire of honest Peter, he received private intelligence of the dark conspiracy matured in the British cabinet, with the astounding fact that a British squadron was already on the way to invade New Amsterdam by sea, and that the grand council of Amphictyons, while thus beguiling him with subtleties, were actually prepared to coöperate by land!

Oh! how did the sturdy old warrior rage and roar, when he found himself thus entrapped, like a lion in the hunter's toil! Now did he draw his trusty sword, and determine to break in upon the council of the Amphictyons and put every mother's son of them to death. Now did he resolve to fight his way throughout all the region of the east and to lay waste Connecticut river!

Gallant, but unfortunate Peter! Did I not enter with sad forebodings on this ill-starred expedition? Did I not tremble when I saw thee, with no other counsellor than thine own head; no other armor but an honest tongue, a spotless conscience, and a rusty sword; no other protector but St. Nicholas, and no other attendant but a trumpeter; did I not tremble when I beheld thee thus sally forth to contend with all the knowing powers of New England?

It was a long time before the kind-hearted expostulations of Antony Van Corlear, aided by the soothing melody of his trumpet, could lower the spirits of Peter Stuyvesant from their warlike and vindictive tones, and prevent his making widows and orphans of half the population of Boston. With great difficulty he was prevailed upon to bottle up his wrath for the present, to conceal from the council his knowledge of their machinations, and by effecting his escape, to be able to arrive in time for the salvation of the Manhattoes.

The latter suggestion awakened a new ray of hope in his bosom; he forthwith dispatched a secret message to his councillors at New Amsterdam, apprising them of their danger, and commanding them to put the city in a posture of defence, promising to come as soon as possible to their assistance. This done, he felt marvellously relieved, rose slowly, shook himself like a rhinoceros, and issued forth from his den, in much the same manner as Giant Despair is described to have issued from Doubting Castle, in the chivalric history of the Pilgrim's Progress.

And now much does it grieve me that I must leave the gallant Peter in this imminent jeopardy; but it behooves us to hurry back and see what is going on at New Amsterdam, for greatly do I fear that city is already in a turmoil. Such was ever the fate of

Peter Stuyvesant; while doing one thing with heart and soul, he was too apt to leave everything else at sixes and sevens. While, like a potentate of yore, he was was absent attending to those things in person which in modern days are trusted to generals and ambassadors, his little territory at home was sure to get in an uproar; all which was owing to that uncommon strength of intellect, which induced him to trust to nobody but himself, and which had acquired him the renowned appellation of Peter the Headstrong.

CHAPTER VII

How the People of New Amsterdam Were Thrown into a Great Panic by the News of the Threatened Invasion, and the Manner in Which They Fortified Themselves

THERE is no sight more truly interesting to a philosopher than a community where every individual has a voice in public affairs, where every individual considers himself the Atlas of the nation, and where every individual thinks it his duty to bestir himself for the good of his country: I say, there is nothing more interesting to a philosopher than such a community in a sudden bustle of war. Such clamor of tongues—such patriotic bawling—such running hither and thither—everybody in a hurry—everybody in trouble—everybody in the way, and everybody interrupting his neighbor—who is busily employed in doing nothing! It is like witnessing a great fire, where the whole community are agog—some dragging about empty engines—others scampering with full buckets, and spilling the contents into their neighbor's boots—and others ringing the church-bells all night, by way of putting out the fire. Little firemen, like sturdy little knights storming a breach, clambering up and down scaling-ladders, and bawling through tin trumpets, by way of directing the attack. Here a fellow, in his great zeal to save the property of the unfortunate, catches up an anonymous chamber-utensil, and gallants it off with an air of as much self-importance as if he had rescued a pot of money; there another throws looking-glasses and china out of the window, to save them from the flames; whilst those who can do nothing else run up and down the streets, keeping up an incessant cry of *Fire! Fire! Fire!*

"When the news arrived at Sinope," says Lucian—though I own the story is rather trite—"that Philip was about to attack them, the inhabitants were thrown into a violent alarm. Some ran to furbish up their arms; others rolled stones to build up the walls—everybody, in short, was employed, and everybody in the way of his neighbor. Diogenes alone could find nothing to do; whereupon, not to be idle when the welfare of his country was at stake, he tucked up his robe, and fell to rolling his tub with might and main up and down the Gymnasium." In like manner did every mother's son in the patriotic community of New Amsterdam, on receiving the missive of Peter Stuyvesant, busy himself most mightily in putting things in confusion, and assisting the general uproar. "Every man"—saith the Stuyvesant manuscript—"flew to arms!"—by which is meant, that not one of our honest Dutch citizens would venture to church or to market without an old-fashioned spit of a sword dangling at his side, and a long Dutch fowling-piece on his shoulder; nor would he go out of a night without a lantern; nor turn a corner without first peeping cautiously round, lest he should come unawares upon a British army; and we are informed that Stoffel Brinkerhoff, who was considered by the old women almost as brave a man as the governor himself, actually had two one-pound swivels mounted in his entry, one pointing out at the front door, and the other at the back.

But the most strenuous measure resorted to on this awful occasion, and one which has since been found of wonderful efficacy, was to assemble popular meetings. These brawling convocations, I have already shown, were extremely offensive to Peter Stuyvesant; but as this was a moment of unusual agitation, and as the old governor was not present to repress them, they broke out with intolerable violence. Hither, therefore, the orators and politicians repaired, striving who should bawl loudest, and exceed the others in hyperbolical bursts of patriotism, and in resolutions to uphold and defend the government. In these sage meetings it was resolved that they were the most enlightened, the most dignified, the most formidable, and the most ancient community upon the face of the earth. This resolution being carried unanimously, another was immediately proposed—whether it were not possible and politic to exterminate Great Britain? upon which sixty-nine members spoke in the affirmative, and only one arose to suggest some doubts—who, as a punishment for his treasonable presumption, was immediately seized by the mob, and tarred and feathered—which punishment being equivalent to the Tarpeian Rock, he was afterwards considered as an outcast from society, and his opinion went for nothing. The question, therefore, being unanimously carried in the affirmative, it was recommended to the grand council to pass it into a law; which was accordingly done. By this measure the hearts of the people at large were wonderfully encouraged, and they waxed exceedingly choleric and valorous. Indeed, the first paroxysm of alarm having in some measure subsided—the old women having buried all the money they could lay their hands on, and their husbands daily getting fuddled with what was left—the community began even to stand on the offensive. Songs were manufactured in Low Dutch and sung about the streets, wherein the English were most wofully beaten, and shown no quarter; and popular addresses were made, wherein it was proved, to a certainty, that the fate of Old England depended upon the will of the New Amsterdammers.

Finally, to strike a violent blow at the very vitals of Great Britain, a multitude of the wiser inhabitants assembled, and having purchased all the British manufactures they could find, they made thereof a huge bonfire; and, in the patriotic glow of the moment, every man present, who had a hat or breeches of English workmanship, pulled it off, and threw it into the flames—to the irreparable detriment, loss, and ruin of the English manufacturers. In commemoration of this great exploit, they erected a pole on the spot, with a device on the top intended to represent the province of Nieuw Nederlands destroying Great Britain, under the similitude of an Eagle picking the little Island of Old England out of the globe; but either through the unskilfulness of the sculptor, or his ill-timed waggery, it bore a striking resemblance to a goose, vainly striving to get hold of a dumpling.

CHAPTER VIII

How the Grand Council of the New Netherlands Were Miraculously Gifted with Long Tongues in the Moment of Emergency—Showing the Value of Words in Warfare

IT will need but little penetration in any one conversant with the ways of that wise but windy potentate, the sovereign people, to discover that notwithstanding all the warlike bluster and bustle of the last chapter, the city of New Amsterdam was not a whit more prepared for war than before. The privy councillors of Peter Stuyvesant were aware of this; and, having received his private orders to put the city in an immediate posture of defence, they called a meeting of the oldest and richest burghers to assist them with their wisdom. These were that order of citizens commonly termed "men of the greatest weight in the community"; their weight being estimated by the heaviness of their heads and of their purses. Their wisdom in fact is apt to be of a ponderous kind, and to hang like a mill-stone round the neck of the community.

Two things were unanimously determined in this assembly of venerables: First, that the city required to be put in a state of defence; and, Second, that, as the danger was imminent, there should be no time lost: which points being settled, they fell to making long speeches and belaboring one another in endless and intemperate disputes. For about this time was this unhappy city first visited by that talking endemic so prevalent in this country, and which so invariably evinces itself wherever a number of wise men assemble together, breaking out in long, windy speeches, caused, as physicians suppose, by the foul air which is ever generated in a crowd. Now it was, moreover, that they first introduced the ingenious method of measuring the merits of an harangue by the hour-glass, he being considered the ablest orator who spoke longest on a question. For which excellent invention, it is recorded, we are indebted to the same profound Dutch critic who judged of books by their size.

This sudden passion for endless harangues, so little consonant with the customary gravity and taciturnity of our sage forefathers, was supposed by certain philosophers to have been imbibed, together with divers other barbarous propensities, from their savage neighbors; who were peculiarly noted for *long talks* and *council-fires*, and never undertook any affair of the least importance without previous debates and harangues among their chiefs and *old men*. But the real cause was, that the people, in electing their representatives to the grand council, were particular in choosing them for their talents at talking, without inquiring whether they possessed the more rare, difficult, and ofttimes important talent of holding their tongues. The consequence was, that this deliberative body was composed of the most loquacious men in the community. As they considered themselves placed there to talk, every man concluded that his duty to his constituents, and, what is more, his popularity with them, required that he should harangue on every subject, whether he understood it or not. There was an ancient mode of burying a chieftain, by every soldier throwing his shield full of earth on the corpse, until a mighty mound was formed; so, whenever a question was brought forward in this assembly, every member pressing forward to throw on his quantum of wisdom, the subject was quickly buried under a mountain of words.

We are told that disciples, on entering the school of Pythagoras, were for two years enjoined silence, and forbidden either to ask questions, or make remarks. After they had thus acquired the inestimable art of holding their tongues, they were gradually permitted to make inquiries, and finally to communicate their own opinions.

With what a beneficial effect could this wise regulation of Pythagoras be introduced in modern legislative bodies—and how wonderfully would it have tended to expedite business in the grand council of the Manhattoes!

At this perilous juncture the fatal word *economy*, the stumbling-block of William the Testy, had been once more set afloat, according to which the cheapest plan of defence was insisted upon as the best; it being deemed a great stroke of policy in furnishing powder to economize in ball.

Thus did dame Wisdom (whom the wags of antiquity have humorously personified as a woman) seem to take a mischievous pleasure in jilting the venerable councillors of New Amsterdam. To add to the confusion, the old factions of Short Pipes and

Long Pipes, which had been almost strangled by the Herculean grasp of Peter Stuyvesant, now sprang up with tenfold vigor. Whatever was proposed by Short Pipe was opposed by the whole tribe of Long Pipes, who, like true partisans, deemed it their first duty to effect the downfall of their rivals, their second, to elevate themselves, and their third, to consult the public good; though many left the third consideration out of question altogether.

In this great collision of hard heads it is astonishing the number of projects that were struck out—projects which threw the wind-mill system of William the Testy completely in the background. These were almost uniformly opposed by the "men of the greatest weight in the community!" your weighty men, though slow to devise, being always great at "negativing." Among these were a set of fat, self-important old burghers, who smoked their pipes, and said nothing except to negative every plan of defence proposed. These were that class of "conservatives" who, having amassed a fortune, button up their pockets, shut their mouths, sink, as it were, into themselves, and pass the rest of their lives in the indwelling beatitude of conscious wealth; as some phlegmatic oyster, having swallowed a pearl, closes its shell, sinks in the mud, and devotes the rest of its life to the conservation of its treasure. Every plan of defence seemed to these worthy old gentlemen pregnant with ruin. An armed force was a legion of locusts preying upon the public property; to fit out a naval armament was to throw their money into the sea; to build fortifications was to bury it in the dirt. In short, they settled it as a sovereign maxim, so long as their pockets were full, no matter how much they were drubbed. A kick left no scar; a broken head cured itself; but an empty purse was of all maladies the slowest to heal, and one in which nature did nothing for the patient.

Thus did this venerable assembly of sages lavish away that time which the urgency of affairs rendered invaluable, in empty brawls and long-winded speeches, without ever agreeing, except on the point with which they started, namely, that there was no time to be lost, and delay was ruinous. At length, St. Nicholas taking compassion on their distracted situation, and anxious to preserve them from anarchy, so ordered, that in the midst of one of their most noisy debates, on the subject of fortification and defence, when they had nearly fallen to loggerheads in consequence of not being able to convince each other, the question was happily settled by the sudden entrance of a messenger, who informed them that a hostile fleet had arrived, and was actually advancing up the bay!

CHAPTER IX

In Which the Troubles of New Amsterdam Appeared to Thicken—Showing the Bravery, in Time of Peril, of a People Who Defend Themselves by Resolution

LIKE as an assemblage of belligerent cats, gibbering and caterwauling, eying one another with hideous grimaces and contortions, spitting in each other's faces, and on the point of a general clapper-clawing, are suddenly put to scampering rout and confusion by the appearance of a house-dog, so was the no less vociferous council of New Amsterdam amazed, astounded, and totally dispersed, by the sudden arrival of the enemy. Every member waddled home as fast as his short legs could carry him, wheezing as he went with corpulency and terror. Arrived at his castle, he barricadoed the street-door, and buried himself in the cider-cellar, without venturing to peep out, lest he should have his head carried off by a cannon-ball.

The sovereign people crowded into the market-place, herding together with the instinct of sheep, who seek safety in each other's company when the shepherd and his dog are absent, and the wolf is prowling round the fold. Far from finding relief, however, they only increased each other's terrors. Each man looked ruefully in his neighbor's face, in search of encouragement, but only found in its woe-begone lineaments a confirmation of his own dismay. Not a word now was to be heard of conquering Great Britain, not a whisper about the sovereign virtues of economy—while the old women heightened the general gloom by clamorously bewailing their fate, and calling for protection on St. Nicholas and Peter Stuyvesant.

Oh, how did they bewail the absence of the lion-hearted

Peter! and how did they long for the comforting presence of Antony Van Corlear! Indeed, a gloomy uncertainty hung over the fate of these adventurous heroes. Day after day had elapsed since the alarming message from the governor, without bringing any further tidings of his safety. Many a fearful conjecture was hazarded as to what had befallen him and his loyal squire. Had they not been devoured alive by the cannibals of Marblehead and Cape Cod?—had they not been put to the question by the great council of Amphictyons?—had they not been smothered in onions by the terrible men of Pyquag? In the midst of this consternation and perplexity, when horror, like a mighty nightmare, sat brooding upon the little, fat, plethoric city of New Amsterdam, the ears of the multitude were suddenly startled by the distant sound of a trumpet: it approached, it grew louder and louder, and now it resounded at the city gate. The public could not be mistaken in the well-known sound; a shout of joy burst from their lips, as the gallant Peter, covered with dust, and followed by his faithful trumpeter, came galloping into the market-place.

The first transports of the populace having subsided, they gathered round the honest Antony, as he dismounted, overwhelming him with greetings and congratulations. In breathless accents he related to them the marvellous adventures through which the old governor and himself had gone, in making their escape from the clutches of the terrible Amphictyons. But though the Stuyvesant manuscript, with its customary minuteness where anything touching the great Peter is concerned, is very particular as to the incidents of this masterly retreat, the state of the public affairs will not allow me to indulge in a full recital thereof. Let it suffice to say, that, while Peter Stuyvesant was anxiously revolving in his mind how he could make good his escape with honor and dignity, certain of the ships sent out for the conquest of the Manhattoes touched at the eastern ports to obtain supplies, and to call on the grand council of the league for its promised coöperation. Upon hearing of this, the vigilant Peter, perceiving that a moment's delay were fatal, made a secret and precipitate decampment; though much did it grieve his lofty soul to be obliged to turn his back even upon a nation of foes. Many hair-breadth 'scapes and divers perilous mishaps did they sustain, as they scoured, without sound of trumpet, through the fair regions of the east. Already was the country in an uproar with hostile preparations, and they were obliged to take a large circuit in their flight, lurking along through the woody mountains of the Devil's backbone; whence the valiant Peter sallied forth one day like a lion, and put to rout a whole legion of squatters, consisting of three generations of a prolific family, who were already on their way to take possession of some corner of the New Netherlands. Nay, the faithful Antony had great difficulty, at sundry times, to prevent him, in the excess of his wrath, from descending down from the mountains, and falling, sword in hand, upon certain of the border-towns, who were marshalling forth their draggle-tailed militia.

The first movement of the governor, on reaching his dwelling, was to mount the roof, whence he contemplated with rueful aspect the hostile squadron. This had already come to anchor in the bay, and consisted of two stout frigates, having on board, as John Josselyn, Gent., informs us, "three hundred valiant redcoats." Having taken this survey, he sat himself down and wrote an epistle to the commander, demanding the reason of his anchoring in the harbor without obtaining previous permission so to do. This letter was couched in the most dignified and courteous terms, though I have it from undoubted authority that his teeth were clinched, and he had a bitter, sardonic grin upon his visage all the while he wrote. Having dispatched his letter, the grim Peter stumped to and fro about the town with a most war-betokening countenance, his hands thrust into his breeches-pockets, and whistling a Low-Dutch psalm-tune, which bore no small resemblance to the music of a northeast wind, when a storm is brewing. The very dogs as they eyed him skulked away in dismay; while all the old and ugly women of New Amsterdam ran howling at his heels, imploring him to save them from murder, robbery, and pitiless ravishment!

The reply of Colonel Nicholas, who commanded the invaders, was couched in terms of equal courtesy with the letter of the governor; declaring the right and title of his British Majesty to the province; where he affirmed the Dutch to be mere interlopers; and demanding that the town, forts, etc., should be forthwith rendered into his Majesty's obedience and protection; promising, at the same time, life, liberty, estate, and free trade to every Dutch denizen who should readily submit to his Majesty's government.

Peter Stuyvesant read over this friendly epistle with some such harmony of aspect as we may suppose a crusty farmer reads the loving letter of John Stiles, warning him of an action of ejectment. He was not, however, to be taken by surprise; but, thrusting the summons into his breeches-pocket, stalked three times across the room, took a pinch of snuff with great vehemence, and then, loftily waving his hand, promised to send an answer the next morning. He now summoned a general meeting of his privy councillors and burgomasters, not to ask their advice, for, confident in his own strong head, he needed no man's counsel, but apparently to give them a piece of his mind on their late craven conduct.

His orders being duly promulgated, it was a piteous sight to behold the late valiant burgomasters, who had demolished the whole British empire in their harangues, peeping ruefully out of their hiding-places; crawling cautiously forth; dodging through narrow lanes and alleys; starting at every little dog that barked; mistaking lamp-posts for British grenadiers; and, in the excess of their panic, metamorphosing pumps into formidable soldiers levelling blunderbusses at their bosoms! Having, however, in despite of numerous perils and difficulties of the kind, arrived safe, without the loss of a single man, at the hall of assembly, they took their seats, and awaited in fearful silence the arrival of the governor. In a few moments the wooden leg of the intrepid Peter was heard in regular and stout-hearted thumps upon the staircase. He entered the chamber, arrayed in full suit of regimentals, and carrying his trusty toledo, not girded on his thigh, but tucked under his arm. As the governor never equipped himself in this portentous manner unless something of martial nature were working within his pericranium, his council regarded him ruefully, as if they saw fire and sword in his iron countenance, and forgot to light their pipes in breathless suspense.

His first words were, to rate his council soundly for having wasted in idle debate and party feud the time which should have been devoted to putting the city in a state of defence. He was particularly indignant at those brawlers who had disgraced the councils of the province by empty bickerings and scurrilous invectives against an absent enemy. He now called upon them to make good their words by deeds, as the enemy they had defied and derided was at the gate. Finally, he informed them of the summons he had received to surrender, but concluded by swearing to defend the province as long as Heaven was on his side and he had a wooden leg to stand upon; which warlike sentence he emphasized by a thwack with the flat of his sword upon the table, that quite electrified his auditors.

The privy councillors, who had long since been brought into as perfect discipline as were ever the soldiers of the great Frederick, knew there was no use in saying a word—so lighted their pipes, and smoked away in silence, like fat and discreet councillors. But the burgomasters, being inflated with considerable importance and self-sufficiency, acquired at popular meetings, were not so easily satisfied. Mustering up fresh spirit, when they found there was some chance of escaping from their present jeopardy without the disagreeable alternative of fighting, they requested a copy of the summons to surrender, that they might show it to a general meeting of the people.

So insolent and mutinous a request would have been enough to have roused the gorge of the tranquil Van Twiller himself—what then must have been its effect upon the great Stuyvesant, who was not only a Dutchman, a governor, and a valiant wooden-legged soldier to boot, but withal a man of the most stomachful and gunpowder disposition? He burst forth into a blaze of indignation—swore not a mother's son of them should see a syllable of it—that as to their advice or concurrence, he did not care a whiff of tobacco for either—that they might go home, and go to bed like old women; for he was determined to defend the colony himself, without the assistance of them or their adherents! So saying he tucked his sword under his arm, cocked his hat upon his head, and girding up his loins, stumped indignantly out of the council-chamber, everybody making room for him as he passed.

No sooner was he gone than the busy burgomasters called a public meeting in front of the Stadthouse, where they appointed as chairman one Dofue Roerback, formerly a meddlesome member of the cabinet during the reign of William the Testy, but kicked out of office by Peter Stuyvesant on taking the reins of government. He was, withal, a mighty gingerbread baker in the land, and reverenced by the populace as a man of dark knowledge, seeing that he was the first to imprint New-Year cakes with the mysterious hieroglyphics of the Cock and Breeches, and such like magical devices.

This burgomaster, who still chewed the cud of ill-will against Peter Stuyvesant, addressed the multitude in what is called a patriotic speech, informing them of the courteous summons which the governor had received, to surrender, of his refusal to comply therewith, and of his denying the public even a sight of the summons, which doubtless contained conditions highly to the honor and advantage of the province.

He then proceeded to speak of his Excellency in high-sounding terms of vituperation, suited to the dignity of his station; comparing him to Nero, Caligula, and other flagrant great men of yore; assuring the people that the history of the world did not contain a despotic outrage equal to the present. That it would be recorded in letters of fire, on the blood-stained tablet of history! That ages would roll back with sudden horror when they came to view it! That the womb of time (by the way, your orators and writers take strange liberties with the womb of time, though some would fain have us believe that time is an old gentleman) —that the womb of time, pregnant as it was with direful horrors, would never produce a parallel enormity!—with a variety of other heart-rending, soul-stirring tropes and figures, which I cannot enumerate; neither, indeed, need I, for they were of the kind which even to the present day form the style of popular harangues and patriotic orations, and may be classed in rhetoric under the general title of RIGMAROLE.

The result of this speech of the inspired burgomaster was a memorial addressed to the governor, remonstrating in good round terms on his conduct. It was proposed that Dofue Roerback himself should be the bearer of this memorial; but this he warily declined, having no inclination of coming again within kicking distance of his Excellency. Who did deliver it has never been named in history, in which neglect he has suffered grievous wrong; seeing that he was equally worthy of blazon with him perpetuated in Scottish song and story by the surname of Bell-the-cat. All we know of the fate of this memorial is, that it was used by the grim Peter to light his pipe; which, from the vehemence with which he smoked it, was evidently anything but a pipe of peace.

CHAPTER X

Containing a Doleful Disaster of Antony the Trumpeter—and How Peter Stuyvesant, Like a Second Cromwell, Suddenly Dissolved a Rump Parliament

NOW did the high-minded Pieter de Groodt shower down a pannier-load of maledictions upon his burgomasters for a set of self-willed, obstinate, factious varlets, who would neither be convinced nor persuaded. Nor did he omit to bestow some left-handed compliments upon the sovereign people, as a herd of poltroons, who had no relish for the glorious hardships and illustrious misadventures of battle, but would rather stay at home, and eat and sleep in ignoble ease, than fight in a ditch for immortality and a broken head.

Resolutely bent, however, upon defending his beloved city, in despite even of itself, he called unto him his trusty Van Corlear, who was his right-hand man in all times of emergency. Him did he adjure to take his war-denouncing trumpet, and mounting his horse, to beat up the country night and day—sounding the alarm along the pastoral borders of the Bronx—startling the wild solitudes of Croton—arousing the rugged yeomanry of Weehawk and Hoboken—the mighty men of battle of Tappan Bay—and the brave boys of Tarry-Town, Petticoat-Lane, and Sleepy-Hollow—charging them one and all to sling their powder-horns, shoulder their fowling-pieces, and march merrily down to the Manhattoes.

Now there was nothing in all the world, the divine sex excepted, that Antony Van Corlear loved better than errands of this kind. So just stopping to take a lusty dinner, and bracing to his side his junk-bottle, well charged with heart-inspiring Hollands, he issued jollily from the city gate, which looked out upon what is at present called Broadway, sounding a farewell strain, that rung in sprightly echoes through the winding streets of New

Amsterdam. Alas! never more were they to be gladdened by the melody of their favorite trumpeter!

It was a dark and stormy night when the good Antony arrived at the creek (sagely denominated Haerlem *river*) which separates the island of Manna-hata from the mainland. The wind was high, the elements were in an uproar, and no Charon could be found to ferry the adventurous sounder of brass across the water. For a short time he vapored like an impatient ghost upon the brink, and then bethinking himself of the urgency of his errand, took a hearty embrace of his stone bottle, swore most valorously that he would swim across in spite of the devil! (Spyt den Duyvel!) and daringly plunged into the stream. Luckless Antony! Scarce had he buffeted half-way over, when he was observed to struggle violently, as if battling with the spirit of the waters—instinctively he put his trumpet to his mouth, and giving a vehement blast—sank forever to the bottom!

The clangor of his trumpet, like that of the ivory horn of the renowned Paladin Orlando, when expiring in the glorious field of Roncesvalles, rang far and wide through the country, alarming the neighbors round, who hurried in amazement to the spot. Here an old Dutch burgher, famed for his veracity, and who had been a witness of the fact, related to them the melancholy affair; with the fearful addition (to which I am slow in giving belief) that he saw the duyvel, in the shape of a huge moss-bonker, seize the sturdy Antony by the leg, and drag him beneath the waves. Certain it is, the place, with the adjoining promontory, which projects into the Hudson, has been called *Spyt den Duyvel* ever since; the ghost of the unfortunate Antony still haunts the surrounding solitudes, and his trumpet has often been heard by the neighbors, of a stormy night, mingling with the howling of the blast. Nobody ever attempts to swim across the creek after dark; on the contrary, a bridge has been built to guard against such melancholy accidents in future; and as to the moss-bonkers, they are held in such abhorrence, that no true Dutchman will admit them to his table, who loves good fish and hates the devil.

Such was the end of Antony Van Corlear—a man deserving of a better fate. He lived roundly and soundly, like a true and jolly bachelor, until the day of his death; but though he was never married, yet did he leave behind some two or three dozen children, in different parts of the country—fine, chubby, brawling, flatulent little urchins; from whom, if legends speak true (and they are not apt to lie), did descend the innumerable race of editors, who people and defend this country, and who are bountifully paid by the people for keeping up a constant alarm —and making them miserable. It is hinted, too, that in his various expeditions into the East he did much towards promoting the population of the country; in proof of which is adduced the notorious propensity of the people of those parts to sound their own trumpet.

As some way-worn pilgrim, when the tempest whistles through his locks, and night is gathering round, beholds his faithful dog, the companion and solace of his journeying, stretched lifeless at his feet, so did the generous-hearted hero of the Manhattoes contemplate the untimely end of Antony Van Corlear. He had been the faithful attendant of his footsteps; he had charmed him in many a weary hour by his honest gayety and the martial melody of his trumpet, and had followed him with unflinching loyalty and affection through many a scene of direful peril and mishap. He was gone forever! and that, too, at a moment when every mongrel cur was skulking from his side. This —Peter Stuyvesant—was the moment to try thy fortitude; and this was the moment when thou didst indeed shine forth Peter the *Headstrong!*

The glare of day had long dispelled the horrors of the stormy night; still all was dull and gloomy. The late jovial Apollo hid his face behind lugubrious clouds, peeping out now and then for an instant, as if anxious, yet fearful, to see what was going on in his favorite city. This was the eventful morning when the great Peter was to give his reply to the summons of the invaders. Already was he closeted with his privy council, sitting in grim state, brooding over the fate of his favorite trumpeter, and anon boiling with indignation as the insolence of his recreant burgomasters flashed upon his mind. While in this state of irritation, a courier arrived in all haste from Winthrop, the subtle governor of Connecticut, counselling him, in the most affectionate and disinterested manner, to surrender the province, and magnifying the dangers and calamities to which a refusal would subject him. —What a moment was this to intrude officious advice upon a man who never took advice in his whole life!—The fiery old governor strode up and down the chamber with a vehemence that made the bosoms of his councillors to quake with awe—railing at his unlucky fate, that thus made him the constant butt of factious subjects, and jesuitical advisers.

Just at this ill-chosen juncture, the officious burgomasters, who had heard of the arrival of mysterious despatches, came marching in a body into the room, with a legion of schepens and toad-eaters at their heels, and abruptly demanded a perusal of the letter. This was too much for the spleen of Peter Stuyvesant. He tore the letter in a thousand pieces—threw it in the face of the nearest burgomaster—broke his pipe over the head of the next—hurled his spitting-box at an unlucky schepen, who was just retreating out at the door, and finally prorogued the whole meeting *sine die*, by kicking them down-stairs with his wooden leg.

As soon as the burgomasters could recover from their confusion and had time to breathe, they called a public meeting, where they related at full length, and with appropriate coloring and exaggeration, the despotic and vindictive deportment of the governor; declaring that, for their own parts, they did not value a straw the being kicked, cuffed, and mauled by the timber toe of his Excellency, but that they felt for the dignity of the sovereign people, thus rudely insulted by the outrage committed on the seat of honor of their representatives. The latter part of the harangue came home at once to that delicacy of feeling and jealous pride of character vested in all true mobs—who, though they may bear injuries without a murmur, yet are marvellously jealous of their sovereign dignity; and there is no knowing to what act of resentment they might have been provoked, had they not been somewhat more afraid of their sturdy old governor than they were of St. Nicholas, the English—or the d—l himself.

CHAPTER XI

How Peter Stuyvesant Defended the City of New Amsterdam for Several Days, by Dint of the Strength of His Head

THERE is something exceedingly sublime and melancholy in the spectacle which the present crisis of our history presents. An illustrious and venerable little city—the metropolis of a vast extent of uninhabited country—garrisoned by a doughty host of orators, chairmen, committee-men, burgomasters, schepens, and old women—governed by a determined and strong-headed warrior, and fortified by mud batteries, palisadoes, and resolutions—blockaded by sea, beleagured by land, and threatened with direful desolation from without, while its very vitals are torn with internal faction and commotion! Never did historic pen record a page of more complicated distress, unless it be the strife that distracted the Israelites, during the siege of Jerusalem—where discordant parties were cutting each other's throats, at the moment when the victorious legions of Titus had toppled down their bulwarks, and were carrying fire and sword into the very *sanctum sanctorum* of the temple.

Governor Stuyvesant having triumphantly put his grand council to the rout, and delivered himself from a multitude of impertinent advisers, dispatched a categorical reply to the commanders of the invading squadron; wherein he asserted the right and title of their High Mightinesses the Lords States General to the province of New Netherlands, and trusting in the righteousness of his cause, set the whole British nation at defiance!

My anxiety to extricate my readers and myself from these disastrous scenes prevents me from giving the whole of this gallant letter, which concluded in these manly and affectionate terms:

"As touching the threats in your conclusion, we have nothing to answer, only that we fear nothing but what God (who is as just as merciful) shall lay upon us; all things being in his gracious disposal, and we may as well be preserved by him with small forces as by a great army; which makes us to wish you all happiness and prosperity, and recommend you to his protection. My lords, your thrice humble and affectionate servant and friend,

P. STUYVESANT."

Thus having thrown his gauntlet, the brave Peter stuck a pair of horse-pistols in his belt, girded an immense powder-horn on his side—thrust his sound leg into a Hessian boot, and clapping his fierce little war-hat on the top of his head—paraded up and down in front of his house, determined to defend his beloved city to the last.

While all these struggles and dissensions were prevailing in the unhappy city of New Amsterdam, and while its worthy but ill-starred governor was framing the above-quoted letter, the English commanders did not remain idle. They had agents secretly employed to foment the fears and clamors of the populace; and moreover circulated far and wide, through the adjacent country, a proclamation, repeating the terms they had already held out in their summons to surrender, at the same time beguiling the simple Nederlanders with the most crafty and conciliating professions. They promised that every man who voluntarily submitted to the authority of his British Majesty should retain peaceful possession of his house, his vrouw, and his cabbage-garden. That he should be suffered to smoke his pipe, speak Dutch, wear as many breeches as he pleased, and import bricks, tiles, and stone jugs from Holland, instead of manufacturing them on the spot. That he should on no account be compelled to learn the English language, nor eat codfish on Saturdays, nor keep accounts in any other way than by casting them up on his fingers, and chalking them down upon the crown of his hat; as is observed among the Dutch yeomanry at the present day. That every man should be allowed quietly to inherit his father's hat, coat, shoe-buckles, pipe, and every other personal appendage; and that no man should be obliged to conform to any improvements, inventions, or any other modern innovations; but, on the contrary, should be permitted to build his house, follow his trade, manage his farm, rear his hogs, and educate his children, precisely as his ancestors had done before him from time immemorial. Finally, that he should have all the benefits of free trade, and should not be required to acknowledge any other saint in the calendar than St. Nicholas, who should thenceforward, as before, be considered the tutelar saint of the city.

These terms, as may be supposed, appeared very satisfactory to the people, who had a great disposition to enjoy their property unmolested, and a most singular aversion to engage in a contest, where they could gain little more than honor and broken heads —the first of which they held in philosophic indifference, the latter in utter detestation. By these insidious means, therefore, did the English succeed in alienating the confidence and affections of the populace from their gallant old governor, whom they considered as obstinately bent upon running them into hideous misadventures; and did not hesitate to speak their minds freely, and abuse him most heartily—behind his back.

Like as a mighty grampus when assailed and buffeted by roaring waves and brawling surges, still keeps on an undeviating course, rising above the boisterous billows, spouting and blowing as he emerges—so did the inflexible Peter pursue, unwavering, his determined career, and rise, contemptuous, above the clamors of the rabble.

But when the British warriors found that he set their power at defiance, they dispatched recruiting officers to Jamaica, and Jericho, and Nineveh, and Quag, and Patchog, and all those towns on Long Island which had been subdued of yore by Stoffel Brinkerhoff; stirring up the progeny of Preserved Fish, and Determined Cock, and those other New-England squatters, to assail the city of New Amsterdam by land, while the hostile ships prepared for an assault by water.

The streets of New Amsterdam now presented a scene of wild dismay and consternation. In vain did Peter Stuyvesant order the citizens to arm and assemble on the Battery. Blank terror reigned over the community. The whole party of Short Pipes in the course of a single night had changed into arrant old women—a metamorphosis only to be paralleled by the prodigies recorded by Livy as having happened at Rome at the approach of Hannibal, when statues sweated in pure affright, goats were converted into sheep, and cocks, turning into hens, ran cackling about the street.

Thus baffled in all attempts to put the city in a state of defence, blockaded from without, tormented from within, and menaced with a Yankee invasion, even the stiff-necked will of Peter Stuyvesant for once gave way, and in spite of his mighty heart, which swelled in his throat until it nearly choked him, he consented to a treaty of surrender.

Words cannot express the transports of the populace, on receiving this intelligence; had they obtained a conquest over their enemies, they could not have indulged greater delight. The streets resounded with their congratulations—they extolled their governor as the father and deliverer of his country—they crowded to his house to testify their gratitude, and were ten times more noisy in their plaudits than when he returned, with victory perched upon his beaver, from the glorious capture of Fort Christina. But the indignant Peter shut his doors and windows, and took refuge in the innermost recesses of his mansion, that he might not hear the ignoble rejoicings of the rabble.

Commissioners were now appointed on both sides, and a capitulation was speedily arranged; all that was wanting to ratify it was that it should be signed by the governor. When the commissioners waited upon him for this purpose, they were received with grim and bitter courtesy. His warlike accoutrements were laid aside—an old Indian night-gown was wrapped about his rugged limbs, a red night-cap overshadowed his frowning brow, an iron-gray beard of three days' growth gave additional grimness to his visage. Thrice did he seize a worn-out stump of a pen, and essay to sign the loathsome paper—thrice did he clinch his teeth, and make a horrible countenance, as though a dose of rhubarb, senna, and ipecacuanha had been offered to his lips; at length, dashing it from him, he seized his brass-hilted sword, and jerking it from the scabbard, swore by St. Nicholas, to sooner die than yield to any power under heaven.

For two whole days did he persist in this magnanimous resolution, during which his house was besieged by the rabble, and menaces and clamorous revilings exhausted to no purpose. And now another course was adopted to soothe, if possible, his mighty ire. A procession was formed by the burgomasters and schepens, followed by the populace, to bear the capitulation in state to the governor's dwelling. They found the castle strongly barricadoed, and the old hero in full regimentals, with his cocked hat on his head, posted with a blunderbuss at the garret-window.

There was something in this formidable position that struck even the ignoble vulgar with awe and admiration. The brawling multitude could not but reflect with self-abasement upon their own pusillanimous conduct, when they beheld their hardy but deserted old governor, thus faithful to his post, like a forlorn hope, and fully prepared to defend his ungrateful city to the last. These compunctions, however, were soon overwhelmed by the recurring tide of public apprehension. The populace arranged themselves before the house, taking off their hats with most respectful humility; Burgomaster Roerback, who was of that popular class of orators described by Sallust as being "talkative rather than eloquent," stepped forth and addressed the governor in a speech of three hours' length, detailing, in the most pathetic terms, the calamitous situation of the province, and urging him in a constant repetition of the same arguments and words to sign the capitulation.

The mighty Peter eyed him from his garret-window in grim silence—now and then his eye would glance over the surrounding rabble, and an indignant grin, like that of an angry mastiff, would mark his iron visage. But though a man of most undaunted mettle—though he had a heart as big as an ox, and a head that would have set adamant to scorn—yet after all he was a mere mortal. Wearied out by these repeated oppositions, and this eternal haranguing, and perceiving that unless he complied, the inhabitants would follow their own inclination, or rather their fears, without waiting for his consent, or, what was still worse, the Yankees would have time to pour in their forces and claim a share in the conquest, he testily ordered them to hand up the paper. It was accordingly hoisted to him on the end of a pole; and having scrawled his name at the bottom of it, he anathematized them all for a set of cowardly, mutinous, degenerate poltroons, threw the capitulation at their heads, slammed down the window, and was heard stumping down-stairs with vehement indignation. The rabble incontinently took to their heels; even the burgomasters were not slow in evacuating the premises, fearing lest the sturdy Peter might issue from his den, and greet them with some unwelcome testimonial of his displeasure.

Within three hours after the surrender, a legion of British beef-fed warriors poured into New Amsterdam, taking possession of the fort and batteries. And now might be heard, from all quarters, the sound of hammers made by the old Dutch burghers, in nailing up their doors and windows, to protect their vrouws from these fierce barbarians, whom they contemplated in silent sullenness from the garret-windows as they paraded through the streets.

Thus did Colonel Richard Nichols, the commander of the British forces, enter into quiet possession of the conquered realm as *locum tenens* for the Duke of York. The victory was attended with no other outrage than that of changing the name of the province and its metropolis, which thenceforth were denominated New York, and so have continued to be called unto the present day. The inhabitants, according to treaty, were allowed to maintain quiet possession of their property; but so inveterately did they retain their abhorrence of the British nation, that in a private meeting of the leading citizens it was unanimously determined never to ask any of their conquerors to dinner.

NOTE

Modern historians assert that when the New Netherlands were thus overrun by the British, as Spain in ancient days by the Saracens, a resolute band refused to bend the neck to the invader. Led by one Garret Van Horne, a valorous and gigantic Dutchman, they crossed the bay and buried themselves among the marshes and cabbage-gardens of Communipaw; as did Pelayo and his followers among the mountains of Asturias. Here their descendants have remained ever since, keeping themselves apart, like seed-corn, to re-people the city with the genuine breed whenever it shall be effectually recovered from its intruders. It is said the genuine descendants of the Nederlanders who inhabit New York, still look with longing eyes to the green marshes of ancient Pavonia, as did the conquered Spaniards of yore to the stern mountains of Asturias, considering these the regions whence deliverance is to come.

CHAPTER XII

Containing the Dignified Retirement, and Mortal Surrender of Peter the Headstrong

THUS, then, have I concluded this great historical enterprise; but before I lay aside my weary pen, there yet remains to be performed one pious duty. If among the variety of readers who may peruse this book, there should haply be found any of those souls of true nobility, which glow with celestial fire as the history of the generous and the brave, they will doubtless be anxious to know the fate of the gallant Peter Stuyvesant. To gratify one such sterling heart of gold I would go more lengths than to instruct the cold-blooded curiosity of a whole fraternity of philosophers.

No sooner had that high-mettled cavalier signed the articles of capitulation, than, determined not to witness the humiliation of his favorite city, he turned his back on its walls and made a growling retreat to his *bouwery*, or country-seat, which was situated about two miles off; where he passed the remainder of his days in patriarchal retirement. There he enjoyed that tranquillity of mind which he had never known amid the distracting cares of government; and tasted the sweets of absolute and uncontrolled authority, which his factious subjects had so often dashed with the bitterness of opposition.

No persuasions could ever induce him to revisit the city; on the contrary, he would always have his great arm-chair placed with its back to the windows which looked in that direction, until a thick grove of trees planted by his own hand grew up and formed a screen that effectually excluded it from the prospect. He railed continually at the degenerate innovations and improvements introduced by the conquerors; forbade a word of their detested language to be spoken in his family—a prohibition readily obeyed, since none of the household could speak anything but Dutch—and even ordered a fine avenue to be cut down in front of his house because it consisted of English cherry-trees.

The same incessant vigilance, which blazed forth when he had a vast province under his care, now showed itself with equal vigor, though in narrower limits. He patrolled with unceasing watchfulness the boundaries of his little territory; repelled every encroachment with intrepid promptness; punished every vagrant depredation upon his orchard or his farm-yard with inflexible severity; and conducted every stray hog or cow in triumph to the pound. But to the indigent neighbor, the friendless stranger, or the weary wanderer, his spacious doors were ever open, and his capacious fireplace, that emblem of his own warm and generous heart, had always a corner to receive and cherish them. There was an exception to this, I must confess, in case the ill-starred applicant were an Englishman or a Yankee; to whom, though he might extend the hand of assistance, he could never be brought to yield the rites of hospitality. Nay, if peradventure some straggling merchant of the East should stop at his door, with his cart-load of tin ware or wooden bowls, the fiery Peter would issue forth like a giant from his castle, and make such a furious clattering among his pots and kettles, that the vender of "*notions*" was fain to betake himself to instant flight.

His suit of regimentals, worn threadbare by the brush, was carefully hung up in the state bed-chamber, and regularly aired the first fair day of every month; and his cocked hat and trusty sword were suspended in grim repose over the parlor mantel-piece, forming supporters to a full-length portrait of the renowned Admiral Van Tromp. In his domestic empire he maintained strict discipline and a well-organized despotic government; but though his own will was the supreme law, yet the good of his subjects was his constant object. He watched over, not merely their immediate comforts, but their morals, and their ultimate welfare; for he gave them abundance of excellent admonition, nor could any of them complain, that, when occasion required, he was by any means niggardly in bestowing wholesome correction.

The good old Dutch festivals, those periodical demonstrations of an overflowing heart and a thankful spirit, which are falling into sad disuse among my fellow-citizens, were faithfully observed in the mansion of Governor Stuyvesant. New-Year was truly a day of open-handed liberality, of jocund revelry, and warm-hearted congratulation, when the bosom swelled with genial good-fellowship, and the plenteous table was attended with an unceremonious freedom, and honest broad-mouthed merriment, unknown in these days of degeneracy and refinement. Paas and Pinxter were scrupulously observed throughout his dominions; nor was the day of St. Nicholas suffered to pass by, without making presents, hanging the stocking in the chimney, and complying with all its other ceremonies.

Once a year, on the first day of April, he used to array himself in full regimentals, being the anniversary of his triumphal entry into New Amsterdam, after the conquest of New Sweden.

This was always a kind of saturnalia among the domestics, when they considered themselves at liberty, in some measure, to say and do what they pleased; for on this day their master was always observed to unbend, and become exceeding pleasant and jocose, sending the old gray-headed Negroes on April-fool's errands for pigeon's milk; not one of whom but allowed himself to be taken in, and humored his old master's jokes, as became a faithful and well-disciplined dependant. Thus did he reign, happily and peacefully on his own land—injuring no man—envying no man—molested by no outward strifes—perplexed by no internal commotions; and the mighty monarchs of the earth, who were vainly seeking to maintain peace, and promote the welfare of mankind, by war and desolation, would have done well to have made a voyage to the little island of Manna-hata, and learned a lesson in government from the domestic economy of Peter Stuyvesant.

In process of time, however, the old governor, like all other children of mortality, began to exhibit evident tokens of decay. Like an aged oak, which, though it long has braved the fury of the elements, and still retains its gigantic proportions, begins to shake and groan with every blast—so was it with the gallant Peter; for though he still bore the port and semblance of what he was in the days of his hardihood and chivalry, yet did age and infirmity begin to sap the vigor of his frame—but his heart, that unconquerable citadel, still triumphed unsubdued. With matchless avidity would he listen to every article of intelligence concerning the battles between the English and Dutch—still would his pulse beat high whenever he heard of the victories of De Ruyter, and his countenance lower, and his eyebrows knit, when fortune turned in favor of the English. At length, as on a certain day he had just smoked his fifth pipe, and was napping after dinner, in his arm-chair, conquering the whole British nation in his dreams, he was suddenly aroused by a ringing of bells, rattling of drums, and roaring of cannon, that put all his blood in a ferment. But when he learnt that these rejoicings were in honor of a great victory obtained by the combined English and French fleets over the brave De Ruyter, and the younger Van Tromp, it went so much to his heart, that he took to his bed, and in less than three days was brought to death's door, by a violent cholera morbus! Even in this extremity he still displayed the unconquerable spirit of Peter *the Headstrong*; holding out to the last gasp, with inflexible obstinacy, against a whole army of old women who were bent upon driving the enemy out of his bowels, in the true Dutch mode of defence, by inundation.

While he thus lay, lingering on the verge of dissolution, news was brought him that the brave De Ruyter had made good his retreat, with little loss, and meant once more to meet the enemy in battle. The closing eye of the old warrior kindled with martial fire at the words—he partly raised himself in bed—clinched his withered hand, as if he felt within his grip that sword which waved in triumph before the walls of Fort Christina, and giving a grim smile of exultation, sank back upon his pillow, and expired.

Thus died Peter Stuyvesant—a valiant soldier—a loyal subject—an upright governor, and an honest Dutchman—who wanted only a few empires to desolate, to have been immortalized as a hero!

His funeral obsequies were celebrated with the utmost grandeur and solemnity. The town was perfectly emptied of its inhabitants, who crowded in throngs to pay the last sad honors to their good old governor. All his sterling qualities rushed in full tide upon their recollection, while the memory of his foibles and his faults had expired with him. The ancient burghers contended who should have the privilege of bearing the pall; the populace strove who should walk nearest to the bier; and the melancholy procession was closed by a number of gray-headed Negroes, who had wintered and summered in the household of their departed master for the greater part of a century.

With sad and gloomy countenances, the multitude gathered round the grave. They dwelt with mournful hearts on the sturdy virtues, the signal services, and the gallant exploits of the brave old worthy. They recalled, with secret upbraidings, their own factious oppositions to his government; and many an ancient burgher, whose phlegmatic features had never been known to relax, nor his eyes to moisten, was now observed to puff a pensive pipe, and the big drop to steal down his cheek, while he muttered, with affectionate accent, and melancholy shake of the head—"Well, den!—Hardkoppig Peter ben gone at last!"

His remains were deposited in the family vault, under a chapel which he had piously erected on his estate, and dedicated to St. Nicholas—and which stood on the identical spot at present occupied by St. Mark's church, where his tombstone is still to be seen. His estate, or *bouwery*, as it was called, has ever continued in the possession of his descendants, who, by the uniform integrity of their conduct, and their strict adherence to the customs and manners that prevailed in the "*good old times*," have proved themselves worthy of their illustrious ancestor. Many a time and oft has the farm been haunted at night by enterprising money-diggers, in quest of pots of gold, said to have been buried by the old governor, though I cannot learn that any of them have ever been enriched by their researches; and who is there, among my native-born fellow-citizens, that does not remember when, in the mischievous days of his boyhood, he conceived it a great exploit to rob "Stuyvesant's orchard" on a holiday afternoon?

At this stronghold of the family may still be seen certain memorials of the immortal Peter. His full-length portrait frowns in martial terrors from the parlor-wall; his cocked hat and sword still hang up in the best bedroom; his brimstone-colored breeches were for a long while suspended in the hall, until some years since they occasioned a dispute between a new-married couple; and his silver-mounted wooden leg is still treasured up in the store-room, as an invaluable relique.

CHAPTER XIII

The Author's Reflections upon What Has Been Said

AMONG the numerous events, which are each in their turn the most direful and melancholy of all possible occurrences, in your interesting and authentic history, there is none that occasions such deep and heart-rending grief as the decline and fall of your renowned and mighty empires. Where is the reader who can contemplate without emotion the disastrous events by which the great dynasties of the world have been extinguished? While wandering, in imagination, among the gigantic ruins of states and empires, and marking the tremendous convulsions that wrought their overthrow, the bosom of the melancholy inquirer swells with sympathy commensurate to the surrounding desolation. Kingdoms, principalities, and powers, have each had their rise, their progress, and their downfall—each in its turn has swayed a potent sceptre—each has returned to its primeval nothingness. And thus did it fare with the empire of their High Mightinesses, at the Manhattoes, under the peaceful reign of Walter the Doubter, the fretful reign of William the Testy, and the chivalric reign of Peter the Headstrong.

Its history is fruitful of instruction, and worthy of being pondered over attentively, for it is by thus raking among the ashes of departed greatness, that the sparks of true knowledge are to be found, and the lamp of wisdom illuminated. Let then the reign of Walter the Doubter warn against yielding to that sleek, contented security, and that overweening fondness for comfort and repose, which are produced by a state of prosperity and peace. These tend to unnerve a nation; to destroy its pride of character; to render it patient of insult; deaf to the calls of honor and of justice; and cause it to cling to peace, like the sluggard to his pillow, at the expense of every valuable duty and consideration. Such supineness insures the very evil from which it shrinks. One right yielded up produces the usurpation of a second; one encroachment passively suffered makes way for another; and the nation which thus, through a doting love of peace, has sacrificed honor and interest, will at length have to fight for existence.

Let the disastrous reign of William the Testy serve as a salutary warning against that fitful, feverish mode of legislation, which acts without system; depends on shifts and projects, and trusts to lucky contingencies. Which hesitates, and wavers, and at length decides with the rashness of ignorance and imbecility. Which stoops for popularity by courting the prejudices and flattering the arrogance, rather than commanding the respect of the rabble. Which seeks safety in a multitude of counsellors, and distracts itself by a variety of contradictory schemes and opinions. Which mistakes procrastination for wariness—hurry for decision—parsimony for economy—bustle for business—and vaporing for valor. Which is violent in council, sanguine in expectation, precipitate in action, and feeble in execution. Which undertakes enterprises without forethought, enters upon them without preparation, conducts them without energy, and ends them in confusion and defeat.

Let the reign of the good Stuyvesant show the effects of vigor and decision even when destitute of cool judgment, and surrounded by perplexities. Let it show how frankness, probity, and high-souled courage will command respect, and secure honor, even where success is unattainable. But at the same time, let it caution against a too ready reliance on the good faith of others, and a too honest confidence in the loving professions of powerful neighbors, who are most friendly when they most mean to betray. Let it teach a judicious attention to the opinions and wishes of the many, who, in times of peril, must be soothed and led, or apprehension will overpower the deference to authority.

Let the empty wordiness of his factious subjects; their intemperate harangues; their violent "resolutions"; their hectorings against an absent enemy, and their pusillanimity on his approach, teach us to distrust and despise those clamorous patriots whose courage dwells but in the tongue. Let them serve as a lesson to repress that insolence of speech, destitute of real force, which too often breaks forth in popular bodies, and bespeaks the vanity rather than the spirit of a nation. Let them caution us against vaunting too much of our own power and prowess, and reviling a noble enemy. True gallantry of soul would always lead us to treat a foe with courtesy and proud punctilio; a contrary conduct but takes from the merit of victory, and renders defeat doubly disgraceful.

But I cease to dwell on the stores of excellent examples to be drawn from the ancient chronicles of the Manhattoes. He who reads attentively will discover the threads of gold which run throughout the web of history, and are invisible to the dull eye of ignorance. But, before I conclude, let me point out a solemn warning, furnished in the subtle chain of events by which the capture of Fort Casimir has produced the present convulsions of our globe.

Attend then, gentle reader, to this plain deduction, which, if thou art a king, an emperor, or other powerful potentate, I advise thee to treasure up in thy heart—though little expectation have I that my work shall fall into such hands, for well I know the care of crafty ministers, to keep all grave and edifying books of the kind out of the way of unhappy monarchs—lest peradventure they should read them and learn wisdom.

By the treacherous surprisal of Fort Casimir, then, did the crafty Swedes enjoy a transient triumph; but drew upon their heads the vengeance of Peter Stuyvesant, who wrested all New Sweden from their hands. By the conquest of New Sweden, Peter Stuyvesant aroused the claims of Lord Baltimore, who appealed to the Cabinet of Great Britain; who subdued the whole province of New Netherlands. By this great achievement the whole extent of North America, from Nova Scotia to the Floridas, was rendered one entire dependency upon the British crown. But mark the consequence: the hitherto scattered colonies being thus consolidated, and having no rival colonies to check or keep them in awe, waxed great and powerful, and finally becoming too strong for the mother-country, were enabled to shake off its bonds, and by a glorious revolution became an independent empire. But the chain of effect stopped not here: the successful revolution in America produced the sanguinary revolution in France; which produced the puissant Bonaparte; who produced the French despotism; which has thrown the whole world in confusion! Thus have these great powers been successively punished for their ill-starred conquests; and thus, as I asserted, have all the present convulsions, revolutions, and disasters that overwhelm mankind, originated in the capture of the little Fort Casimir, as recorded in this eventful history.

And now, worthy reader, ere I take a sad farewell—which, alas! must be forever—willingly would I part in cordial fellowship, and bespeak thy kind-hearted remembrance. That I have not written a better history of the days of the patriarchs is not my fault; had any other person written one as good, I should not have attempted it at all. That many will hereafter spring up and surpass me in excellence, I have very little doubt, and still less care; well knowing that, when the great Christovallo Colon (who is vulgarly called Columbus) had once stood his egg upon its end, every one at table could stand his up a thousand times more dexterously. Should any reader find matter of offence in this history, I should heartily grieve, though I would on no account question his penetration by telling him he was mistaken—his good-nature by telling him he was captious—or his pure conscience by telling him he was startled at a shadow. Surely when so ingenious in finding offence where none was intended, it were a thousand pities he should not be suffered to enjoy the benefit of his discovery.

I have too high an opinion of the understanding of my fellow-citizens to think of yielding them instruction, and I covet too much their good-will, to forfeit it by giving them good advice. I am none of those cynics who despise the world, because it despises them: on the contrary, though but low in its regard, I look up to it with the most perfect good-nature, and my only sorrow is, that it does not prove itself more worthy of the unbounded love I bear it. If, however, in this my historic production—the scanty fruit of a long and laborious life—I have failed to gratify the dainty palate of the age, I can only lament my misfortune—for it is too late in the season for me even to hope to repair it. Already has withering age showered his sterile snows upon my brow; in a little while, and this genial warmth which still lingers around my heart, and throbs—worthy reader—throbs kindly towards thyself, will be chilled forever. Haply this frail compound of dust, which while alive may have given birth to naught but unprofitable weeds, may form a humble sod of the valley, whence may spring many a sweet wild flower, to adorn my beloved island of Manna-hata!

249 CALDWELL, ERSKINE: *Tobacco Road*
352 CAMUS, ALBERT: *The Fall & Exile and the Kingdom*
109 CAMUS, ALBERT: *The Plague*
349 CAMUS, ALBERT: *Notebooks 1935–1942*
353 CAPOTE, TRUMAN: *Selected Writings*
339 CAMUS, ALBERT: *Resistance, Rebellion and Death*
79 CARROLL, LEWIS: *Alice in Wonderland, etc.*
165 CASANOVA, JACQUES: *Memoirs of Casanova*
150 CELLINI, BENVENUTO: *Autobiography of Cellini*
174 CERVANTES: *Don Quixote*
161 CHAUCER: *The Canterbury Tales*
171 CHEKHOV, ANTON: *Best Plays*
50 CHEKHOV, ANTON: *Short Stories*
272 CICERO: *Basic Works*
279 COLERIDGE: *Selected Poetry and Prose*
251 COLETTE: *Six Novels*
235 COMMAGER, HENRY STEELE & NEVINS, ALLAN: *A Short History of the United States*
306 CONFUCIUS: *The Wisdom of Confucius*
186 CONRAD, JOSEPH: *Lord Jim*
275 CONRAD, JOSEPH: *Nostromo*
34 CONRAD, JOSEPH: *Victory*
105 COOPER, JAMES FENIMORE: *The Pathfinder*
194 CORNEILLE & RACINE: *Six Plays by Corneille and Racine*
130 CRANE, STEPHEN: *The Red Badge of Courage*
214 CUMMINGS, E. E.: *The Enormous Room*

236 DANA, RICHARD HENRY: *Two Years Before the Mast*
208 DANTE: *The Divine Comedy*
122 DEFOE, DANIEL: *Moll Flanders*
92 DEFOE, DANIEL: *Robinson Crusoe* and *A Journal of the Plague Year*
43 DESCARTES, RENÉ: *Philosophical Writings*
173 DEWEY, JOHN: *Human Nature and Conduct*
348 DEWEY, JOHN: *John Dewey on Education*
110 DICKENS, CHARLES: *David Copperfield*
204 DICKENS, CHARLES: *Pickwick Papers*
308 DICKENS, CHARLES: *Our Mutual Friend*
189 DICKENS, CHARLES: *A Tale of Two Cities*
25 DICKINSON, EMILY: *Selected Poems*
23 DINESEN, ISAK: *Out of Africa*
54 DINESEN, ISAK: *Seven Gothic Tales*
12 DONNE, JOHN: *Complete Poetry and Selected Prose*
205 DOS PASSOS, JOHN: *Three Soldiers*
293 DOSTOYEVSKY, FYODOR: *Best Short Stories*
151 DOSTOYEVSKY, FYODOR: *The Brothers Karamazov*
199 DOSTOYEVSKY, FYODOR: *Crime and Punishment*
55 DOSTOYEVSKY, FYODOR: *The Possessed*
5 DOUGLAS, NORMAN: *South Wind*
206 DOYLE, SIR ARTHUR CONAN: *The Adventure and Memoirs of Sherlock Holmes*
8 DREISER, THEODORE: *Sister Carrie*
69 DUMAS, ALEXANDRE: *Camille*
143 DUMAS, ALEXANDRE: *The Three Musketeers*
227 DU MAURIER, DAPHNE: *Rebecca*

338 ELLISON, RALPH: *Invisible Man*
192 EMERSON, RALPH WALDO: *The Journals*
91 EMERSON, RALPH WALDO: *Essays and Other Writings*
331 ERASMUS, DESIDERIUS: *The Praise of Folly*
314 EURIPIDES: *The Complete Greek Tragedies,* VOL. V
315 EURIPIDES: *The Complete Greek Tragedies,* VOL. VI
316 EURIPIDES: *The Complete Greek Tragedies,* VOL. VII

271 FAULKNER, WILLIAM: *Absalom, Absalom!*
175 FAULKNER, WILLIAM: *Go Down, Moses*
351 FAULKNER, WILLIAM: *Intruder in the Dust*
88 FAULKNER, WILLIAM: *Light in August*
61 FAULKNER, WILLIAM: *Sanctuary*
187 FAULKNER, WILLIAM: *The Sound and the Fury* and *As I Lay Dying*
324 FAULKNER, WILLIAM: *Selected Short Stories*
117 FIELDING, HENRY: *Joseph Andrews*
185 FIELDING, HENRY: *Tom Jones*
28 FLAUBERT, GUSTAVE: *Madame Bovary*
102 FORESTER, C. S.: *The African Queen*
210 FRANCE, ANATOLE: *Penguin Island*
298 FRANK, ANNE: *Diary of a Young Girl*
39 FRANKLIN, BENJAMIN: *Autobiography,* etc.
96 FREUD, SIGMUND: *The Interpretation of Dreams*

358 GENET, JEAN: *Our Lady of the Flowers*
36 GEORGE, HENRY: *Progress and Poverty*
327 GIDE, ANDRÉ: *The Counterfeiters*
177 GOETHE: *Faust*
40 GOGOL, NICHOLAI: *Dead Souls*
291 GOLDSMITH, OLIVER: *The Vicar of Wakefield and Other Writings*
20 GRAVES, ROBERT: *I, Claudius*
286 GUNTHER, JOHN: *Death Be Not Proud*

265 HACKETT, FRANCIS: *The Personal History of Henry the Eighth*
163 HAGGARD, H. RIDER: *She* and *King Solomon's Mines*
320 HAMILTON, EDITH: *The Greek Way*
135 HARDY, THOMAS: *Jude the Obscure*
17 HARDY, THOMAS: *The Mayor of Casterbridge*
121 HARDY, THOMAS: *The Return of the Native*
72 HARDY, THOMAS: *Tess of the D'Urbervilles*
233 HART & KAUFMAN: *Six Plays*
329 HART, MOSS: *Act One*
250 HARTE, BRET: *Best Stories*
93 HAWTHORNE, NATHANIEL: *The Scarlet Letter*
239 HEGEL: *The Philosophy of Hegel*
223 HELLMAN, LILLIAN: *Six Plays*
26 HENRY, O.: *Best Short Stories*
255 HERODOTUS: *The Persian Wars*
328 HERSEY, JOHN: *Hiroshima*
334 HESSE, HERMAN: *Steppenwolf*
166 HOMER: *The Iliad*
167 HOMER: *The Odyssey*
141 HORACE: *Complete Works*
302 HOWARD, JOHN TASKER: *World's Great Operas*
277 HOWELLS, WILLIAM DEAN: *The Rise of Silas Lapham*

89 Hudson, W. H.: *Green Mansions*
35 Hugo, Victor: *The Hunchback of Notre Dame*
340 Hume, David: *Philosophy*
209 Huxley, Aldous: *Antic Hay*
48 Huxley, Aldous: *Brave New World*
180 Huxley, Aldous: *Point Counter Point*

305 Ibsen, Henrik: *Six Plays*
307 Ibsen, Henrik: *The Wild Duck and Other Plays*
240 Irving, Washington: *Selected Writings*

16 James, Henry: *The Bostonians*
107 James, Henry: *The Portrait of a Lady*
169 James, Henry: *The Turn of the Screw*
269 James, Henry: *Washington Square*
244 James, Henry: *The Wings of the Dove*
114 James, William: *The Philosophy of William James*
70 James, William: *The Varieties of Religious Experience*
234 Jefferson, Thomas: *The Life* and *Selected Writings*
355 Johnson, Samuel: *Johnson's Dictionary: A Modern Selection*
124 Joyce, James: *Dubliners*
300 Jung, C. G.: *Basic Writings*

318 Kafka, Franz: *The Trial*
283 Kafka, Franz: *Selected Stories*
297 Kant: *Critique of Pure Reason*
266 Kant: *The Philosophy of Kant*
233 Kaufman & Hart: *Six Plays*
273 Keats: *Complete Poetry and Selected Prose*
303 Kierkegaard, Søren: *A Kierkegaard Anthology*
99 Kipling, Rudyard: *Kim*
74 Koestler, Arthur: *Darkness at Noon*

262 Laotse: *The Wisdom of Laotse*
148 Lawrence, D. H.: *Lady Chatterley's Lover*
128 Lawrence, D. H.: *The Rainbow*
333 Lawrence, D. H.: *Sons and Lovers*
68 Lawrence, D. H.: *Women in Love*
252 Lewis, Sinclair: *Dodsworth*
221 Lewis, Sinclair: *Cass Timberlane*
325 Livy: *A History of Rome*
56 Longfellow, Henry W.: *Poems*
77 Louys, Pierre: *Aphrodite*
95 Ludwig, Emil: *Napoleon*

65 Machiavelli: *The Prince* and *The Discourses*
321 Mailer, Norman: *The Naked and the Dead*
317 Malamud, Bernard: *Two Novels*
33 Malraux, André: *Man's Fate*
309 Malthus, Thomas Robert: *On Population*
360 Mann, Thomas: *Confessions of Felix Krull*
182 Marquand, John P.: *The Late George Apley*
202 Marx, Karl: *Capital and Other Writings*
14 Maugham, W. Somerset: *Best Short Stories*
170 Maugham, W. Somerset: *Cakes and Ale*

27 MAUGHAM, W. SOMERSET: *The Moon and Sixpence*
176 MAUGHAM, W. SOMERSET: *Of Human Bondage*
98 MAUPASSANT, GUY DE: *Best Short Stories*
46 MAUROIS, ANDRÉ: *Disraeli*
119 MELVILLE, HERMAN: *Moby Dick*
253 MEREDITH, GEORGE: *The Egoist*
134 MEREDITH, GEORGE: *The Ordeal of Richard Feverel*
138 MEREJKOWSKI, DMITRI: *The Romance of Leonardo da Vinci*
296 MICHENER, JAMES A.: *Selected Writings*
322 MILL, JOHN STUART: *Selections*
132 MILTON, JOHN: *Complete Poetry and Selected Prose*
78 MOLIÈRE: *Eight Plays*
218 MONTAIGNE: *Selected Essays*

343 NASH, OGDEN: *Verses From 1929 On*
235 NEVINS, ALLAN & COMMAGER, HENRY STEELE: *A Short History of the United States*
113 NEWMAN, CARDINAL JOHN H.: *Apologia Pro Vita Sua*
9 NIETZSCHE, FRIEDRICH: *Thus Spake Zarathustra*
81 NOSTRADAMUS: *Oracles*

67 ODETS, CLIFFORD: *Six Plays*
42 O'HARA, JOHN: *Appointment in Samarra*
211 O'HARA, JOHN: *Selected Short Stories*
323 O'HARA, JOHN: *Butterfield 8*
342 O'NEILL, EUGENE: *Ah, Wilderness! and Two Other Plays*
146 O'NEILL, EUGENE: *The Emperor Jones, Anna Christie* and *The Hairy Ape*
111 O'NEILL, EUGENE: *The Long Voyage Home: Seven Plays of the Sea*

232 PALGRAVE, FRANCIS (editor): *The Golden Treasury*
123 PARKER, DOROTHY: *Collected Short Stories*
237 PARKER, DOROTHY: *Collected Poetry*
267 PARKMAN, FRANCIS: *The Oregon Trail*
164 PASCAL, BLAISE: *Penseés* and *The Provincial Letters*
86 PATER, WALTER: *The Renaissance*
103 PEPYS, SAMUEL: *Passages from the Diary*
247 PERELMAN, S. J.: *The Best of S. J. Perelman*
153 PLATO: *The Republic*
181 PLATO: *The Works of Plato*
82 POE, EDGAR ALLAN: *Selected Poetry and Prose*
196 POLO, MARCO: *The Travels of Marco Polo*
257 POPE, ALEXANDER: *Selected Works*
284 PORTER, KATHERINE ANNE: *Flowering Judas*
45 PORTER, KATHERINE ANNE: *Pale Horse, Pale Rider*
120 PROUST, MARCEL: *The Captive*
220 PROUST, MARCEL: *Cities of the Plain*
213 PROUST, MARCEL: *The Guermantes Way*
278 PROUST, MARCEL: *The Past Recaptured*
59 PROUST, MARCEL: *Swann's Way*
260 PROUST, MARCEL: *The Sweet Cheat Gone*
172 PROUST, MARCEL: *Within a Budding Grove*

194 RACINE & CORNEILLE: *Six Plays by Corneille and Racine*
62 READE, CHARLES: *The Cloister and the Hearth*

215 Reed, John: *Ten Days That Shook the World*
140 Renan, Ernest: *The Life of Jesus*
336 Renault, Mary: *The Last of the Wine*
10 Richardson, Samuel: *Clarissa*
200 Rodgers & Hammerstein: *Six Plays*
154 Rostand, Edmond: *Cyrano de Bergerac*
243 Rousseau, Jean Jacques: *The Confessions*
53 Runyon, Damon: *Famous Stories*
137 Russell, Bertrand: *Selected Papers of Betrand Russell*

280 Saki: *Short Stories*
301 Salinger, J. D.: *Nine Stories*
90 Salinger, J. D.: *The Catcher in the Rye*
292 Santayana, George: *The Sense of Beauty*
335 Sartre, Jean-Paul: *The Age of Reason*
52 Schopenhauer: *The Philosophy of Schopenhauer*
281 Schulberg, Budd: *What Makes Sammy Run?*
2,3 Shakespeare, William: *Tragedies*—complete, 2 vols.
4,5 Shakespeare, William: *Comedies*—complete, 2 vols.
6 Shakespeare, William: *Histories* } complete, 2 vols.
7 Shakespeare, William: *Histories, Poems* }
19 Shaw, Bernard: *Four Plays*
294 Shaw, Bernard: *Saint Joan, Major Barbara,* and *Androcles [and the Lion*
112 Shaw, Irwin: *The Young Lions*
319 Shaw, Irwin: *Selected Short Stories*
274 Shelley: *Selected Poetry and Prose*
159 Smollett, Tobias: *Humphry Clinker*
312 Sophocles I: *Complete Greek Tragedies,* vol. III
313 Sophocles II: *Complete Greek Tragedies,* vol. IV
60 Spinoza: *The Philosophy of Spinoza*
332 Stein, Gertrude: *Selected Writings*
115 Steinbeck, John: *In Dubious Battle*
29 Steinbeck, John: *Of Mice and Men*
216 Steinbeck, John: *Tortilla Flat*
157 Stendhal: *The Red and the Black*
147 Sterne, Laurence: *Tristram Shandy*
254 Stewart, George R.: *Storm*
31 Stoker, Bram: *Dracula*
11 Stone, Irving: *Lust for Life*
261 Stowe, Harriet Beecher: *Uncle Tom's Cabin*
212 Strachey, Lytton: *Eminent Victorians*
351 Styron, William: *Lie Down in Darkness*
188 Suetonius: *Lives of the Twelve Caesars*
100 Swift, Jonathan: *Gulliver's Travels and Other Writings*
49 Symonds, John A.: *The Life of Michelangelo*

222 Tacitus: *Complete Works*
230 Tennyson: *Selected Poetry*
80 Thackeray, William: *Henry Esmond*
131 Thackeray, William: *Vanity Fair*
38 Thompson, Francis: *Complete Poems*
155 Thoreau, Henry David: *Walden and Other Writings*
58 Thucydides: *Complete Writings*
85 Thurber, James: *The Thurber Carnival*
37 Tolstoy, Leo: *Anna Karenina*—tr. revised

347 TOLSTOY, LEO: *Selected Essays*
354 TOLSTOY, LEO: *Short Novels*
346 TOLSTOY, LEO: *Short Stories*
361 TOLSTOY, LEO: *Short Stories*, VOL. II
41 TROLLOPE, ANTHONY: *Barchester Towers* and *The Warden*
21 TURGENEV, IVAN: *Fathers and Sons*
162 TWAIN, MARK: *A Connecticut Yankee in King Arthur's Court*

357 UPDIKE, JOHN: *The Poorhouse Fair* and *Rabbit, Run*

190 VASARI, GIORGIO: *Lives of the Most Eminent Painters, Sculptors and Architects*
63 VEBLEN, THORSTEIN: *The Theory of the Leisure Class*
156 VINCI, LEONARDO DA: *The Notebooks*
75 VIRGIL: *The Aeneid, Eclogues* and *Georgics*
47 VOLTAIRE: *Candide and Other Writings*

178 WALPOLE, HUGH: *Fortitude*
170 WARREN, ROBERT PENN: *All The King's Men*
219 WEBB, MARY: *Precious Bane*
225 WEIDMAN, JEROME: *I Can Get It for You Wholesale*
197 WELLS, H. G.: *Tono Bungay*
290 WELTY, EUDORA: *Selected Stories*
299 WHARTON, EDITH: *The Age of Innocence*
97 WHITMAN, WALT: *Leaves of Grass*
125 WILDE, OSCAR: *Dorian Gray* and *De Profundis*
83 WILDE, OSCAR: *The Plays of Oscar Wilde*
84 WILDE, OSCAR: *Poems* and *Fairy Tales*
126 WODEHOUSE, P. J.: *Selected Stories*
268 WORDSWORTH: *Selected Poetry*

44 YEATS, W. B. (editor): *Irish Fairy and Folk Tales*
179 YOUNG, G. F.: *The Medici*

207 ZIMMERN, ALFRED: *The Greek Commonwealth*
142 ZOLA, ÉMILE: *Nana*

MISCELLANEOUS

288 *An Anthology of Irish Literature*
330 *Anthology of Medieval Lyrics*
326 *The Apocrypha*
201 *The Arabian Nights' Entertainments*
87 *Best American Humorous Short Stories*
18 *Best Russian Short Stories*
129 *Best Spanish Stories*
Complete Greek Tragedies
310 VOL. I (Aeschylus I); 311 VOL. II (Aeschylus II); **312** VOL. III (Sophocles I); 313 VOL. IV (Sophocles II); 314 VOL. V (Euripides I); 315 VOL. VI (Euripides II)
359 *Complete Poems and Selected Letters of Michelangelo*
101 *A Comprehensive Anthology of American Poetry*
226 *The Consolation of Philosophy*
94 *Eight Famous Elizabethan Plays*
345 *Eight Spanish Plays of the Golden Age*
224 *Eighteenth-Century Plays*
73 *Famous Ghost Stories*
139 *The Federalist*
30 *Five Great Modern Irish Plays*
144 *Fourteen Great Detective Stories*
108 *Great German Short Novels and Stories*
168 *Great Modern Short Stories*
238 *Great Tales of the American West*
203 *The Greek Poets*
356 *Hellenistic Philosophy*
217 *The Latin Poets*
149 *The Making of Man: An Outline of Anthropology*
183 *Making of Society*
344 *Medieval Philosophy*
133 *Medieval Romances*
1 *The Modern Library Dictionary*
258 *New Voices in the American Theatre*
152 *Outline of Abnormal Psychology*
66 *Outline of Psychoanalysis*
287 *Restoration Plays*
337 *Roman Comedies*
158 *Seven Famous Greek Plays*
57 *The Short Bible*
276 *Six Modern American Plays*
38 *Six American Plays for Today*
118 *Stories of Modern Italy*
127 *Twentieth-Century American Poetry*—revised
341 *Twenty German Poets*

MODERN LIBRARY GIANTS

A series of sturdily bound and handsomely printed, full-sized library editions of books formerly available only in expensive sets. These volumes contain from 600 to 1,400 pages each.

THE MODERN LIBRARY GIANTS REPRESENT A SELECTION OF THE WORLD'S GREATEST BOOKS

G76 ANDERSEN & GRIMM: *Tales*
G74 AUGUSTINE, ST.: *The City of God*
G58 AUSTEN, JANE: *Complete Novels*
G70 BLAKE, WILLIAM & DONNE, JOHN: *Complete Poetry*
G2 BOSWELL, JAMES: *Life of Samuel Johnson*
G17 BROWNING, ROBERT: *Poems and Plays*
G14 BULFINCH: *Mythology* (ILLUSTRATED)
G35 BURY, J. B.: *A History of Greece*
G13 CARLYLE, THOMAS: *The French Revolution*
G28 CARROLL, LEWIS: *Complete Works*
G15 CERVANTES: *Don Quixote*
G33 COLLINS, WILKIE: *The Moonstone* and *The Woman in White*
G27 DARWIN, CHARLES: *Origin of Species* and *The Descent of Man*
G43 DEWEY, JOHN: *Intelligence in the Modern World: John Dewey's Philosophy*
G70 DONNE, JOHN & BLAKE, WILLIAM: *Complete Poetry*
G36 DOSTOYEVSKY, FYODOR: *The Brothers Karamazov*
G60 DOSTOYEVSKY, FYODOR: *The Idiot*
G51 ELIOT, GEORGE: *Best-Known Novels*
G41 FARRELL, JAMES T.: *Studs Lonigan*
G82 FAULKNER, WILLIAM: *The Faulkner Reader*
G39 FREUD, SIGMUND: *The Basic Writings*
G6, G7, G8 GIBBON, EDWARD: *The Decline and Fall of the Roman Empire* (COMPLETE IN THREE VOLUMES)
G25 GILBERT & SULLIVAN: *Complete Plays*
G76 GRIMM & ANDERSEN: *Tales*
G37 HAWTHORNE, NATHANIEL: *Compl. Novels & Selected Tales*
G78 HOLMES, OLIVER WENDELL: *The Mind and Faith of Justice Holmes*
G19 HOMER: *Complete Works*
G3 HUGO, VICTOR: *Les Miserables*
G18 IBSEN, HENRIK: *Eleven Plays*
G11 JAMES, HENRY: *Short Stories*
G52 JOYCE, JAMES: *Ulysses*
G4 KEATS & SHELLEY: *Complete Poems*
G24 LAMB, CHARLES: *The Complete Works and Letters*
G20 LINCOLN, ABRAHAM: *The Life and Writings of Abraham Lincoln*
G84 MANN, THOMAS: *Stories of Three Decades*
G26 MARX, KARL: *Capital*
G57 MELVILLE, HERMAN: *Selected Writings*
G38 MURASAKA, LADY: *The Tale of Genji*
G30 MYERS, GUSTAVUS: *History of the Great American Fortunes*
G34 NIETZSCHE, FRIEDRICH: *The Philosophy of Nietzsche*
G88 O'HARA, JOHN: *49 Stories*

G55 O'NEILL, EUGENE: *Nine Plays*
G68 PAINE, TOM: *Selected Work*
G86 PASTERNAK, BORIS: *Doctor Zhivago*
G5 PLUTARCH: *Lives* (The Dryden Translation)
G40 POE, EDGAR ALLAN: *Complete Tales and Poems*
G29 PRESCOTT, WILLIAM H.: *The Conquest of Mexico* and *The Conquest of Peru*
G62 PUSHKIN: *Poems, Prose and Plays*
G65 RABELAIS: *Complete Works*
G12 SCOTT, SIR WALTER: *The Most Popular Novels* (Quentin Durward, Ivanhoe & Kenilworth)
G4 SHELLEY & KEATS: *Complete Poems*
G32 SMITH, ADAM: *The Wealth of Nations*
G61 SPAETH, SIGMUND: *A Guide to Great Orchestral Music*
G92 SPENGLER, OSWALD: *The Decline of the West* (one volume)
G91 SPENSER, EDMUND: *Selected Poetry*
G75 STEVENSON, ROBERT LOUIS: *Selected Writings*
G53 SUE, EUGENE: *The Wandering Jew*
G42 TENNYSON: *The Poems and Plays*
G23 TOLSTOY, LEO: *Anna Karenina*—tr. revised
G1 TOLSTOY, LEO: *War and Peace*
G49 TWAIN, MARK: *Tom Sawyer* and *Huckleberry Finn*
G50 WHITMAN, WALT: *Leaves of Grass*
G83 WILSON, EDMUND: *The Shock of Recognition*

MISCELLANEOUS

G77 *An Anthology of Famous American Stories*
G54 *An Anthology of Famous British Stories*
G67 *Anthology of Famous English and American Poetry*
G81 *An Encyclopedia of Modern American Humor*
G47 *The English Philosophers from Bacon to Mill*
G16 *The European Philosophers from Descartes to Nietzsche*
G31 *Famous Science-Fiction Stories*
G85 *Great Ages and Ideas of the Jewish People*
G89 *Great Classical Myths*
G72 *Great Tales of Terror and the Supernatural*
G9 *Great Voices of the Reformation*
G87 *Medieval Epics*
G48 *The Metropolitan Opera Guide*
G46 *A New Anthology of Modern Poetry*
G69 *One Hundred and One Years' Entertainment*
G93 *Parodies: An Anthology from Chaucer to Beerbohm and After*
G90 *Philosophies of Art and Beauty: Readings in Aesthetics from Plato to Heidegger*
G21 *Sixteen Famous American Plays*
G63 *Sixteen Famous British Plays*
G71 *Sixteen Famous European Plays*
G45 *Stoic and Epicurean Philosophers*
G22 *Thirty Famous One-Act Plays*
G66 *Three Famous Murder Novels, Before the Fact,* FRANCIS ILES, *Trent's Last Case,* E. C. BENTLEY, *The House of the Arrow,* A. E. W. MASON
G10 *Twelve Famous Plays of the Restoration and Eighteenth Century* (1660–1820): Dryden, Congreve, Wycherley, Gay, etc.
G56 *The Wisdom of Catholicism*
G59 *The Wisdom of China and India*
G79 *The Wisdom of Israel*